Student Solutions Manual

to accompany

Chemistry

The Molecular Nature of Matter and Change

Seventh Edition

Martin S. Silberberg

and

Patricia G. Amateis

Virginia Tech

Prepared by

MaryKay Orgill

University of Nevada, Las Vegas

CHEM 211

Volume I

George Mason University

6 7 8 9 10 11 QVS/QVS 20 19 18 17 16

ISBN-13: 978-1-259-34194-6
ISBN-10: 1-259-34194-1

Learning Solutions Consultant: Dave Fleming
Project Manager: Nina Meyer

CONTENTS

PREFACE

WELCOME TO YOUR STUDENT SOLUTIONS MANUAL

Your Student Solutions Manual (SSM) includes detailed solutions for the Follow-up Problems, selected Boxed Reading Problems, and highlighted End-of-Chapter Problems in the seventh edition of *Chemistry: The Molecular Nature of Matter and Change* by Martin Silberberg and Patricia Amateis.

You should use the SSM in your study of chemistry as a study tool:

- to better understand the reasoning behind problem solutions. The plan-solution-check format illustrates the problem-solving thought process for the Follow-up Problems and for selected End-of-Chapter Problems.
- to better understand the concepts through their applications in problems. Explanations and hints for problems are in response to questions from students in general chemistry courses.
- to check your problem solutions. Solutions provide comments on the solution process as well as the answer.

To succeed in general chemistry you must develop skills in problem solving. Not only does this mean being able to follow a solution path and reproduce it on your own, but also to analyze problems you have never seen before and develop a solution strategy. Chemistry problems are story problems that bring together chemistry concepts and mathematical reasoning. The analysis of new problems is the most challenging step for general chemistry students. You may face this in the initial few chapters or not until later in the year when the material is less familiar. When you find that you are having difficulty starting problems, do not be discouraged. This is an opportunity to learn new skills that will benefit you in future courses and your future career. The following two strategies, tested and found successful by many students, may help you develop the skills you need.

The first strategy is to become aware of your own thought processes as you solve problems. As you solve a problem, make notes in the margin concerning your thoughts. Why are you doing each step and what questions do you ask yourself during the solution? After you complete the problem, review your notes and make an outline of the process you used in the solution while reviewing the reasoning behind the solution. It may be useful to write a paragraph describing the solution process you used.

The second strategy helps you develop the ability to transfer a solution process to a new problem. After solving a problem, rewrite the problem to ask a different question. One way to rewrite the question is to ask the question backwards—find what has been given in the problem from the answer to the problem. Another approach is to change the conditions—for instance, ask yourself what if the temperature is higher or there is twice as much carbon dioxide present? A third method is to change the reaction or process taking place—what if the substance is melting instead of boiling?

At times, you may find slight differences between your answer and the one in the SSM. Two reasons may account for the differences. First, SSM calculations do not round answers until the final step so this may impact the exact numerical answer. Note that in preliminary calculations extra significant figures are retained and shown in the intermediate answers. The second reason for discrepancies may be that your solution route was different from the one given in the SSM. Valid alternate paths exist for many problems, but the SSM does not have space to show all alternate solutions. So, trust your solution as long as the discrepancy with the SSM answer is small, and use the different solution route to understand the concepts used in the problem.

Some problems have more than one correct answer. For example, if you are asked to name a metal, there are over 80 correct answers.

I would like to thank Lora Neyens and the staff at McGraw-Hill for their assistance in completing this project.

MaryKay Orgill
University of Nevada, Las Vegas

CHAPTER 1 KEYS TO THE STUDY OF CHEMISTRY

FOLLOW–UP PROBLEMS

1.1A Plan: The real question is "Does the substance change composition or just change form?" A change in composition is a chemical change while a change in form is a physical change.
Solution:
The figure on the left shows red atoms and molecules composed of one red atom and one blue atom. The figure on the right shows a change to blue atoms and molecules containing two red atoms. The change is **chemical** since the substances themselves have changed in composition.

1.1B Plan: The real question is "Does the substance change composition or just change form?" A change in composition is a chemical change while a change in form is a physical change.
Solution:
The figure on the left shows red atoms that are close together, in the solid state. The figure on the right shows red atoms that are far apart from each other, in the gaseous state. The change is **physical** since the substances themselves have not changed in composition.

1.2A Plan: The real question is "Does the substance change composition or just change form?" A change in composition is a chemical change while a change in form is a physical change.
Solution:
a) Both the solid and the vapor are iodine, so this must be a **physical** change.
b) The burning of the gasoline fumes produces energy and products that are different gases. This is a **chemical** change.
c) The scab forms due to a **chemical** change.

1.2B Plan: The real question is "Does the substance change composition or just change form?" A change in composition is a chemical change while a change in form is a physical change.
Solution:
a) Clouds form when gaseous water (water vapor) changes to droplets of liquid water. This is a **physical** change.
b) When old milk sours, the compounds in milk undergo a reaction to become different compounds (as indicated by a change in the smell, the taste, the texture, and the consistency of the milk). This is a **chemical** change.
c) Both the solid and the liquid are butter, so this must be a **physical** change.

1.3A Plan: We need to find the amount of time it takes for the professor to walk 10,500 m. We know how many miles she can walk in 15 min (her speed), so we can convert the distance the professor walks to miles and use her speed to calculate the amount of time it will take to walk 10,500 m.
Solution:

$$\text{Time (min)} = 10{,}500\text{ m}\left(\frac{1\text{ km}}{1000\text{ m}}\right)\left(\frac{1\text{ mi}}{1.609\text{ km}}\right)\left(\frac{15\text{ min}}{1\text{ mi}}\right) = 97.8869 = \mathbf{98\ min}$$

Road map:

Distance (m)

↓ 1000 m = 1 km

Distance (km)

↓ 1.609 km = 1 mi

Distance (mi)

1 mi = 15 min

Time (min)

1.3B Plan: We need to find the number of virus particles that can line up side by side in a 1 inch distance. We know the diameter of a virus in nm units. If we convert the 1 inch distance to nm, we can use the diameter of the virus to calculate the number of virus particles we can line up over a 1 inch distance.

Solution:

$$\text{No. of virus particles} = 1.0\ \text{in}\left(\frac{2.54\ \text{cm}}{1\ \text{in}}\right)\left(\frac{1 \times 10^7\ \text{nm}}{1\ \text{cm}}\right)\left(\frac{1\ \text{virus particle}}{30\ \text{nm}}\right) = 8.4667 \times 10^5 = \mathbf{8.5 \times 10^5\ virus\ particles}$$

Road map:

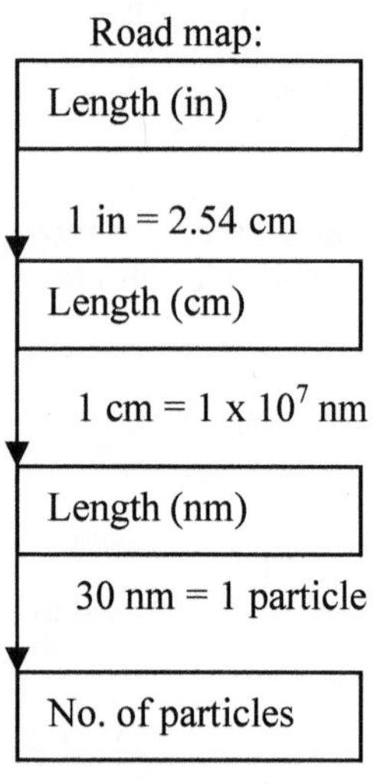

1.4A Plan: The diameter in nm is used to obtain the radius in nm, which is converted to the radius in dm. The volume of the ribosome in dm^3 is then determined using the equation for the volume of a sphere given in the problem. This volume may then be converted to volume in μL.

Solution:

$$\text{Radius (dm)} = \frac{\text{diameter}}{2} = \left(\frac{21.4\ \text{nm}}{2}\right)\left(\frac{1\ \text{m}}{1 \times 10^9\ \text{nm}}\right)\left(\frac{1\ \text{dm}}{0.1\ \text{m}}\right) = 1.07 \times 10^{-7}\ \text{dm}$$

$$\text{Volume (dm}^3\text{)} = \frac{4}{3}\pi r^3 = \frac{4}{3}(3.14159)\left(1.07 \times 10^{-7}\ \text{dm}\right)^3 = 5.13145 \times 10^{-21} = \mathbf{5.13 \times 10^{-21}\ dm^3}$$

$$\text{Volume (μL)} = \left(5.13145 \times 10^{-21}\ \text{dm}^3\right)\left(\frac{1\ \text{L}}{(1\ \text{dm})^3}\right)\left(\frac{1\ \text{μL}}{10^{-6}\ \text{L}}\right) = 5.13145 \times 10^{-15} = \mathbf{5.13 \times 10^{-15}\ μL}$$

Road map:

Diameter (dm)

diameter = $2r$

Radius (dm)

$V = 4/3\pi r^3$

Volume (dm^3)

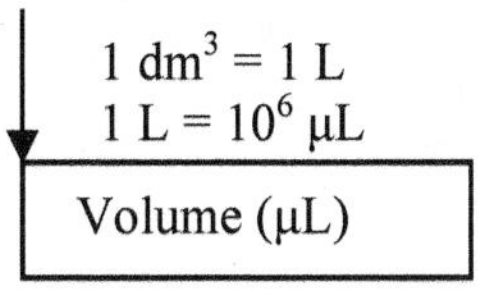

1 dm³ = 1 L
1 L = 10^6 µL

Volume (µL)

1.4B Plan: We need to convert gallon units to liter units. If we first convert gallons to dm^3, we can then convert to L.
Solution:

$$\text{Volume (L)} = 8400 \text{ gal}\left(\frac{3.785 \text{ dm}^3}{1 \text{ gal}}\right)\left(\frac{1 \text{ L}}{1 \text{ dm}^3}\right) = 31{,}794 = \mathbf{32{,}000\ L}$$

Road map:

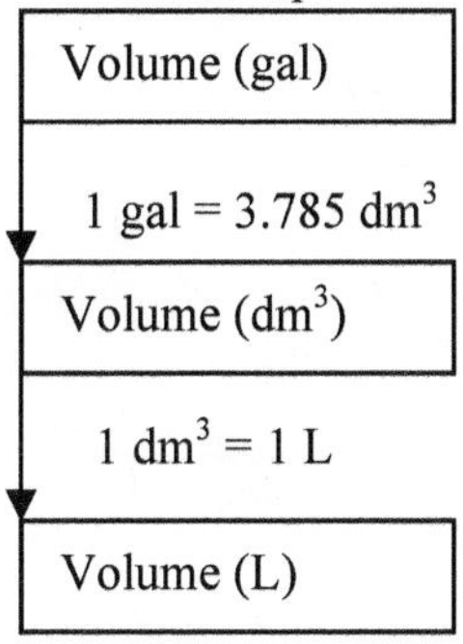

Volume (gal)

↓ 1 gal = 3.785 dm^3

Volume (dm^3)

↓ 1 dm^3 = 1 L

Volume (L)

1.5A Plan: The time is given in hours and the rate of delivery is in drops per second. Conversions relating hours to seconds are needed. This will give the total number of drops, which may be combined with their mass to get the total mass. The mg of drops will then be changed to kilograms.
Solution:

$$\text{Mass (kg)} = 8.0 \text{ h}\left(\frac{60 \text{ min}}{1 \text{ h}}\right)\left(\frac{60 \text{s}}{1 \text{ min}}\right)\left(\frac{1.5 \text{ drops}}{1 \text{ s}}\right)\left(\frac{65 \text{ mg}}{1 \text{ drop}}\right)\left(\frac{10^{-3} \text{ g}}{1 \text{ mg}}\right)\left(\frac{1 \text{ kg}}{10^3 \text{ g}}\right) = 2.808 = \mathbf{2.8\ kg}$$

Road map:

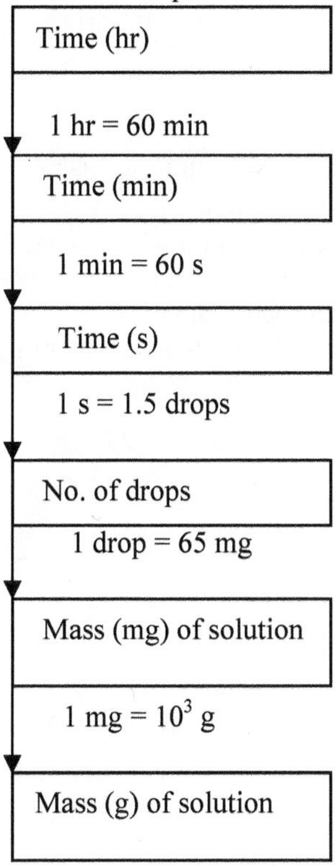

Time (hr)

↓ 1 hr = 60 min

Time (min)

↓ 1 min = 60 s

Time (s)

↓ 1 s = 1.5 drops

No. of drops

↓ 1 drop = 65 mg

Mass (mg) of solution

↓ 1 mg = 10^3 g

Mass (g) of solution

10^3 g = 1 kg

Mass (kg) of solution

1.5B Plan: We have the mass of apples in kg and need to find the mass of potassium in those apples in g. The number of apples per pound and the mass of potassium per apple are given. Convert the mass of apples in kg to pounds. Then use the number of apples per pound to calculate the number of apples. Use the mass of potassium in one apple to calculate the mass (mg) of potassium in the group of apples. Finally, convert the mass in mg to g.

Solution:

$$\text{Mass (g)} = 3.25\ \text{kg}\left(\frac{1\ \text{lb}}{0.4536\ \text{kg}}\right)\left(\frac{3\ \text{apples}}{1\ \text{lb}}\right)\left(\frac{159\ \text{mg potassium}}{1\ \text{apple}}\right)\left(\frac{1\ \text{g}}{10^3\ \text{mg}}\right) = 3.4177 = \mathbf{3.42\ g}$$

Road map:

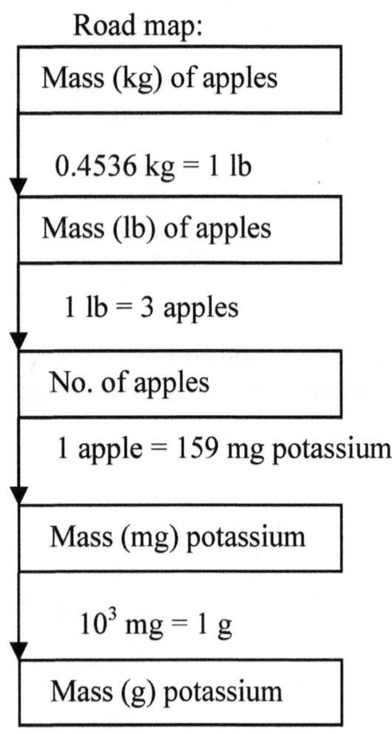

1.6A Plan: We know the area of a field in m^2. We need to know how many bottles of herbicide will be needed to treat that field. The volume of each bottle (in fl oz) and the volume of herbicide needed to treat 300 ft^2 of field are given. Convert the area of the field from m^2 to ft^2 (don't forget to square the conversion factor when converting from squared units to squared units!). Then use the given conversion factors to calculate the number of bottles of herbicide needed. Convert first from ft^2 of field to fl oz of herbicide (because this conversion is from a squared unit to a non-squared unit, we do not need to square the conversion factor). Then use the number of fl oz per bottle to calculate the number of bottles needed.

Solution:

$$\text{No. of bottles} = 2050\ \text{m}^2\left(\frac{1\ \text{ft}^2}{(0.3048)^2\ \text{m}^2}\right)\left(\frac{1.5\ \text{fl oz}}{300\ \text{ft}^2}\right)\left(\frac{1\ \text{bottle}}{16\ \text{fl oz}}\right) = 6.8956 = \mathbf{7\ bottles}$$

Road map:

Area (m^2)

$(0.3048)^2\ m^2 = 1\ ft^2$

Area (ft^2)

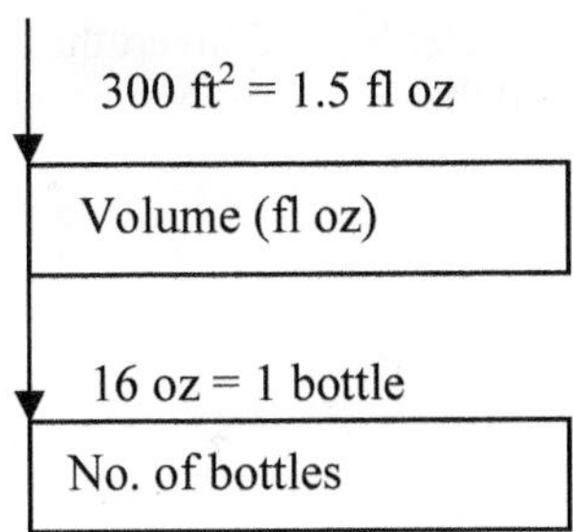

1.6B Plan: Calculate the mass of mercury in g. Convert the surface area of the lake form mi^2 to ft^2. Find the volume of the lake in ft^3 by multiplying the surface area (in ft^2) by the depth (in ft). Then convert the volume of the lake to mL by converting first from ft^3 to m^3, then from m^3 to cm^3, and from cm^3 to mL. Finally, divide the mass in g by the volume in mL to find the mass of mercury in each mL of the lake.

Solution:

$$\text{Mass (g)} = 75{,}000 \text{ kg}\left(\frac{1000 \text{ g}}{1 \text{ kg}}\right) = 7.5 \times 10^7 \text{ g}$$

$$\text{Volume (mL)} = 4.5 \text{ mi}^2\left(\frac{(5280)^2 \text{ ft}^2}{1 \text{ mi}^2}\right)(35 \text{ ft})\left(\frac{0.02832 \text{ m}^3}{1 \text{ ft}^3}\right)\left(\frac{1 \times 10^6 \text{ cm}^3}{1 \text{ m}^3}\right)\left(\frac{1 \text{ mL}}{1 \text{ cm}^3}\right) = 1.2 \times 10^{14} \text{ mL}$$

$$\text{Mass (g) of mercury per mL} = \frac{7.5 \times 10^7 \text{ g}}{1.2 \times 10^{14} \text{ mL}} = \mathbf{6.2 \times 10^{-7} \text{ g/mL}}$$

Road map:

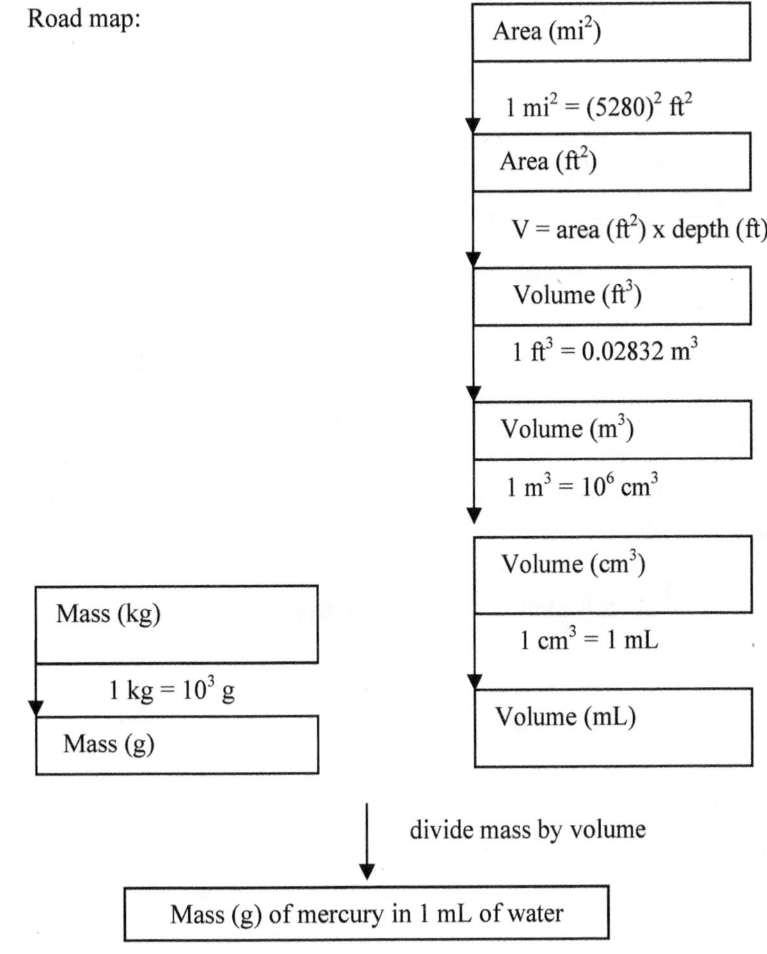

1.7A Plan: Find the mass of Venus in g. Calculate the radius of Venus by dividing its diameter by 2. Convert the radius from km to cm. Use the radius to calculate the volume of Venus. Finally, find the density of Venus by dividing the mass of Venus (in g) by the volume of Venus (in cm^3).

Solution:

$$\text{Mass (g)} = 4.9 \times 10^{24}\ \text{kg}\left(\frac{10^3\ \text{g}}{1\ \text{kg}}\right) = 4.9 \times 10^{27}\ \text{g}$$

$$\text{Radius (cm)} = \left(\frac{12{,}100\ \text{km}}{2}\right)\left(\frac{10^3\ \text{m}}{1\ \text{km}}\right)\left(\frac{10^2\ \text{cm}}{1\ \text{m}}\right) = 6.05 \times 10^8\ \text{cm}$$

$$\text{Volume (cm}^3) = \frac{4}{3}\pi r^3 = \frac{4}{3}(3.14)(6.05 \times 10^8\ \text{cm})^3 = 9.27 \times 10^{26}\ \text{cm}^3$$

$$\text{Density (g/cm}^3) = \frac{4.9 \times 10^{27}\ \text{g}}{9.27 \times 10^{26}\ \text{cm}^3} = \mathbf{5.3\ g/cm^3}$$

Road map:

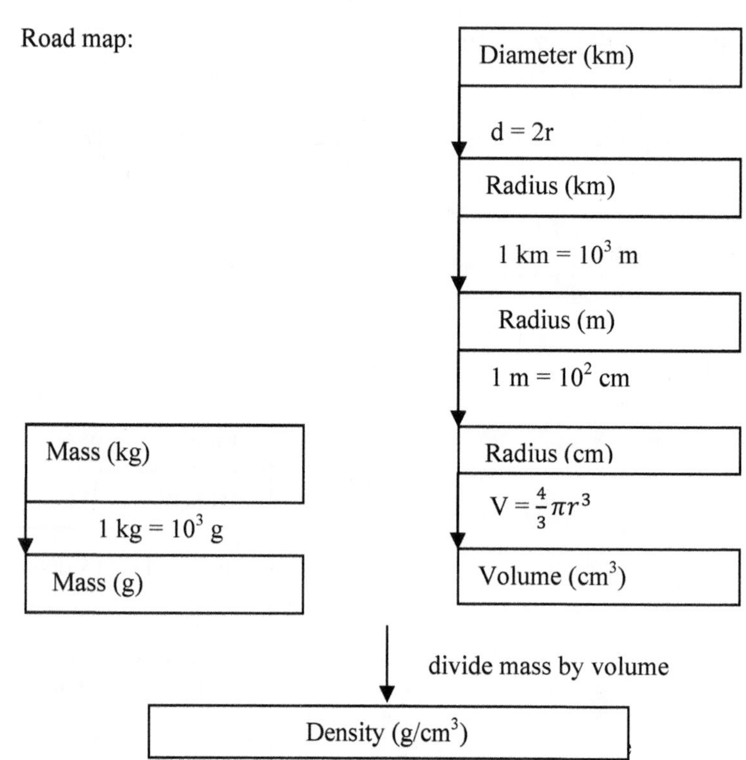

1.7B Plan: The volume unit may be factored away by multiplying by the density. Then it is simply a matter of changing grams to kilograms.

Solution:

$$\text{Mass (kg)} = \left(4.6\ \text{cm}^3\right)\left(\frac{7.5\ \text{g}}{\text{cm}^3}\right)\left(\frac{1\ \text{kg}}{1000\ \text{g}}\right) = 0.0345 = \mathbf{0.034\ kg}$$

Road map:

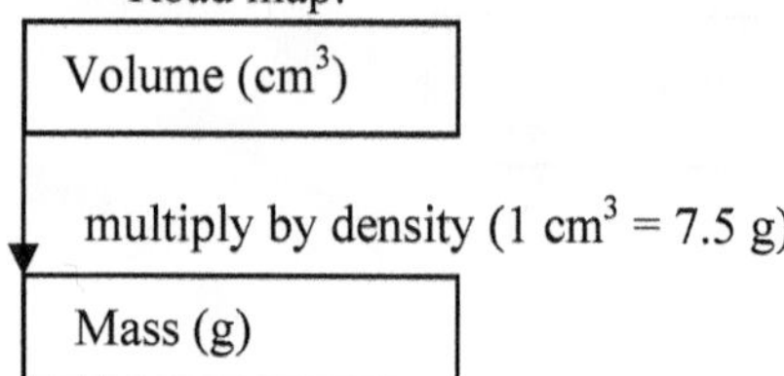

10^3 g = 1 kg

Mass (kg)

1.8A Plan: Using the relationship between the Kelvin and Celsius scales, change the Kelvin temperature to the Celsius temperature. Then convert the Celsius temperature to the Fahrenheit value using the relationship between these two scales.
Solution:
T (in °C) = T (in K) – 273.15 = 234 K – 273.15 = –39.15 = **–39°C**

$T \text{ (in °F)} = \frac{9}{5} \text{T (in °C)} + 32 = \frac{9}{5} (-39.15\text{°C}) + 32 = -38.47 = \mathbf{-38°F}$

Check: Since the Kelvin temperature is below 273, the Celsius temperature must be negative. The low Celsius value gives a negative Fahrenheit value.

1.8B Plan: Convert the Fahrenheit temperature to the Celsius value using the relationship between these two scales. Then use the relationship between the Kelvin and Celsius scales to change the Celsius temperature to the Kelvin temperature.
Solution:

$T \text{ (in °C)} = \frac{5}{9} (\text{T (in °F)} - 32) = \frac{5}{9} (2325 \text{ °F} - 32) = 1273.8889 = 1274 \text{ °C}$

T (in K) = T (in °C) + 273.15 = 1274 °C + 273.15 = 1547.15 = 1547 K
Check: Since the Fahrenheit temperature is large and positive, both the Celsius and Kelvin temperatures should also be positive. Because the Celsius temperature is greater than 273, the Kelvin temperature should be greater than 273, which it is.

1.9A Plan: Determine the significant figures by counting the digits present and accounting for the zeros. Zeros between non-zero digits are significant, as are trailing zeros to the right of a decimal point. Trailing zeros to the left of a decimal point are only significant if the decimal point is present.
Solution:
a) 31.070 mg; **five** significant figures
b) 0.06060 g; **four** significant figures
c) 850.°C; **three** significant figures — note the decimal point that makes the zero significant.
Check: All significant zeros must come after a significant digit.

1.9B Plan: Determine the significant figures by counting the digits present and accounting for the zeros. Zeros between non-zero digits are significant, as are trailing zeros to the right of a decimal point. Trailing zeros to the left of a decimal point are only significant if the decimal point is present.
Solution:
a) 2.000×10^2 mL; **four** significant figures
b) 3.9×10^{-6} m; **two** significant figures — note that none of the zeros are significant.
c) 4.01×10^{-4} L; **three** significant figures
Check: All significant zeros must come after a significant digit.

1.10A Plan: Use the rules presented in the text. Add the two values in the numerator before dividing. The time conversion is an exact conversion and, therefore, does not affect the significant figures in the answer.
Solution:
The addition of 25.65 mL and 37.4 mL gives an answer where the last significant figure is the one after the decimal point (giving three significant figures total):

25.65 mL + 37.4 mL = 63.05 = 63.0 mL

When a four significant figure number divides a three significant figure number, the answer must round to three significant figures. An exact number (1 min / 60 s) will have no bearing on the number of significant figures.

$$\frac{63.0\text{ mL}}{73.55\text{ s}\left(\frac{1\text{ min}}{60\text{ s}}\right)} = 51.394 = \mathbf{51.4\text{ mL/min}}$$

1.10B Plan: Use the rules presented in the text. Subtract the two values in the numerator and multiply the numbers in the denominator before dividing.
Solution:
The subtraction of 35.26 from 154.64 gives an answer in which the last significant figure is two places after the decimal point (giving five significant figures total):

$$154.64\text{ g} - 35.26\text{ g} = 119.38\text{ g}$$

The multiplication of 4.20 cm (three significant figures) by 5.12 cm (three significant figures) by 6.752 cm (four significant figures) gives a number with three significant figures.

$$4.20\text{ cm x }5.12\text{ cm x }6.752\text{ cm} = 145.1950 = 145\text{ cm}^3$$

When a three significant figure number divides a five significant figure number, the answer must round to three significant figures.

$$\frac{119.38\text{ g}}{145\text{ cm}^3} = 0.8233 = \mathbf{0.823\text{ g/cm}^3}$$

END–OF–CHAPTER PROBLEMS

1.2 Plan: Apply the definitions of the states of matter to a container. Next, apply these definitions to the examples. Gas molecules fill the entire container; the volume of a gas is the volume of the container. Solids and liquids have a definite volume. The volume of the container does not affect the volume of a solid or liquid.
Solution:
a) The helium fills the volume of the entire balloon. The addition or removal of helium will change the volume of a balloon. Helium is a **gas**.
b) At room temperature, the mercury does not completely fill the thermometer. The surface of the **liquid** mercury indicates the temperature.
c) The soup completely fills the bottom of the bowl, and it has a definite surface. The soup is a **liquid**, though it is possible that solid particles of food will be present.

1.4 Plan: Define the terms and apply these definitions to the examples.
Solution:
Physical property – A characteristic shown by a substance itself, without interacting with or changing into other substances.
Chemical property – A characteristic of a substance that appears as it interacts with, or transforms into, other substances.
a) The change in color (yellow–green and silvery to white), and the change in physical state (gas and metal to crystals) are examples of **physical properties**. The change in the physical properties indicates that a chemical change occurred. Thus, the interaction between chlorine gas and sodium metal producing sodium chloride is an example of a **chemical property**.
b) The sand and the iron are still present. Neither sand nor iron became something else. Colors along with magnetism are **physical properties**. No chemical changes took place, so there are no chemical properties to observe.

1.6 Plan: Apply the definitions of chemical and physical changes to the examples.
Solution:
a) Not a chemical change, but a **physical change** — simply cooling returns the soup to its original form.
b) There is a **chemical change** — cooling the toast will not "un–toast" the bread.
c) Even though the wood is now in smaller pieces, it is still wood. There has been no change in composition, thus this is a **physical change**, and not a chemical change.
d) This is a **chemical change** converting the wood (and air) into different substances with different compositions. The wood cannot be "unburned."

1.8 Plan: A system has a higher potential energy before the energy is released (used).

Solution:
a) The exhaust is lower in energy than the fuel by an amount of energy equal to that released as the fuel burns. The **fuel** has a higher potential energy.
b) **Wood,** like the fuel, is higher in energy by the amount released as the wood burns.

1.13 Lavoisier measured the total mass of the reactants and products, not just the mass of the solids. The total mass of the reactants and products remained constant. His measurements showed that a gas was involved in the reaction. He called this gas oxygen (one of his key discoveries).

1.16 A well-designed experiment must have the following essential features:
1) There must be two variables that are expected to be related.
2) There must be a way to control all the variables, so that only one at a time may be changed.
3) The results must be reproducible.

1.20 Plan: Density $= \frac{\text{mass}}{\text{volume}}$. An increase in mass or a decrease in volume will increase the density. A decrease in density will result if the mass is decreased or the volume increased.
Solution:
a) Density **increases.** The mass of the chlorine gas is not changed, but its volume is smaller.
b) Density **remains the same.** Neither the mass nor the volume of the solid has changed.
c) Density **decreases.** Water is one of the few substances that expands on freezing. The mass is constant, but the volume increases.
d) Density **increases.** Iron, like most materials, contracts on cooling; thus the volume decreases while the mass does not change.
e) Density **remains the same.** The water does not alter either the mass or the volume of the diamond.

1.23 Plan: Review the definitions of extensive and intensive properties.
Solution:
An extensive property depends on the amount of material present. An intensive property is the same regardless of how much material is present.
a) Mass is an **extensive property**. Changing the amount of material will change the mass.
b) Density is an **intensive property**. Changing the amount of material changes both the mass and the volume, but the ratio (density) remains fixed.
c) Volume is an **extensive property**. Changing the amount of material will change the size (volume).
d) The melting point is an **intensive property**. The melting point depends on the substance, not on the amount of substance.

1.24 Plan: Review the table of conversions in the chapter or inside the back cover of the book. Write the conversion factor so that the unit initially given will cancel, leaving the desired unit.
Solution:

a) To convert from in^2 to cm^2, use $\frac{\mathbf{(2.54\ cm)^2}}{\mathbf{(1\ in)^2}}$; to convert from cm^2 to m^2, use $\frac{\mathbf{(1\ m)^2}}{\mathbf{(100\ cm)^2}}$

b) To convert from km^2 to m^2, use $\frac{\mathbf{(1000\ m)^2}}{\mathbf{(1\ km)^2}}$; to convert from m^2 to cm^2, use $\frac{\mathbf{(100\ cm)^2}}{\mathbf{(1\ m)^2}}$

c) This problem requires two conversion factors: one for distance and one for time. It does not matter which conversion is done first. Alternate methods may be used.
To convert distance, mi to m, use:

$$\left(\frac{1.609\ \text{km}}{1\ \text{mi}}\right)\left(\frac{1000\ \text{m}}{1\ \text{km}}\right) = \mathbf{1.609x10^3\ m/mi}$$

To convert time, h to s, use:

$$\left(\frac{1\text{ h}}{60\text{ min}}\right)\left(\frac{1\text{ min}}{60\text{ s}}\right) = \mathbf{1\ h/3600\ s}$$

Therefore, the complete conversion factor is $\left(\frac{1.609 \times 10^3\text{ m}}{1\text{ mi}}\right)\left(\frac{1\text{ h}}{3600\text{ s}}\right) = \frac{\mathbf{0.4469\ m \bullet h}}{\mathbf{mi \bullet s}}$.

Do the units cancel when you start with a measurement of mi/h?

d) To convert from pounds (lb) to grams (g), use $\frac{\mathbf{1000\ g}}{\mathbf{2.205\ lb}}$.

To convert volume from ft^3 to cm^3 use, $\left(\frac{(1\text{ ft})^3}{(12\text{ in})^3}\right)\left(\frac{(1\text{ in})^3}{(2.54\text{ cm})^3}\right) = \mathbf{3.531x10^{-5}\ ft^3/cm^3}$.

1.26 Plan: Use conversion factors from the inside back cover: 1 pm = 10^{-12} m; 10^{-9} m = 1 nm.
Solution:

$$\text{Radius (nm)} = (1430\text{ pm})\left(\frac{10^{-12}\text{ m}}{1\text{ pm}}\right)\left(\frac{1\text{ nm}}{10^{-9}\text{ m}}\right) = \mathbf{1.43\ nm}$$

1.28 Plan: Use conversion factors: 0.01 m = 1 cm; 2.54 cm = 1 in.
Solution:

$$\text{Length (in)} = (100.\text{ m})\left(\frac{1\text{ cm}}{0.01\text{ m}}\right)\left(\frac{1\text{ in}}{2.54\text{ cm}}\right) = 3.9370\text{x}10^3 = \mathbf{3.94x10^3\ in}$$

1.30 Plan: Use conversion factors $(1\text{ cm})^2 = (0.01\text{ m})^2$; $(1000\text{ m})^2 = (1\text{ km})^2$ to express the area in km^2. To calculate the cost of the patch, use the conversion factor: $(2.54\text{ cm})^2 = (1\text{ in})^2$.
Solution:

$$\text{a) Area (km}^2) = (20.7\text{ cm}^2)\left(\frac{(0.01\text{ m})^2}{(1\text{ cm})^2}\right)\left(\frac{(1\text{ km})^2}{(1000\text{ m})^2}\right) = \mathbf{2.07x10^{-9}\ km^2}$$

$$\text{b) Cost} = (20.7\text{ cm}^2)\left(\frac{(1\text{ in})^2}{(2.54\text{ cm})^2}\right)\left(\frac{\$3.25}{1\text{ in}^2}\right) = 10.4276 = \mathbf{\$10.43}$$

1.32 Plan: Use conversion factor 1 kg = 2.205 lb. The following assumes a body weight of 155 lbs. Use your own body weight in place of the 155 lbs.
Solution:

$$\text{Body weight (kg)} = (155\text{ lb})\left(\frac{1\text{ kg}}{2.205\text{ lb}}\right) = \mathbf{70.3\ kg}$$

Answers will vary, depending on the person's mass.

1.34 Plan: Mass in g is converted to kg in part a) with the conversion factor 1000 g = 1 kg; mass in g is converted to lb in part b) with the conversion factors 1000 g = 1 kg; 1 kg = 2.205 lb. Volume in cm^3 is converted to m^3 with the conversion factor $(1\text{ cm})^3 = (0.01\text{ m})^3$ and to ft^3 with the conversion factors $(2.54\text{ cm})^3 = (1\text{ in})^3$; $(12\text{ in})^3 = (1\text{ ft})^3$. The conversions may be performed in any order.
Solution:

$$\text{a) Density (kg/m}^3) = \left(\frac{5.52\text{ g}}{\text{cm}^3}\right)\left(\frac{(1\text{ cm})^3}{(0.01\text{ m})^3}\right)\left(\frac{1\text{ kg}}{1000\text{ g}}\right) = \mathbf{5.52x10^3\ kg/m^3}$$

b) Density (lb/ft^3) = $\left(\frac{5.52\ g}{cm^3}\right)\left(\frac{(2.54\ cm)^3}{(1\ in)^3}\right)\left(\frac{(12\ in)^3}{(1\ ft)^3}\right)\left(\frac{1\ kg}{1000\ g}\right)\left(\frac{2.205\ lb}{1\ kg}\right)$ = 344.661 = **345 lb/ft³**

1.36 Plan: Use the conversion factors $(1\ \mu m)^3 = (1\text{x}10^{-6}\ m)^3$; $(1\text{x}10^{-3}\ m)^3 = (1\ mm)^3$ to convert to mm^3. To convert to L, use the conversion factors $(1\ \mu m)^3 = (1\text{x}10^{-6}\ m)^3$; $(1\text{x}10^{-2}\ m)^3 = (1\ cm)^3$; $1\ cm^3 = 1\ mL$; $1\ mL = 1\text{x}10^{-3}\ L$.
Solution:

a) Volume (mm^3) = $\left(\frac{2.56\ \mu m^3}{cell}\right)\left(\frac{(1\text{x}10^{-6}\ m)^3}{(1\ \mu m)^3}\right)\left(\frac{(1\ mm)^3}{(1\text{x}10^{-3}\ m)^3}\right)$ = **2.56x10⁻⁹ mm³/cell**

b) Volume (L) = $(10^5\ cells)\left(\frac{2.56\ \mu m^3}{cell}\right)\left(\frac{(1\text{x}10^{-6}\ m)^3}{(1\ \mu m)^3}\right)\left(\frac{(1\ cm)^3}{(1\text{x}10^{-2}\ m)^3}\right)\left(\frac{1\ mL}{1\ cm^3}\right)\left(\frac{1\text{x}10^{-3}\ L}{1\ mL}\right)$

= $2.56\text{x}10^{-10}$ = **10⁻¹⁰ L**

1.38 Plan: The mass of the mercury in the vial is the mass of the vial filled with mercury minus the mass of the empty vial. Use the density of mercury and the mass of the mercury in the vial to find the volume of mercury and thus the volume of the vial. Once the volume of the vial is known, that volume is used in part b. The density of water is used to find the mass of the given volume of water. Add the mass of water to the mass of the empty vial.
Solution:
a) Mass (g) of mercury = mass of vial and mercury – mass of vial = 185.56 g – 55.32 g = 130.24 g

Volume (cm^3) of mercury = volume of vial = $(130.24\ g)\left(\frac{1\ cm^3}{13.53\ g}\right)$ = 9.626016 = **9.626 cm³**

b) Volume (cm^3) of water = volume of vial = 9.626016 cm^3

Mass (g) of water = $(9.626016\ cm^3)\left(\frac{0.997\ g}{1\ cm^3}\right)$ = 9.59714 g water

Mass (g) of vial filled with water = mass of vial + mass of water = 55.32 g + 9.59714 g = 64.91714 = **64.92 g**

1.40 Plan: Calculate the volume of the cube using the relationship Volume = (length of side)³. The length of side in mm must be converted to cm so that volume will have units of cm^3. Divide the mass of the cube by the volume to find density.
Solution:

Side length (cm) = $(15.6\ mm)\left(\frac{10^{-3}\ m}{1\ mm}\right)\left(\frac{1\ cm}{10^{-2}\ m}\right)$ = 1.56 cm (convert to cm to match density unit)

Al cube volume (cm^3) = (length of side)³ = (1.56 cm)³ = 3.7964 cm^3

Density (g/cm^3) = $\frac{mass}{volume} = \frac{10.25\ g}{3.7964\ cm^3}$ = 2.69993 = **2.70 g/cm³**

1.42 Plan: Use the equations given in the text for converting between the three temperature scales.
Solution:
a) T (in °C) = [T (in °F) – 32]$\frac{5}{9}$ = [68°F – 32]$\frac{5}{9}$ = **20.°C**
T (in K) = T (in °C) + 273.15 = 20.°C + 273.15 = 293.15 = **293 K**
b) T (in K) = T (in °C) + 273.15 = –164°C + 273.15 = 109.15 = **109 K**
T (in °F) = $\frac{9}{5}$ T (in °C) + 32 = $\frac{9}{5}$(–164°C) + 32 = –263.2 = **–263°F**
c) T (in °C) = T (in K) – 273.15 = 0 K – 273.15 = –273.15 = **–273°C**
T (in °F) = $\frac{9}{5}$ T (in °C) + 32 = $\frac{9}{5}$(–273.15°C) + 32 = –459.67 = **–460.°F**

1.45 Plan: Use 1 nm = 10^{-9} m to convert wavelength in nm to m. To convert wavelength in pm to Å, use 1 pm = 0.01 Å.
Solution:

$$\text{a) Wavelength (m)} = (247\ \text{nm})\left(\frac{10^{-9}\ \text{m}}{1\ \text{nm}}\right) = \mathbf{2.47x10^{-7}\ m}$$

$$\text{b) Wavelength (Å)} = (6760\ \text{pm})\left(\frac{0.01\ \text{Å}}{1\ \text{pm}}\right) = \mathbf{67.6\ Å}$$

1.52 Plan: Review the rules for significant zeros.
Solution:
a) No significant zeros (leading zeros are not significant)
b) No significant zeros (leading zeros are not significant)
c) $0.041\underline{0}$ (terminal zeros to the right of the decimal point are significant)
d) $4.\underline{0}1\underline{00}\text{x}10^4$ (zeros between nonzero digits are significant; terminal zeros to the right of the decimal point are significant)

1.54 Plan: Review the rules for rounding.
Solution: (significant figures are underlined)
a) $0.000\underline{35}54$: the extra digits are 54 at the end of the number. When the digit to be removed is 5 and that 5 is followed by nonzero numbers, the last digit kept is increased by 1: **0.00036**
b) $\underline{35.83}48$: the extra digits are 48. Since the digit to be removed (4) is less than 5, the last digit kept is unchanged: **35.83**
c) $\underline{22.4}555$: the extra digits are 555. When the digit to be removed is 5 and that 5 is followed by nonzero numbers, the last digit kept is increased by 1: **22.5**

1.56 Plan: Review the rules for rounding.
Solution:
19 rounds to 20: the digit to be removed (9) is greater than 5 so the digit kept is increased by 1.
155 rounds to 160: the digit to be removed is 5 and the digit to be kept is an odd number, so that digit kept is increased by 1.
8.3 rounds to 8: the digit to be removed (3) is less than 5 so the digit kept remains unchanged.
3.2 rounds to 3: the digit to be removed (2) is less than 5 so the digit kept remains unchanged.
2.9 rounds to 3: the digit to be removed (9) is greater than 5 so the digit kept is increased by 1.
4.7 rounds to 5: the digit to be removed (7) is greater than 5 so the digit kept is increased by 1.

$$\left(\frac{20\ \text{x}\ 160\ \text{x}\ 8}{3\ \text{x}\ 3\ \text{x}\ 5}\right) = 568.89 = \mathbf{6x10^2}$$

Since there are numbers in the calculation with only one significant figure, the answer can be reported only to one significant figure. (Note that the answer is 560 with the original number of significant digits.)

1.58 Plan: Use a calculator to obtain an initial value. Use the rules for significant figures and rounding to get the final answer.
Solution:
a) $\frac{(2.795\ \text{m})(3.10\ \text{m})}{6.48\ \text{m}} = 1.3371 = \mathbf{1.34\ m}$ (maximum of 3 significant figures allowed since two of the original numbers in the calculation have only 3 significant figures)

b) $V = \left(\frac{4}{3}\right)\pi(17.282\ \text{mm})^3 = 21{,}620.74 = \mathbf{21{,}621\ mm^3}$ (maximum of 5 significant figures allowed)

c) 1.110 cm + 17.3 cm + 108.2 cm + 316 cm = 442.61 = **443 cm** (no digits allowed to the right of the decimal since 316 has no digits to the right of the decimal point)

1.60 Plan: Review the procedure for changing a number to scientific notation. There can be only 1 nonzero digit to the left of the decimal point in correct scientific notation. Moving the decimal point to the left results in a positive exponent while moving the decimal point to the right results in a negative exponent.

Solution:

a) $\mathbf{1.310000x10^5}$ (Note that all zeros are significant.)
b) $\mathbf{4.7x10^{-4}}$ (No zeros are significant.)
c) $\mathbf{2.10006x10^5}$
d) $\mathbf{2.1605x10^3}$

1.62 Plan: Review the examples for changing a number from scientific notation to standard notation. If the exponent is positive, move the decimal back to the right; if the exponent is negative, move the decimal point back to the left.

Solution:

a) **5550** (Do not use terminal decimal point since the zero is not significant.)
b) **10070.** (Use terminal decimal point since final zero is significant.)
c) **0.000000885**
d) **0.003004**

1.64 Plan: In most cases, this involves a simple addition or subtraction of values from the exponents. There can be only 1 nonzero digit to the left of the decimal point in correct scientific notation.

Solution:

a) $\mathbf{8.025x10^4}$ (The decimal point must be moved an additional 2 places to the left: $10^2 + 10^2 = 10^4$)
b) $\mathbf{1.0098x10^{-3}}$ (The decimal point must be moved an additional 3 places to the left: $10^3 + 10^{-6} = 10^{-3}$)
c) $\mathbf{7.7x10^{-11}}$ (The decimal point must be moved an additional 2 places to the right: $10^{-2} + 10^{-9} = 10^{-11}$)

1.66 Plan: Calculate a temporary answer by simply entering the numbers into a calculator. Then you will need to round the value to the appropriate number of significant figures. Cancel units as you would cancel numbers, and place the remaining units after your numerical answer.

Solution:

a) $$\frac{\left(6.626\text{x}10^{-34}\ \text{J}\bullet\text{s}\right)\left(2.9979\text{x}10^{8}\ \text{m/s}\right)}{489\text{x}10^{-9}\ \text{m}} = 4.062185\text{x}10^{-19}$$

$\mathbf{4.06x10^{-19}}$ **J** ($489\text{x}10^{-9}$ m limits the answer to 3 significant figures; units of m and s cancel)

b) $$\frac{\left(6.022\ \text{x}\ 10^{23}\ \text{molecules/mol}\right)\left(1.23\ \text{x}\ 10^{2}\ \text{g}\right)}{46.07\ \text{g/mol}} = 1.6078\text{x}10^{24}$$

$\mathbf{1.61x10^{24}}$ **molecules** ($1.23\text{x}10^2$ g limits answer to 3 significant figures; units of mol and g cancel)

c) $$\left(6.022\ \text{x}\ 10^{23}\ \text{atoms/mol}\right)\left(2.18\ \text{x}\ 10^{-18}\ \text{J/atom}\right)\left(\frac{1}{2^2}-\frac{1}{3^2}\right) = 1.82333\text{x}10^{5}$$

$\mathbf{1.82x10^5}$ **J/mol** ($2.18\text{x}10^{-18}$ J/atom limits answer to 3 significant figures; unit of atoms cancels)

1.68 Plan: Exact numbers are those which have no uncertainty. Unit definitions and number counts of items in a group are examples of exact numbers.

Solution:

a) The height of Angel Falls is a measured quantity. This is **not** an exact number.
b) The number of planets in the solar system is a number count. This **is** an exact number.
c) The number of grams in a pound is not a unit definition. This is **not** an exact number.
d) The number of millimeters in a meter is a definition of the prefix "milli–." This **is** an exact number.

1.70 Plan: Observe the figure, and estimate a reading the best you can.

Solution:

The scale markings are 0.2 cm apart. The end of the metal strip falls between the mark for 7.4 cm and 7.6 cm. If we assume that one can divide the space between markings into fourths, the uncertainty is one-fourth the separation between the marks. Thus, since the end of the metal strip falls between 7.45 and 7.55 we can report its length as **7.50 ± 0.05 cm**. (Note: If the assumption is that one can divide the space between markings into halves only, then the result is 7.5 ± 0.1 cm.)

1.72 Plan: Calculate the average of each data set. Remember that accuracy refers to how close a measurement is to the actual or true value while precision refers to how close multiple measurements are to each other.
Solution:

a) $I_{avg} = \dfrac{8.72\text{ g} + 8.74\text{ g} + 8.70\text{ g}}{3} = 8.7200 = \mathbf{8.72\text{ g}}$

$II_{avg} = \dfrac{8.56\text{ g} + 8.77\text{ g} + 8.83\text{ g}}{3} = 8.7200 = \mathbf{8.72\text{ g}}$

$III_{avg} = \dfrac{8.50\text{ g} + 8.48\text{ g} + 8.51\text{ g}}{3} = 8.4967 = \mathbf{8.50\text{ g}}$

$IV_{avg} = \dfrac{8.41\text{ g} + 8.72\text{ g} + 8.55\text{ g}}{3} = 8.5600 = \mathbf{8.56\text{ g}}$

Sets **I** and **II** are most accurate since their average value, 8.72 g, is closest to the true value, 8.72 g.
b) To get an idea of precision, calculate the range of each set of values: largest value – smallest value. A small range is an indication of good precision since the values are close to each other.
I_{range} = 8.74 g – 8.70 g = 0.04 g
II_{range} = 8.83 g – 8.56 g = 0.27 g
III_{range} = 8.51 g – 8.48 g = 0.03 g
IV_{range} = 8.72 g – 8.41 g = 0.31 g
Set III is the most precise (smallest range), but is the least accurate (the average is the farthest from the actual value).
c) **Set I** has the best combination of high accuracy (average value = actual value) and high precision (relatively small range).
d) **Set IV** has both low accuracy (average value differs from actual value) and low precision (has the largest range).

1.74 Plan: If it is necessary to force something to happen, the potential energy will be higher.
Solution:
a)

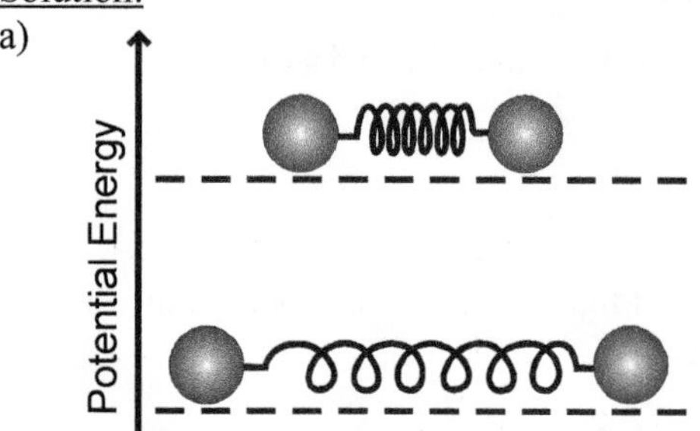

b)

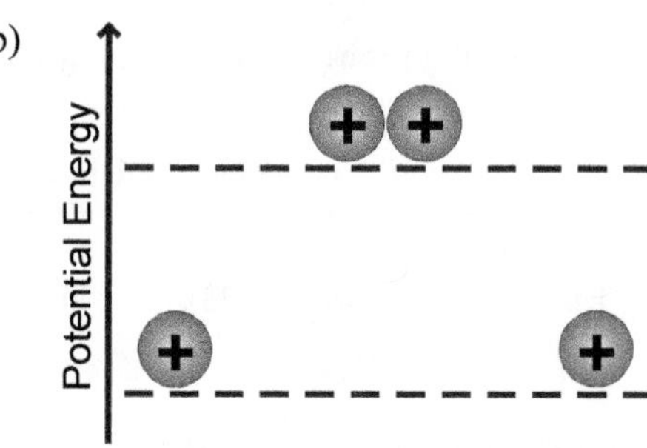

a) The balls on the relaxed spring have a lower potential energy and are more stable. The balls on the compressed spring have a higher potential energy, because the balls will move once the spring is released. This configuration is less stable.
b) The two + charges apart from each other have a lower potential energy and are more stable. The two + charges near each other have a higher potential energy, because they repel one another. This arrangement is less stable.

1.76 Plan: Use the concentrations of bromine given.
Solution:

$\dfrac{\text{Mass bromine in Dead Sea}}{\text{Mass bromine in seawater}} = \dfrac{0.50\text{ g/L}}{0.065\text{ g/L}} = \mathbf{7.7 / 1}$

1.78 Plan: In each case, calculate the overall density of the ball and contents and compare to the density of air. The volume of the ball in cm^3 is converted to units of L to find the density of the ball itself in g/L. The densities of the ball and the gas in the ball are additive because the volume of the ball and the volume of the gas are the same.
Solution:
a) Density of evacuated ball: the mass is only that of the sphere itself:

$$\text{Volume of ball (L)} = \left(560\ \text{cm}^3\right)\left(\frac{1\ \text{mL}}{1\ \text{cm}^3}\right)\left(\frac{10^{-3}\ \text{L}}{1\ \text{mL}}\right) = 0.560 = 0.56\ \text{L}$$

$$\text{Density of evacuated ball} = \frac{\text{mass}}{\text{volume}} = \frac{0.12\ \text{g}}{0.560} = 0.21\ \text{g/L}$$

The evacuated ball will **float** because its density is less than that of air.
b) Because the density of CO_2 is greater than that of air, a ball filled with CO_2 will **sink**.
c) Density of ball + density of hydrogen = 0.0899 + 0.21 g/L = 0.30 g/L
The ball will **float** because the density of the ball filled with hydrogen is less than the density of air.
d) Because the density of O_2 is greater than that of air, a ball filled with O_2 will **sink**.
e) Density of ball + density of nitrogen = 0.21 g/L + 1.165 g/L = 1.38 g/L
The ball will **sink** because the density of the ball filled with nitrogen is greater than the density of air.

f) To sink, the total mass of the ball and gas must weigh $\left(\frac{0.560\ \text{L}}{}\right)\left(\frac{1.189\ \text{g}}{1\ \text{L}}\right) = 0.66584\ \text{g}$

For the evacuated ball:
0.66584 – 0.12 g = 0.54585 = **0.55 g**. More than 0.55 g would have to be added to make the ball sink.
For ball filled with hydrogen:

$$\text{Mass of hydrogen in the ball} = (0.56\ \text{L})\left(\frac{0.0899\ \text{g}}{1\ \text{L}}\right) = 0.0503\ \text{g}$$

Mass of hydrogen and ball = 0.0503 g + 0.12 g = 0.17 g
0.66584 – 0.17 g = 0.4958 = **0.50 g**. More than 0.50 g would have to be added to make the ball sink.

1.80 Plan: Convert the surface area to m^2 and then use the surface area and the depth to determine the volume of the oceans (area x depth = volume) in m^3. The volume is then converted to liters, and finally to the mass of gold using the density of gold in g/L. Once the mass of the gold is known, its density is used to find the volume of that amount of gold. The mass of gold is converted to troy oz and the price of gold per troy oz gives the total price.
Solution:

$$\text{a) Area of ocean (m}^2) = \left(3.63\text{x}10^8\ \text{km}^2\right)\left(\frac{(1000\ \text{m})^2}{(1\ \text{km})^2}\right) = 3.63\text{x}10^{14}\ \text{m}^2$$

$$\text{Volume of ocean (m}^3) = \text{(area)(depth)} = (3.63\text{x}10^{14}\ \text{m}^2)(3800\ \text{m}) = 1.3794\text{x}10^{18}\ \text{m}^3$$

$$\text{Mass of gold (g)} = \left(1.3794\ \text{x}\ 10^{18}\ \text{m}^3\right)\left(\frac{1\ \text{L}}{10^{-3}\ \text{m}^3}\right)\left(\frac{5.8\ \text{x}\ 10^{-9}\ \text{g}}{\text{L}}\right) = 8.00052\text{x}10^{12} = \mathbf{8.0x10^{12}\ g}$$

b) Use the density of gold to convert mass of gold to volume of gold:

$$\text{Volume of gold (m}^3) = \left(8.00052\ \text{x}\ 10^{12}\ \text{g}\right)\left(\frac{1\ \text{cm}^3}{19.3\ \text{g}}\right)\left(\frac{(0.01\ \text{m})^3}{(1\ \text{cm})^3}\right) = 4.14535\text{x}10^5 = \mathbf{4.1x10^5\ m^3}$$

$$\text{c) Value of gold} = \left(8.00052\ \text{x}\ 10^{12}\ \text{g}\right)\left(\frac{1\ \text{tr. oz}}{31.1\ \text{g}}\right)\left(\frac{\$1595}{1\ \text{tr. oz.}}\right) = 4.1032\ \text{x}\ 10^{14} = \mathbf{\$4.1\ x\ 10^{14}}$$

1.82 Plan: Use the equations for temperature conversion given in the chapter. The mass of nitrogen is conserved when the gas is liquefied; the mass of the nitrogen gas equals the mass of the liquid nitrogen. Use the density of nitrogen gas to find the mass of the nitrogen; then use the density of liquid nitrogen to find the volume of that mass of liquid nitrogen.
Solution:
a) T(in °C) = T(in K) – 273.15 = 77.36 K – 273.15 = **–195.79°C**

b) T (in °F) = $\frac{9}{5}$ T(in °C) + 32 = $\frac{9}{5}$ (–195.79°C) + 32 = –320.422 = **–320.42°F**

c) Mass of liquid nitrogen = mass of gaseous nitrogen = $(895.0 \text{ L})\left(\frac{4.566 \text{ g}}{1 \text{ L}}\right)$ = 4086.57 g N_2

Volume of liquid N_2 = $(4086.57 \text{ g})\left(\frac{1 \text{ L}}{809 \text{ g}}\right)$ = 5.0514 = **5.05 L**

1.83 Plan: For part a), convert mi to m and h to s. For part b), time is converted from h to min and length from mi to km. For part c), convert the distance in ft to mi and use the average speed in mi/h to find the time necessary to cover the given distance.
Solution:

a) Speed (m/s) = $\left(\frac{5.9 \text{ mi}}{\text{h}}\right)\left(\frac{1000 \text{ m}}{0.62 \text{ mi}}\right)\left(\frac{1 \text{ h}}{3600 \text{ s}}\right)$ = 2.643 = **2.6 m/s**

b) Distance (km) = $(98 \text{ min})\left(\frac{1 \text{ h}}{60 \text{ min}}\right)\left(\frac{5.9 \text{ mi}}{\text{h}}\right)\left(\frac{1 \text{ km}}{0.62 \text{ mi}}\right)$ = 15.543 = **16 km**

c) Time (h) = $(4.75\text{x}10^4 \text{ ft})\left(\frac{1 \text{ mi}}{5280 \text{ ft}}\right)\left(\frac{1 \text{ h}}{5.9 \text{ mi}}\right)$ = 1.5248 = 1.5 h

If she starts running at 11:15 am, 1.5 hours later the time is **12:45 pm**.

1.85 Plan: In visualizing the problem, the two scales can be set next to each other.
Solution:

There are 50 divisions between the freezing point and boiling point of benzene on the °X scale and 74.6 divisions (80.1°C – 5.5°C) on the °C scale. So °X = $\left(\frac{50°\text{X}}{74.6°\text{C}}\right)$ °C

This does not account for the offset of 5.5 divisions in the °C scale from the zero point on the °X scale.

So °X = $\left(\frac{50°\text{X}}{74.6°\text{C}}\right)$ (°C – 5.5°C)

Check: Plug in 80.1°C and see if result agrees with expected value of 50°X.

So °X = $\left(\frac{50°\text{X}}{74.6°\text{C}}\right)$ (80.1°C – 5.5°C) = 50°X

Use this formula to find the freezing and boiling points of water on the °X scale.

fp_{water} °X = $\left(\frac{50°\text{X}}{74.6°\text{C}}\right)$ (0.00°C – 5.5°C) = 3.68°X = **–3.7°X**

bp_{water} °X = $\left(\frac{50°\text{X}}{74.6°\text{C}}\right)$ (100.0°C – 5.5°C) = **63.3°X**

1.86 Plan: Determine the total mass of Earth's crust in metric tons (t) by finding the volume of crust (surface area x depth) in km^3 and then in cm^3 and then using the density to find the mass of this volume, using conversions from the inside back cover. The mass of each individual element comes from the concentration of that element multiplied by the mass of the crust.
Solution:

Volume of crust (km^3) = area x depth = $(35 \text{ km})(5.10\text{x}10^8 \text{ km}^2)$ = $1.785\text{x}10^{10}$ km^3

Volume of crust (cm^3) = $(1.785 \text{ x } 10^{10} \text{ km}^3)\left(\frac{(1000 \text{ m})^3}{(1 \text{ km})^3}\right)\left(\frac{(1 \text{ cm})^3}{(0.01 \text{ m})^3}\right)$ = $1.785\text{x}10^{25}$ cm^3

$$\text{Mass of crust (t)} = \left(1.785 \times 10^{25}\ \text{cm}^3\right)\left(\frac{2.8\ \text{g}}{1\ \text{cm}^3}\right)\left(\frac{1\ \text{kg}}{1000\ \text{g}}\right)\left(\frac{1\ \text{t}}{1000\ \text{kg}}\right) = 4.998\text{x}10^{19}\ \text{t}$$

$$\text{Mass of oxygen (g)} = \left(4.998 \times 10^{19}\ \text{t}\right)\left(\frac{4.55 \times 10^5\ \text{g oxygen}}{1\ \text{t}}\right) = 2.2741\text{x}10^{25} = \mathbf{2.3x10^{25}\ g\ oxygen}$$

$$\text{Mass of silicon (g)} = \left(4.998 \times 10^{19}\ \text{t}\right)\left(\frac{2.72 \times 10^5\ \text{g silicon}}{1\ \text{t}}\right) = 1.3595\text{x}10^{25} = \mathbf{1.4x10^{25}\ g\ silicon}$$

$$\text{Mass of ruthenium} = \text{mass of rhodium} = \left(4.998 \times 10^{19}\ \text{t}\right)\left(\frac{1 \times 10^{-4}\ \text{g element}}{1\ \text{t}}\right)$$

$$= 4.998\text{x}10^{15} = \mathbf{5x10^{15}\ g\ each\ of\ ruthenium\ and\ rhodium}$$

CHAPTER 2 THE COMPONENTS OF MATTER

FOLLOW–UP PROBLEMS

2.1A Plan: An element has only one kind of atom; a compound is composed of at least two kinds of atoms. A mixture consists of two or more substances mixed together in the same container.
Solution:
(a) There is only one type of atom (blue) present, so this is an **element**.
(b) Two different atoms (brown and green) appear in a fixed ratio of 1/1, so this is a **compound**.
(c) These molecules consist of one type of atom (orange), so this is an **element**.

2.1B Plan: An element has only one kind of atom; a compound is composed of at least two kinds of atoms.
Solution:
The circle on the left contains molecules with either only orange atoms or only blue atoms. This is a **mixture of two different elements**. In the circle on the right, the molecules are composed of one orange atom and one blue atom so this is a **compound**.

2.2A Plan: Use the mass fraction of uranium in pitchblende (from Sample Problem 2.2) to find the mass of pitchblende that contains 2.3 t of uranium. Subtract the amount of uranium from that amount of pitchblende to obtain the mass of oxygen in that amount of pitchblende. Find the mass fraction of oxygen in pitchblende and multiply the amount of pitchblende by the mass fraction of oxygen to determine the mass of oxygen in the sample.
Solution:

$$\text{Mass (t) of pitchblende} = (2.3\ \text{t uranium})\left(\frac{84.2\ \text{t pitchblende}}{71.4\ \text{t uranium}}\right) = 2.7123 = \mathbf{2.7\ t\ pitchblende}$$

Mass (t) of oxygen in 84.2 t of pitchblende = 84.2 t pitchblende – 71.4 t uranium = 12.8 t oxygen

$$\text{Mass (t) of oxygen} = (2.7123\ \text{t pitchblende})\left(\frac{12.8\ \text{t oxygen}}{84.2\ \text{t pitchblende}}\right) = 0.4123 = \mathbf{0.41\ t\ oxygen}$$

2.2B Plan: Subtract the amount of silver from the amount of silver bromide to find the mass of bromine in 26.8 g of silver bromide. Use the mass fraction of silver in silver bromide to find the mass of silver in 3.57 g of silver bromide. Use the mass fraction of bromine in silver bromide to find the mass of bromine in 3.57 g of silver bromide.
Solution:
Mass (g) of bromine in 26.8 g silver bromide = 26.8 g silver bromide – 15.4 g silver = 11.4 g bromine

$$\text{Mass (g) of silver in 3.57 g silver bromide} = 3.57\ \text{g silver bromide}\left(\frac{15.4\ \text{g silver}}{26.8\ \text{g silver bromide}}\right) = \mathbf{2.05\ g\ silver}$$

$$\text{Mass (g) of bromine in 3.57 g silver bromide} = 3.57\ \text{g silver bromide}\left(\frac{11.4\ \text{g bromine}}{26.8\ \text{g silver bromide}}\right) = \mathbf{1.52\ g\ bromine}$$

2.3A Plan: The law of multiple proportions states that when two elements react to form two compounds, the different masses of element B that react with a fixed mass of element A is a ratio of small whole numbers. The law of definite composition states that the elements in a compound are present in fixed parts by mass. The law of mass conversation states that the total mass before and after a reaction is the same.
Solution:
The law of **mass conservation** is illustrated because the number of atoms does not change as the reaction proceeds (there are 14 red spheres and 12 black spheres before and after the reaction occurs). The law of **multiple proportions** is illustrated because two compounds are formed as a result of the reaction. One of the compounds has a ratio of 2 red spheres to 1 black sphere. The other has a ratio of 1 red sphere to 1 black sphere. The law of **definite proportions** is illustrated because each compound has a fixed ratio of red-to-black atoms.

2.3B Plan: The law of multiple proportions states that when two elements react to form two compounds, the different masses of element B that react with a fixed mass of element A is a ratio of small whole numbers.
Solution:
Only **Sample B** shows two different bromine-fluorine compounds. In one compound there are three fluorine atoms for every one bromine atom; in the other compound, there is one fluorine atom for every bromine atom.

2.4A Plan: The subscript (atomic number = Z) gives the number of protons, and for an atom, the number of electrons. The atomic number identifies the element. The superscript gives the mass number (A) which is the total of the protons plus neutrons. The number of neutrons is simply the mass number minus the atomic number ($A - Z$).
Solution:
^{46}Ti $Z = 22$ and $A = 46$, there are **22 p^+** and **22 e^-** and $46 - 22 =$ **24 n^0**
^{47}Ti $Z = 22$ and $A = 47$, there are **22 p^+** and **22 e^-** and $46 - 22 =$ **25 n^0**
^{48}Ti $Z = 22$ and $A = 48$, there are **22 p^+** and **22 e^-** and $46 - 22 =$ **26 n^0**
^{49}Ti $Z = 22$ and $A = 49$, there are **22 p^+** and **22 e^-** and $46 - 22 =$ **27 n^0**
^{50}Ti $Z = 22$ and $A = 50$, there are **22 p^+** and **22 e^-** and $46 - 22 =$ **28 n^0**

2.4B Plan: The subscript (atomic number = Z) gives the number of protons, and for an atom, the number of electrons. The atomic number identifies the element. The superscript gives the mass number (A) which is the total of the protons plus neutrons. The number of neutrons is simply the mass number minus the atomic number ($A - Z$).
Solution:
a) $Z = 5$ and $A = 11$, there are 5 p^+ and 5 e^- and $11 - 5 = 6$ n^0; Atomic number = 5 = **B.**
b) $Z = 20$ and $A = 41$, there are 20 p^+ and 20 e^- and $41 - 20 = 21$ n^0; Atomic number = 20 = **Ca.**
c) $Z = 53$ and $A = 131$, there are 53 p^+ and 53 e^- and $131 - 53 = 78$ n^0; Atomic number = 53 = **I.**

2.5A Plan: First, divide the percent abundance value (found in Figure B2.2C, Tools of the Laboratory, p. 57) by 100 to obtain the fractional value for each isotope. Multiply each isotopic mass by the fractional value, and add the resulting masses to obtain neon's atomic mass.
Solution:
Atomic Mass = (^{20}Ne mass) (fractional abundance of ^{20}Ne) + (^{21}Ne mass) (fractional abundance of ^{21}Ne) + (^{22}Ne mass) (fractional abundance of ^{22}Ne)
^{20}Ne = (19.99244 amu)(0.9048) = 18.09 amu
^{21}Ne = (20.99385 amu)(0.0027) = 0.057 amu
^{22}Ne = (21.99139 amu)(0.0925) = 2.03 amu
20.177 amu = **20.18 amu**

2.5B Plan: To find the percent abundance of each B isotope, let x equal the fractional abundance of ^{10}B and (1 – x) equal the fractional abundance of ^{11}B. Remember that atomic mass = isotopic mass of ^{10}B x fractional abundance) + (isotopic mass of ^{11}B x fractional abundance).
Solution:
Atomic Mass = (^{10}B mass) (fractional abundance of ^{10}B) + (^{11}B mass) (fractional abundance of ^{11}B)
Amount of ^{10}B + Amount ^{11}B = 1 (setting ^{10}B = x gives ^{11}B = 1 – x)
10.81 amu = (10.0129 amu)(x) + (11.0093 amu) (1 – x)
10.81 amu = 11.0093 – 11.0093x + 10.0129 x
10.81 amu = 11.0093 – 0.9964 x
–0.1993 = – 0.9964x
x = 0.20; 1 – x = 0.80
(10.81 – 11.0093 limits the answer to 2 significant figures)
Fraction x 100% = percent abundance.
% abundance of ^{10}B = **20.%**; % abundance of ^{11}B = **80.%**

2.6A Plan: Use the provided atomic numbers (the Z numbers) to locate these elements on the periodic table. The name of the element is on the periodic table or on the list of elements inside the front cover of the textbook. Use the periodic table to find the group/column number (listed at the top of each column) and the period/row number (listed at the left of each row) in which the element is located. Classify the element from the color coding in the periodic table.

Solution:
(a) Z = 14: Silicon, Si; Group 4A(14) and Period 3; metalloid
(b) Z = 55: Cesium, Cs; Group 1A(1) and Period 6; main-group metal
(c) Z = 54: Xenon, Xe; Group 8A(18) and Period 5; nonmetal

2.6B Plan: Use the provided atomic numbers (the Z numbers) to locate these elements on the periodic table. The name of the element is on the periodic table or on the list of elements inside the front cover of the textbook. Use the periodic table to find the group/column number (listed at the top of each column) and the period/row number (listed at the left of each row) in which the element is located. Classify the element from the color coding in the periodic table.
Solution:
(a) Z = 12: Magnesium, Mg; Group 2A(2) and Period 3; main-group metal
(b) Z = 7: Nitrogen, N; Group 5A(15) and Period 2; nonmetal
(c) Z = 30: Zinc, Zn; Group 2B(12) and Period 4; transition metal

2.7A Plan: Locate these elements on the periodic table and predict what ions they will form. For A-group cations (metals), ion charge = group number; for anions (nonmetals), ion charge = group number – 8. Or, relate the element's position to the nearest noble gas. Elements after a noble gas lose electrons to become positive ions, while those before a noble gas gain electrons to become negative ions.
Solution:
a) $_{16}\mathbf{S}^{2-}$ [Group 6A(16); 6 – 8 = –2]; sulfur needs to gain 2 electrons to match the number of electrons in $_{18}$Ar.
b) $_{37}\mathbf{Rb}^{+}$ [Group 1A(1)]; rubidium needs to lose 1 electron to match the number of electrons in $_{36}$Kr.
c) $_{56}\mathbf{Ba}^{2+}$ [Group 2A(2)]; barium needs to lose 2 electrons to match the number of electrons in $_{54}$Xe.

2.7B Plan: Locate these elements on the periodic table and predict what ions they will form. For A-group cations (metals), ion charge = group number; for anions (nonmetals), ion charge = group number – 8. Or, relate the element's position to the nearest noble gas. Elements after a noble gas lose electrons to become positive ions, while those before a noble gas gain electrons to become negative ions.
Solution:
a) $_{38}\mathbf{Sr}^{2+}$ [Group 2A(2)]; strontium needs to lose 2 electrons to match the number of electrons in $_{36}$Kr.
b) $_{8}\mathbf{O}^{2-}$ [Group 6A(16); 6 – 8 = –2]; oxygen needs to gain 2 electrons to match the number of electrons in $_{10}$Ne.
c) $_{55}\mathbf{Cs}^{+}$ [Group 1A(1)]; cesium needs to lose 1 electron to match the number of electrons in $_{54}$Xe.

2.8A Plan: When dealing with ionic binary compounds, the first name is that of the metal and the second name is that of the nonmetal. If there is any doubt, refer to the periodic table. The metal name is unchanged, while the nonmetal has an -ide suffix added to the nonmetal root.
Solution:
a) **Zinc** is in **Group 2B(12)** and **oxygen**, from oxide, is in **Group 6A(16)**.
b) **Silver** is in **Group 1B(11)** and **bromine**, from bromide, is in **Group 7A(17)**.
c) **Lithium** is in **Group 1A(1)** and **chlorine**, from chloride, is in **Group 7A(17)**.
d) **Aluminum** is in **Group 3A(13)** and **sulfur**, from sulfide, is in **Group 6A(16)**.

2.8B Plan: When dealing with ionic binary compounds, the first name is that of the metal and the second name is that of the nonmetal. If there is any doubt, refer to the periodic table. The metal name is unchanged, while the nonmetal has an -ide suffix added to the nonmetal root.
Solution:
a) **Potassium** is in **Group 1A(1)** and **sulfur**, from sulfide, is in **Group 6A(16)**.
b) **Barium** is in **Group 2A(2)** and **chlorine**, from chloride, is in **Group 7A(17)**.
c) **Cesium** is in **Group 1A(1)** and **nitrogen**, from nitride, is in **Group 5A(15)**.
d) **Sodium** is in **Group 1A(1)** and **hydrogen**, from hydride, is in **Group 1A(1)**.

2.9A Plan: Use the charges of the ions to predict the lowest ratio leading to a neutral compound. The sum of the total charges must be 0.
Solution:
a) Zinc should form Zn^{2+} and oxygen should form O^{2-}; these will combine to give **ZnO**. The charges cancel (+2 + –2 = 0), so this is an acceptable formula.

b) Silver should form Ag^+ and bromine should form Br^-; these will combine to give **AgBr**. The charges cancel (+1 + –1 = 0), so this is an acceptable formula.
c) Lithium should form Li^+ and chlorine should form Cl^-; these will combine to give **LiCl**. The charges cancel (+1 + –1 = 0), so this is an acceptable formula.
d) Aluminum should form Al^{3+} and sulfur should form S^{2-}; to produce a neutral combination the formula is $\mathbf{Al_2S_3}$. This way the charges will cancel [2(+3) + 3(–2) = 0], so this is an acceptable formula.

2.9B Plan: Use the charges of the ions to predict the lowest ratio leading to a neutral compound. The sum of the total charges must be 0.
Solution:
a) Potassium should form K^+ and sulfur should form S^{2-}; these will combine to give $\mathbf{K_2S}$. The charges cancel [2(+1) + 1(–2) = 0], so this is an acceptable formula.
b) Barium should form Ba^{2+} and chlorine should form Cl^-; these will combine to give $\mathbf{BaCl_2}$. The charges cancel [1(+2) + 2(–1) = 0], so this is an acceptable formula.
c) Cesium should form Cs^+ and nitrogen should form N^{3-}; these will combine to give $\mathbf{Cs_3N}$. The charges cancel [3(+1) + 1(–3) = 0], so this is an acceptable formula.
d) Sodium should form Na^+ and hydrogen should form H^-; to produce a neutral combination the formula is **NaH**. This way the charges will cancel (+1 + –1 = 0), so this is an acceptable formula.

2.10A Plan: Determine the names or symbols of each of the species present. Then combine the species to produce a name or formula. The metal or positive ions are written first. Review the rules for nomenclature covered in the chapter. For metals like many transition metals, that can form more than one ion each with a different charge, the ionic charge of the metal ion is indicated by a Roman numeral within parentheses immediately following the metal's name.
Solution:
a) The Roman numeral means that the lead is Pb^{4+}; oxygen produces the usual O^{2-}. The neutral combination is [+4 + 2(–2) = 0], so the formula is $\mathbf{PbO_2}$.
b) Sulfide (Group 6A(16)), like oxide, is –2 (6 – 8 = – 2). This is split between two copper ions, each of which must be +1. This is one of the two common charges for copper ions. The +1 charge on the copper is indicated with a Roman numeral. This gives the name **copper(I) sulfide** (common name = cuprous sulfide).
c) Bromine (Group 7A(17)), like other elements in the same column of the periodic table, forms a –1 ion. Two of these ions require a total of +2 to cancel them out. Thus, the iron must be +2 (indicated with a Roman numeral). This is one of the two common charges on iron ions. This gives the name **iron(II) bromide** (or ferrous bromide).
d) The mercuric ion is Hg^{2+}, and two –1 ions (Cl^-) are needed to cancel the charge. This gives the formula $\mathbf{HgCl_2}$.

2.10B Plan: Determine the names or symbols of each of the species present. Then combine the species to produce a name or formula. The metal or positive ions are written first. Review the rules for nomenclature covered in the chapter. For metals like many transition metals, that can form more than one ion each with a different charge, the ionic charge of the metal ion is indicated by a Roman numeral within parentheses immediately following the metal's name.
Solution:
a) Stannous is the Sn^{2+} ion; fluoride is F^-. Two F^- ions balance one Sn^{2+} ion: stannous fluoride is $\mathbf{SnF_2}$. (The systematic name is tin(II) fluoride.)
b) The anion is I^-, iodide, and the formula shows two I^-. Therefore, the cation must be Pb^{2+}, lead(II) ion: PbI_2 is **lead(II) iodide**. (The common name is plumbous iodide.)
c) Chromic is the common name for chromium(III) ion, Cr^{3+}; sulfide ion is S^{2-}. To balance the charges, the formula is $\mathbf{Cr_2S_3}$. [The systematic name is chromium(III) sulfide.]
d) The anion is oxide, O^{2-}, which requires that the cation be Fe^{2+}. The name is **iron(II) oxide**. (The common name is ferrous oxide.)

2.11A Plan: Determine the names or symbols of each of the species present. Then combine the species to produce a name or formula. The metal or positive ions always go first.
Solution:
a) The cupric ion, Cu^{2+}, requires two nitrate ions, NO_3^-, to cancel the charges. Trihydrate means three water molecules. These combine to give $\mathbf{Cu(NO_3)_2{\cdot}3H_2O}$.
b) The zinc ion, Zn^{2+}, requires two hydroxide ions, OH^-, to cancel the charges. These combine to give $\mathbf{Zn(OH)_2}$.

c) Lithium only forms the Li^+ ion, so Roman numerals are unnecessary. The cyanide ion, CN^-, has the appropriate charge. These combine to give **lithium cyanide.**

2.11B Plan: Determine the names or symbols of each of the species present. Then combine the species to produce a name or formula. The metal or positive ions always go first.
Solution:
a) Two ammonium ions, NH_4^+, are needed to balance the charge on one sulfate ion, SO_4^{2-}. These combine to give **$(NH_4)_2SO_4$.**
b) The nickel ion is combined with two nitrate ions, NO_3^-, so the charge on the nickel ion is 2+, Ni^{2+}. There are 6 water molecules (hexahydrate). Therefore, the name is **nickel(II) nitrate hexahydrate**.
c) Potassium forms the K^+ ion. The bicarbonate ion, HCO_3^-, has the appropriate charge to balance out one potassium ion. Therefore, the formula of this compound is **$KHCO_3$.**

2.12A Plan: Determine the names or symbols of each of the species present. Then combine the species to produce a name or formula. The metal or positive ions always go first. Make corrections accordingly.
Solution:
a) The ammonium ion is NH_4^+ and the phosphate ion is PO_4^{3-}. To give a neutral compound they should combine $[3(+1) + (-3) = 0]$ to give the correct formula **$(NH_4)_3PO_4$.**
b) Aluminum gives Al^{3+} and the hydroxide ion is OH^-. To give a neutral compound they should combine $[+3 + 3(-1) =0]$ to give the correct formula **$Al(OH)_3$**. Parentheses are required around the polyatomic ion.
c) Manganese is Mn, and Mg, in the formula, is magnesium. Magnesium only forms the Mg^{2+} ion, so Roman numerals are unnecessary. The other ion is HCO_3^-, which is called the hydrogen carbonate (or bicarbonate) ion. The correct name is **magnesium hydrogen carbonate** or **magnesium bicarbonate**.

2.12B Plan: Determine the names or symbols of each of the species present. Then combine the species to produce a name or formula. The metal or positive ions always go first. Make corrections accordingly.
Solution:
a) Either use the "-ic" suffix or the "(III)" but not both. Nitr*ide* is N^{3-}, and nitr*ate* is NO_3^-. This gives the correct name: **chromium(III) nitrate** (the common name is chromic nitrate).
b) Cadmium is Cd, and Ca, in the formula, is calcium. Nitr*ate* is NO_3^-, and nitr*ite* is NO_2^-. The correct name is **calcium nitrite.**
c) Potassium is K, and P, in the formula, is phosphorus. *Per*chlorate is ClO_4^-, and chlorate is ClO_3^-. Additionally, parentheses are not needed when there is only one of a given polyatomic ion. The correct formula is **$KClO_3$.**

2.13A Plan: Use the name of the acid to determine the name of the anion of the acid. The name *hydro_______ic acid* indicates that the anion is a monatomic nonmetal. The name _______*ic acid* indicates that the anion is an oxoanion with an –ate ending. The name _______*ous acid* indicates that the anion is an oxoanion with an –ite ending.
Solution:
a) Chloric acid is derived from the **chlorate ion, ClO_3^-**. The –1 charge on the ion requires one hydrogen. These combine to give the formula $HClO_3$.
b) Hydrofluoric acid is derived from the **fluoride** ion, **F^-**. The –1 charge on the ion requires one hydrogen. These combine to give the formula HF.
c) Acetic acid is derived from the **acetate ion**, which may be written as **CH_3COO^-** or as **$C_2H_3O_2^-$**. The –1 charge means that one H is needed. These combine to give the formula CH_3COOH or $HC_2H_3O_2$.
d) Nitrous acid is derived from the **nitrite ion, NO_2^-**. The –1 charge on the ion requires one hydrogen. These combine to give the formula HNO_2.

2.13B Plan: Remove a hydrogen ion to determine the formula of the anion. Identify the corresponding name of the anion and use the name of the anion to name the acid. For the oxoanions, the -ate suffix changes to -ic acid and the -ite suffix changes to -ous acid. For the monatomic nonmetal anions, the name of the acid includes a hydro- prefix and the –ide suffix changes to –ic acid.
Solution:
a) Removing a hydrogen ion from the formula H_2SO_3 gives the oxoanion **HSO_3^-, hydrogen sulfite**; removing two hydrogen ions gives the oxoanion **SO_3^{2-}, sulfite** To name the acid, the "-ite of "sulfite" must be replaced with "-ous." The corresponding name is **sulfurous acid**.

b) HBrO is an oxoacid containing the **BrO^-** ion (**hypobromite** ion). To name the acid, the "-ite" must be replaced with "-ous". This gives the name: **hypobromous acid.**
c) $HClO_2$ is an oxoacid containing the **ClO_2^-** ion (**chlorite** ion). To name the acid, the "-ite" must be replaced with "-ous". This gives the name: **chlorous acid.**
d) HI is a binary acid containing the **I^-** ion (**iodide** ion). To name the acid, a "hydro-" prefix is used, and the "-ide" must be replaced with "-ic". This gives the name: **hydroiodic acid.**

2.14A Plan: Determine the names or symbols of each of the species present. Since these are binary compounds consisting of two nonmetals, the number of each type of atom is indicated with a Greek prefix.
Solution:
a) **Sulfur trioxide** — one sulfur and three (tri) oxygens, as oxide, are present.
b) **Silicon dioxide** — one silicon and two (di) oxygens, as oxide, are present.
c) **N_2O** Nitrogen has the prefix "di" = 2, and oxygen has the prefix "mono" = 1 (understood in the formula).
d) **SeF_6** Selenium has no prefix (understood as = 1), and the fluoride has the prefix "hexa" = 6.

2.14B Plan: Determine the names or symbols of each of the species present. Since these are binary compounds consisting of two nonmetals, the number of each type of atom is indicated with a Greek prefix.
Solution:
a) **Sulfur dichloride** — one sulfur and two (di) chlorines, as chloride, are present.
b) **Dinitrogen pentoxide** — two (di) nitrogen and five (penta) oxygens, as oxide, are present. Note that the "a" in "penta" is dropped when this prefix is combined with "oxide".
c) **BF_3** Boron doesn't have a prefix, so there is one boron atom present. Fluoride has the prefix "tri" = 3.
d) **IBr_3** Iodine has no prefix (understood as = 1), and the bromide has the prefix "tri" = 3.

2.15A Plan: Determine the names or symbols of each of the species present. For compounds between nonmetals, the number of atoms of each type is indicated by a Greek prefix. If both elements in the compound are in the same group, the one with the higher period number is named first.
Solution:
a) Suffixes are not used in the common names of the nonmetal listed first in the formula. Sulfur does not qualify for the use of a suffix. Chlorine correctly has an "ide" suffix. There are two of each nonmetal atom, so both names require a "di" prefix. This gives the name **disulfur dichloride.**
b) Both elements are nonmetals, and there is just one nitrogen and one oxygen. These combine to give the formula **NO.**
c) Br has a higher period number than Cl and should be named first. The three chlorides are correctly named. The correct name is **bromine trichloride.**

2.15B Plan: Determine the names or symbols of each of the species present. For compounds between nonmetals, the number of atoms of each type is indicated by a Greek prefix. If both elements in the compound are in the same group, the one with the higher period number is named first.
Solution:
a) The name of the element phosphorus ends in *–us*, not *–ous*. Additionally, the prefix *hexa-* is shortened to *hex-* before oxide. The correct name is **tetraphosphorus hexoxide.**
b) Because sulfur is listed first in the formula (and has a lower group number), it should be named first. The fluorine should come second in the name, modified with an *–ide* ending. The correct name is **sulfur hexafluoride.**
c) Nitrogen's symbol is N, not Ni. Additionally, the second letter of an element symbol should be lowercase (Br, not BR). The correct formula is **NBr_3.**

2.16A Plan: First, write a formula to match the name. Next, multiply the number of each type of atom by the atomic mass of that atom. Sum all the masses to get an overall mass.
Solution:
a) The peroxide ion is O_2^{2-}, which requires two hydrogen atoms to cancel the charge: H_2O_2.
Molecular mass = (2 x 1.008 amu) + (2 x 16.00 amu) = 34.016 = **34.02 amu.**
b) Two Cs^+ ions are required to balance the charge on one CO_3^{2-} ion: Cs_2CO_3;
formula mass = (2 x 132.9 amu) + (1 x 12.01 amu) + (3 x 16.00 amu) = 325.81 = **325.8 amu.**

2.16B Plan: First, write a formula to match the name. Next, multiply the number of each type of atom by the atomic mass of that atom. Sum all the masses to get an overall mass.
Solution:
a) Sulfuric acid contains the sulfate ion, SO_4^{2-}, which requires two hydrogen atoms to cancel the charge: H_2SO_4; molecular mass = (2 x 1.008 amu) + 32.06 amu + (4 x 16.00 amu) = 98.076 = **98.08 amu.**
b) The sulfate ion, SO_4^{2-}, requires two +1 potassium ions, K^+, to give K_2SO_4;
formula mass = (2 x 39.10 amu) + 32.06 amu + (4 x 16.00 amu) = **174.26 amu.**

2.17A Plan: Since the compounds only contain two elements, finding the formulas by counting each type of atom and developing a ratio. Name the compounds. Multiply the number of each type of atom by the atomic mass of that atom. Sum all the masses to get an overall mass.
Solution:
a) There are two brown atoms (sodium) for every red (oxygen). The compound contains a metal with a nonmetal. Thus, the compound is **sodium oxide**, with the formula $\mathbf{Na_2O}$. The formula mass is twice the mass of sodium plus the mass of oxygen:
2 (22.99 amu) + (16.00 amu) = **61.98 amu**
b) There is one blue (nitrogen) and two reds (oxygen) in each molecule. The compound only contains nonmetals. Thus, the compound is **nitrogen dioxide**, with the formula $\mathbf{NO_2}$. The molecular mass is the mass of nitrogen plus twice the mass of oxygen: (14.01 amu) + 2 (16.00 amu) = **46.01 amu.**

2.17B Plan: Since the compounds only contain two elements, finding the formulas by counting each type of atom and developing a ratio. Name the compounds. Multiply the number of each type of atom by the atomic mass of that atom. Sum all the masses to get an overall mass.
Solution:
a) There is one gray (magnesium) for every two green (chlorine). The compound contains a metal with a nonmetal. Thus, the compound is **magnesium chloride**, with the formula $\mathbf{MgCl_2}$. The formula mass is the mass of magnesium plus twice the mass of chlorine: (24.31 amu) + 2 (35.45 amu) = **95.21 amu**
b) There is one green (chlorine) and three golds (fluorine) in each molecule. The compound only contains nonmetals. Thus, the compound is **chlorine trifluoride**, with the formula $\mathbf{ClF_3}$. The molecular mass is the mass of chlorine plus three times the mass of fluorine: (35.45 amu) + 3 (19.00 amu) = **92.45 amu.**

TOOLS OF THE LABORATORY BOXED READING PROBLEMS

B2.1 Plan: There is one peak for each type of Cl atom and peaks for the Cl_2 molecule. The *m/e* ratio equals the mass divided by 1+.
Solution:
a) There is one peak for the ^{35}Cl atom and another peak for the ^{37}Cl atom. There are three peaks for the three possible Cl_2 molecules: $^{35}Cl^{35}Cl$ (both atoms are mass 35), $^{37}Cl^{37}Cl$ (both atoms are mass 37), and $^{35}Cl^{37}Cl$ (one atom is mass 35 and one is mass 37). So the mass of chlorine will have **5 peaks.**

b)

Peak	*m/e* ratio	
^{35}Cl	**35**	**lightest particle**
^{37}Cl	37	
$^{35}Cl^{35}Cl$	70 (35 + 35)	
$^{35}Cl^{37}Cl$	72 (35 + 37)	
$^{37}Cl^{37}Cl$	**74** (35 + 37)	**heaviest particle**

B2.2 Plan: Each peak in the mass spectrum of carbon represents a different isotope of carbon. The heights of the peaks correspond to the natural abundances of the isotopes.
Solution:
Carbon has three naturally occurring isotopes: ^{12}C, ^{13}C, and ^{14}C. ^{12}C has an abundance of 98.89% and would have the tallest peak in the mass spectrum as the most abundant isotope. ^{13}C has an abundance of 1.11% and thus would have a significantly shorter peak; the shortest peak in the mass spectrum would correspond to the least abundant isotope, ^{14}C, the abundance of which is less than 0.01%. Peak Y, as the tallest peak, has a *m/e* ratio of 12 (^{12}C); X, the shortest peak, has a *m/e* ratio of 14(^{14}C). Peak Z corresponds to ^{13}C with a *m/e* ratio of **13.**

B2.3 Plan: Review the discussion on separations.
Solution:
a) Salt dissolves in water and pepper does not. Procedure: add water to mixture and filter to remove solid pepper. Evaporate water to recover solid salt.
b) The water/soot mixture can be filtered; the water will flow through the filter paper, leaving the soot collected on the filter paper.
c) Allow the mixture to warm up, and then pour off the melted ice (water); or, add water, and the glass will sink and the ice will float.
d) Heat the mixture; the alcohol will boil off (distill), while the sugar will remain behind.
e) The spinach leaves can be extracted with a solvent that dissolves the pigments.
Chromatography can be used to separate one pigment from the other.

END–OF–CHAPTER PROBLEMS

2.1 Plan: Refer to the definitions of an element and a compound.
Solution:
Unlike compounds, elements cannot be broken down by chemical changes into simpler materials. Compounds contain different types of atoms; there is only one type of atom in an element.

2.4 Plan: Remember that an element contains only one kind of atom while a compound contains at least two different elements (two kinds of atoms) in a fixed ratio. A mixture contains at least two different substances in a composition that can vary.
Solution:
a) The presence of more than one element (calcium and chlorine) makes this pure substance a **compound**.
b) There are only atoms from one element, sulfur, so this pure substance is an **element**.
c) This is a combination of two compounds and has a varying composition, so this is a **mixture**.
d) The presence of more than one type of atom means it cannot be an element. The specific, not variable, arrangement means it is a **compound**.

2.12 Plan: Restate the three laws in your own words.
Solution:
a) The law of mass conservation applies to all substances — **elements, compounds, and mixtures**. Matter can neither be created nor destroyed, whether it is an element, compound, or mixture.
b) The law of definite composition applies to **compounds** only, because it refers to a constant, or definite, composition of elements within a compound.
c) The law of multiple proportions applies to **compounds** only, because it refers to the combination of elements to form compounds.

2.14 Plan: Review the three laws: law of mass conservation, law of definite composition, and law of multiple proportions.
Solution:
a) **Law of Definite Composition** — The compound potassium chloride, KCl, is composed of the same elements and same fraction by mass, regardless of its source (Chile or Poland).
b) **Law of Mass Conservation** — The mass of the substances inside the flashbulb did not change during the chemical reaction (formation of magnesium oxide from magnesium and oxygen).
c) **Law of Multiple Proportions** — Two elements, O and As, can combine to form two different compounds that have different proportions of As present.

2.16 Plan: Review the definition of percent by mass.
Solution:
a) **No**, the mass percent of each element in a compound is fixed. The percentage of Na in the compound NaCl is 39.34% (22.99 amu/58.44 amu), whether the sample is 0.5000 g or 50.00 g.

b) **Yes**, the mass of each element in a compound depends on the mass of the compound. A 0.5000 g sample of NaCl contains 0.1967 g of Na (39.34% of 0.5000 g), whereas a 50.00 g sample of NaCl contains 19.67 g of Na (39.34% of 50.00 g).

2.18 Plan: Review the mass laws: law of mass conservation, law of definite composition, and law of multiple proportions. For each experiment, compare the mass values before and after each reaction and examine the ratios of the mass of white compound to the mass of colorless gas.

Solution:

Experiment 1: mass before reaction = 1.00 g; mass after reaction = 0.64 g + 0.36 g = 1.00 g
Experiment 2: mass before reaction = 3.25 g; mass after reaction = 2.08 g + 1.17 g = 3.25 g
Both experiments demonstrate the **law of mass conservation** since the total mass before reaction equals the total mass after reaction.

Experiment 1: mass white compound/mass colorless gas = 0.64 g/0.36 g = 1.78
Experiment 2: mass white compound/mass colorless gas = 2.08 g/1.17 g = 1.78
Both Experiments 1 and 2 demonstrate the **law of definite composition** since the compound has the same composition by mass in each experiment.

2.20 Plan: Fluorite is a mineral containing only calcium and fluorine. The difference between the mass of fluorite and the mass of calcium gives the mass of fluorine. Mass fraction is calculated by dividing the mass of element by the mass of compound (fluorite) and mass percent is obtained by multiplying the mass fraction by 100.

Solution:

a) Mass (g) of fluorine = mass of fluorite – mass of calcium = 2.76 g – 1.42 g = **1.34 g fluorine**

b) Mass fraction of Ca = $\frac{\text{mass Ca}}{\text{mass fluorite}} = \frac{1.42 \text{ g Ca}}{2.76 \text{ g fluorite}} = 0.51449 = \mathbf{0.514}$

Mass fraction of F = $\frac{\text{mass F}}{\text{mass fluorite}} = \frac{1.34 \text{ g F}}{2.76 \text{ g fluorite}} = 0.48551 = \mathbf{0.486}$

c) Mass percent of Ca = 0.51449 x 100 = 51.449 = **51.4%**
Mass percent of F = 0.48551 x 100 = 48.551 = **48.6%**

2.22 Plan: Dividing the mass of magnesium by the mass of the oxide gives the ratio. Multiply the mass of the second sample of magnesium oxide by this ratio to determine the mass of magnesium.

Solution:

a) If 1.25 g of MgO contains 0.754 g of Mg, then the mass ratio (or fraction) of magnesium in the oxide compound is $\frac{\text{mass Mg}}{\text{mass MgO}} = \frac{0.754 \text{ g Mg}}{1.25 \text{ g MgO}} = 0.6032 = \mathbf{0.603}$.

b) Mass (g) of magnesium = $(534 \text{ g MgO})\left(\frac{0.6032 \text{ g Mg}}{1 \text{ g MgO}}\right) = 322.109 = \mathbf{322\ g\ magnesium}$

2.24 Plan: Since copper is a metal and sulfur is a nonmetal, the sample contains 88.39 g Cu and 44.61 g S. Calculate the mass fraction of each element in the sample by dividing the mass of element by the total mass of compound. Multiply the mass of the second sample of compound in grams by the mass fraction of each element to find the mass of each element in that sample.

Solution:

Mass (g) of compound = 88.39 g copper + 44.61 g sulfur = 133.00 g compound

Mass fraction of copper = $\left(\frac{88.39 \text{ g copper}}{133.00 \text{ g compound}}\right) = 0.664586$

Mass (g) of copper = $(5264 \text{ kg compound})\left(\frac{10^3 \text{ g compound}}{1 \text{ kg compound}}\right)\left(\frac{0.664586 \text{ g copper}}{1 \text{ g compound}}\right)$

$= 3.49838 \times 10^6 = \mathbf{3.498 \times 10^6\ g\ copper}$

$$\text{Mass fraction of sulfur} = \left(\frac{44.61 \text{ g sulfur}}{133.00 \text{ g compound}}\right) = 0.335414$$

$$\text{Mass (g) of sulfur} = (5264 \text{ kg compound})\left(\frac{10^3 \text{ g compound}}{1 \text{ kg compound}}\right)\left(\frac{0.335414 \text{ g sulfur}}{1 \text{ g compound}}\right)$$

$$= 1.76562 \times 10^6 = \mathbf{1.766 \times 10^6 \text{ g sulfur}}$$

2.26 Plan: The law of multiple proportions states that if two elements form two different compounds, the relative amounts of the elements in the two compounds form a whole-number ratio. To illustrate the law we must calculate the mass of one element to one gram of the other element for each compound and then compare this mass for the two compounds. The law states that the ratio of the two masses should be a small whole-number ratio such as 1:2, 3:2, 4:3, etc.

Solution:

Compound 1: $\frac{47.5 \text{ mass \% S}}{52.5 \text{ mass \% Cl}} = 0.90476 = 0.905$

Compound 2: $\frac{31.1 \text{ mass \% S}}{68.9 \text{ mass \% Cl}} = 0.451379 = 0.451$

Ratio: $\frac{0.905}{0.451} = 2.0067 = 2.00{:}1.00$

Thus, the ratio of the mass of sulfur per gram of chlorine in the two compounds is a small whole-number ratio of 2:1, which agrees with the law of multiple proportions.

2.29 Plan: Determine the mass percent of sulfur in each sample by dividing the grams of sulfur in the sample by the total mass of the sample and multiplying by 100. The coal type with the smallest mass percent of sulfur has the smallest environmental impact.

Solution:

$$\text{Mass \% in Coal A} = \left(\frac{11.3 \text{ g sulfur}}{378 \text{ g sample}}\right)(100\%) = 2.9894 = 2.99\% \text{ S (by mass)}$$

$$\text{Mass \% in Coal B} = \left(\frac{19.0 \text{ g sulfur}}{495 \text{ g sample}}\right)(100\%) = 3.8384 = 3.84\% \text{ S (by mass)}$$

$$\text{Mass \% in Coal C} = \left(\frac{20.6 \text{ g sulfur}}{675 \text{ g sample}}\right)(100\%) = 3.0519 = 3.05\% \text{ S (by mass)}$$

Coal A has the smallest environmental impact.

2.31 Plan: This question is based on the law of definite composition. If the compound contains the same types of atoms, they should combine in the same way to give the same mass percentages of each of the elements.

Solution:

Potassium nitrate is a compound composed of three elements — potassium, nitrogen, and oxygen — in a specific ratio. If the ratio of these elements changed, then the compound would be changed to a different compound, for example, to potassium nitrite, with different physical and chemical properties. Dalton postulated that atoms of an element are identical, regardless of whether that element is found in India or Italy. Dalton also postulated that compounds result from the chemical combination of specific ratios of different elements. Thus, Dalton's theory explains why potassium nitrate, a compound comprised of three different elements in a specific ratio, has the same chemical composition regardless of where it is mined or how it is synthesized.

2.32 Plan: Review the discussion of the experiments in this chapter.

Solution:

Millikan determined the minimum *charge* on an oil drop and that the minimum charge was equal to the charge on one electron. Using Thomson's value for the *mass/charge ratio* of the electron and the determined value for the charge on one electron, Millikan calculated the mass of an electron (charge/(charge/mass)) to be 9.109×10^{-28} g.

2.36 Plan: Re-examine the definitions of atomic number and the mass number.

Solution:

The atomic number is the number of protons in the nucleus of an atom. When the atomic number changes, the identity of the element also changes. The mass number is the total number of protons and neutrons in the nucleus of an atom. Since the identity of an element is based on the number of protons and not the number of neutrons, the mass number can vary (by a change in number of neutrons) without changing the identity of the element.

2.39 Plan: The superscript is the mass number, the sum of the number of protons and neutrons. Consult the periodic table to get the atomic number (the number of protons). The mass number – the number of protons = the number of neutrons. For atoms, the number of protons and electrons are equal.

Solution:

Isotope	Mass Number	# of Protons	# of Neutrons	# of Electrons
^{36}Ar	36	18	18	18
^{38}Ar	38	18	20	18
^{40}Ar	40	18	22	18

2.41 Plan: The superscript is the mass number (A), the sum of the number of protons and neutrons; the subscript is the atomic number (Z, number of protons). The mass number – the number of protons = the number of neutrons. For atoms, the number of protons = the number of electrons.

Solution:

a) $^{16}_{8}O$ and $^{17}_{8}O$ have the **same number of protons and electrons** (8), but different numbers of neutrons.

$^{16}_{8}O$ and $^{17}_{8}O$ are isotopes of oxygen, and $^{16}_{8}O$ has 16 – 8 = 8 neutrons whereas $^{17}_{8}O$ has 17 – 8 = 9 neutrons.

Same *Z* value

b) $^{40}_{18}Ar$ and $^{41}_{19}K$ have the **same number of neutrons** (Ar: 40 – 18 = 22; K: 41 – 19 = 22) but different numbers of protons and electrons (Ar = 18 protons and 18 electrons; K = 19 protons and 19 electrons).

Same *N* value

c) $^{60}_{27}Co$ and $^{60}_{28}Ni$ have different numbers of protons, neutrons, and electrons. Co: 27 protons, 27 electrons, and 60 – 27 = 33 neutrons; Ni: 28 protons, 28 electrons and 60 – 28 = 32 neutrons. However, both have a mass number of 60. **Same *A* value**

2.43 Plan: Combine the particles in the nucleus (protons + neutrons) to give the mass number (superscript, A). The number of protons gives the atomic number (subscript, Z) and identifies the element.

Solution:

a) $A = 18 + 20 = 38$; $Z = 18$; $\mathbf{^{38}_{18}Ar}$

b) $A = 25 + 30 = 55$; $Z = 25$; $\mathbf{^{55}_{25}Mn}$

c) $A = 47 + 62 = 109$; $Z = 47$; $\mathbf{^{109}_{47}Ag}$

2.45 Plan: Determine the number of each type of particle. The superscript is the mass number (A) and the subscript is the atomic number (Z, number of protons). The mass number – the number of protons = the number of neutrons. For atoms, the number of protons = the number of electrons. The protons and neutrons are in the nucleus of the atom.

Solution:

a) $^{48}_{22}Ti$	b) $^{79}_{34}Se$	c) $^{11}_{5}B$
22 protons	34 protons	5 protons
22 electrons	34 electrons	5 electrons
48 – 22 = 26 neutrons	79 – 34 = 45 neutrons	11 – 5 = 6 neutrons

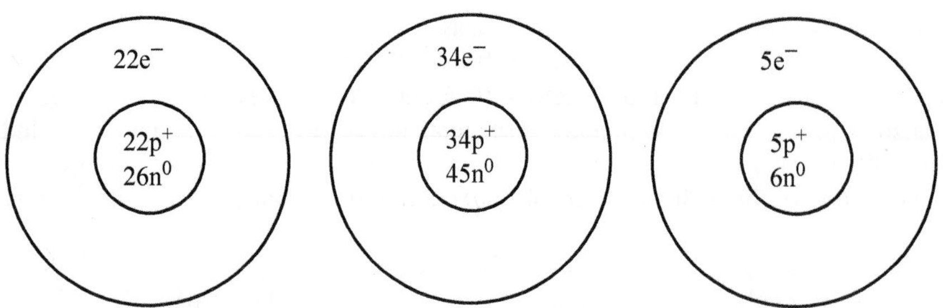

2.47 Plan: To calculate the atomic mass of an element, take a weighted average based on the natural abundance of the isotopes: (isotopic mass of isotope 1 x fractional abundance) + (isotopic mass of isotope 2 x fractional abundance).

Solution:

$$\text{Atomic mass of gallium} = (68.9256\ \text{amu})\left(\frac{60.11\%}{100\%}\right) + (70.9247\ \text{amu})\left(\frac{39.89\%}{100\%}\right) = 69.7230 = \mathbf{69.72\ amu}$$

2.49 Plan: To find the percent abundance of each Cl isotope, let x equal the fractional abundance of ^{35}Cl and (1 – x) equal the fractional abundance of ^{37}Cl since the sum of the fractional abundances must equal 1. Remember that atomic mass = (isotopic mass of ^{35}Cl x fractional abundance) + (isotopic mass of ^{37}Cl x fractional abundance).
Solution:
Atomic mass = (isotopic mass of ^{35}Cl x fractional abundance) + (isotopic mass of ^{37}Cl x fractional abundance)

35.4527 amu = 34.9689 amu(x) + 36.9659 amu(1 – x)
35.4527 amu = 34.9689 amu(x) + 36.9659 amu – 36.9659 amu(x)
35.4527 amu = 36.9659 amu – 1.9970 amu(x)
1.9970 amu(x) = 1.5132 amu
x = 0.75774 and 1 – x = 1 – 0.75774 = 0.24226
% abundance ^{35}**Cl = 75.774%** % abundance ^{37}**Cl = 24.226%**

2.52 Plan: Review the section in the chapter on the periodic table.
Solution:
a) In the modern periodic table, the elements are arranged in order of increasing atomic **number**.
b) Elements in a **column or group** (or family) have similar chemical properties, not those in the same period or row.
c) Elements can be classified as **metals**, metalloids, or nonmetals.

2.55 Plan: Review the properties of these two columns in the periodic table.
Solution:
The alkali metals (Group 1A(1)) are metals and readily lose one electron to form cations whereas the halogens (Group 7A(17)) are nonmetals and readily gain one electron to form anions.

2.56 Plan: Locate each element on the periodic table. The Z value is the atomic number of the element. Metals are to the left of the "staircase," nonmetals are to the right of the "staircase," and the metalloids are the elements that lie along the "staircase" line.
Solution:

a) Germanium	Ge	4A(14)	metalloid
b) Phosphorus	P	5A(15)	nonmetal
c) Helium	He	8A(18)	nonmetal
d) Lithium	Li	1A(1)	metal
e) Molybdenum	Mo	6B(6)	metal

2.58 Plan: Review the section in the chapter on the periodic table. Remember that alkaline earth metals are in Group 2A(2), the halogens are in Group 7A(17), and the metalloids are the elements that lie along the "staircase" line; periods are horizontal rows.

Solution:
a) The symbol and atomic number of the heaviest alkaline earth metal are **Ra** and **88**.
b) The symbol and atomic number of the lightest metalloid in Group 4A(14) are **Si** and **14**.
c) The symbol and atomic mass of the coinage metal whose atoms have the fewest electrons are **Cu** and **63.55 amu**.
d) The symbol and atomic mass of the halogen in Period 4 are **Br** and **79.90 amu**.

2.60 Plan: Review the section of the chapter on the formation of ionic compounds.
Solution:
Reactive metals and nometals will form **ionic** bonds, in which one or more electrons are transferred from the metal atom to the nonmetal atom to form a cation and an anion, respectively. The oppositely charged ions attract, forming the ionic bond.

2.63 Plan: Assign charges to each of the ions. Since the sizes are similar, there are no differences due to the sizes.
Solution:
Coulomb's law states the energy of attraction in an ionic bond is directly proportional to the *product of charges* and inversely proportional to the *distance between charges*. The *product of charges* in MgO (+2 x –2 = –4) is greater than the *product of charges* in LiF (+1 x –1 = –1). Thus, **MgO** has stronger ionic bonding.

2.66 Plan: Locate these groups on the periodic table and assign charges to the ions that would form.
Solution:
The monatomic ions of Group 1A(1) have a +1 charge (e.g., Li^+, Na^+, and K^+) whereas the monatomic ions of Group 7A(17) have a –1 charge (e.g., F^-, Cl^-, and Br^-). Elements gain or lose electrons to form ions with the same number of electrons as the nearest noble gas. For example, Na loses one electron to form a cation with the same number of electrons as Ne. The halogen F gains one electron to form an anion with the same number of electrons as Ne.

2.68 Plan: A metal and a nonmetal will form an ionic compound. Locate these elements on the periodic table and predict their charges.
Solution:
Potassium sulfide (K_2S) is an ionic compound formed from a metal (potassium) and a nonmetal (sulfur). Potassium atoms transfer electrons to sulfur atoms. Each potassium atom loses one electron to form an ion with +1 charge and the same number of electrons (18) as the noble gas argon. Each sulfur atom gains two electrons to form an ion with a –2 charge and the same number of electrons (18) as the noble gas argon. The oppositely charged ions, K^+ and S^{2-}, attract each other to form an ionic compound with the ratio of two K^+ ions to one S^{2-} ion. The total number of electrons lost by the potassium atoms equals the total number of electrons gained by the sulfur atoms.

2.70 Plan: Locate these elements on the periodic table and predict what ions they will form. For A group cations (metals), ion charge = group number; for anions (nonmetals), ion charge = group number minus 8.
Solution:
Potassium (K) is in Group **1**A(1) and forms the $\mathbf{K^+}$ ion. Bromine (Br) is in Group **7**A(17) and forms the $\mathbf{Br^-}$ ion (7 – 8 = –1).

2.72 Plan: Use the number of protons (atomic number) to identify the element. Add the number of protons and neutrons together to get the mass number. Locate the element on the periodic table and assign its group and period number.
Solution:

a) Oxygen (atomic number = 8)	mass number = 8p + 9n = 17	Group 6A(16)	Period 2
b) Fluorine (atomic number = 9)	mass number = 9p + 10n = 19	Group 7A(17)	Period 2
c) Calcium (atomic number = 20)	mass number = 20p + 20n = 40	Group 2A(2)	Period 4

2.74 Plan: Determine the charges of the ions based on their position on the periodic table. For A group cations (metals), ion charge = group number; for anions (nonmetals), ion charge = group number minus 8. Next, determine the ratio of the charges to get the ratio of the ions.

Solution:
Lithium [Group 1A(1)] forms the Li^+ ion; oxygen [Group 6A(16)] forms the O^{2-} ion (6 – 8 = –2). The ionic compound that forms from the combination of these two ions must be electrically neutral, so two Li^+ ions combine with one O^{2-} ion to form the compound Li_2O. There are twice as many Li^+ ions as O^{2-} ions in a sample of Li_2O.

$$\text{Number of } O^{2-} \text{ ions} = (8.4\text{x}10^{21}\ Li^+ \text{ ions})\left(\frac{1\ O^{2-} \text{ ion}}{2\ Li^+ \text{ ions}}\right) = \mathbf{4.2x10^{21}\ O^{2-}\ ions}$$

2.76 Plan: The key is the size of the two alkali metal ions. The charges on the sodium and potassium ions are the same as both are in Group 1A(1), so there will be no difference due to the charge. The chloride ions are the same in size and charge, so there will be no difference due to the chloride ion.

Solution:
Coulomb's law states that the energy of attraction in an ionic bond is directly proportional to the *product of charges* and inversely proportional to the *distance between charges*. The *product of the charges* is the same in both compounds because both sodium and potassium ions have a +1 charge. Attraction increases as distance decreases, so the ion with the smaller radius, Na^+, will form a stronger ionic interaction (**NaCl**).

2.78 Plan: Review the definition of molecular formula.
Solution:
The subscripts in the formula, MgF_2, give the number of ions in a formula unit of the ionic compound. The subscripts indicate that there are two F^- ions for every one Mg^{2+} ion. Using this information and the mass of each element, we could calculate the percent mass of each element.

2.80 Plan: Review the concepts of atoms and molecules.
Solution:
The mixture is similar to the sample of hydrogen peroxide in that both contain 20 billion oxygen atoms and 20 billion hydrogen atoms since both O_2 and H_2O_2 contain 2 oxygen atoms per molecule and both H_2 and H_2O_2 contain 2 hydrogen atoms per molecule. They differ in that they contain different types of molecules: H_2O_2 molecules in the hydrogen peroxide sample and H_2 and O_2 molecules in the mixture. In addition, the mixture contains 20 billion molecules (10 billion H_2 molecules + 10 billion O_2 molecules) while the hydrogen peroxide sample contains 10 billion molecules.

2.84 Plan: Locate each of the individual elements on the periodic table, and assign charges to each of the ions. For A group cations (metals), ion charge = group number; for anions (nonmetals), ion charge = group number minus 8. Find the smallest number of each ion that gives a neutral compound. To name ionic compounds with metals that form only one ion, name the metal, followed by the nonmetal name with an -ide suffix.
Solution:
a) Sodium is a metal that forms a +1 (Group **1**A) ion and nitrogen is a nonmetal that forms a –3 ion (Group **5**A, 5 – 8 = –3).

+3 –3
+1 –3 +1
Na N Na_3N The compound is **Na_3N, sodium nitride.**

b) Oxygen is a nonmetal that forms a –2 ion (Group **6**A, 6 – 8 = –2) and strontium is a metal that forms a +2 ion (Group **2**A). +2 –2
Sr O The compound is **SrO, strontium oxide.**

c) Aluminum is a metal that forms a +3 ion (Group **3**A) and chlorine is a nonmetal that forms a –1 ion (Group 7A, 7– 8 = –1). +3 –3
+3 –1 +3 –1
Al Cl $AlCl_3$ The compound is **$AlCl_3$, aluminum chloride.**

2.86 Plan: Based on the atomic numbers (the subscripts) locate the elements on the periodic table. Once the atomic numbers are located, identify the element and based on its position, assign a charge. For A group cations (metals), ion charge = group number; for anions (nonmetals), ion charge = group number minus 8. Find the smallest number of each ion that gives a neutral compound. To name ionic compounds with metals that form only one ion, name the metal, followed by the nonmetal name with an -ide suffix.

Solution:

a) ${}_{12}L$ is the element Mg ($Z = 12$). Magnesium [Group **2**A(2)] forms the Mg^{2+} ion. ${}_{9}M$ is the element F ($Z = 9$). Fluorine [Group **7**A(17)] forms the F^- ion ($7 - 8 = -1$). The compound formed by the combination of these two elements is **MgF_2, magnesium fluoride**.

b) ${}_{30}L$ is the element Zn ($Z = 30$). Zinc forms the Zn^{2+} ion (see Table 2.3). ${}_{16}M$ is the element S ($Z = 16$). Sulfur [Group **6**A(16)] will form the S^{2-} ion ($6 - 8 = -2$). The compound formed by the combination of these two elements is **ZnS, zinc sulfide**.

c) ${}_{17}L$ is the element Cl ($Z = 17$). Chlorine [Group **7**A(17)] forms the Cl^- ion ($7 - 8 = -1$). ${}_{38}M$ is the element Sr ($Z = 38$). Strontium [Group **2**A(2)] forms the Sr^{2+} ion. The compound formed by the combination of these two elements is **$SrCl_2$, strontium chloride**.

2.88 Plan: Review the rules for nomenclature covered in the chapter. For ionic compounds, name the metal, followed by the nonmetal name with an -ide suffix. For metals, like many transition metals, that can form more than one ion each with a different charge, the ionic charge of the metal ion is indicated by a Roman numeral within parentheses immediately following the metal's name.

Solution:

a) tin(IV) chloride = **$SnCl_4$** The (IV) indicates that the metal ion is Sn^{4+} which requires 4 Cl^- ions for a neutral compound.

b) $FeBr_3$ = **iron(III) bromide** (common name is ferric bromide); the charge on the iron ion is +3 to match the –3 charge of 3 Br^- ions. The +3 charge of the Fe is indicated by (III).

c) cuprous bromide = **CuBr** (cuprous is +1 copper ion, cupric is +2 copper ion).

d) Mn_2O_3 = **manganese(III) oxide** Use (III) to indicate the +3 ionic charge of Mn:

$$\begin{matrix} +6 & -6 \\ +3 & -2 \\ Mn_2 & O_3 \end{matrix}$$

2.90 Plan: Review the rules for nomenclature covered in the chapter. For ionic compounds, name the metal, followed by the nonmetal name with an -ide suffix. For metals, like many transition metals, that can form more than one ion each with a different charge, the ionic charge of the metal ion is indicated by a Roman numeral within parentheses immediately following the metal's name. Hydrates, compounds with a specific number of water molecules associated with them, are named with a prefix before the word hydrate to indicate the number of water molecules.

Solution:

a) **cobalt(II) oxide** Cobalt forms more than one monatomic ion so the ionic charge must be indicated with a Roman numeral. Since the Co is paired with one O^{2-} ion, the charge of Co is +2.

b) **Hg_2Cl_2** The Roman numeral I indicates that mercury has an ionic charge of +1; mercury is an unusual case in which the +1 ion formed is Hg_2^{2+}, not Hg^+.

c) **lead(II) acetate trihydrate** The $C_2H_3O_2^-$ ion has a –1 charge (see Table 2.5); since there are two of these ions, the lead ion has a +2 charge which must be indicated with the Roman numeral II. The •$3H_2O$ indicates a hydrate in which the number of H_2O molecules is indicated by the prefix tri-.

d) **Cr_2O_3** "chromic" denotes a +3 charge (see Table 2.4), oxygen has a –2 charge:

$$\overset{+3\,-2}{CrO} \rightarrow \overset{+6\,-6}{Cr_2O_3}$$

2.92 Plan: Review the rules for nomenclature covered in the chapter. For metals, like many transition metals, that can form more than one ion each with a different charge, the ionic charge of the metal ion is indicated by a Roman numeral within parentheses immediately following the metal's name. Compounds must be neutral.

Solution:

a) Barium [Group **2**A(2)] forms Ba^{2+} and oxygen [Group 6A(16)] forms O^{2-} ($6 - 8 = -2$) so the neutral compound forms from one Ba^{2+} ion and one O^{2-} ion. Correct formula is **BaO**.

b) Iron(II) indicates Fe^{2+} and nitrate is NO_3^- so the neutral compound forms from one iron(II) ion and two nitrate ions. Correct formula is **$Fe(NO_3)_2$**.

c) Mn is the symbol for manganese. Mg is the correct symbol for magnesium. Correct formula is **MgS**. Sulfide is the S^{2-} ion and sulfite is the SO_3^{2-} ion.

2.94 Plan: Acids donate H^+ ion to the solution, so the acid is a combination of H^+ and a negatively charged ion. Binary acids (H plus one other nonmetal) are named hydro- + nonmetal root + -ic acid. Oxoacids (H + an oxoanion) are named by changing the suffix of the oxoanion: -ate becomes -ic acid and -ite becomes -ous acid.

Solution:
a) Hydrogen carbonate is HCO_3^-, so its source acid is **H_2CO_3**. The name of the acid is **carbonic acid** (-ate becomes –ic acid).
b) **HIO_4, periodic acid.** IO_4^- is the periodate ion: -ate becomes –ic acid.
c) Cyanide is CN^-; its source acid is **HCN hydrocyanic acid** (binary acid).
d) **H_2S, hydrosulfuric acid** (binary acid).

2.96 Plan: Use the formulas of the polyatomic ions. Recall that oxoacids are named by changing the suffix of the oxoanion: -ate becomes -ic acid and -ite becomes -ous acid. Compounds must be neutral.
Solution:
a) ammonium ion = **NH_4^+** ammonia = **NH_3**
b) magnesium sulfide = **MgS** magnesium sulfite = **$MgSO_3$** magnesium sulfate = **$MgSO_4$**
Sulfide = S^{2-}; sulfite = SO_3^{2-}; sulfate = SO_4^{2-}.
c) hydrochloric acid = **HCl** chloric acid = **$HClO_3$** chlorous acid = **$HClO_2$**
Binary acids (H plus one other nonmetal) are named hydro- + nonmetal root + -ic acid. Chloric indicates the polyatomic ion ClO_3^- while chlorous indicates the polyatomic ion ClO_2^-.
d) cuprous bromide = **CuBr** cupric bromide = **$CuBr_2$**
The suffix -ous indicates the lower charge, +1, while the suffix -ic indicates the higher charge, +2.

2.98 Plan: This compound is composed of two nonmetals. The element with the lower group number is named first. Greek numerical prefixes are used to indicate the number of atoms of each element in the compound.
Solution:
disulfur tetrafluoride **S_2F_4** Di- indicates two S atoms and tetra- indicates four F atoms.

2.100 Plan: Review the nomenclature rules in the chapter. For ionic compounds, name the metal, followed by the nonmetal name with an -ide suffix. For metals, like many transition metals, that can form more than one ion each with a different charge, the ionic charge of the metal ion is indicated by a Roman numeral within parentheses immediately following the metal's name. Binary acids (H plus one other nonmetal) are named hydro- + nonmetal root + -ic acid.
Solution:
a) Calcium(II) dichloride, $CaCl_2$: The name becomes **calcium chloride** because calcium does not require "(II)" since it only forms +2 ions. Prefixes like di- are only used in naming covalent compounds between nonmetal elements.
b) Copper(II) oxide, Cu_2O: The charge on the oxide ion is O^{2-}, which makes each copper a Cu^+. The name becomes **copper(I) oxide** to match the charge on the copper.
c) Stannous fluoride, SnF_4: Stannous refers to Sn^{2+}, but the tin in this compound is Sn^{4+} due to the charge on the fluoride ion. The tin(IV) ion is the stannic ion; this gives the name **stannic fluoride or tin(IV) fluoride**.
d) Hydrogen chloride acid, HCl: Binary acids consist of the root name of the nonmetal (chlor in this case) with a hydro- prefix and an -ic suffix. The word acid is also needed. This gives the name **hydrochloric acid**.

2.102 Plan: Review the rules for nomenclature covered in the chapter. For ionic compounds containing polyatomic ions, name the metal, followed by the name of the polyatomic ion. The molecular (formula) mass is the sum of the atomic masses of all of the atoms.
Solution:
a) **$(NH_4)_2SO_4$** ammonium is NH_4^+ and sulfate is SO_4^{2-}

N	=	2(14.01 amu)	=	28.02 amu
H	=	8(1.008 amu)	=	8.064 amu
S	=	1(32.06 amu)	=	32.06 amu
O	=	4(16.00 amu)	=	64.00 amu
				132.14 amu

b) **NaH_2PO_4** sodium is Na^+ and dihydrogen phosphate is $H_2PO_4^-$

Na	=	1(22.99 amu)	=	22.99 amu
H	=	2(1.008 amu)	=	2.016 amu
P	=	1(30.97 amu)	=	30.97 amu
O	=	4(16.00 amu)	=	64.00 amu
				119.98 amu

c) **$KHCO_3$** potassium is K^+ and bicarbonate is HCO_3^-

K	=	1(39.10 amu)	=	39.10 amu
H	=	1(1.008 amu)	=	1.008 amu
C	=	1(12.01 amu)	=	12.01 amu
O	=	3(16.00 amu)	=	48.00 amu
				100.12 amu

2.104 Plan: Convert the names to the appropriate chemical formulas. The molecular (formula) mass is the sum of the masses of each atom times its atomic mass.

Solution:

a) dinitrogen pentoxide N_2O_5 (di- = 2 and penta- = 5)

N	=	2(14.01 amu)	=	28.02 amu
O	=	5(16.00 amu)	=	80.00 amu
				108.02 amu

b) lead(II) nitrate $Pb(NO_3)_2$ (lead(II) is Pb^{2+} and nitrate is NO_3^-)

Pb	=	1(207.2 amu)	=	207.2 amu
N	=	2(14.01 amu)	=	28.02 amu
O	=	6(16.00 amu)	=	96.00 amu
				331.2 amu

c) calcium peroxide CaO_2 (calcium is Ca^{2+} and peroxide is O_2^{2-})

Ca	=	1(40.08 amu)	=	40.08 amu
O	=	2(16.00 amu)	=	32.00 amu
				72.08 amu

2.106 Plan: Break down each formula to the individual elements and count the number of atoms of each element by observing the subscripts. The molecular (formula) mass is the sum of the atomic masses of all of the atoms.

Solution:

a) There are **12 atoms of oxygen** in $Al_2(SO_4)_3$. The molecular mass is:

Al	=	2(26.98 amu)	=	53.96 amu
S	=	3(32.06 amu)	=	96.18 amu
O	=	12(16.00 amu)	=	192.00 amu
				342.14 amu

b) There are **9 atoms of hydrogen** in $(NH_4)_2HPO_4$. The molecular mass is:

N	=	2(14.01 amu)	=	28.02 amu
H	=	9(1.008 amu)	=	9.072 amu
P	=	1(30.97 amu)	=	30.97 amu
O	=	4(16.00 amu)	=	64.00 amu
				132.06 amu

c) There are **8 atoms of oxygen** in $Cu_3(OH)_2(CO_3)_2$. The molecular mass is:

Cu	=	3(63.55 amu)	=	190.65 amu
O	=	8(16.00 amu)	=	128.00 amu
H	=	2(1.008 amu)	=	2.016 amu
C	=	2(12.01 amu)	=	24.02 amu
				344.69 amu

2.108 Plan: Use the chemical symbols and count the atoms of each type to give a molecular formula. Use the nomenclature rules in the chapter to derive the name. The molecular (formula) mass is the sum of the masses of each atom times its atomic mass.

Solution:

a) Formula is **SO_3**. Name is **sulfur trioxide** (the prefix tri- indicates 3 oxygen atoms).

S	=	1(32.06 amu)	=	32.06 amu
O	=	3(16.00 amu)	=	48.00 amu
				80.06 amu

b) Formula is **C_3H_8**. Since it contains only carbon and hydrogen it is a hydrocarbon and with three carbons its name is **propane**.

C	=	3(12.01 amu)	=	36.03 amu
H	=	8(1.008 amu)	=	8.064 amu
				44.09 amu

2.112 Plan: Review the discussion on separations.
Solution:
Separating the components of a mixture requires physical methods only; that is, no chemical changes (no changes in composition) take place and the components maintain their chemical identities and properties throughout. Separating the components of a compound requires a chemical change (change in composition).

2.115 Plan: Review the definitions of homogeneous and heterogeneous. The key is that a homogeneous mixture has a uniform composition while a heterogeneous mixture does not. A mixture consists of two or more substances physically mixed together while a compound is a pure substance.
Solution:
a) Distilled water is a **compound** that consists of H_2O molecules only.
b) Gasoline is a **homogeneous mixture** of hydrocarbon compounds of uniform composition that can be separated by physical means (distillation).
c) Beach sand is a **heterogeneous mixture** of different size particles of minerals and broken bits of shells.
d) Wine is a **homogeneous mixture** of water, alcohol, and other compounds that can be separated by physical means (distillation).
e) Air is a **homogeneous mixture** of different gases, mainly N_2, O_2, and Ar.

2.117 Plan: Review the discussion on separations.
Solution:
a) Filtration — separating the mixture on the basis of differences in particle size. The water moves through the holes in the colander but the larger pasta cannot.
b) **Extraction** — The colored impurities are extracted into a solvent that is rinsed away from the raw sugar (or **chromatography**). A sugar solution is passed through a column in which the impurities stick to the stationary phase and the sugar moves through the column in the mobile phase.

2.119 Plan: Use the equation for the volume of a sphere in part a) to find the volume of the nucleus and the volume of the atom. Calculate the fraction of the atom volume that is occupied by the nucleus. For part b), calculate the total mass of the two electrons; subtract the electron mass from the mass of the atom to find the mass of the nucleus. Then calculate the fraction of the atom's mass contributed by the mass of the nucleus.
Solution:

$$\text{a) Volume (m}^3\text{) of nucleus} = \frac{4}{3}\pi r^3 = \frac{4}{3}\pi\left(2.5\text{x}10^{-15}\ \text{m}\right)^3 = 6.54498\text{x}10^{-44}\ \text{m}^3$$

$$\text{Volume (m}^3\text{) of atom} = \frac{4}{3}\pi r^3 = \frac{4}{3}\pi\left(3.1\text{x}10^{-11}\ \text{m}\right)^3 = 1.24788\text{x}10^{-31}\ \text{m}^3$$

$$\text{Fraction of volume} = \frac{\text{volume of Nucleus}}{\text{volume of Atom}} = \frac{6.54498\text{x}10^{-44}\ \text{m}^3}{1.24788\text{x}10^{-31}\ \text{m}^3} = 5.2449\text{x}10^{-13} = \mathbf{5.2x10^{-13}}$$

b) Mass of nucleus = mass of atom – mass of electrons

$$= 6.64648\text{x}10^{-24}\ \text{g} - 2(9.10939\text{x}10^{-28}\ \text{g}) = 6.64466\text{x}10^{-24}\ \text{g}$$

$$\text{Fraction of mass} = \frac{\text{mass of Nucleus}}{\text{mass of Atom}} = \frac{\left(6.64466\text{x}10^{-24}\ \text{g}\right)}{\left(6.64648\text{x}10^{-24}\ \text{g}\right)} = 0.99972617 = \mathbf{0.999726}$$

As expected, the volume of the nucleus relative to the volume of the atom is small while its relative mass is large.

2.120 Plan: Use Coulomb's law which states that the energy of attraction in an ionic bond is directly proportional to the *product of charges* and inversely proportional to the *distance between charges*. Choose the largest ionic charges and smallest radii for the strongest ionic bonding and the smallest ionic charges and largest radii for the weakest ionic bonding.

Solution:
Strongest ionic bonding: **MgO**. Mg^{2+}, Ba^{2+}, and O^{2-} have the largest charges. Attraction increases as distance decreases, so the positive ion with the smaller radius, Mg^{2+}, will form a stronger ionic bond than the larger ion Ba^{2+}.
Weakest ionic bonding: **RbI**. K^+, Rb^+, Cl^-, and I^- have the smallest charges. Attraction decreases as distance increases, so the ions with the larger radii, Rb^+ and I^-, will form the weakest ionic bond.

2.124 Plan: Determine the percent oxygen in each oxide by subtracting the percent nitrogen from 100%. Express the percentage in amu and divide by the atomic mass of the appropriate elements. Then divide each amount by the smaller number and convert to the simplest whole-number ratio. To find the mass of oxygen per 1.00 g of nitrogen, divide the mass percentage of oxygen by the mass percentage of nitrogen.
Solution:

a) I

$$(100.00 - 46.69 \text{ N})\% = 53.31\% \text{ O}$$

$$\left(\frac{46.69 \text{ amu N}}{14.01 \text{ amu N}}\right) = 3.3326 \text{ N} \qquad \left(\frac{53.31 \text{ amu O}}{16.00 \text{ amu O}}\right) = 3.3319 \text{ O}$$

$$\frac{3.3326 \text{ N}}{3.3319} = 1.0002 \text{ N} \qquad \frac{3.3319 \text{ O}}{3.3319} = 1.0000 \text{ O}$$

The simplest whole-number ratio is **1:1 N:O.**

II

$$(100.00 - 36.85 \text{ N})\% = 63.15\% \text{ O}$$

$$\left(\frac{36.85 \text{ amu N}}{14.01 \text{ amu N}}\right) = 2.6303 \text{ N} \qquad \left(\frac{63.15 \text{ amu O}}{16.00 \text{ amu O}}\right) = 3.9469 \text{ O}$$

$$\frac{2.6303 \text{ N}}{2.6303} = 1.0000 \text{ mol N} \qquad \frac{3.9469 \text{ O}}{2.6303} = 1.5001 \text{ O}$$

The simplest whole-number ratio is 1:1.5 N:O = **2:3 N:O.**

III

$$(100.00 - 25.94 \text{ N})\% = 74.06\% \text{ O}$$

$$\left(\frac{25.94 \text{ amu N}}{14.01 \text{ amu N}}\right) = 1.8515 \text{ N} \qquad \left(\frac{74.06 \text{ amu O}}{16.00 \text{ amu O}}\right) = 4.6288 \text{ O}$$

$$\frac{1.8515 \text{ N}}{1.8515} = 1.0000 \text{ N} \qquad \frac{4.6288 \text{ O}}{1.8515} = 2.5000 \text{ O}$$

The simplest whole-number ratio is 1:2.5 N:O = **2:5 N:O.**

b) I

$$\left(\frac{53.31 \text{ amu O}}{46.69 \text{ amu N}}\right) = 1.1418 = \mathbf{1.14 \text{ g O}}$$

II

$$\left(\frac{63.15 \text{ amu O}}{36.85 \text{ amu N}}\right) = 1.7137 = \mathbf{1.71 \text{ g O}}$$

III

$$\left(\frac{74.06 \text{ amu O}}{25.94 \text{ amu N}}\right) = 2.8550 = \mathbf{2.86 \text{ g O}}$$

2.128 Plan: To find the mass percent divide the mass of each substance in mg by the amount of seawater in mg and multiply by 100. The percent of an ion is the mass of that ion divided by the total mass of ions.
Solution:

$$\text{a) Mass (mg) of seawater} = (1 \text{ kg})\left(\frac{1000 \text{ g}}{1 \text{ kg}}\right)\left(\frac{1000 \text{ mg}}{1 \text{ g}}\right) = 1\text{x}10^6 \text{ mg}$$

$$\text{Mass \%} = \left(\frac{\text{mass of substance}}{\text{mass of seawater}}\right)(100\%)$$

$$\text{Mass \% Cl}^- = \left(\frac{18{,}980 \text{ mg Cl}^-}{1\text{x}10^6 \text{ mg seawater}}\right)(100\%) = \mathbf{1.898\% \ Cl^-}$$

$$\text{Mass \% Na}^+ = \left(\frac{10.560 \text{ mg Na}^+}{1\text{x}10^6 \text{ mg seawater}}\right)(100\%) = \mathbf{1.056\% \ Na^+}$$

$$\text{Mass \% } SO_4^{2-} = \left(\frac{2650 \text{ mg } SO_4^{2-}}{1\text{x}10^6 \text{ mg seawater}}\right)(100\%) = \mathbf{0.265\% \ SO_4^{2-}}$$

$$\text{Mass \% } Mg^{2+} = \left(\frac{1270 \text{ mg } Mg^{2+}}{1\text{x}10^6 \text{ mg seawater}}\right)(100\%) = \mathbf{0.127\% \ Mg^{2+}}$$

$$\text{Mass \% } Ca^{2+} = \left(\frac{400 \text{ mg } Ca^{2+}}{1\text{x}10^6 \text{ mg seawater}}\right)(100\%) = \mathbf{0.04\% \ Ca^{2+}}$$

$$\text{Mass \% } K^{+} = \left(\frac{380 \text{ mg } K^{+}}{1\text{x}10^6 \text{ mg seawater}}\right)(100\%) = \mathbf{0.038\% \ K^{+}}$$

$$\text{Mass \% } HCO_3^{-} = \left(\frac{140 \text{ mg } HCO_3^{-}}{1\text{x}10^6 \text{ mg seawater}}\right)(100\%) = \mathbf{0.014\% \ HCO_3^{-}}$$

The mass percents do not add to 100% since the majority of seawater is H_2O.

b) Total mass of ions in 1 kg of seawater

= 18,980 mg + 10,560 mg + 2650 mg + 1270 mg + 400 mg + 380 mg + 140 mg = 34,380 mg

$$\% \ Na^{+} = \left(\frac{10{,}560 \text{ mg } Na^{+}}{34{,}380 \text{ mg total ions}}\right)(100) = 30.71553 = \mathbf{30.72\%}$$

c) Alkaline earth metal ions are Mg^{2+} and Ca^{2+} (Group 2 ions).

Total mass % = 0.127% Mg^{2+} + 0.04% Ca^{2+} = 0.167%

Alkali metal ions are Na^{+} and K^{+} (Group 1 ions). Total mass % = 1.056% Na^{+} + 0.038% K^{+} = 1.094%

$$\frac{\text{Mass \% of alkali metal ions}}{\text{Mass \% of alkaline earth metal ions}} = \frac{1.094\%}{0.167\%} = 6.6$$

Total mass percent for alkali metal ions is **6.6 times greater** than the total mass percent for alkaline earth metal ions. Sodium ions (alkali metal ions) are dominant in seawater.

d) Anions are Cl^{-}, SO_4^{2-}, and HCO_3^{-}.

Total mass % = 1.898% Cl^{-} + 0.265% SO_4^{2-} + 0.014% HCO_3^{-} = 2.177% anions

Cations are Na^{+}, Mg^{2+}, Ca^{2+}, and K^{+}.

Total mass % = 1.056% Na^{+} + 0.127% Mg^{2+} + 0.04% Ca^{2+} + 0.038% K^{+} = 1.2610 = 1.26% cations

The mass fraction of **anions** is larger than the mass fraction of cations. Is the solution neutral since the mass of anions exceeds the mass of cations? Yes, although the mass is larger, the number of positive charges equals the number of negative charges.

2.131 Plan: First, count each type of atom present to produce a molecular formula. The molecular (formula) mass is the sum of the atomic masses of all of the atoms. Divide the mass of each element in the compound by the molecular mass and multiply by 100 to obtain the mass percent of each element.

Solution:

The molecular formula of succinic acid is $\mathbf{C_4H_6O_4}$.

C	=	4(12.01 amu)	=	48.04 amu
H	=	6(1.008 amu)	=	6.048 amu
O	=	4 (16.00 amu)	=	64.00 amu
				118.09 amu

$$\% \ C = \left(\frac{48.04 \text{ amu C}}{118.088 \text{ amu}}\right)100\% = 40.6815 = \mathbf{40.68\% \ C}$$

$$\% \ H = \left(\frac{6.048 \text{ amu H}}{118.088 \text{ amu}}\right)100\% = 5.1216 = \mathbf{5.122\% \ H}$$

$$\% \text{ O} = \left(\frac{64.00 \text{ amu O}}{118.088 \text{ amu}}\right)100\% = 54.1969 = \mathbf{54.20\% \text{ O}}$$

Check: Total = (40.68 + 5.122 + 54.20)% = 100.00% The answer checks.

2.134 Plan: List all possible combinations of the isotopes. Determine the masses of each isotopic composition. The molecule consisting of the lower abundance isotopes (N-15 and O-18) is the least common, and the one containing only the more abundant isotopes (N-14 and O-16) will be the most common.

Solution:

a) Formula	Mass (amu)	b)
$\mathbf{^{15}N_2{}^{18}O}$	2(15 amu N) + 18 amu O = **48**	**least common**
$\mathbf{^{15}N_2{}^{16}O}$	2(15 amu N) + 16 amu O = **46**	
$\mathbf{^{14}N_2{}^{18}O}$	2(14 amu N) + 18 amu O = **46**	
$\mathbf{^{14}N_2{}^{16}O}$	2(14 amu N) + 16 amu O = **44**	**most common**
$\mathbf{^{15}N^{14}N^{18}O}$	1(15 amu N) + 1(14 amu N) + 18 amu O = **47**	
$\mathbf{^{15}N^{14}N^{16}O}$	1(15 amu N) + 1(14 amu N) + 16 amu O = **45**	

2.136 Plan: To find the formula mass of potassium fluoride, add the atomic masses of potassium and fluorine. Fluorine has only one naturally occurring isotope, so the mass of this isotope equals the atomic mass of fluorine. The atomic mass of potassium is the weighted average of the two isotopic masses: (isotopic mass of isotope 1 x fractional abundance) + (isotopic mass of isotope 2 x fractional abundance).

Solution:

Average atomic mass of K =

(isotopic mass of ^{39}K x fractional abundance) + (isotopic mass of ^{41}K x fractional abundance)

$$\text{Average atomic mass of K} = (38.9637\text{ amu})\left(\frac{93.258\%}{100\%}\right) + (40.9618\text{ amu})\left(\frac{6.730\%}{100\%}\right) = 39.093 \text{ amu}$$

The formula for potassium fluoride is KF, so its molecular mass is (39.093 + 18.9984) = **58.091 amu**

2.138 Plan: One molecule of NO is released per atom of N in the medicine. Divide the total mass of NO released by the molecular mass of the medicine and multiply by 100 for mass percent.

Solution:

NO = (14.01 + 16.00) amu = 30.01 amu

Nitroglycerin:

$C_3H_5N_3O_9$ = 3(12.01 amu C) + 5(1.008 amu H) + 3(14.01 amu N) + 9(16.00 amu O) = 227.10 amu

In $C_3H_5N_3O_9$ (molecular mass = 227.10 amu), there are 3 atoms of N; since 1 molecule of NO is released per atom of N, this medicine would release 3 molecules of NO. The molecular mass of NO = 30.01 amu.

$$\text{Mass percent of NO} = \frac{\text{total mass of NO}}{\text{mass of compound}}(100) = \frac{3(30.01 \text{ amu})}{227.10 \text{ amu}}(100) = 39.6433 = \mathbf{39.64\%}$$

Isoamyl nitrate:

$C_5H_{11}NO_3$ = 5(12.01 amu C) + 11(1.008 amu H) + 1(14.01 amu N) + 3(16.00 amu O) = 133.15 amu

In $(CH_3)_2CHCH_2CH_2ONO_2$ (molecular mass = 133.15 amu), there is one atom of N; since 1 molecule of NO is released per atom of N, this medicine would release 1 molecule of NO.

$$\text{Mass percent of NO} = \frac{\text{total mass of NO}}{\text{mass of compound}}(100) = \frac{1(30.01 \text{ amu})}{133.15 \text{ amu}}(100) = 22.5385 = \mathbf{22.54\%}$$

2.139 Plan: First, count each type of atom present to produce a molecular formula. Determine the mass fraction of each element. Mass fraction = $\frac{\text{total mass of the element}}{\text{molecular mass of TNT}}$. The mass of TNT multiplied by the mass fraction of each element gives the mass of that element.

Solution:
The molecular formula for TNT is $C_7H_5O_6N_3$. The molecular mass of TNT is:

C	=	7(12.01 amu)	=	84.07 amu
H	=	5(1.008 amu)	=	5.040 amu
O	=	6(16.00 amu)	=	96.00 amu
N	=	3(14.01 amu)	=	42.03 amu
				227.14 amu

The mass fraction of each element is:

$$C = \frac{84.07 \text{ amu}}{227.14 \text{ amu}} = 0.3701 \text{ C} \qquad H = \frac{5.040 \text{ amu}}{227.14 \text{ amu}} = 0.02219 \text{ H}$$

$$O = \frac{96.00 \text{ amu}}{227.14 \text{ amu}} = 0.4226 \text{ O} \qquad N = \frac{42.03 \text{ amu}}{227.14 \text{ amu}} = 0.1850 \text{ N}$$

Masses of each element in 1.00 lb of TNT = mass fraction of element x 1.00 lb.

Mass (lb) C = 0.3701 x 1.00 lb = **0.370 lb C**
Mass (lb) H = 0.02219 x 1.00 lb = **0.0222 lb H**
Mass (lb) O = 0.4226 x 1.00 lb = **0.423 lb O**
Mass (lb) N = 0.1850 x 1.00 lb = **0.185 lb N**

2.144 Plan: A change is physical when there has been a change in physical form but not a change in composition. In a chemical change, a substance is converted into a different substance.
Solution:
1) Initially, all the molecules are present in blue-blue or red-red pairs. After the change, there are no red-red pairs, and there are now red-blue pairs. Changing some of the pairs means there has been a **chemical change.**
2) There are two blue-blue pairs and four red-blue pairs both before and after the change, thus no chemical change occurred. The different types of molecules are separated into different boxes. This is a **physical change.**
3) The identity of the box contents has changed from pairs to individuals. This requires a **chemical change.**
4) The contents have changed from all pairs to all triplets. This is a change in the identity of the particles, thus, this is a **chemical change.**
5) There are four red-blue pairs both before and after, thus there has been no change in the identity of the individual units. There has been a **physical change.**

CHAPTER 3 STOICHIOMETRY OF FORMULAS AND EQUATIONS

FOLLOW–UP PROBLEMS

3.1A Plan: The mass of carbon must be changed from mg to g. The molar mass of carbon can then be used to determine the number of moles.

Solution:

$$\text{Moles of carbon} = 315 \text{ mg C}\left(\frac{1\text{g}}{10^3 \text{ mg}}\right)\left(\frac{1 \text{ mol C}}{12.01 \text{ g C}}\right) = 2.6228 \times 10^{-2} = \mathbf{2.62 \times 10^{-2} \text{ mol C}}$$

Road map:

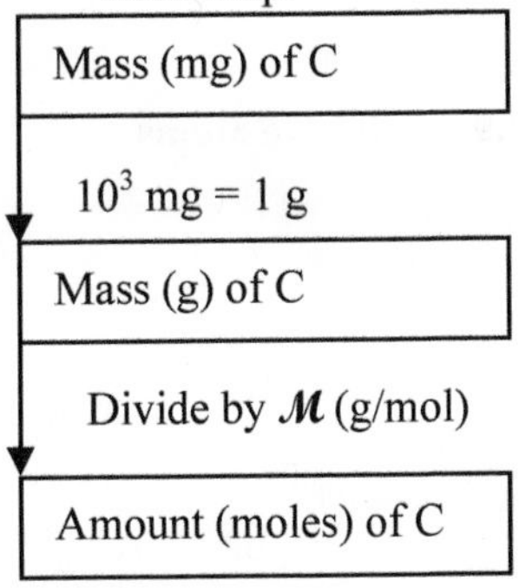

Mass (mg) of C

↓ 10^3 mg = 1 g

Mass (g) of C

↓ Divide by $\mathcal{M}$ (g/mol)

Amount (moles) of C

3.1B Plan: The number of moles of aluminum must be changed to g. Then the mass of aluminum per can can be used to calculate the number of soda cans that can be made from 52 mol of Al.

Solution:

$$\text{Number of soda cans} = 52 \text{ mol Al}\left(\frac{26.98 \text{ g Al}}{1 \text{ mol Al}}\right)\left(\frac{1 \text{ soda can}}{14 \text{ g Al}}\right) = 100.21 = \mathbf{100 \text{ soda cans}}$$

Road map:

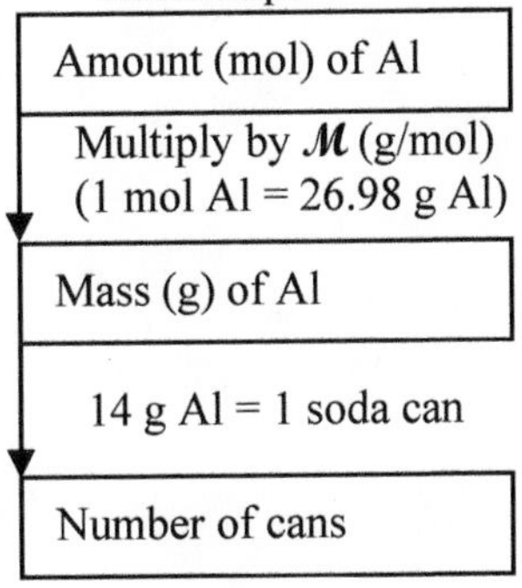

Amount (mol) of Al

↓ Multiply by $\mathcal{M}$ (g/mol) (1 mol Al = 26.98 g Al)

Mass (g) of Al

↓ 14 g Al = 1 soda can

Number of cans

3.2A Plan: Avogadro's number is needed to convert the number of nitrogen molecules to moles. Since nitrogen molecules are diatomic (composed of two N atoms), the moles of molecules must be multiplied by 2 to obtain moles of atoms.

Solution:

$$\text{Moles of N atoms} = \left(9.72 \times 10^{21} \text{ N}_2 \text{ molecules}\right)\left(\frac{1 \text{ mol N}_2}{6.022 \times 10^{23} \text{ N}_2 \text{ molecules}}\right)\left(\frac{2 \text{ N atoms}}{1 \text{ mol N}_2}\right)$$

$$= 3.2281634 \times 10^{-2} = \mathbf{3.23 \times 10^{-2} \text{ mol N}}$$

Road map:

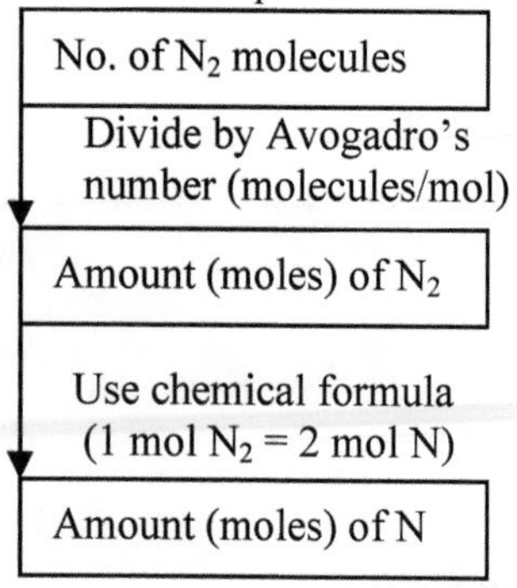

No. of N_2 molecules
↓ Divide by Avogadro's number (molecules/mol)
Amount (moles) of N_2
↓ Use chemical formula (1 mol N_2 = 2 mol N)
Amount (moles) of N

3.2B Plan: Avogadro's number is needed to convert the number of moles of He to atoms.
Solution:

$$\text{Number of He atoms} = 325 \text{ mol He} \left(\frac{6.022 \text{ x } 10^{23} \text{ He atoms}}{1 \text{ mol He}}\right) = 1.9572 \text{ x } 10^{26} = \mathbf{1.96 \text{ x } 10^{26} \text{ He atoms}}$$

Road map:

Amount (mol) of He
↓ Multiply by Avogadro's number (1 mol He = $6.022 \text{ x } 10^{23}$ He atoms)
Number of He atoms

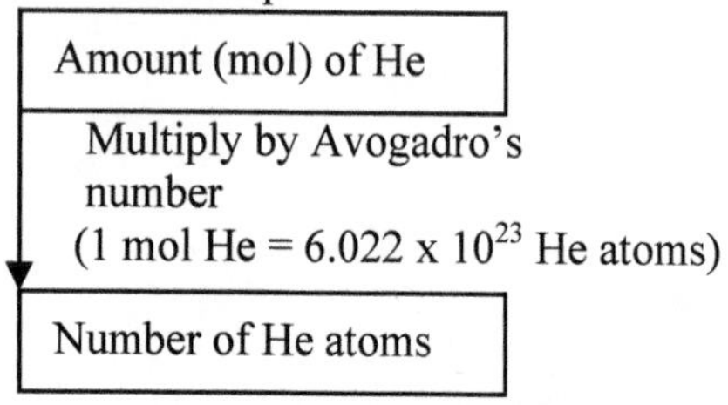

3.3A Plan: Avogadro's number is needed to convert the number of atoms to moles. The molar mass of manganese can then be used to determine the number of grams.
Solution:

$$\text{Mass (g) of Mn} = \left(3.22 \text{ x } 10^{20} \text{ Mn atoms}\right)\left(\frac{1 \text{ mol Mn}}{6.022 \text{ x } 10^{23} \text{ Mn atoms}}\right)\left(\frac{54.94 \text{ g Mn}}{1 \text{ mol Mn}}\right)$$

$$= 2.9377 \text{ x } 10^{-2} = \mathbf{2.94 \text{ x } 10^{-2} \text{ g Mn}}$$

Road map:

No. of Mn atoms
↓ Divide by Avogadro's number (molecules/mol)
Amount (moles) of Mn
↓ Multiply by $\mathcal{M}$ (g/mol)
Mass (g) of Mn

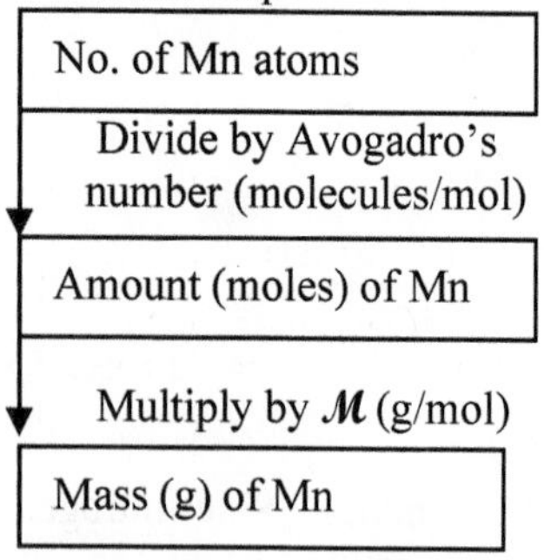

3.3B Plan: Use the molar mass of copper to calculate the number of moles of copper present in a penny. Avogadro's number is then needed to convert the number of moles of Cu to Cu atoms.
Solution:

$$\text{Number of Cu atoms} = 0.0625 \text{ g Cu} \left(\frac{1 \text{ mol Cu}}{63.55 \text{ g Cu}}\right)\left(\frac{6.022 \text{ x } 10^{23} \text{ Cu atoms}}{1 \text{ mol Cu}}\right)$$

$$= 5.9225 \text{ x } 10^{20} = \mathbf{5.92 \text{ x } 10^{20} \text{ Cu atoms}}$$

Road map:

Mass (g) of Cu

↓ Divide by $\mathcal{M}$ (g/mol)
(1 mol Cu = 63.55 g Cu)

Amount (moles) of Cu

↓ Multiply by Avogadro's number
(1 mol Cu = 6.022×10^{23} Cu atoms)

No. of Cu atoms

3.4A Plan: Avogadro's number is used to change the number of formula units to moles. Moles may be changed to mass using the molar mass of sodium fluoride, which is calculated from its formula.
Solution:
The formula of sodium fluoride is NaF.
$\mathcal{M}$ of NaF = (1 x $\mathcal{M}$ of Na) + (1 x $\mathcal{M}$ of F) = 22.99 g/mol + 19.00 g/mol = 41.99 g/mol

$$\text{Mass (g) of NaF} = \left(1.19 \times 10^{19} \text{ NaF formula units}\right)\left(\frac{1 \text{ mol NaF}}{6.022 \times 10^{23} \text{ NaF formula units}}\right)\left(\frac{41.99 \text{ g NaF}}{1 \text{ mol NaF}}\right)$$

$= 8.29759 \times 10^{-4} =$ **8.30×10^{-4} g NaF**

Road map:

No. of NaF formula units

↓ Divide by Avogadro's number (molecules/mol)

Amount (moles) of NaF

↓ Multiply by $\mathcal{M}$ (g/mol)

Mass (g) of NaF

3.4B Plan: Convert the mass of calcium chloride from pounds to g. Use the molar mass to calculate the number of moles of calcium chloride in the sample. Finally, use Avogadro's number to change the number of moles to formula units.
Solution:
$\mathcal{M}$ of $CaCl_2$ = (1 x $\mathcal{M}$ of Ca) + (2 x $\mathcal{M}$ of Cl) = 40.08 g/mol + 2(35.45 g/mol) = 110.98 g/mol

$$\text{Number of formula units of } CaCl_2 = 400 \text{ lb}\left(\frac{453.6 \text{ g}}{1 \text{ lb}}\right)\left(\frac{1 \text{ mol } CaCl_2}{110.98 \text{ g } CaCl_2}\right)\left(\frac{6.022 \times 10^{23} \text{ formula units } CaCl_2}{1 \text{ mol } CaCl_2}\right)$$

$= 9.8453 \times 10^{26} =$ **1×10^{27} formula units $CaCl_2$**

Road map:

Mass (lb) of $CaCl_2$

↓ 1 lb = 453.6 g

Mass (g) of $CaCl_2$

↓ Divide by $\mathcal{M}$ (g/mol)
(1 mol $CaCl_2$ = 110.98 g $CaCl_2$)

Amount (mol) of $CaCl_2$

Multiply by Avogadro's number
(1 mol $CaCl_2$ = 6.022 x 10^{23} $CaCl_2$ formula units)

No. of formula units of $CaCl_2$

3.5A Plan: Avogadro's number is used to change the number of molecules to moles. Moles may be changed to mass by multiplying by the molar mass. The molar mass of tetraphosphorus decoxide is obtained from its chemical formula. Each molecule has four phosphorus atoms, so the total number of atoms is four times the number of molecules.

Solution:

a) Tetra = 4, and deca = 10 to give P_4O_{10}.

The molar mass, $\mathcal{M}$, is the sum of the atomic weights, expressed in g/mol:

$$P = 4(30.97) = 123.88 \text{ g/mol}$$
$$O = 10(16.00) = \underline{160.00 \text{ g/mol}}$$
$$= 283.88 \text{ g/mol of } P_4O_{10}$$

$$\text{Mass (g) of } P_4O_{10} = \left(4.65 \text{ x } 10^{22} \text{ molecules } P_4O_{10}\right)\left(\frac{1 \text{ mol}}{6.022 \text{ x } 10^{23} \text{ molecules}}\right)\left(\frac{283.88 \text{ g}}{1 \text{ mol}}\right)$$

$$= 21.9203 = \mathbf{21.9 \text{ g } P_4O_{10}}$$

$$\text{b) Number of P atoms} = 4.65 \text{ x } 10^{22} \text{ molecules } P_4O_{10}\left(\frac{4 \text{ atoms P}}{1\ P_4O_{10} \text{ molecule}}\right) = \mathbf{1.86 \text{ x } 10^{23} \text{ P atoms}}$$

3.5B Plan: The mass of calcium phosphate is converted to moles of calcium phosphate by dividing by the molar mass. Avogadro's number is used to change the number of moles to formula units. Each formula unit has two phosphate ions, so the total number of phosphate ions is two times the number of formula units.

Solution:

a) The formula of calcium phosphate is $Ca_3(PO_4)_2$.

The molar mass, $\mathcal{M}$, is the sum of the atomic weights, expressed in g/mol:

$$\mathcal{M} = (3 \text{ x } \mathcal{M} \text{ of Ca}) + (2 \text{ x } \mathcal{M} \text{ of P}) + (8 \text{ x } \mathcal{M} \text{ of O})$$
$$= (3 \text{ x } 40.08 \text{ g/mol Ca}) + (2 \text{ x } 30.97 \text{ g/mol P}) + (8 \text{ x } 16.00 \text{ g/mol O})$$
$$= 310.18 \text{ g/mol } Ca_3(PO_4)_2$$

$$\text{No. of formula units } Ca_3(PO_4)_2 = 75.5 \text{ g } Ca_3(PO_4)_2\left(\frac{1 \text{ mol } Ca_3(PO_4)_2}{310.18 \text{ g } Ca_3(PO_4)_2}\right)\left(\frac{6.022 \text{ x } 10^{23} \text{ formula units } Ca_3(PO_4)_2}{1 \text{ mol } Ca_3(PO_4)_2}\right)$$

$$= 1.4658 \text{ x } 10^{23} = \mathbf{1.47 \text{ x } 10^{23} \text{ formula units } Ca_3(PO_4)_2}$$

$$\text{b) No. of phosphate } (PO_4^{3-}) \text{ ions} = 1.47 \text{ x } 10^{23} \text{ formula units } Ca_3(PO_4)_2\left(\frac{2\ PO_4^{3-} \text{ ions}}{1 \text{ formula unit } Ca_3(PO_4)_2}\right)$$

$$= \mathbf{2.94 \text{ x } 10^{23} \text{ phosphate ions}}$$

3.6A Plan: Calculate the molar mass of glucose. The total mass of carbon in the compound divided by the molar mass of the compound, multiplied by 100% gives the mass percent of C.

Solution:

The formula for glucose is $C_6H_{12}O_6$. There are 6 atoms of C per each formula.

$$\text{Molar mass of } C_6H_{12}O_6 = (6 \text{ x } \mathcal{M} \text{ of C}) + (12 \text{ x } \mathcal{M} \text{ of H}) + (6 \text{ x } \mathcal{M} \text{ of O})$$
$$= (6 \text{ x } 12.01 \text{ g/mol}) + (12 \text{ x } 1.008 \text{ g/mol}) + (6 \text{ x } 16.00 \text{ g/mol})$$
$$= 180.16 \text{ g/mol}$$

$$\text{Mass \% of C} = \frac{\text{total mass of C}}{\text{molar mass of } C_6H_{12}O_6}(100) = \frac{6 \times 12.01 \text{ g/mol}}{180.16 \text{ g/mol}}(100) = 39.9978 = \mathbf{40.00\% \ C}$$

3.6B Plan: Calculate the molar mass of CCl_3F. The total mass of chlorine in the compound divided by the molar mass of the compound, multiplied by 100% gives the mass percent of Cl.

Solution:

The formula is CCl_3F. There are 3 atoms of Cl per each formula.

Molar mass of CCl_3F = (1 x $\mathcal{M}$ of C) + (3 x $\mathcal{M}$ of Cl) + (1 x $\mathcal{M}$ of F)

= (1 x 12.01 g/mol) + (3 x 35.45 g/mol) + (1 x 19.00 g/mol)

= 137.36 g/mol

$$\text{Mass \% of Cl} = \frac{\text{total mass of Cl}}{\text{molar mass of } CCl_3F}(100) = \frac{3 \times 35.45 \text{ g/mol}}{137.36 \text{ g/mol}}(100) = 77.4243 = \mathbf{77.42\% \ Cl}$$

3.7A Plan: Multiply the mass of the sample by the mass fraction of C found in the preceding problem.

Solution:

$$\text{Mass (g) of C} = 16.55 \text{ g } C_6H_{12}O_6 \left(\frac{72.06 \text{ g C}}{180.16 \text{ g } C_6H_{12}O_6}\right) = 6.6196 = \mathbf{6.620 \ g \ C}$$

3.7B Plan: Multiply the mass of the sample by the mass fraction of Cl found in the preceding problem.

Solution:

$$\text{Mass (g) of Cl} = 112 \text{ g } CCl_3F \left(\frac{106.35 \text{ g Cl}}{137.36 \text{ g } CCl_3F}\right) = 86.6900 = \mathbf{86.7 \ g \ Cl}$$

3.8A Plan: We are given fractional amounts of the elements as subscripts. Convert the fractional amounts to whole numbers by dividing each number by the smaller number and then multiplying by the smallest integer that will turn both subscripts into integers.

Solution:

Divide each subscript by the smaller value, 0.170: $B_{\frac{0.170}{0.170}}O_{\frac{0.255}{0.170}} = B_1O_{1.5}$

Multiply the subscripts by 2 to obtain integers: $B_{1 \times 2}O_{1.5 \times 2} = \mathbf{B_2O_3}$

3.8B Plan: We are given fractional amounts of the elements as subscripts. Convert the fractional amounts to whole numbers by dividing each number by the smaller number and then multiplying by the smallest integer that will turn both subscripts into integers.

Solution:

Divide each subscript by the smaller value, 6.80: $C_{\frac{6.80}{6.80}}H_{\frac{18.1}{6.80}} = C_1H_{2.67}$

Multiply the subscripts by 3 to obtain integers: $C_{1x3}H_{2.66x3} = \mathbf{C_3H_8}$

3.9A Plan: Calculate the number of moles of each element in the sample by dividing by the molar mass of the corresponding element. The calculated numbers of moles are the fractional amounts of the elements and can be used as subscripts in a chemical formula. Convert the fractional amounts to whole numbers by dividing each number by the smallest subscripted number.

Solution:

$$\text{Moles of H} = 1.23 \text{ g H}\left(\frac{1 \text{ mol H}}{1.008 \text{ g H}}\right) = 1.22 \text{ mol H}$$

$$\text{Moles of P} = 12.64 \text{ g P}\left(\frac{1 \text{ mol P}}{30.97 \text{ g P}}\right) = 0.408 \text{ mol P}$$

$$\text{Moles of O} = 26.12 \text{ g O}\left(\frac{1 \text{ mol O}}{16.00 \text{ g O}}\right) = 1.63 \text{ mol O}$$

Divide each subscript by the smaller value, 0.408: $H_{\frac{1.22}{0.408}}P_{\frac{0.408}{0.408}}O_{\frac{1.63}{0.408}} = \mathbf{H_3PO_4}$

3.9B Plan: The moles of sulfur may be calculated by dividing the mass of sulfur by the molar mass of sulfur. The moles of sulfur and the chemical formula will give the moles of M. The mass of M divided by the moles of M will give the molar mass of M. The molar mass of M can identify the element.

Solution:

$$\text{Moles of S} = (2.88 \text{ g S})\left(\frac{1 \text{ mol S}}{32.06 \text{ g S}}\right) = 0.0898 \text{ mol S}$$

$$\text{Moles of M} = (0.0898 \text{ mol S})\left(\frac{2 \text{ mol M}}{3 \text{ mol S}}\right) = 0.0599 \text{ mol M}$$

$$\text{Molar mass of M} = \frac{3.12 \text{ g M}}{0.0599 \text{ mol M}} = 52.0868 = 52.1 \text{ g/mol}$$

The element is Cr (52.00 g/mol); M is **Chromium** and M_2S_3 is **chromium(III) sulfide.**

3.10A Plan: If we assume there are 100 grams of this compound, then the masses of carbon and hydrogen, in grams, are numerically equivalent to the percentages. Divide the atomic mass of each element by its molar mass to obtain the moles of each element. Dividing each of the moles by the smaller value gives the simplest ratio of C and H. The smallest multiplier to convert the ratios to whole numbers gives the empirical formula. To obtain the molecular formula, divide the given molar mass of the compound by the molar mass of the empirical formula to find the whole-number by which the empirical formula is multiplied.

Solution:

Assuming 100 g of compound gives 95.21 g C and 4.79 g H:

$$\text{Moles of C} = 95.21 \text{ g C}\left(\frac{1 \text{ mol C}}{12.01 \text{ g C}}\right) = 7.92756 \text{ mol C}$$

$$\text{Mole of H} = 4.79 \text{ g H}\left(\frac{1 \text{ mol H}}{1.008 \text{ g H}}\right) = 4.75198 \text{ mol H}$$

Divide each of the moles by 4.75198, the smaller value:

$$C_{\frac{7.92756}{4.75198}}H_{\frac{4.75198}{4.75198}} = C_{1.6683}H_1$$

The value 1.668 is 5/3, so the moles of C and H must each be multiplied by 3. If it is not obvious that the value is near 5/3, use a trial and error procedure whereby the value is multiplied by the successively larger integer until a value near an integer results. This gives C_5H_3 as the empirical formula. The molar mass of this formula is:

$$(5 \text{ x } 12.01 \text{ g/mol}) + (3 \text{ x } 1.008 \text{ g/mol}) = 63.074 \text{ g/mol}$$

$$\text{Whole-number multiple} = \frac{\text{molar mass of compound}}{\text{molar mass of empirical formula}} = \frac{252.30 \text{ g/mol}}{63.074 \text{ g/mol}} = 4$$

Thus, the empirical formula must be multiplied by 4 to give $4(C_5H_3) = \mathbf{C_{20}H_{12}}$ as the molecular formula of benzo[*a*]pyrene.

3.10B Plan: If we assume there are 100 grams of this compound, then the masses of carbon, hydrogen, nitrogen, and oxygen, in grams, are numerically equivalent to the percentages. Divide the atomic mass of each element by its molar mass to obtain the moles of each element. Dividing each of the moles by the smaller value gives the simplest ratio of C, H, N, and O. To obtain the molecular formula, divide the given molar mass of the compound by the molar mass of the empirical formula to find the whole-number by which the empirical formula is multiplied.

Solution:

Assuming 100 g of compound gives 49.47 g C, 5.19 g H, 28.86 g N, and 16.48 g O:

$$\text{Moles of C} = 49.47 \text{ g C}\left(\frac{1 \text{ mol C}}{12.01 \text{ g C}}\right) = 4.119 \text{ mol C}$$

$$\text{Moles of H} = 5.19 \text{ g H}\left(\frac{1 \text{ mol H}}{1.008 \text{ g H}}\right) = 5.15 \text{ mol H}$$

$$\text{Moles of N} = 28.86 \text{ g N}\left(\frac{1 \text{ mol N}}{14.01 \text{ g N}}\right) = 2.060 \text{ mol N}$$

$$\text{Moles of O} = 16.48 \text{ g O}\left(\frac{1 \text{ mol O}}{16.00 \text{ g O}}\right) = 1.030 \text{ mol O}$$

Divide each subscript by the smaller value, 1.030: $C_{\frac{4.119}{1.030}}H_{\frac{5.15}{1.030}}N_{\frac{2.060}{1.030}}O_{\frac{1.030}{1.030}} = C_4H_5N_2O$

This gives $C_4H_5N_2O$ as the empirical formula. The molar mass of this formula is:

(4 x 12.01 g/mol) + (5 x 1.008 g/mol) + (2 x 14.01 g/mol) + (1 x 16.00 g/mol) = 97.10 g/mol

The molar mass of caffeine is 194.2 g/mol, which is larger than the empirical formula mass of 97.10 g/mol, so the molecular formula must be a whole-number multiple of the empirical formula.

$$\text{Whole-number multiple} = \frac{\text{molar mass of compound}}{\text{molar mass of empirical formula}} = \frac{194.2 \text{ g/mol}}{97.10 \text{ g/mol}} = 2$$

Thus, the empirical formula must be multiplied by 2 to give $2(C_4H_5N_2O) = \mathbf{C_8H_{10}N_4O_2}$ as the molecular formula of caffeine.

3.11A Plan: The carbon in the sample is converted to carbon dioxide, the hydrogen is converted to water, and the remaining material is chlorine. The grams of carbon dioxide and the grams of water are both converted to moles. One mole of carbon dioxide gives one mole of carbon, while one mole of water gives two moles of hydrogen. Using the molar masses of carbon and hydrogen, the grams of each of these elements in the original sample may be determined. The original mass of sample minus the masses of carbon and hydrogen gives the mass of chlorine. The mass of chlorine and the molar mass of chlorine will give the moles of chlorine. Once the moles of each of the elements have been calculated, divide by the smallest value, and, if necessary, multiply by the smallest number required to give a set of whole numbers for the empirical formula. Compare the molar mass of the empirical formula to the molar mass given in the problem to find the molecular formula.

Solution:

Determine the moles and the masses of carbon and hydrogen produced by combustion of the sample.

$$0.451 \text{ g } CO_2\left(\frac{1 \text{ mol } CO_2}{44.01 \text{ g } CO_2}\right)\left(\frac{1 \text{ mol C}}{1 \text{ mol } CO_2}\right) = 0.010248 \text{ mol C}\left(\frac{12.01 \text{ g C}}{1 \text{ mol C}}\right) = 0.12307 \text{ g C}$$

$$0.0617 \text{ g } H_2O\left(\frac{1 \text{ mol } H_2O}{18.016 \text{ g } H_2O}\right)\left(\frac{2 \text{ mol H}}{1 \text{ mol } H_2O}\right) = 0.0068495 \text{ mol H}\left(\frac{1.008 \text{ g H}}{1 \text{ mol H}}\right) = 0.006904 \text{ g H}$$

The mass of chlorine is given by: 0.250 g sample – (0.12307 g C + 0.006904 g H) = 0.120 g Cl

The moles of chlorine are:

$$0.120 \text{ g Cl}\left(\frac{1 \text{ mol Cl}}{35.45 \text{ g Cl}}\right) = 0.0033850 \text{ mol Cl. This is the smallest number of moles.}$$

Divide each mole value by the lowest value, 0.0033850: $C_{\frac{0.010248}{0.0033850}}H_{\frac{0.0068495}{0.0033850}}Cl_{\frac{0.0033850}{0.0033850}} = C_3H_2Cl$

The empirical formula has the following molar mass:

(3 x 12.01 g/mol) + (2 x 1.008 g/mol) + (35.45 g/mol) = 73.496 g/mol C_3H_2Cl

$$\text{Whole-number multiple} = \frac{\text{molar mass of compound}}{\text{molar mass of empirical formula}} = \frac{146.99 \text{ g/mol}}{73.496 \text{ g/mol}} = 2$$

Thus, the molecular formula is two times the empirical formula, $2(C_3H_2Cl) = \mathbf{C_6H_4Cl_2}$.

3.11B Plan: The carbon in the sample is converted to carbon dioxide, the hydrogen is converted to water, and the remaining material is oxygen. The grams of carbon dioxide and the grams of water are both converted to moles. One mole of carbon dioxide gives one mole of carbon, while one mole of water gives two moles of hydrogen. Using the molar masses of carbon and hydrogen, the grams of each of these elements in the original sample may be determined. The original mass of sample minus the masses of carbon and hydrogen gives the mass of oxygen. The mass of oxygen and the molar mass of oxygen will give the moles of oxygen. Once the moles of each of the elements have been calculated, divide by the smallest value, and, if necessary, multiply by the smallest number required to give a set of whole numbers for the empirical formula. Compare the molar mass of the empirical formula to the molar mass given in the problem to find the molecular formula.

Solution:

Determine the moles and the masses of carbon and hydrogen produced by combustion of the sample.

$$3.516 \text{ g CO}_2 \left(\frac{1 \text{ mol CO}_2}{44.01 \text{ g CO}_2}\right)\left(\frac{1 \text{ mol C}}{1 \text{ mol CO}_2}\right) = 0.07989 \text{ mol C} \left(\frac{12.01 \text{ g C}}{1 \text{ mol C}}\right) = 0.9595 \text{ g C}$$

$$1.007 \text{ g H}_2\text{O} \left(\frac{1 \text{ mol H}_2\text{O}}{18.02 \text{ g H}_2\text{O}}\right)\left(\frac{2 \text{ mol H}}{1 \text{ mol H}_2\text{O}}\right) = 0.1118 \text{ mol H} \left(\frac{1.008 \text{ g H}}{1 \text{ mol H}}\right) = 0.1127 \text{ g H}$$

The mass of oxygen is given by: 1.200 g sample – (0.9595 g C + 0.1127 g H) = 0.128 g O
The moles of C and H are calculated above. The moles of oxygen are:

$0.128 \text{ g O} \left(\frac{1 \text{ mol O}}{16.00 \text{ g O}}\right) = 0.00800$ mol O. This is the smallest number of moles.

Divide each subscript by the smallest value, 0.00800: $C_{\frac{0.07989}{0.00800}}H_{\frac{0.1118}{0.00800}}O_{\frac{0.00800}{0.00800}} = C_{10}H_{14}O$

This gives $C_{10}H_{14}O$ as the empirical formula. The molar mass of this formula is:
(10 x 12.01 g/mol) + (14 x 1.008 g/mol) + (1 x 16.00 g/mol) = 150.21 g/mol
The molar mass of the steroid is 300.42 g/mol, which is larger than the empirical formula mass of 150.21 g/mol, so the molecular formula must be a whole-number multiple of the empirical formula.

$$\text{Whole-number multiple} = \frac{\text{molar mass of compound}}{\text{molar mass of empirical formula}} = \frac{300.42 \text{ g/mol}}{150.21 \text{ g/mol}} = 2$$

Thus, the empirical formula must be multiplied by 2 to give $2(C_{10}H_{14}O)$ = $\mathbf{C_{20}H_{28}O_2}$ as the molecular formula of the steroid.

3.12A Plan: In each part it is necessary to determine the chemical formulas, including the physical states, for both the reactants and products. The formulas are then placed on the appropriate sides of the reaction arrow. The equation is then balanced.

Solution:

a) Sodium is a metal (solid) that reacts with water (liquid) to produce hydrogen (gas) and a solution of sodium hydroxide (aqueous). Sodium is Na; water is H_2O; hydrogen is H_2; and sodium hydroxide is NaOH.

$Na(s) + H_2O(l) \rightarrow H_2(g) + NaOH(aq)$ is the equation.

Balancing will precede one element at a time. One way to balance hydrogen gives:

$Na(s) + 2H_2O(l) \rightarrow H_2(g) + 2NaOH(aq)$

Next, the sodium will be balanced:

$\mathbf{2Na(s) + 2H_2O(l) \rightarrow H_2(g) + 2NaOH(aq)}$

On inspection, we see that the oxygen is already balanced.

b) Aqueous nitric acid reacts with calcium carbonate (solid) to produce carbon dioxide (gas), water (liquid), and aqueous calcium nitrate. Nitric acid is HNO_3; calcium carbonate is $CaCO_3$; carbon dioxide is CO_2; water is H_2O; and calcium nitrate is $Ca(NO_3)_2$. The starting equation is

$HNO_3(aq) + CaCO_3(s) \rightarrow CO_2(g) + H_2O(l) + Ca(NO_3)_2(aq)$

Initially, Ca and C are balanced. Proceeding to another element, such as N, or better yet the group of elements in NO_3^- gives the following partially balanced equation:

$\mathbf{2HNO_3(aq) + CaCO_3(s) \rightarrow CO_2(g) + H_2O(l) + Ca(NO_3)_2(aq)}$

Now, all the elements are balanced.

c) We are told all the substances involved are gases. The reactants are phosphorus trichloride and hydrogen fluoride, while the products are phosphorus trifluoride and hydrogen chloride. Phosphorus trifluoride is PF_3; phosphorus trichloride is PCl_3; hydrogen fluoride is HF; and hydrogen chloride is HCl. The initial equation is:

$PCl_3(g) + HF(g) \rightarrow PF_3(g) + HCl(g)$

Initially, P and H are balanced. Proceed to another element (either F or Cl); if we will choose Cl, it balances as:

$PCl_3(g) + HF(g) \rightarrow PF_3(g) + 3HCl(g)$

The balancing of the Cl unbalances the H, this should be corrected by balancing the H as:

$\mathbf{PCl_3(g) + 3HF(g) \rightarrow PF_3(g) + 3HCl(g)}$

Now, all the elements are balanced.

3.12B Plan: In each part it is necessary to determine the chemical formulas, including the physical states, for both the reactants and products. The formulas are then placed on the appropriate sides of the reaction arrow. The equation is then balanced.

Solution:

a) We are told that nitroglycerine is a liquid reactant, and that all the products are gases. The formula for nitroglycerine is given. Carbon dioxide is CO_2; water is H_2O; nitrogen is N_2; and oxygen is O_2. The initial equation is:

$$C_3H_5N_3O_9(l) \rightarrow CO_2(g) + H_2O(g) + N_2(g) + O_2(g)$$

Counting the atoms shows no atoms are balanced.

One element should be picked and balanced. Any element except oxygen will work. Oxygen will not work in this case because it appears more than once on one side of the reaction arrow. We will start with carbon. Balancing C gives:

$$C_3H_5N_3O_9(l) \rightarrow 3CO_2(g) + H_2O(g) + N_2(g) + O_2(g)$$

Now balancing the hydrogen gives:

$$C_3H_5N_3O_9(l) \rightarrow 3CO_2(g) + 5/2H_2O(g) + N_2(g) + O_2(g)$$

Similarly, if we balance N we get:

$$C_3H_5N_3O_9(l) \rightarrow 3CO_2(g) + 5/2H_2O(g) + 3/2N_2(g) + O_2(g)$$

Clear the fractions by multiplying everything except the unbalanced oxygen by 2:

$$2C_3H_5N_3O_9(l) \rightarrow 6CO_2(g) + 5H_2O(g) + 3N_2(g) + O_2(g)$$

This leaves oxygen to balance. Balancing oxygen gives:

$$2C_3H_5N_3O_9(l) \rightarrow 6CO_2(g) + 5H_2O(g) + 3N_2(g) + 1/2O_2(g)$$

Again clearing fractions by multiplying everything by 2 gives:

$$\mathbf{4C_3H_5N_3O_9(\mathit{l}) \rightarrow 12CO_2(\mathit{g}) + 10H_2O(\mathit{g}) + 6N_2(\mathit{g}) + O_2(\mathit{g})}$$

Now all the elements are balanced.

b) Potassium superoxide (KO_2) is a solid. Carbon dioxide (CO_2) and oxygen (O_2) are gases. Potassium carbonate (K_2CO_3) is a solid. The initial equation is:

$$KO_2(s) + CO_2(g) \rightarrow O_2(g) + K_2CO_3(s)$$

Counting the atoms indicates that the carbons are balanced, but none of the other atoms are balanced. One element should be picked and balanced. Any element except oxygen will work (oxygen will be more challenging to balance because it appears more than once on each side of the reaction arrow). Because the carbons are balanced, we will start with potassium. Balancing potassium gives:

$$2KO_2(s) + CO_2(g) \rightarrow O_2(g) + K_2CO_3(s)$$

Now all elements except for oxygen are balanced. Balancing oxygen by adding a coefficient in front of the O_2 gives:

$$2KO_2(s) + CO_2(g) \rightarrow 3/2O_2(g) + K_2CO_3(s)$$

Clearing the fractions by multiplying everything by 2 gives:

$$\mathbf{4KO_2(\mathit{s}) + 2CO_2(\mathit{g}) \rightarrow 3O_2(\mathit{g}) + 2K_2CO_3(\mathit{s})}$$

Now all the elements are balanced.

c) Iron(III) oxide (Fe_2O_3) is a solid, as is iron metal (Fe). Carbon monoxide (CO) and carbon dioxide (CO_2) are gases. The initial equation is:

$$Fe_2O_3(s) + CO(g) \rightarrow Fe(s) + CO_2(g)$$

Counting the atoms indicates that the carbons are balanced, but none of the other atoms are balanced. One element should be picked and balanced. Because oxygen appears in more than one compound on one side of the reaction arrow, it is best not to start with that element. Because the carbons are balanced, we will start with iron. Balancing iron gives:

$$Fe_2O_3(s) + CO(g) \rightarrow 2Fe(s) + CO_2(g)$$

Now all the atoms but oxygen are balanced. There are 4 oxygen atoms on the left hand side of the reaction arrow and 2 oxygen atoms on the right hand side of the reaction arrow. In order to balance the oxygen, we want to change the coefficients in front of the carbon-containing compounds (if we changed the coefficient in front of the iron(III) oxide, the iron atoms would no longer be balanced). To maintain the balance of carbons, the coefficients in front of the carbon monoxide and the carbon dioxide must be the same. On the left hand side of the equation, there are 3 oxygens in Fe_2O_3 plus 1X oxygen atoms from the CO (where X is the coefficient in the balanced equation). On the right hand side of the equation, there are 2X oxygen atoms. The number of oxygen atoms on both sides of the equation should be the same:

$3 + 1X = 2X$
$3 = X$

Balancing oxygen by adding a coefficient of 3 in front of the CO and CO_2 gives:

$$\mathbf{Fe_2O_3(s) + 3CO(g) \rightarrow 2Fe(s) + 3CO_2(g)}$$

Now all the elements are balanced.

3.13A Plan: Count the number of each type of atom in each molecule to write the formulas of the reactants and products.
Solution:

$$6CO(g) + 3O_2(g) \rightarrow 6CO_2(g)$$

or, $\mathbf{2CO(g) + O_2(g) \rightarrow 2CO_2(g)}$

3.13B Plan: Count the number of each type of atom in each molecule to write the formulas of the reactants and products.
Solution:

$$6H_2(g) + 2N_2(g) \rightarrow 4NH_3(g)$$

or, $\mathbf{3H_2(g) + N_2(g) \rightarrow 2NH_3(g)}$

3.14A Plan: The reaction, like all reactions, needs a balanced chemical equation. The balanced equation gives the molar ratio between the moles of iron and moles of iron(III) oxide.
Solution:
The names and formulas of the substances involved are: iron(III) oxide, Fe_2O_3, and aluminum, Al, as reactants, and aluminum oxide, Al_2O_3, and iron, Fe, as products. The iron is formed as a liquid; all other substances are solids. The equation begins as:

$$Fe_2O_3(s) + Al(s) \rightarrow Al_2O_3(s) + Fe(l)$$

There are 2 Fe, 3 O, and 1 Al on the reactant side and 1 Fe, 3 O, and 2 Al on the product side.

Balancing aluminum: $Fe_2O_3(s) + 2Al(s) \rightarrow Al_2O_3(s) + Fe(l)$
Balancing iron: $Fe_2O_3(s) + 2Al(s) \rightarrow Al_2O_3(s) + 2Fe(l)$

$$\text{Moles of } Fe_2O_3 = \left(3.60 \times 10^3 \text{ mol Fe}\right)\left(\frac{1 \text{ mol } Fe_2O_3}{2 \text{ mol Fe}}\right) = \mathbf{1.80 \times 10^3 \text{ mol } Fe_2O_3}$$

Road map:

Amount (moles) of Fe
↓ Molar ratio (2 mol Fe = 1 mol Fe_2O_3)
Amount (moles) of Fe_2O_3

3.14B Plan: The reaction, like all reactions, needs a balanced chemical equation. The balanced equation gives the molar ratio between the moles of aluminum and moles of silver sulfide.
Solution:
The names and formulas of the substances involved are: silver sulfide, Ag_2S, and aluminum, Al, as reactants; and aluminum sulfide, Al_2S_3, and silver, Ag, as products. All reactants and compounds are solids. The equation begins as:

$$Ag_2S(s) + Al(s) \rightarrow Al_2S_3(s) + Ag(s)$$

There are 2 Ag, 1 S, and 1 Al on the reactant side and 2 Al, 3 S, and 1 Ag on the product side.

Balancing sulfur: $3Ag_2S(s) + Al(s) \rightarrow Al_2S_3(s) + Ag(s)$
Balancing silver: $3Ag_2S(s) + Al(s) \rightarrow Al_2S_3(s) + 6Ag(s)$
Balancing aluminum: $3Ag_2S(s) + 2Al(s) \rightarrow Al_2S_3(s) + 6Ag(s)$

$$\text{Moles of Al} = 0.253 \text{ mol } Ag_2S\left(\frac{2 \text{ mol Al}}{3 \text{ mol } Ag_2S}\right) = 0.1687 = \mathbf{0.169 \text{ mol Al}}$$

Road map:

Amount (moles) of Ag_2S
↓ Molar ratio
(3 mol Ag_2S = 2 mol Al)
Amount (moles) of Al

3.15A Plan: Divide the formula units of aluminum oxide by Avogadro's number to obtain moles of compound. The balanced equation gives the molar ratio between moles of iron(III) oxide and moles of iron.
Solution:

$$\text{Moles of Fe} = \left(1.85 \times 10^{25}\ Fe_2O_3\ \text{formula units}\right)\left(\frac{1\ \text{mol}\ Fe_2O_3}{6.022 \times 10^{23}\ Fe_2O_3\ \text{formula units}}\right)\left(\frac{2\ \text{mol Fe}}{1\ \text{mol}\ Fe_2O_3}\right)$$

61.4414 = **61.4 mol Fe**

Road map:

No. of Fe_2O_3 formula units
↓ Divide by Avogadro's number
(6.022×10^{23} Fe_2O_3 formula units = 1 mol Fe_2O_3)
Amount (moles) of Fe_2O_3
↓ Molar ratio
(1 mol Fe_2O_3 = 2 mol Fe)
Amount (moles) of Fe

3.15B Plan: Divide the mass of silver sulfide by its molar mass to obtain moles of the compound. The balanced equation gives the molar ratio between moles of silver sulfide and moles of silver.
Solution:

$$\text{Moles of Ag} = 32.6\ \text{g}\ Ag_2S\left(\frac{1\ \text{mol}\ Ag_2S}{247.9\ \text{g}\ Ag_2S}\right)\left(\frac{6\ \text{mol Ag}}{3\ \text{mol}\ Ag_2S}\right) = 0.2630 = \mathbf{0.263\ mol\ Ag}$$

Road map:

Mass (g) of Ag_2S
↓ Divide by $\mathcal{M}$ (g/mol)
(247.9 g Ag_2S = 1 mol Ag_2S)
Amount (moles) of Ag_2S
↓ Molar ratio
(3 mol Ag_2S = 6 mol Ag)
Amount (moles) of Ag

3.16A Plan: The mass of aluminum oxide must be converted to moles by dividing by its molar mass. The balanced chemical equation (follow-up problem 3.14A) shows there are two moles of aluminum for every mole of aluminum oxide. Multiply the moles of aluminum by Avogadro's number to obtain atoms of Al.

Solution:

$$\text{Atoms of Al} = (1.00\ \text{g Al}_2\text{O}_3)\left(\frac{1\ \text{mol Al}_2\text{O}_3}{101.96\ \text{g Al}_2\text{O}_3}\right)\left(\frac{2\ \text{mol Al}}{1\ \text{mol Al}_2\text{O}_3}\right)\left(\frac{6.022 \times 10^{23}\ \text{atoms Al}}{1\ \text{mol Al}}\right)$$

$$= 1.18125 \times 10^{22} = \mathbf{1.18 \times 10^{22}\ atoms\ Al}$$

Road map:

Mass (g) of Al_2O_3

↓ Divide by $\mathcal{M}$ (g/mol)

Amount (moles) of Al_2O_3

↓ Molar ratio

Amount (moles) of Al

↓ Multiply by Avogadro's number

Number of Al atoms

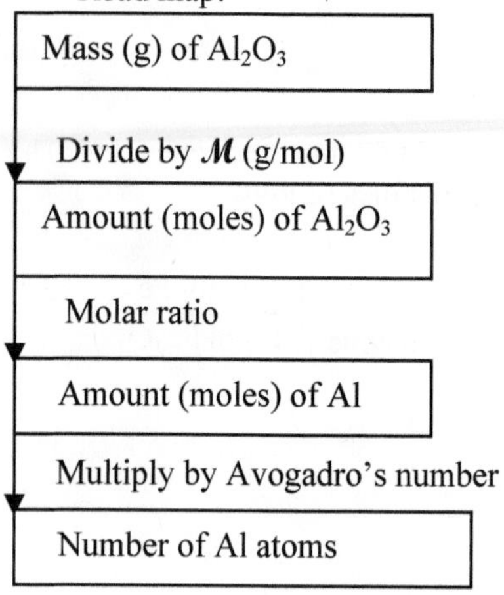

3.16B Plan: The mass of aluminum sulfide must be converted to moles by dividing by its molar mass. The balanced chemical equation (follow-up problem 3.14B) shows there are two moles of aluminum for every mole of aluminum sulfide. Multiply the moles of aluminum by its molar mass to obtain the mass (g) of aluminum.
Solution:

$$\text{Mass (g) of Al} = 12.1\ \text{g Al}_2\text{S}_3\left(\frac{1\ \text{mol Al}_2\text{S}_3}{150.14\ \text{g Al}_2\text{S}_3}\right)\left(\frac{2\ \text{mol Al}}{1\ \text{mol Al}_2\text{S}_3}\right)\left(\frac{26.98\ \text{g Al}}{1\ \text{mol Al}}\right) = 4.3487 = \mathbf{4.35\ g\ Al}$$

Road map:

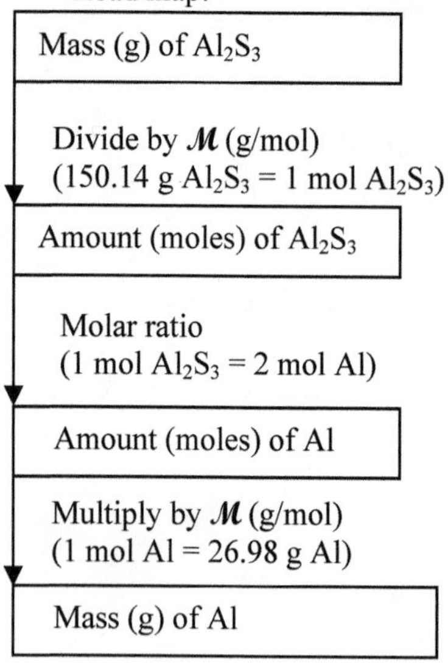

Mass (g) of Al_2S_3

↓ Divide by $\mathcal{M}$ (g/mol)
($150.14\ g\ Al_2S_3 = 1\ mol\ Al_2S_3$)

Amount (moles) of Al_2S_3

↓ Molar ratio
($1\ mol\ Al_2S_3 = 2\ mol\ Al$)

Amount (moles) of Al

↓ Multiply by $\mathcal{M}$ (g/mol)
(1 mol Al = 26.98 g Al)

Mass (g) of Al

3.17A Plan: Write the balanced chemical equation for each step. Add the equations, canceling common substances.
Solution:

Step 1 $2SO_2(g) + O_2(g) \rightarrow 2SO_3(g)$

Step 2 $SO_3(g) + H_2O(l) \rightarrow H_2SO_4(aq)$

Adjust the coefficients since 2 moles of SO_3 are produced in Step 1 but only 1 mole of SO_3 is consumed in Step 2. We have to double all of the coefficients in Step 2 so that the amount of SO_3 formed in Step 1 is used in Step 2.

Step 1 $2SO_2(g) + O_2(g) \rightarrow 2SO_3(g)$

Step 2 $2SO_3(g) + 2H_2O(l) \rightarrow 2H_2SO_4(aq)$

Add the two equations and cancel common substances.

Step 1 $2SO_2(g) + O_2(g) \rightarrow 2SO_3(g)$

Step 2 $2SO_3(g) + 2H_2O(l) \rightarrow 2H_2SO_4(aq)$

$2SO_2(g) + O_2(g) +$ ~~$2SO_3(g)$~~ $+ 2H_2O(l) \rightarrow$ ~~$2SO_3(g)$~~ $+ 2H_2SO_4(aq)$

Or **$2SO_2(g) + O_2(g) + 2H_2O(l) \rightarrow 2H_2SO_4(aq)$**

3.17B <u>Plan:</u> Write the balanced chemical equation for each step. Add the equations, canceling common substances.

<u>Solution:</u>

Step 1 $N_2(g) + O_2(g) \rightarrow 2NO(g)$

Step 2 $NO(g) + O_3(g) \rightarrow NO_2(g) + O_2(g)$

Adjust the coefficients since 2 moles of NO are produced in Step 1 but only 1 mole of NO is consumed in Step 2. We have to double all of the coefficients in Step 2 so that the amount of NO formed in Step 1 is used in Step 2.

Step 1 $N_2(g) + O_2(g) \rightarrow 2NO(g)$

Step 2 $2NO(g) + 2O_3(g) \rightarrow 2NO_2(g) + 2O_2(g)$

Add the two equations and cancel common substances.

Step 1 $N_2(g) + O_2(g) \rightarrow 2NO(g)$

Step 2 $2NO(g) + 2O_3(g) \rightarrow 2NO_2(g) + 2O_2(g)$

$N_2(g) +$ ~~$O_2(g)$~~ $+$ ~~$2NO(g)$~~ $+ 2O_3(g) \rightarrow$ ~~$2NO(g)$~~ $+ 2NO_2(g) +$ ~~2~~$O_2(g)$

Or **$N_2(g) + 2O_3(g) \rightarrow 2NO_2(g) + O_2(g)$**

3.18A <u>Plan:</u> Count the molecules of each type, and find the simplest ratio. The simplest ratio leads to a balanced chemical equation. The substance with no remaining particles is the limiting reagent.

<u>Solution:</u>

4 AB molecules react with 3 B_2 molecules to produce 4 molecules of AB_2, with 1 B_2 molecule remaining unreacted. The balanced chemical equation is

$4AB(g) + 2B_2(g) \rightarrow 4AB_2(g)$ or **$2AB(g) + B_2(g) \rightarrow 2AB_2(g)$**

The limiting reagent is **AB** since there is a B_2 molecule left over (excess).

3.18B <u>Plan:</u> Write a balanced equation for the reaction. Use the molar ratios in the balanced equation to find the amount (molecules) of SO_3 produced when each reactant is consumed. The reactant that gives the smaller amount of product is the limiting reagent.

<u>Solution:</u>

5 SO_2 molecules react with 2 O_2 molecules to produce molecules of SO_3. The balanced chemical equation is

$2SO_2(g) + O_2(g) \rightarrow 2SO_3(g)$

$$\text{Amount (molecules) of } SO_3 \text{ produced from the } SO_2 = 5 \text{ molecules } SO_2 \left(\frac{2 \text{ molecules } SO_3}{2 \text{ molecules } SO_2}\right) = 5 \text{ molecules } SO_3$$

$$\text{Amount (molecules) of } SO_3 \text{ produced from the } O_2 = 2 \text{ molecules } SO_2 \left(\frac{2 \text{ molecules } SO_3}{1 \text{ molecule } O_2}\right) = 4 \text{ molecules } SO_3$$

O_2 is the limiting reagent since it produces less SO_3 than the SO_2 does.

3.19A <u>Plan:</u> Use the molar ratios in the balanced equation to find the amount of AB_2 produced when 1.5 moles of each reactant is consumed. The smaller amount of product formed is the actual amount.

<u>Solution:</u>

$$\text{Moles of } AB_2 \text{ from AB} = (1.5 \text{ mol AB})\left(\frac{2 \text{ mol } AB_2}{2 \text{ mol AB}}\right) = 1.5 \text{ mol } AB_2$$

Moles of AB_2 from $B_2 = (1.5 \text{ mol } B_2)\left(\frac{2 \text{ mol } AB_2}{1 \text{ mol } B_2}\right) = 3.0 \text{ mol } AB_2$

Thus AB is the limiting reagent and only **1.5 mol of AB_2** will form.

3.19B Plan: Use the molar ratios in the balanced equation to find the amount of SO_3 produced when 4.2 moles of SO_2 are consumed and, separately, the amount of SO_3 produced when 3.6 moles of O_2 are consumed. The smaller amount of product formed is the actual amount.

Solution:

The balanced chemical equation is

$$2SO_2(g) + O_2(g) \rightarrow 2SO_3(g)$$

Amount (mol) of SO_3 produced from the $SO_2 = 4.2 \text{ mol } SO_2 \left(\frac{2 \text{ mol } SO_3}{2 \text{ mol } SO_2}\right) = 4.2 \text{ mol } SO_3$

Amount (mol) of SO_3 produced from the $O_2 = 3.6 \text{ mol } SO_2 \left(\frac{2 \text{ mol } SO_3}{1 \text{ mol } O_2}\right) = 7.2 \text{ mol } SO_3$

4.2 mol of SO_3 (the smaller amount) will be produced.

3.20A Plan: First, determine the formulas of the materials in the reaction and write a balanced chemical equation. Using the molar mass of each reactant, determine the moles of each reactant. Use molar ratios from the balanced equation to determine the moles of aluminum sulfide that may be produced from each reactant. The reactant that generates the smaller number of moles is limiting. Change the moles of aluminum sulfide from the limiting reactant to the grams of product using the molar mass of aluminum sulfide. To find the excess reactant amount, find the amount of excess reactant required to react with the limiting reagent and subtract that amount from the amount given in the problem.

Solution:

The balanced equation is $2Al(s) + 3S(s) \rightarrow Al_2S_3(s)$

Determining the moles of product from each reactant:

Moles of Al_2S_3 from $Al = (10.0 \text{ g Al})\left(\frac{1 \text{ mol Al}}{26.98 \text{ g Al}}\right)\left(\frac{1 \text{ mol } Al_2S_3}{2 \text{ mol Al}}\right) = 0.18532 \text{ mol } Al_2S_3$

Moles of Al_2S_3 from $S = (15.0 \text{ g S})\left(\frac{1 \text{ mol S}}{32.06 \text{ g S}}\right)\left(\frac{1 \text{ mol } Al_2S_3}{3 \text{ mol S}}\right) = 0.155958 \text{ mol } Al_2S_3$

Sulfur produces less product so it is the limiting reactant.

Mass (g) of $Al_2S_3 = (0.155958 \text{ mol } Al_2S_3)\left(\frac{150.14 \text{ g } Al_2S_3}{1 \text{ mol } Al_2S_3}\right) = 23.4155 = \mathbf{23.4 \text{ g } Al_2S_3}$

The mass of aluminum used in the reaction is now determined:

Mass (g) of Al= $(15.0 \text{ g S})\left(\frac{1 \text{ mol S}}{32.06 \text{ g S}}\right)\left(\frac{2 \text{ mol Al}}{3 \text{ mol Al}}\right)\left(\frac{26.98 \text{ g Al}}{1 \text{ mol Al}}\right) = 8.4155 \text{ g Al used}$

Subtracting the mass of aluminum used from the initial aluminum gives the mass remaining.

Excess Al = Initial mass of Al – mass of Al reacted = 10.0 g – 8.4155 g = 1.5845 = **1.6 g Al**

3.20B Plan: First, determine the formulas of the materials in the reaction and write a balanced chemical equation. Using the molar mass of each reactant, determine the moles of each reactant. Use molar ratios and the molar mass of carbon dioxide from the balanced equation to determine the mass of carbon dioxide that may be produced from each reactant. The reactant that generates the smaller mass of carbon dioxide is limiting. To find the excess reactant amount, find the amount of excess reactant required to react with the limiting reagent and subtract that amount from the amount given in the problem.

Solution:

The balanced equation is: $2C_4H_{10}(g) + 13O_2(g) \rightarrow 8CO_2(g) + 10H_2O(g)$

Determining the mass of product formed from each reactant:

Mass (g) of CO_2 from $C_4H_{10} = 4.65 \text{ g } C_4H_{10}\left(\frac{1 \text{ mol } C_4H_{10}}{58.12 \text{ g } C_4H_{10}}\right)\left(\frac{8 \text{ mol } CO_2}{2 \text{ mol } C_4H_{10}}\right)\left(\frac{44.01 \text{ g } CO_2}{1 \text{ mol } CO_2}\right) = 14.0844 = 14.1 \text{ g } CO_2$

$$\text{Mass (g) of } CO_2 \text{ from } O_2 = 10.0 \text{ g } O_2 \left(\frac{1 \text{ mol } O_2}{32.00 \text{ g } O_2}\right)\left(\frac{8 \text{ mol } CO_2}{13 \text{ mol } O_2}\right)\left(\frac{44.01 \text{ g } CO_2}{1 \text{ mol } CO_2}\right) = 8.4635 = 8.46 \text{ g } CO_2$$

Oxygen produces the smallest amount of product, so it is the limiting reagent, and **8.46 g of CO_2 are produced.** The mass of butane used in the reaction is now determined:

$$\text{Mass (g) of } C_4H_{10} = 10.0 \text{ g } O_2 \left(\frac{1 \text{ mol } O_2}{32.00 \text{ g } O_2}\right)\left(\frac{2 \text{ mol } C_4H_{10}}{13 \text{ mol } O_2}\right)\left(\frac{58.12 \text{ g } C_4H_{10}}{1 \text{ mol } C_4H_{10}}\right) = 2.7942 = 2.79 \text{ g } C_4H_{10} \text{ used}$$

Subtracting the mass of butane used from the initial butane gives the mass remaining.
Excess butane = Initial mass of butane – mass of butane reacted = 4.65 g – 2.79 g = **1.86 g butane**

3.21A Plan: Determine the formulas, and then balance the chemical equation. The mass of marble is converted to moles, the molar ratio (from the balanced equation) gives the moles of CO_2, and finally the theoretical yield of CO_2 is determined from the moles of CO_2 and its molar mass. To calculate percent yield, divide the given actual yield of CO_2 by the theoretical yield, and multiply by 100.

Solution:

The balanced equation: $CaCO_3(s) + 2HCl(aq) \rightarrow CaCl_2(aq) + H_2O(l) + CO_2(g)$

Find the theoretical yield of carbon dioxide.

$$\text{Mass (g) of } CO_2 = (10.0 \text{ g } CaCO_3)\left(\frac{1 \text{ mol } CaCO_3}{100.09 \text{ g } CaCO_3}\right)\left(\frac{1 \text{ mol } CO_2}{1 \text{ mol } CaCO_3}\right)\left(\frac{44.01 \text{ g } CO_2}{1 \text{ mol } CO_2}\right)$$

$$= 4.39704 \text{ g } CO_2$$

The percent yield:

$$\left(\frac{\text{actual yield}}{\text{theoretical yield}}\right)(100\%) = \left(\frac{3.65 \text{ g } CO_2}{4.39704 \text{ g } CO_2}\right)(100\%) = 83.0104 = \mathbf{83.0\%}$$

3.21B Plan: Determine the formulas, and then balance the chemical equation. The mass of sodium chloride is converted to moles, the molar ratio (from the balanced equation) gives the moles of sodium carbonate, and finally the theoretical yield of sodium carbonate is determined from the moles of sodium carbonate and its molar mass. To calculate percent yield, divide the given actual yield of sodium carbonate by the theoretical yield, and multiply by 100.

Solution:

The balanced equation: $2NaCl + CaCO_3 \rightarrow CaCl_2 + Na_2CO_3$

Find the theoretical yield of sodium carbonate.

$$\text{Mass (g) of } Na_2CO_3 = 112 \text{ g NaCl} \left(\frac{1 \text{ mol NaCl}}{58.44 \text{ g NaCl}}\right)\left(\frac{1 \text{ mol } Na_2CO_3}{2 \text{ mol NaCl}}\right)\left(\frac{105.99 \text{ g } Na_2CO_3}{1 \text{ mol } Na_2CO_3}\right) = 101.5647 = 102 \text{ g } Na_2CO_3$$

The percent yield:

$$\% \text{ yield of } Na_2CO_3 = \left(\frac{\text{actual yield}}{\text{theoretical yield}}\right)(100\%) = \frac{92.6 \text{ g } Na_2CO_3}{102 \text{ g } Na_2CO_3}(100\%) = 90.7843 = \mathbf{90.8\%}$$

END–OF–CHAPTER PROBLEMS

3.2 Plan: The molecular formula of sucrose tells us that 1 mole of sucrose contains 12 moles of carbon atoms. Multiply the moles of sucrose by 12 to obtain moles of carbon atoms; multiply the moles of carbon atoms by Avogadro's number to convert from moles to atoms.

Solution:

$$\text{a) Moles of C atoms} = (1 \text{ mol } C_{12}H_{22}O_{11})\left(\frac{12 \text{ mol C}}{1 \text{ mol } C_{12}H_{22}O_{11}}\right) = \mathbf{12 \text{ mol C}}$$

$$\text{b) C atoms} = (2 \text{ mol} C_{12}H_{22}O_{11})\left(\frac{12 \text{ mol C}}{1 \text{ mol } C_{12}H_{22}O_{11}}\right)\left(\frac{6.022 \times 10^{23} \text{ C atoms}}{1 \text{ mol C}}\right) = \mathbf{1.445 x 10^{25} \text{ C atoms}}$$

3.7 Plan: The relative atomic masses of each element can be found by counting the number of atoms of each element and comparing the overall masses of the two samples.

Solution:
a) The element on the **left** (green) has the higher molar mass because only 5 green balls are necessary to counterbalance the mass of 6 yellow balls. Since the green ball is heavier, its atomic mass is larger, and therefore its molar mass is larger.
b) The element on the **left** (red) has more atoms per gram. This figure requires more thought because the number of red and blue balls is unequal and their masses are unequal. If each pan contained 3 balls, then the red balls would be lighter. The presence of 6 red balls means that they are that much lighter. Because the red ball is lighter, more red atoms are required to make 1 g.
c) The element on the **left** (orange) has fewer atoms per gram. The orange balls are heavier, and it takes fewer orange balls to make 1 g.
d) **Neither** element has more atoms per mole. Both the left and right elements have the same number of atoms per mole. The number of atoms per mole (6.022×10^{23}) is constant and so is the same for every element.

3.8 Plan: Locate each of the elements on the periodic table and record its atomic mass. The atomic mass of the element multiplied by the number of atoms present in the formula gives the mass of that element in one mole of the substance. The molar mass is the sum of the masses of the elements in the substance expressed in g/mol.
Solution:
a) $\mathcal{M}$ = (1 x $\mathcal{M}$ of Sr) + (2 x $\mathcal{M}$ of O) + (2 x $\mathcal{M}$ of H)
= (1 x 87.62 g/mol Sr) + (2 x 16.00 g/mol O) + (2 x 1.008 g/mol H)
= **121.64 g/mol of $Sr(OH)_2$**
b) $\mathcal{M}$ = (2 x $\mathcal{M}$ of N) + (3 x $\mathcal{M}$ of O)
= (2 x 14.01 g/mol N) + (3 x 16.00 g/mol O)
= **76.02 g/mol of N_2O_3**
c) $\mathcal{M}$ = (1 x $\mathcal{M}$ of Na) + (1 x $\mathcal{M}$ of Cl) + (3 x $\mathcal{M}$ of O)
= (1 x 22.99 g/mol Na) + (1 x 35.45 g/mol Cl) + (3 x 16.00 g/mol O)
= **106.44 g/mol of $NaClO_3$**
d) $\mathcal{M}$ = (2 x $\mathcal{M}$ of Cr) + (3 x $\mathcal{M}$ of O)
= (2 x 52.00 g/mol Cr) + (3 x 16.00 g/mol O)
= **152.00 g/mol of Cr_2O_3**

3.10 Plan: Locate each of the elements on the periodic table and record its atomic mass. The atomic mass of the element multiplied by the number of atoms present in the formula gives the mass of that element in one mole of the substance. The molar mass is the sum of the masses of the elements in the substance expressed in g/mol.
Solution:
a) $\mathcal{M}$ = (1 x $\mathcal{M}$ of Sn) + (1 x $\mathcal{M}$ of O)
= (1 x 118.7 g/mol Sn) + (1 x 16.00 g/mol O)
= **134.7 g/mol of SnO**
b) $\mathcal{M}$ = (1 x $\mathcal{M}$ of Ba) + (2 x $\mathcal{M}$ of F)
= (1 x 137.3 g/mol Ba) + (2 x 19.00 g/mol F)
= **175.3 g/mol of BaF_2**
c) $\mathcal{M}$ = (2 x $\mathcal{M}$ of Al) + (3 x $\mathcal{M}$ of S) + (12 x $\mathcal{M}$ of O)
= (2 x 26.98 g/mol Al) + (3 x 32.06 g/mol S) + (12 x 16.00 g/mol O)
= **342.14 g/mol of $Al_2(SO_4)_3$**
d) $\mathcal{M}$ = (1 x $\mathcal{M}$ of Mn) + (2 x $\mathcal{M}$ of Cl)
= (1 x 54.94 g/mol Mn) + (2 x 35.45 g/mol Cl)
= **125.84 g/mol of $MnCl_2$**

3.12 Plan: Determine the molar mass of each substance; then perform the appropriate molar conversions. To find the mass in part a), multiply the number of moles by the molar mass of Zn. In part b), first multiply by Avogadro's number to obtain the number of F_2 molecules. The molecular formula tells us that there are 2 F atoms in each molecule of F_2; use the 2:1 ratio to convert F_2 molecules to F atoms. In part c), convert mass of Ca to moles of Ca by dividing by the molar mass of Ca. Then multiply by Avogadro's number to obtain the number of Ca atoms.

Solution:

a) $(0.346 \text{ mol Zn})\left(\frac{65.38 \text{ g Zn}}{1 \text{ mol Zn}}\right) = \mathbf{22.6 \text{ g Zn}}$

b) $(2.62 \text{ mol } F_2)\left(\frac{6.022 \times 10^{23} \; F_2 \text{ molecules}}{1 \text{ mol } F_2}\right)\left(\frac{2 \text{ F atoms}}{1 \; F_2 \text{ molecule}}\right) = \mathbf{3.16 \times 10^{24} \text{ F atoms}}$

c) $28.5 \text{ g Ca}\left(\frac{1 \text{ mol Ca}}{40.08 \text{ g Ca}}\right)\left(\frac{6.022 \times 10^{23} \text{ Ca atoms}}{1 \text{ mol Ca}}\right) = \mathbf{4.28 \times 10^{23} \text{ Ca atoms}}$

3.14 Plan: Determine the molar mass of each substance; then perform the appropriate molar conversions. To find the mass in part a), multiply the number of moles by the molar mass of the substance. In part b), first convert mass of compound to moles of compound by dividing by the molar mass of the compound. The molecular formula of the compound tells us that 1 mole of compound contains 6 moles of oxygen atoms; use the 1:6 ratio to convert moles of compound to moles of oxygen atoms. In part c), convert mass of compound to moles of compound by dividing by the molar mass of the compound. Since 1 mole of compound contains 6 moles of oxygen atoms, multiply the moles of compound by 6 to obtain moles of oxygen atoms; then multiply by Avogadro's number to obtain the number of oxygen atoms.

Solution:

a) $\mathcal{M}$ of $KMnO_4$ = (1 x $\mathcal{M}$ of K) + (1 x $\mathcal{M}$ of Mn) + (4 x $\mathcal{M}$ of O)
= (1 x 39.10 g/mol K) + (1 x 54.94 g/mol Mn) + (4 x 16.00 g/mol O) = 158.04 g/mol of $KMnO_4$

$$\text{Mass of } KMnO_4 = (0.68 \text{ mol } KMnO_4)\left(\frac{158.04 \text{ g } KMnO_4}{1 \text{ mol } KMnO_4}\right) = 107.467 = \mathbf{1.1 \times 10^2 \text{ g } KMnO_4}$$

b) $\mathcal{M}$ of $Ba(NO_3)_2$ = (1 x $\mathcal{M}$ of Ba) + (2 x $\mathcal{M}$ of N) + (6 x $\mathcal{M}$ of O)
= (1 x 137.3 g/mol Ba) + (2 x 14.01 g/mol N) + (6 x 16.00 g/mol O) = 261.3 g/mol $Ba(NO_3)_2$

$$\text{Moles of } Ba(NO_3)_2 = (8.18 \text{ g } Ba(NO_3)_2)\left(\frac{1 \text{ mol } Ba(NO_3)_2}{261.3 \text{ g } Ba(NO_3)_2}\right) = 0.031305 \text{ mol } Ba(NO_3)_2$$

$$\text{Moles of O atoms} = (0.031305 \text{ mol } Ba(NO_3)_2)\left(\frac{6 \text{ mol O atoms}}{1 \text{ mol } Ba(NO_3)_2}\right) = 0.18783 = \mathbf{0.188 \text{ mol O atoms}}$$

c) $\mathcal{M}$ of $CaSO_4 \cdot 2H_2O$ = (1 x $\mathcal{M}$ of Ca) + (1 x $\mathcal{M}$ of S) + (6 x $\mathcal{M}$ of O) + (4 x $\mathcal{M}$ of H)
= (1 x 40.08 g/mol Ca) + (1 x 32.06 g/mol S) + (6 x 16.00 g/mol O) + (4 x 1.008 g/mol H)
= 172.17 g/mol

(Note that the waters of hydration are included in the molar mass.)

$$\text{Moles of } CaSO_4 \cdot 2H_2O = (7.3 \times 10^{-3} \text{ g } CaSO_4 \cdot 2H_2O)\left(\frac{1 \text{ mol } CaSO_4 \cdot 2H_2O}{172.17 \text{ g } CaSO_4 \cdot 2H_2O}\right) = 4.239995 \times 10^{-5} \text{ mol}$$

$$\text{Moles of O atoms} = (4.239995 \times 10^{-5} \text{ mol } CaSO_4 \cdot 2H_2O)\left(\frac{6 \text{ mol O atoms}}{1 \text{ mol } CaSO_4 \cdot 2H_2O}\right)$$

$$= 2.543997 \times 10^{-5} \text{ mol O atoms}$$

$$\text{Number of O atoms} = (2.543997 \times 10^{-4} \text{ mol O atoms})\left(\frac{6.022 \times 10^{23} \text{ O atoms}}{1 \text{ mol O atoms}}\right)$$

$$= 1.5320 \times 10^{20} = \mathbf{1.5 \times 10^{20} \text{ O atoms}}$$

3.16 Plan: Determine the molar mass of each substance; then perform the appropriate molar conversions. To find the mass in part a), multiply the number of moles by the molar mass of the substance. In part b), first convert the mass of compound in kg to mass in g and divide by the molar mass of the compound to find moles of compound. In part c), convert mass of compound in mg to mass in g and divide by the molar mass of the compound to find moles of compound. Since 1 mole of compound contains 2 moles of nitrogen atoms, multiply the moles of compound by 2 to obtain moles of nitrogen atoms; then multiply by Avogadro's number to obtain the number of nitrogen atoms.

Solution:
a) $\mathcal{M}$ of $MnSO_4$ = (1 x $\mathcal{M}$ of Mn) + (1 x $\mathcal{M}$ of S) + (4 x $\mathcal{M}$ of O)
= (1 x 54.94 g/mol Mn) + (1 x 32.06 g/mol S) + (4 x 16.00 g/mol O) = 151.00 g/mol of $MnSO_4$

$$\text{Mass (g) of } MnSO_4 = \left(6.44\text{x}10^{-2}\text{ mol } MnSO_4\right)\left(\frac{151.00\text{ g } MnSO_4}{1\text{ mol } MnSO_4}\right) = 9.7244 = \mathbf{9.72\text{ g } MnSO_4}$$

b) $\mathcal{M}$ of $Fe(ClO_4)_3$ = (1 x $\mathcal{M}$ of Fe) + (3 x $\mathcal{M}$ of Cl) + (12 x $\mathcal{M}$ of O)
= (1 x 55.85 g/mol Fe) + (3 x 35.45 g/mol S) + (12 x 16.00 g/mol O)
= 354.20 g/mol of $Fe(ClO_4)_3$

$$\text{Mass (g) of } Fe(ClO_4)_3 = \left(15.8\text{ kg } Fe(ClO_4)_3\right)\left(\frac{10^3\text{ g}}{1\text{ kg}}\right) = 1.58 \text{ x } 10^4\text{ kg } Fe(ClO_4)_3$$

$$\text{Moles of } Fe(ClO_4)_3 = \left(1.58\text{x}10^4\text{ g } Fe(ClO_4)_3\right)\left(\frac{1\text{ mol } Fe(ClO_4)_3}{354.20\text{ g } Fe(ClO_4)_3}\right) = 44.6076 = \mathbf{44.6\ \ mol\ Fe(ClO_4)_3}$$

c) $\mathcal{M}$ of NH_4NO_2 = (2 x $\mathcal{M}$ of N) + (4 x $\mathcal{M}$ of H) + (2 x $\mathcal{M}$ of O)
= (2 x 14.01 g/mol N) + (4 x 1.008 g/mol H) + (2 x 16.00 g/mol O) = 64.05 g/mol NH_4NO_2

$$\text{Mass (g) of } NH_4NO_2 = \left(92.6\text{ mg } NH_4NO_2\right)\left(\frac{10^{-3}\text{ g}}{1\text{ mg}}\right) = 0.0926\text{ g } NH_4NO_2$$

$$\text{Moles of } NH_4NO_2 = \left(0.0926\text{ g } NH_4NO_2\right)\left(\frac{1\text{ mol } NH_4NO_2}{64.05\text{ g } NH_4NO_2}\right) = 1.44575\text{x}10^{-3}\text{ mol } NH_4NO_2$$

$$\text{Moles of N atoms} = \left(1.44575\text{x}10^{-3}\text{ mol } NH_4NO_2\right)\left(\frac{2\text{ mol N atoms}}{1\text{ mol } NH_4NO_2}\right) = 2.8915\text{x}10^{-3}\text{ mol N atoms}$$

$$\text{Number of N atoms} = \left(2.8915\text{x}10^{-3}\text{ mol N atoms}\right)\left(\frac{6.022\text{ x }10^{23}\text{ N atoms}}{1\text{ mol N atoms}}\right)$$

$$= 1.74126 \text{ x } 10^{21} = \mathbf{1.74 \text{ x } 10^{21}\text{ N atoms}}$$

3.18 Plan: The formula of each compound must be determined from its name. The molar mass for each formula comes from the formula and atomic masses from the periodic table. Determine the molar mass of each substance, then perform the appropriate molar conversions. In part a), multiply the moles by the molar mass of the compound to find the mass of the sample. In part b), divide the number of molecules by Avogadro's number to find moles; multiply the number of moles by the molar mass to obtain the mass. In part c), divide the mass by the molar mass to find moles of compound and multiply moles by Avogadro's number to find the number of formula units. In part d), use the fact that each formula unit contains 1 Na ion, 1 perchlorate ion, 1 Cl atom, and 4 O atoms.

Solution:
a) Carbonate is a polyatomic anion with the formula, CO_3^{2-}. Copper(I) indicates Cu^+. The correct formula for this ionic compound is Cu_2CO_3.
$\mathcal{M}$ of Cu_2CO_3 = (2 x $\mathcal{M}$ of Cu) + (1 x $\mathcal{M}$ of C) + (3 x $\mathcal{M}$ of O)
= (2 x 63.55 g/mol Cu) + (1 x 12.01 g/mol C) + (3 x 16.00 g/mol O) = 187.11 g/mol of Cu_2CO_3

$$\text{Mass (g) of } Cu_2CO_3 = \left(8.35\text{ mol } Cu_2CO_3\right)\left(\frac{187.11\text{ g } Cu_2CO_3}{1\text{ mol } Cu_2CO_3}\right) = 1562.4 = \mathbf{1.56\text{x}10^3\text{ g } Cu_2CO_3}$$

b) Dinitrogen pentaoxide has the formula N_2O_5. Di- indicates 2 N atoms and penta- indicates 5 O atoms.
$\mathcal{M}$ of N_2O_5 = (2 x $\mathcal{M}$ of N) + (5 x $\mathcal{M}$ of O)
= (2 x 14.01 g/mol N) + (5 x 16.00 g/mol O) = 108.02 g/mol of N_2O_5

Moles of N_2O_5 = $\left(4.04\text{x}10^{20}\ N_2O_5\ \text{molecules}\right)\left(\frac{1\ \text{mol}\ N_2O_5}{6.022\text{x}10^{23}\ N_2O_5\ \text{molecules}}\right)$ = 6.7087x10^{-4} mol N_2O_5

Mass (g) of N_2O_5 = $\left(6.7087\text{x}10^{-4}\ \text{mol}\ N_2O_5\right)\left(\frac{108.02\ \text{g}\ N_2O_5}{1\ \text{mol}\ N_2O_5}\right)$ = 0.072467 = **0.0725 g N_2O_5**

c) The correct formula for this ionic compound is $NaClO_4$; Na has a charge of +1 (Group 1 ion) and the perchlorate ion is ClO_4^- .

$\mathcal{M}$ of $NaClO_4$ = (1x $\mathcal{M}$ of Na) + (1 x $\mathcal{M}$ of Cl) + (4 x $\mathcal{M}$ of O)
= (1 x 22.99 g/mol Na) + (1 x 35.45 g/mol Cl) + (4 x 16.00 g/mol O) = 122.44 g/mol of $NaClO_4$

Moles of $NaClO_4$ = $\left(78.9\ \text{g}\ NaClO_4\right)\left(\frac{1\ \text{mol}\ NaClO_4}{122.44\ \text{g}\ NaClO_4}\right)$ = 0.644397 = **0.644 mol $NaClO_4$**

FU = formula units

FU of $NaClO_4$ = $\left(0.644397\ \text{mol}\ NaClO_4\right)\left(\frac{6.022\text{x}10^{23}\ \text{FU}\ NaClO_4}{1\ \text{mol}\ NaClO_4}\right)$
= 3.88056x10^{23} = **3.88x10^{23} FU $NaClO_4$**

d) Number of Na^+ ions = $\left(3.88056\text{x}10^{23}\ \text{FU}\ NaClO_4\right)\left(\frac{1\ Na^+\ \text{ion}}{1\ \text{FU}\ NaClO_4}\right)$ = **3.88x10^{23} Na^+ ions**

Number of ClO_4^- ions = $\left(3.88056\text{x}10^{23}\ \text{FU}\ NaClO_4\right)\left(\frac{1\ ClO_4^-\ \text{ion}}{1\ \text{FU}\ NaClO_4}\right)$ = **3.88x10^{23} ClO_4^- ions**

Number of Cl atoms = $\left(3.88056\text{x}10^{23}\ \text{FU}\ NaClO_4\right)\left(\frac{1\ \text{Cl atom}}{1\ \text{FU}\ NaClO_4}\right)$ = **3.88x10^{23} Cl atoms**

Number of O atoms = $\left(3.88056\text{x}10^{23}\ \text{FU}\ NaClO_4\right)\left(\frac{4\ \text{O atoms}}{1\ \text{FU}\ NaClO_4}\right)$ = **1.55x10^{24} O atoms**

3.20 Plan: Determine the formula and the molar mass of each compound. The formula gives the relative number of moles of each element present. Multiply the number of moles of each element by its molar mass to find the total mass of element in 1 mole of compound. Mass percent = $\frac{\text{total mass of element}}{\text{molar mass of compound}}(100)$.

Solution:

a) Ammonium bicarbonate is an ionic compound consisting of ammonium ions, NH_4^+ and bicarbonate ions, HCO_3^-. The formula of the compound is NH_4HCO_3.

$\mathcal{M}$ of NH_4HCO_3 = (1 x $\mathcal{M}$ of N) + (5 x $\mathcal{M}$ of H) + (1 x $\mathcal{M}$ of C) + (3 x $\mathcal{M}$ of O)
= (1 x 14.01 g/mol N) + (5 x 1.008 g/mol H) + (1 x 12.01 g/mol C) + (3 x 16.00 g/mol O)
= 79.06 g/mol of NH_4HCO_3

There are 5 moles of H in 1 mole of NH_4HCO_3.

Mass (g) of H = $\left(5\ \text{mol H}\right)\left(\frac{1.008\ \text{g H}}{1\ \text{mol H}}\right)$ = 5.040 g H

Mass percent = $\frac{\text{total mass H}}{\text{molar mass of compound}}(100) = \frac{5.040\ \text{g H}}{79.06\ \text{g}\ NH_4HCO_3}(100)$ = 6.374905 = **6.375% H**

b) Sodium dihydrogen phosphate heptahydrate is a salt that consists of sodium ions, Na^+, dihydrogen phosphate ions, $H_2PO_4^-$, and seven waters of hydration. The formula is $NaH_2PO_4{\bullet}7H_2O$. Note that the waters of hydration are included in the molar mass.

$\mathcal{M}$ of $NaH_2PO_4{\bullet}7H_2O$ = (1 x $\mathcal{M}$ of Na) + (16 x $\mathcal{M}$ of H) + (1 x $\mathcal{M}$ of P) + (11 x $\mathcal{M}$ of O)
= (1 x 22.99 g/mol Na) + (16 x 1.008 g/mol H) + (1 x 30.97 g/mol P) + (11 x 16.00 g/mol O)
= 246.09 g/mol $NaH_2PO_4{\bullet}7H_2O$

There are 11 moles of O in 1 mole of $NaH_2PO_4 \bullet 7H_2O$.

$$\text{Mass (g) of O} = (11 \text{ mol O})\left(\frac{16.00 \text{ g O}}{1 \text{ mol O}}\right) = 176.00 \text{ g O}$$

$$\text{Mass percent} = \frac{\text{total mass O}}{\text{molar mass of compound}}(100) = \frac{176.00 \text{ g O}}{246.09 \text{ g } NaH_2PO_4 \bullet 7H_2O}(100)$$
$$= 71.51855 = \mathbf{71.52\% \ O}$$

3.22 Plan: Determine the formula and the molar mass of each compound. The formula gives the relative number of moles of each element present. Multiply the number of moles of each element by its molar mass to find the total mass of element in 1 mole of compound. Mass fraction = $\dfrac{\text{total mass of element}}{\text{molar mass of compound}}$.

Solution:

a) Cesium acetate is an ionic compound consisting of Cs^+ cations and $C_2H_3O_2^-$ anions. (Note that the formula for acetate ions can be written as either $C_2H_3O_2^-$ or CH_3COO^-.) The formula of the compound is $CsC_2H_3O_2$.

$\mathcal{M}$ of $CsC_2H_3O_2$ = (1 x $\mathcal{M}$ of Cs) + (2 x $\mathcal{M}$ of C) + (3 x $\mathcal{M}$ of H) + (2 x $\mathcal{M}$ of O)
= (1 x 132.9 g/mol Cs) + (2 x 12.01 g/mol C) + (3 x 1.008 g/mol H) + (2 x 16.00 g/mol O)
= 191.9 g/mol of $CsC_2H_3O_2$

There are 2 moles of C in 1 mole of $CsC_2H_3O_2$.

$$\text{Mass (g) of C} = (2 \text{ mol C})\left(\frac{12.01 \text{ g C}}{1 \text{ mol C}}\right) = 24.02 \text{ g C}$$

$$\text{Mass fraction} = \frac{\text{total mass C}}{\text{molar mass of compound}} = \frac{24.02 \text{ g C}}{191.9 \text{ g } CsC_2H_3O_2} = 0.125169 = \mathbf{0.1252 \text{ mass fraction C}}$$

b) Uranyl sulfate trihydrate is is a salt that consists of uranyl ions, UO_2^{2+}, sulfate ions, SO_4^{2-}, and three waters of hydration. The formula is $UO_2SO_4 \bullet 3H_2O$. Note that the waters of hydration are included in the molar mass.

$\mathcal{M}$ of $UO_2SO_4 \bullet 3H_2O$ = (1 x $\mathcal{M}$ of U) + (9 x $\mathcal{M}$ of O) + (1 x $\mathcal{M}$ of S) + (6 x $\mathcal{M}$ of H)
= (1 x 238.0 g/mol U) + (9 x 16.00 g/mol O) + (1 x 32.06 g/mol S) + (6 x 1.008 g/mol H)
= 420.1 g/mol of $UO_2SO_4 \bullet 3H_2O$

There are 9 moles of O in 1 mole of $UO_2SO_4 \bullet 3H_2O$.

$$\text{Mass (g) of O} = (9 \text{ mol O})\left(\frac{16.00 \text{ g O}}{1 \text{ mol O}}\right) = 144.0 \text{ g O}$$

$$\text{Mass fraction} = \frac{\text{total mass O}}{\text{molar mass of compound}} = \frac{144.0 \text{ g O}}{420.1 \text{ g } UO_2SO_4 \bullet 3H_2O} = 0.3427755 = \mathbf{0.3428 \text{ mass fraction O}}$$

3.25 Plan: Determine the formula of cisplatin from the figure, and then calculate the molar mass from the formula. Divide the mass given by the molar mass to find moles of cisplatin. Since 1 mole of cisplatin contains 6 moles of hydrogen atoms, multiply the moles given by 6 to obtain moles of hydrogen and then multiply by Avogadro's number to obtain the number of atoms.

Solution:

The formula for cisplatin is $Pt(Cl)_2(NH_3)_2$.

$\mathcal{M}$ of $Pt(Cl)_2(NH_3)_2$ = (1 x $\mathcal{M}$ of Pt) + (2 x $\mathcal{M}$ of Cl) + (2 x $\mathcal{M}$ of N) + (6 x $\mathcal{M}$ of H)
= (1 x 195.1 g/mol Pt) + (2 x 35.45 g/mol Cl) + (2 x 14.01 g/mol N) + (6 x 1.008 g/mol H)
= 300.1 g/mol of $Pt(Cl)_2(NH_3)_2$

$$\text{a) Moles of cisplatin} = (285.3 \text{ g cisplatin})\left(\frac{1 \text{ mol cisplatin}}{300.1 \text{ g cisplatin}}\right) = 0.9506831 = \mathbf{0.9507 \text{ mol cisplatin}}$$

$$\text{b) Moles of H atoms} = (0.98 \text{ mol cisplatin})\left(\frac{6 \text{ mol H}}{1 \text{ mol cisplatin}}\right) = 5.88 \text{ mol H atoms}$$

$$\text{Number of H atoms} = (5.88 \text{ mol H atoms})\left(\frac{6.022 \times 10^{23} \text{ H atoms}}{1 \text{ mol H atoms}}\right) = 3.540936 \times 10^{24} = \mathbf{3.5 \times 10^{24} \text{ H atoms}}$$

3.27 Plan: Determine the molar mass of rust. Convert mass in kg to mass in g and divide by the molar mass to find the moles of rust. Since each mole of rust contains 1 mole of Fe_2O_3, multiply the moles of rust by 1 to obtain moles of Fe_2O_3. Multiply the moles of Fe_2O_3 by 2 to obtain moles of Fe (1:2 Fe_2O_3:Fe mole ratio) and multiply by the molar mass of Fe to convert to mass.

Solution:

a) $\mathcal{M}$ of $Fe_2O_3 \cdot 4H_2O$ = (2 x $\mathcal{M}$ of Fe) + (7 x $\mathcal{M}$ of O) + (8 x $\mathcal{M}$ of H)
= (2 x 55.85 g/mol Fe) + (7 x 16.00 g/mol O) + (8 x 1.008 g/mol H) = 231.76 g/mol

$$\text{Mass (g) of rust} = (45.2 \text{ kg rust})\left(\frac{10^3 \text{ g}}{1 \text{ kg}}\right) = 4.52\text{x}10^4 \text{ g}$$

$$\text{Moles of rust} = (4.52\text{x}10^4 \text{ g rust})\left(\frac{1 \text{ mol rust}}{231.76 \text{ g rust}}\right) = 195.029 = \mathbf{195 \text{ mol rust}}$$

b) The formula shows that there is 1 mole of Fe_2O_3 for every mole of rust, so there are also **195 mol of Fe_2O_3**.

$$\text{c) Moles of iron} = (195.029 \text{ mol } Fe_2O_3)\left(\frac{2 \text{ mol Fe}}{1 \text{ mol } Fe_2O_3}\right) = 390.058 \text{ mol Fe}$$

$$\text{Mass (g) of iron} = (390.058 \text{ mol Fe})\left(\frac{55.85 \text{ g Fe}}{1 \text{ mol Fe}}\right) = 21784.74 = \mathbf{2.18\text{x}10^4 \text{ g Fe}}$$

3.29 Plan: Determine the formula and the molar mass of each compound. The formula gives the relative number of moles of nitrogen present. Multiply the number of moles of nitrogen by its molar mass to find the total mass of nitrogen in 1 mole of compound. Divide the total mass of nitrogen by the molar mass of compound and multiply by 100 to determine mass percent. Mass percent = $\frac{(\text{mol N})\text{x }(\text{molar mass N})}{\text{molar mass of compound}}(100)$. Then rank the values in order of decreasing mass percent N.

Solution:

Name	Formula	Molar Mass (g/mol)
Potassium nitrate	KNO_3	101.11
Ammonium nitrate	NH_4NO_3	80.05
Ammonium sulfate	$(NH_4)_2SO_4$	132.14
Urea	$CO(NH_2)_2$	60.06

$$\text{Mass \% N in potassium nitrate} = \frac{(1 \text{ mol N})(14.01 \text{ g/mol N})}{101.11 \text{ g/mol}} \text{ x } 100 = 13.856196 = \mathbf{13.86\% \text{ N}}$$

$$\text{Mass \% N in ammonium nitrate} = \frac{(2 \text{ mol N})(14.01 \text{ g/mol N})}{80.05 \text{ g/mol}} \text{ x } 100 = 35.003123 = \mathbf{35.00\% \text{ N}}$$

$$\text{Mass \% N in ammonium sulfate} = \frac{(2 \text{ mol N})(14.01 \text{ g/mol N})}{132.14 \text{ g/mol}} \text{ x } 100 = 21.20478 = \mathbf{21.20\% \text{ N}}$$

$$\text{Mass \% N in urea} = \frac{(2 \text{ mol N})(14.01 \text{ g/mol N})}{60.06 \text{ g/mol}} \text{ x } 100 = 46.6533 = \mathbf{46.65\% \text{ N}}$$

Rank is **$CO(NH_2)_2$ > NH_4NO_3 > $(NH_4)_2SO_4$ > KNO_3**

3.30 Plan: The volume must be converted from cubic feet to cubic centimeters. The volume and the density will give the mass of galena which is then divided by molar mass to obtain moles. Part b) requires a conversion from cubic decimeters to cubic centimeters. The density allows a change from volume in cubic centimeters to mass which is then divided by the molar mass to obtain moles; the amount in moles is multiplied by Avogadro's number to obtain formula units of PbS which is also the number of Pb atoms due to the 1:1 PbS:Pb mole ratio.

Solution:
Lead(II) sulfide is composed of Pb^{2+} and S^{2-} ions and has a formula of PbS.
$\mathcal{M}$ of PbS = (1 x $\mathcal{M}$ of Pb) + (1 x $\mathcal{M}$ of S) = (1 x 207.2 g/mol Pb) + (1 x 32.06 g/mol S) = 239.3 g/mol

$$\text{a) Volume (cm}^3) = \left(1.00 \text{ ft}^3 \text{ PbS}\right)\left(\frac{(12 \text{ in})^3}{(1 \text{ ft})^3}\right)\left(\frac{(2.54 \text{ cm})^3}{(1 \text{ in})^3}\right) = 28316.85 \text{ cm}^3$$

$$\text{Mass (g) of PbS} = \left(28316.85 \text{ cm}^3 \text{ PbS}\right)\left(\frac{7.46 \text{ g PbS}}{1 \text{ cm}^3}\right) = 211243.7 \text{ g PbS}$$

$$\text{Moles of PbS} = \left(211243.7 \text{ g PbS}\right)\left(\frac{1 \text{ mol PbS}}{239.3 \text{ g PbS}}\right) = 882.7568 = \mathbf{883 \text{ mol PbS}}$$

$$\text{b) Volume (cm}^3) = \left(1.00 \text{ dm}^3 \text{ PbS}\right)\left(\frac{(0.1 \text{ m})^3}{(1 \text{ dm})^3}\right)\left(\frac{(1 \text{ cm})^3}{(10^{-2} \text{ m})^3}\right) = 1.00\text{x}10^3 \text{ cm}^3$$

$$\text{Mass (g) of PbS} = \left(1.00\text{x}10^3 \text{ cm}^3 \text{ PbS}\right)\left(\frac{7.46 \text{ g PbS}}{1 \text{ cm}^3}\right) = 7460 \text{ g PbS}$$

$$\text{Moles of PbS} = \left(7460 \text{ g PbS}\right)\left(\frac{1 \text{ mol PbS}}{239.3 \text{ g PbS}}\right) = 31.17426 \text{ mol PbS}$$

$$\text{Moles of Pb} = \left(31.17426 \text{ mol PbS}\right)\left(\frac{1 \text{ mol Pb}}{1 \text{ mol PbS}}\right) = 31.17426 \text{ mol Pb}$$

Number of lead atoms =

$$\left(31.17426 \text{ mol Pb}\right)\left(\frac{6.022\text{x}10^{23} \text{ Pb atoms}}{1 \text{ mol Pb}}\right) = 1.87731\text{x}10^{25} = \mathbf{1.88x10^{25} \text{ Pb atoms}}$$

3.34 Plan: Remember that the molecular formula tells the *actual* number of moles of each element in one mole of compound.
Solution:
a) No, this information does not allow you to obtain the molecular formula. You can obtain the empirical formula from the number of moles of each type of atom in a compound, but not the molecular formula.
b) Yes, you can obtain the molecular formula from the mass percentages and the total number of atoms.
Plan:

1) Assume a 100.0 g sample and convert masses (from the mass % of each element) to moles using molar mass.
2) Identify the element with the lowest number of moles and use this number to divide into the number of moles for each element. You now have at least one elemental mole ratio (the one with the smallest number of moles) equal to 1.00 and the remaining mole ratios that are larger than one.
3) Examine the numbers to determine if they are whole numbers. If not, multiply each number by a whole-number factor to get whole numbers for each element. You will have to use some judgment to decide when to round. Write the empirical formula using these whole numbers.
4) Check the total number of atoms in the empirical formula. If it equals the total number of atoms given then the empirical formula is also the molecular formula. If not, then divide the total number of atoms given by the total number of atoms in the empirical formula. This should give a whole number. Multiply the number of atoms of each element in the empirical formula by this whole number to get the molecular formula. If you do not get a whole number when you divide, return to step 3 and revise how you multiplied and rounded to get whole numbers for each element.

Roadmap:

Mass (g) of each element (express mass percent directly as grams)

↓

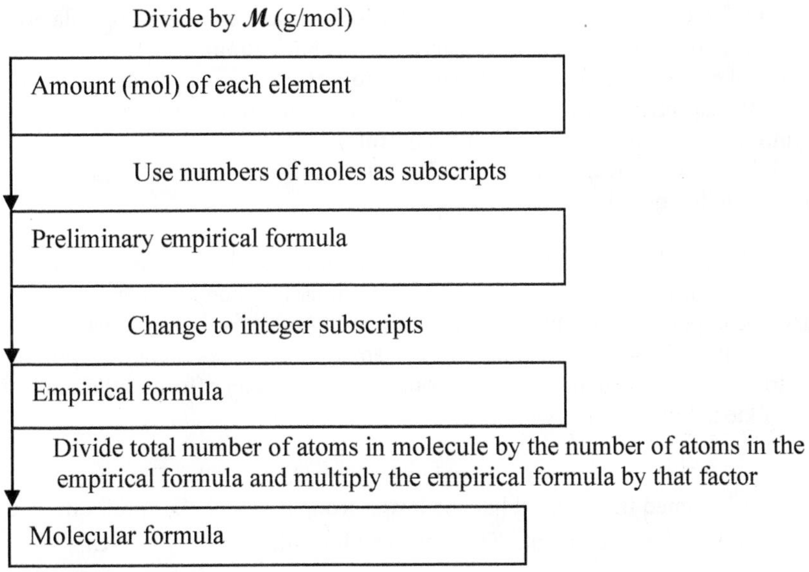

Divide by $\mathcal{M}$ (g/mol)

Amount (mol) of each element

↓ Use numbers of moles as subscripts

Preliminary empirical formula

↓ Change to integer subscripts

Empirical formula

↓ Divide total number of atoms in molecule by the number of atoms in the empirical formula and multiply the empirical formula by that factor

Molecular formula

c) Yes, you can determine the molecular formula from the mass percent and the number of atoms of one element in a compound. Plan:

1) Follow steps 1–3 in part b).

2) Compare the number of atoms given for the one element to the number in the empirical formula. Determine the factor the number in the empirical formula must be multiplied by to obtain the given number of atoms for that element. Multiply the empirical formula by this number to get the molecular formula.

Roadmap:

(Same first three steps as in b).

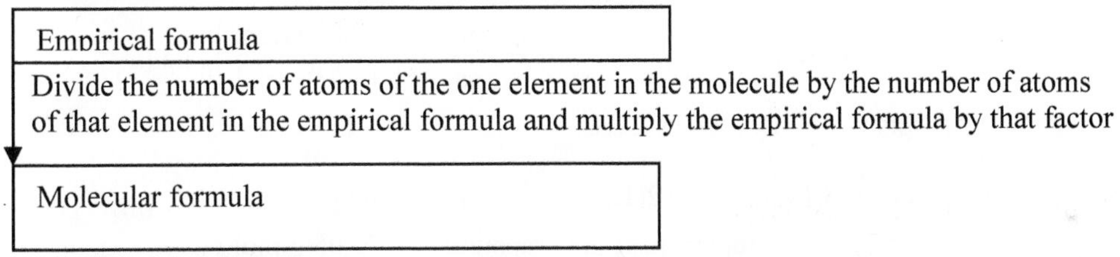

Empirical formula

↓ Divide the number of atoms of the one element in the molecule by the number of atoms of that element in the empirical formula and multiply the empirical formula by that factor

Molecular formula

d) No, the mass % will only lead to the empirical formula.

e) Yes, a structural formula shows all the atoms in the compound. Plan: Count the number of atoms of each type of element and record as the number for the molecular formula.

Roadmap:

Structural formula

↓ Count the number of atoms of each element and use these numbers as subscripts

Molecular formula

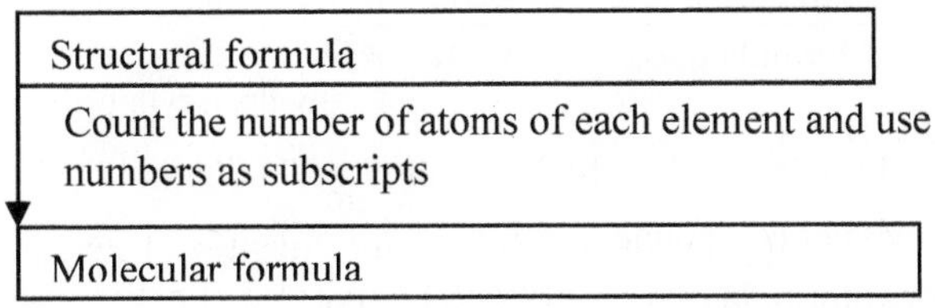

3.36 Plan: Examine the number of atoms of each type in the compound. Divide all atom numbers by the common factor that results in the lowest whole-number values. Add the molar masses of the atoms to obtain the empirical formula mass.

Solution:

a) C_2H_4 has a ratio of 2 carbon atoms to 4 hydrogen atoms, or 2:4. This ratio can be reduced to 1:2, so that the empirical formula is $\mathbf{CH_2}$. The empirical formula mass is 12.01 g/mol C + 2(1.008 g/mol H) = **14.03 g/mol.**

b) The ratio of atoms is 2:6:2, or 1:3:1. The empirical formula is $\mathbf{CH_3O}$ and its empirical formula mass is 12.01 g/mol C + 3(1.008 g/mol H) + 16.00 g/mol O = **31.03 g/mol.**

c) Since, the ratio of elements cannot be further reduced, the molecular formula and empirical formula are the same, $\mathbf{N_2O_5}$. The formula mass is 2(14.01 g/mol N) + 5(16.00 g/mol O) = **108.02 g/mol.**
d) The ratio of elements is 3 atoms of barium to 2 atoms of phosphorus to 8 atoms of oxygen, or 3:2:8. This ratio cannot be further reduced, so the empirical formula is also $\mathbf{Ba_3(PO_4)_2}$, with a formula mass of 3(137.3 g/mol Ba) + 2(30.97 g/mol P) + 8(16.00 g/mol O) = **601.8 g/mol.**
e) The ratio of atoms is 4:16, or 1:4. The empirical formula is $\mathbf{TeI_4}$, and the formula mass is 127.6 g/mol Te + 4(126.9 g/mol I) = **635.2 g/mol.**

3.38 Plan: Use the chemical symbols and count the atoms of each type to obtain the molecular formula. Divide the molecular formula by the largest common factor to give the empirical formula. Use nomenclature rules to derive the name. This compound is composed of two nonmetals. The naming rules for binary covalent compounds indicate that the element with the lower group number is named first. Greek numerical prefixes are used to indicate the number of atoms of each element in the compound. The molecular (formula) mass is the sum of the atomic masses of all of the atoms.
Solution:
The compound has 2 sulfur atoms and 2 chlorine atoms and a molecular formula of S_2Cl_2. The compound's name is **disulfur dichloride**. Sulfur is named first since it has the lower group number. The prefix di- is used for both elements since there are 2 atoms of each element. The empirical formula is $S_{\frac{2}{2}}Cl_{\frac{2}{2}}$ or **SCl**.

$\mathcal{M}$ of S_2Cl_2 = (2 x $\mathcal{M}$ of S) + (2 x $\mathcal{M}$ of Cl) = (2 x 32.06 g/mol S) + (2 x 35.45 g/mol Cl) = **135.02 g/mol**

3.40 Plan: Determine the molar mass of each empirical formula. The subscripts in the molecular formula are whole-number multiples of the subscripts in the empirical formula. To find this whole number, divide the molar mass of the compound by its empirical formula mass. Multiply each subscript in the empirical formula by the whole number.
Solution:
Only approximate whole-number values are needed.
a) CH_2 has empirical mass equal to 12.01 g/mol C + 2(1.008 g/mol C) = 14.03 g/mol

$$\text{Whole-number multiple} = \frac{\text{molar mass of compound}}{\text{empirical formula mass}} = \left(\frac{42.08 \text{ g/mol}}{14.03 \text{ g/mol}}\right) = 3$$

Multiplying the subscripts in CH_2 by 3 gives $\mathbf{C_3H_6}$.

b) NH_2 has empirical mass equal to 14.01 g/mol N + 2(1.008 g/mol H) = 16.03 g/mol

$$\text{Whole-number multiple} = \frac{\text{molar mass of compound}}{\text{empirical formula mass}} = \left(\frac{32.05 \text{ g/mol}}{16.03 \text{ g/mol}}\right) = 2$$

Multiplying the subscripts in NH_2 by 2 gives $\mathbf{N_2H_4}$.
c) NO_2 has empirical mass equal to 14.01 g/mol N + 2(16.00 g/mol O) = 46.01 g/mol

$$\text{Whole-number multiple} = \frac{\text{molar mass of compound}}{\text{empirical formula mass}} = \left(\frac{92.02 \text{ g/mol}}{46.01 \text{ g/mol}}\right) = 2$$

Multiplying the subscripts in NO_2 by 2 gives $\mathbf{N_2O_4}$.
d) CHN has empirical mass equal to 12.01 g/mol C + 1.008 g/mol H + 14.01 g/mol N = 27.03 g/mol

$$\text{Whole-number multiple} = \frac{\text{molar mass of compound}}{\text{empirical formula mass}} = \left(\frac{135.14 \text{ g/mol}}{27.03 \text{ g/mol}}\right) = 5$$

Multiplying the subscripts in CHN by 5 gives $\mathbf{C_5H_5N_5}$.

3.42 Plan: The empirical formula is the smallest whole-number ratio of the atoms or moles in a formula. All data must be converted to moles of an element by dividing mass by the molar mass. Divide each mole number by the smallest mole number to convert the mole ratios to whole numbers.
Solution:
a) 0.063 mol Cl and 0.22 mol O: preliminary formula is $Cl_{0.063}O_{0.22}$
Converting to integer subscripts (dividing all by the smallest subscript):

$$\underset{0.063}{Cl_{0.063}}\underset{0.063}{O_{0.22}} \rightarrow Cl_1O_{3.5}$$

The formula is $Cl_1O_{3.5}$, which in whole numbers (x 2) is $\mathbf{Cl_2O_7}$.

b) Find moles of elements by dividing by molar mass:

$$\text{Moles of Si} = (2.45 \text{ g Si})\left(\frac{1 \text{ mol Si}}{28.09 \text{ g Si}}\right) = 0.08722 \text{ mol Si}$$

$$\text{Moles of Cl} = (12.4 \text{ g Cl})\left(\frac{1 \text{ mol Cl}}{35.45 \text{ g Cl}}\right) = 0.349788 \text{ mol Cl}$$

Preliminary formula is $Si_{0.08722}Cl_{0.349788}$

Converting to integer subscripts (dividing all by the smallest subscript):

$$\underset{0.08722}{Si_{0.08722}}\underset{0.349788}{Cl_{0.349788}} \rightarrow Si_1Cl_4$$

The empirical formula is $\mathbf{SiCl_4}$.

c) Assume a 100 g sample and convert the masses to moles by dividing by the molar mass:

$$\text{Moles of C} = (100 \text{ g})\left(\frac{27.3 \text{ parts C by mass}}{100 \text{ parts by mass}}\right)\left(\frac{1 \text{ mol C}}{12.01 \text{ g C}}\right) = 2.2731 \text{ mol C}$$

$$\text{Moles of O} = (100 \text{ g})\left(\frac{72.7 \text{ parts O by mass}}{100 \text{ parts by mass}}\right)\left(\frac{1 \text{ mol O}}{16.00 \text{ g O}}\right) = 4.5438 \text{ mol O}$$

Preliminary formula is $C_{2.2731}O_{4.5438}$

Converting to integer subscripts (dividing all by the smallest subscript):

$$\underset{2.2731}{C_{2.2731}}\underset{2.2731}{O_{4.5438}} \rightarrow C_1O_2$$

The empirical formula is $\mathbf{CO_2}$.

3.44 Plan: The percent oxygen is 100% minus the percent nitrogen. Assume 100 grams of sample, and then the moles of each element may be found by dividing the mass of each element by its molar mass. Divide each of the moles by the smaller value, and convert to whole numbers to get the empirical formula. The subscripts in the molecular formula are whole-number multiples of the subscripts in the empirical formula. To find this whole number, divide the molar mass of the compound by its empirical formula mass. Multiply each subscript in the empirical formula by the whole number.

Solution:

a) % O = 100% − % N = 100% − 30.45% N = 69.55% O

Assume a 100 g sample and convert the masses to moles by dividing by the molar mass:

$$\text{Moles of N} = (100 \text{ g})\left(\frac{30.45 \text{ parts N by mass}}{100 \text{ parts by mass}}\right)\left(\frac{1 \text{ mol N}}{14.01 \text{ g N}}\right) = 2.1734 \text{ mol N}$$

$$\text{Moles of O} = (100 \text{ g})\left(\frac{69.55 \text{ parts O by mass}}{100 \text{ parts by mass}}\right)\left(\frac{1 \text{ mol O}}{16.00 \text{ g O}}\right) = 4.3469 \text{ mol O}$$

Preliminary formula is $N_{2.1734}O_{4.3469}$

Converting to integer subscripts (dividing all by the smallest subscript):

$$\underset{2.1734}{N_{2.1734}}\underset{2.1734}{O_{4.3469}} \rightarrow N_1O_2$$

The empirical formula is $\mathbf{NO_2}$.

b) Formula mass of empirical formula = 14.01 g/mol N + 2(16.00 g/mol O) = 46.01 g/mol

$$\text{Whole-number multiple} = \frac{\text{molar mass of compound}}{\text{empirical formula mass}} = \left(\frac{90 \text{ g/mol}}{46.01 \text{ g/mol}}\right) = 2$$

Multiplying the subscripts in NO_2 by 2 gives $\mathbf{N_2O_4}$ as the molecular formula.

Note: Only an approximate value of the molar mass is needed.

3.46 Plan: The moles of the metal are known, and the moles of fluorine atoms may be found in part a) from the M:F mole ratio in the compound formula. In part b), convert moles of F atoms to mass and subtract the mass of F from the mass of MF_2 to find the mass of M. In part c), divide the mass of M by moles of M to determine the molar mass of M which can be used to identify the element.

Solution:

a) Determine the moles of fluorine.

$$\text{Moles of F} = (0.600 \text{ mol M})\left(\frac{2 \text{ mol F}}{1 \text{ mol M}}\right) = \mathbf{1.20 \text{ mol F}}$$

b) Determine the mass of M.

$$\text{Mass of F} = (1.20 \text{ mol F})\left(\frac{19.00 \text{ g F}}{1 \text{ mol F}}\right) = 22.8 \text{ g F}$$

$$\text{Mass (g) of M} = MF_2(g) - F(g) = 46.8 \text{ g} - 22.8 \text{ g} = \mathbf{24.0 \text{ g M}}$$

c) The molar mass is needed to identify the element.

$$\text{Molar mass of M} = \frac{24.0 \text{ g M}}{0.600 \text{ mol M}} = 40.0 \text{ g/mol}$$

The metal with the closest molar mass to 40.0 g/mol is **calcium**.

3.49 Plan: The empirical formula is the smallest whole-number ratio of the atoms or moles in a formula. Assume 100 grams of cortisol so the percentages are numerically equivalent to the masses of each element. Convert each of the masses to moles by dividing by the molar mass of each element involved. Divide each mole number by the smallest mole number to convert the mole ratios to whole numbers. The subscripts in the molecular formula are whole-number multiples of the subscripts in the empirical formula. To find this whole number, divide the molar mass of the compound by its empirical formula mass. Multiply each subscript in the empirical formula by the whole number.

Solution:

$$\text{Moles of C} = (69.6 \text{ g C})\left(\frac{1 \text{ mol C}}{12.01 \text{ g C}}\right) = 5.7952 \text{ mol C}$$

$$\text{Moles of H} = (8.34 \text{ g H})\left(\frac{1 \text{ mol H}}{1.008 \text{ g H}}\right) = 8.2738 \text{ mol H}$$

$$\text{Moles of O} = (22.1 \text{ g O})\left(\frac{1 \text{ mol O}}{16.00 \text{ g O}}\right) = 1.38125 \text{ mol O}$$

Preliminary formula is $C_{5.7952}H_{8.2738}O_{1.38125}$

Converting to integer subscripts (dividing all by the smallest subscript):

$$C_{\frac{5.7952}{1.38125}}H_{\frac{8.2738}{1.38125}}O_{\frac{1.38125}{1.38125}} \rightarrow C_{4.2}H_6O_1$$

The carbon value is not close enough to a whole number to round the value. The smallest number that 4.20 may be multiplied by to get close to a whole number is 5. (You may wish to prove this to yourself.) All three ratios need to be multiplied by five: $5(C_{4.2}H_6O_1) = C_{21}H_{30}O_5$.

The empirical formula mass is = 21(12.01 g/mol C) + 30(1.008 g/mol H) + 5(16.00 g/mol O) = 362.45 g/mol

$$\text{Whole-number multiple} = \frac{\text{molar mass of compound}}{\text{empirical formula mass}} = \left(\frac{362.47 \text{ g/mol}}{362.45 \text{ g/mol}}\right) = 1$$

The empirical formula mass and the molar mass given are the same, so the empirical and the molecular formulas are the same. The molecular formula is $\mathbf{C_{21}H_{30}O_5}$.

3.51 Plan: In combustion analysis, finding the moles of carbon and hydrogen is relatively simple because all of the carbon present in the sample is found in the carbon of CO_2, and all of the hydrogen present in the sample is found in the hydrogen of H_2O. Convert the mass of CO_2 to moles and use the ratio between CO_2 and C to find the moles and mass of C present. Do the same to find the moles and mass of H from H_2O. The moles of oxygen are more difficult to find, because additional O_2 was added to cause the combustion reaction. Subtracting the masses of C and H from the mass of the sample gives the mass of O. Convert the mass of O to moles of O. Take the moles of C, H, and O and divide by the smallest value to convert to whole numbers to get the empirical formula. Determine the empirical formula mass and compare it to the molar mass given in the problem to see how the empirical and molecular formulas are related. Finally, determine the molecular formula.

Solution:

$$\text{Moles of C} = (0.449 \text{ g } CO_2)\left(\frac{1 \text{ mol } CO_2}{44.01 \text{ g } CO_2}\right)\left(\frac{1 \text{ mol C}}{1 \text{ mol } CO_2}\right) = 0.010202 \text{ mol C}$$

$$\text{Mass (g) of C} = (0.010202 \text{ mol C})\left(\frac{12.01 \text{ g C}}{1 \text{ mol C}}\right) = 0.122526 \text{ g C}$$

$$\text{Moles of H} = (0.184 \text{ g } H_2O)\left(\frac{1 \text{ mol } H_2O}{18.02 \text{ g } H_2O}\right)\left(\frac{2 \text{ mol H}}{1 \text{ mol } H_2O}\right) = 0.020422 \text{ mol H}$$

$$\text{Mass (g) of H} = (0.020422 \text{ mol H})\left(\frac{1.008 \text{ g H}}{1 \text{ mol H}}\right) = 0.020585 \text{ g H}$$

Mass (g) of O = Sample mass – (mass of C + mass of H)
= 0.1595 g – (0.122526 g C + 0.020585 g H) = 0.016389 g O

$$\text{Moles of O} = (0.016389 \text{ g O})\left(\frac{1 \text{ mol O}}{16.00 \text{ g O}}\right) = 0.0010243 \text{ mol O}$$

Preliminary formula = $C_{0.010202}H_{0.020422}O_{0.0010243}$
Converting to integer subscripts (dividing all by the smallest subscript):

$$C_{\frac{0.010202}{0.0010243}}H_{\frac{0.020422}{0.0010243}}O_{\frac{0.0010243}{0.0010243}} \rightarrow C_{10}H_{20}O_1$$

Empirical formula = $C_{10}H_{20}O$
Empirical formula mass = 10(12.01 g/mol C) + 20(1.008 g/mol H) + 1(16.00 g/mol O) = 156.26 g/mol
The empirical formula mass is the same as the given molar mass so the empirical and molecular formulas are the same. The molecular formula is **$C_{10}H_{20}O$**.

3.52 A balanced chemical equation describes:
1) The identities of the reactants and products.
2) The molar (and molecular) ratios by which reactants form products.
3) The physical states of all substances in the reaction.

3.55 Plan: Examine the diagram and label each formula. We will use A for red atoms and B for green atoms.
Solution:
The reaction shows A_2 and B_2 diatomic molecules forming AB molecules. Equal numbers of A_2 and B_2 combine to give twice as many molecules of AB. Thus, the reaction is $A_2 + B_2 \rightarrow 2\text{ AB}$. This is the balanced equation in **b**.

3.56 Plan: Balancing is a trial-and-error procedure. Balance one element at a time, placing coefficients where needed to have the same number of atoms of a particular element on each side of the equation. The smallest whole-number coefficients should be used.
Solution:
a) __Cu(*s*) + __ S_8(*s*) → __Cu_2S(*s*)
Balance the S first, because there is an obvious deficiency of S on the right side of the equation. The 8 S atoms in S_8 require the coefficient 8 in front of Cu_2S:
__Cu(*s*) + __S_8(*s*) → 8Cu_2S(*s*)
Then balance the Cu. The 16 Cu atoms in Cu_2S require the coefficient 16 in front of Cu:
16Cu(*s*) + S_8(*s*) → 8Cu_2S(*s*)
b) __P_4O_{10}(*s*) + __H_2O(*l*) → __H_3PO_4(*l*)
Balance the P first, because there is an obvious deficiency of P on the right side of the equation. The 4 P atoms in P_4O_{10} require a coefficient of 4 in front of H_3PO_4:
__P_4O_{10}(*s*) + __H_2O(*l*) → 4H_3PO_4(*l*)

Balance the H next, because H is present in only one reactant and only one product. The 12 H atoms in $4H_3PO_4$ on the right require a coefficient of 6 in front of H_2O:

___ $P_4O_{10}(s) + \underline{6}H_2O(l) \rightarrow \underline{4}H_3PO_4(l)$

Balance the O last, because it appears in both reactants and is harder to balance. There are 16 O atoms on each side:

$P_4O_{10}(s) + 6H_2O(l) \rightarrow 4H_3PO_4(l)$

c) __$B_2O_3(s)$ + __$NaOH(aq) \rightarrow$ __$Na_3BO_3(aq)$ + __$H_2O(l)$

Balance oxygen last because it is present in more than one place on each side of the reaction. The 2 B atoms in B_2O_3 on the left require a coefficient of 2 in front of Na_3BO_3 on the right:

__$B_2O_3(s)$ + __$NaOH(aq) \rightarrow \underline{2}Na_3BO_3(aq)$ + __$H_2O(l)$

The 6 Na atoms in $2Na_3BO_3$ on the right require a coefficient of 6 in front of NaOH on the left:

__$B_2O_3(s) + \underline{6}NaOH(aq) \rightarrow \underline{2}Na_3BO_3(aq)$ + __$H_2O(l)$

The 6 H atoms in 6NaOH on the left require a coefficent of 3 in front of H_2O on the right:

__$B_2O_3(s) + \underline{6}NaOH(aq) \rightarrow \underline{2}Na_3BO_3(aq) + \underline{3}H_2O(l)$

The oxygen is now balanced with 9 O atoms on each side:

$B_2O_3(s) + 6NaOH(aq) \rightarrow 2Na_3BO_3(aq) + 3H_2O(l)$

d) __$CH_3NH_2(g)$ + __$O_2(g) \rightarrow$ __$CO_2(g)$ + __$H_2O(g)$ + __$N_2(g)$

There are 2 N atoms on the right in N_2 so a coefficient of 2 is required in front of CH_3NH_2 on the left:

$\underline{2}CH_3NH_2(g)$ + __$O_2(g) \rightarrow$ __$CO_2(g)$ + __$H_2O(g)$ + __$N_2(g)$

There are now 10 H atoms in $2CH_3NH_2$ on the left so a coefficient of 5 is required in front of H_2O on the right:

$\underline{2}CH_3NH_2(g)$ + __$O_2(g) \rightarrow$ __$CO_2(g) + \underline{5}H_2O(g)$ + __$N_2(g)$

The 2 C atoms on the left require a coefficient of 2 in front of CO_2 on the right:

$\underline{2}CH_3NH_2(g)$ + __$O_2(g) \rightarrow \underline{2}CO_2(g) + \underline{5}H_2O(g)$ + __$N_2(g)$

The 9 O atoms on the right (4 O atoms in $2CO_2$ plus 5 in $5H_2O$) require a coefficient of 9/2 in front of O_2 on the left:

$\underline{2}CH_3NH_2(g) + \underline{9/2}O_2(g) \rightarrow \underline{2}CO_2(g) + \underline{5}H_2O(g)$ + __$N_2(g)$

Multiply all coefficients by 2 to obtain whole numbers:

$4CH_3NH_2(g) + 9O_2(g) \rightarrow 4CO_2(g) + 10H_2O(g) + 2N_2(g)$

3.58 Plan: Balancing is a trial-and-error procedure. Balance one element at a time, placing coefficients where needed to have the same number of atoms of a particular element on each side of the equation. The smallest whole-number coefficients should be used.

Solution:

a) __$SO_2(g)$ + __$O_2(g) \rightarrow$ __$SO_3(g)$

There are 4 O atoms on the left and 3 O atoms on the right. Since there is an odd number of O atoms on the right, place a coefficient of 2 in front of SO_3 for an even number of 6 O atoms on the right:

__$SO_2(g)$ + __$O_2(g) \rightarrow \underline{2}SO_3(g)$

Since there are now 2 S atoms on the right, place a coefficient of 2 in front of SO_2 on the left. There are now 6 O atoms on each side:

$2SO_2(g) + O_2(g) \rightarrow 2SO_3(g)$

b) __$Sc_2O_3(s)$ + __$H_2O(l) \rightarrow$ __ $Sc(OH)_3(s)$

The 2 Sc atoms on the left require a coefficient of 2 in front of $Sc(OH)_3$ on the right:

__$Sc_2O_3(s)$ + __$H_2O(l) \rightarrow \underline{2}Sc(OH)_3(s)$

The 6 H atoms in $2Sc(OH)_3$ on the right require a coefficient of 3 in front of H_2O on the left. There are now 6 O atoms on each side:

$Sc_2O_3(s) + 3H_2O(l) \rightarrow 2Sc(OH)_3(s)$

c) __$H_3PO_4(aq)$ + __$NaOH(aq) \rightarrow$ __$Na_2HPO_4(aq)$ + __$H_2O(l)$

The 2 Na atoms in Na_2HPO_4 on the right require a coefficient of 2 in front of NaOH on the left:

__$H_3PO_4(aq) + \underline{2}NaOH(aq) \rightarrow$ __$Na_2HPO_4(aq)$ + __$H_2O(l)$

There are 6 O atoms on the right (4 in H_3PO_4 and 2 in 2NaOH); there are 4 O atoms in Na_2HPO_4 on the right so a coefficient of 2 in front of H_2O will result in 6 O atoms on the right:

__$H_3PO_4(aq) + \underline{2}NaOH(aq) \rightarrow$ __$Na_2HPO_4(aq) + \underline{2}H_2O(l)$

Now there are 4 H atoms on each side:

$H_3PO_4(aq) + 2NaOH(aq) \rightarrow Na_2HPO_4(aq) + 2H_2O(l)$

d) __$C_6H_{10}O_5(s)$ + __$O_2(g) \rightarrow$ __$CO_2(g)$ + __$H_2O(g)$

The 6 C atoms inn $C_6H_{10}O_5$ on the left require a coefficient of 6 in front of CO_2 on the right:

__$C_6H_{10}O_5(s)$ + __$O_2(g) \rightarrow \underline{6}CO_2(g)$ + __$H_2O(g)$

The 10 H atoms in $C_6H_{10}O_5$ on the left require a coefficient of 5 in front of H_2O on the right:

__$C_6H_{10}O_5(s)$ + __$O_2(g) \rightarrow \underline{6}CO_2(g) + \underline{5}H_2O(g)$

There are 17 O atoms on the right (12 in $6CO_2$ and 5 in $5H_2O$); there are 5 O atoms in $C_6H_{10}O_5$ so a coefficient of 6 in front of O_2 will bring the total of O atoms on the left to 17:

$C_6H_{10}O_5(s) + 6O_2(g) \rightarrow 6CO_2(g) + 5H_2O(g)$

3.60 Plan: The names must first be converted to chemical formulas. Balancing is a trial-and-error procedure. Balance one element at a time, placing coefficients where needed to have the same number of atoms of a particular element on each side of the equation. The smallest whole-number coefficients should be used. Remember that oxygen is diatomic.

Solution:

a) Gallium (a solid) and oxygen (a gas) are reactants and solid gallium(III) oxide is the only product:

__$Ga(s)$ + __$O_2(g) \rightarrow$ __$Ga_2O_3(s)$

A coefficient of 2 in front of Ga on the left is needed to balance the 2 Ga atoms in Ga_2O_3:

$\underline{2}Ga(s)$ + __$O_2(g) \rightarrow$ __$Ga_2O_3(s)$

The 3 O atoms in Ga_2O_3 on the right require a coefficient of 3/2 in front of O_2 on the left:

$\underline{2}Ga(s) + \underline{3/2}O_2(g) \rightarrow$ __$Ga_2O_3(s)$

Multiply all coefficients by 2 to obtain whole numbers:

$4Ga(s) + 3O_2(g) \rightarrow 2Ga_2O_3(s)$

b) Liquid hexane and oxygen gas are the reactants while carbon dioxide gas and gaseous water are the products:

__$C_6H_{14}(l)$ + __$O_2(g) \rightarrow$ __$CO_2(g)$ + __$H_2O(g)$

The 6 C atoms in C_6H_{14} on the left require a coefficient of 6 in front of CO_2 on the right:

__$C_6H_{14}(l)$ + __$O_2(g) \rightarrow \underline{6}CO_2(g)$ + __$H_2O(g)$

The 14 H atoms in C_6H_{14} on the left require a coefficient of 7 in front of H_2O on the right:

__$C_6H_{14}(l)$ + __$O_2(g) \rightarrow \underline{6}CO_2(g) + \underline{7}H_2O(g)$

The 19 O atoms on the right (12 in $6CO_2$ and 7 in $7H_2O$) require a coefficient of 19/2 in front of O_2 on the left:
Multiply all coefficients by 2 to obtain whole numbers:

$2C_6H_{14}(l) + 19O_2(g) \rightarrow 12CO_2(g) + 14H_2O(g)$

c) Aqueous solutions of calcium chloride and sodium phosphate are the reactants; solid calcium phosphate and an aqueous solution of sodium chloride are the products:

__$CaCl_2(aq)$ + __$Na_3PO_4(aq) \rightarrow$ __$Ca_3(PO_4)_2(s)$ + __$NaCl(aq)$

The 3 Ca atoms in $Ca_3(PO_4)_2$ on the right require a coefficient of 3 in front of $CaCl_2$ on the left:

$\underline{3}CaCl_2(aq)$ + __$Na_3PO_4(aq) \rightarrow$ __$Ca_3(PO_4)_2(s)$ + __$NaCl(aq)$

The 6 Cl atoms in $3CaCl_2$ on the left require a coefficient of 6 in front of NaCl on the right:

$\underline{3}CaCl_2(aq)$ + __$Na_3PO_4(aq) \rightarrow$ __$Ca_3(PO_4)_2(s) + \underline{6}NaCl(aq)$

The 6 Na atoms in 6NaCl on the right require a coefficient of 2 in front of Na_3PO_4 on the left:

$\underline{3}CaCl_2(aq) + \underline{2}Na_3PO_4(aq) \rightarrow$ __$Ca_3(PO_4)_2(s) + \underline{6}NaCl(aq)$

There are now 2 P atoms on each side:

$3CaCl_2(aq) + 2Na_3PO_4(aq) \rightarrow Ca_3(PO_4)_2(s) + 6NaCl(aq)$

3.66 Plan: First, write a balanced chemical equation. Since A is the limiting reagent (B is in excess), A is used to determine the amount of C formed, using the mole ratio between reactant A and product C.

Solution:

Plan: The balanced equation is aA + bB $\rightarrow$ cC. Divide the mass of A by its molar mass to obtain moles of A. Use the molar ratio from the balanced equation to find the moles of C. Multiply moles of C by its molar mass to obtain mass of C.

Roadmap:

Mass (g) of A

Divide by $\mathcal{M}$ (g/mol)

Amount (mol) of A

Molar ratio between A and C

Amount (moles) of C

Multiply by $\mathcal{M}$ (g/mol)

Mass (g) of C

3.68 Plan: Always check to see if the initial equation is balanced. If the equation is not balanced, it should be balanced before proceeding. Use the mole ratio from the balanced chemical equation to determine the moles of Cl_2 produced. The equation shows that 1 mole of Cl_2 is produced for every 4 moles of HCl that react. Multiply the moles of Cl_2 produced by the molar mass to convert to mass in grams.

Solution:

$4HCl(aq) + MnO_2(s) \rightarrow MnCl_2(aq) + 2H_2O(g) + Cl_2(g)$

a) Moles of $Cl_2 = (1.82\text{ mol HCl})\left(\frac{1\text{ mol }Cl_2}{4\text{ mol HCl}}\right) = \mathbf{0.455\text{ mol }Cl_2}$

b) Mass (g) of $Cl_2 = (0.455\text{ mol }Cl_2)\left(\frac{70.90\text{ g }Cl_2}{1\text{ mol }Cl_2}\right) = 32.2595 = \mathbf{32.3\text{ g }Cl_2}$

3.70 Plan: Convert the kilograms of oxygen to grams of oxygen and then moles of oxygen by dividing by its molar mass. Use the moles of oxygen and the mole ratio from the balanced chemical equation to determine the moles of KNO_3 required. Multiply the moles of KNO_3 by its molar mass to obtain the mass in grams.

Solution:

a) Mass (g) of $O_2 = (56.6\text{ kg }O_2)\left(\frac{10^3\text{ g}}{1\text{ kg}}\right) = 5.66\text{x}10^4\text{ g }O_2$

Moles of $O_2 = (5.66\text{x}10^4\text{ g }O_2)\left(\frac{1\text{ mol }O_2}{32.00\text{ g }O_2}\right) = 1.76875\text{x}10^3\text{ mol }O_2$

Moles of $KNO_3 = (1.76875\text{ mol }O_2)\left(\frac{4\text{ mol }KNO_3}{5\text{ mol }O_2}\right) = 1415 = \mathbf{1.42\text{x}10^3\text{ mol }KNO_3}$

b) Mass (g) of $KNO_3 = (1415\text{ mol }KNO_3)\left(\frac{101.11\text{ g }KNO_3}{1\text{ mol }KNO_3}\right) = 143070.65 = \mathbf{1.43\text{x}10^5\text{ g }KNO_3}$

Combining all steps gives:

$$\text{Mass (g) of }KNO_3 = (56.6\text{ kg }O_2)\left(\frac{10^3\text{ g}}{1\text{ kg}}\right)\left(\frac{1\text{ mol }O_2}{32.00\text{ g }O_2}\right)\left(\frac{4\text{ mol }KNO_3}{5\text{ mol }O_2}\right)\left(\frac{101.11\text{ g }KNO_3}{1\text{ mol }KNO_3}\right)$$
$$= 143070.65 = \mathbf{1.43\text{x}10^5\text{ g }KNO_3}$$

3.72 Plan: First, balance the equation. Convert the grams of diborane to moles of diborane by dividing by its molar mass. Use mole ratios from the balanced chemical equation to determine the moles of the products. Multiply the mole amount of each product by its molar mass to obtain mass in grams.

Solution:

The balanced equation is: $B_2H_6(g) + 6H_2O(l) \rightarrow 2H_3BO_3(s) + 6H_2(g)$.

Moles of B_2H_6 = $(43.82 \text{ g } B_2H_6)\left(\frac{1 \text{ mol } B_2H_6}{27.67 \text{ g } B_2H_6}\right)$ = 1.583665 mol B_2H_6

Moles of H_3BO_3 = $(1.583665 \text{ mol } B_2H_6)\left(\frac{2 \text{ mol } H_3BO_3}{1 \text{ mol } B_2H_6}\right)$ = 3.16733 mol H_3BO_3

Mass (g) of H_3BO_3 = $(3.16733 \text{ mol } H_3BO_3)\left(\frac{61.83 \text{ g } H_3BO_3}{1 \text{ mol } H_3BO_3}\right)$ = 195.83597 = **195.8 g H_3BO_3**

Combining all steps gives:

Mass (g) of H_3BO_3 = $(43.82 \text{ g } B_2H_6)\left(\frac{1 \text{ mol } B_2H_6}{27.67 \text{ g } B_2H_6}\right)\left(\frac{2 \text{ mol } H_3BO_3}{1 \text{ mol } B_2H_6}\right)\left(\frac{61.83 \text{ g } H_3BO_3}{1 \text{ mol } H_3BO_3}\right)$

= 195.83597 = **195.8 g H_3BO_3**

Moles of H_2 = $(1.583665 \text{ mol } B_2H_6)\left(\frac{6 \text{ mol } H_2}{1 \text{ mol } B_2H_6}\right)$ = 9.50199 mol H_2

Mass (g) of H_2 = $(9.50199 \text{ mol } H_2)\left(\frac{2.016 \text{ g } H_2}{1 \text{ mol } H_2}\right)$ = 19.15901 g H_2 = **19.16 g H_2**

Combining all steps gives:

Mass (g) of H_2 = $(43.82 \text{ g } B_2H_6)\left(\frac{1 \text{ mol } B_2H_6}{27.67 \text{ g } B_2H_6}\right)\left(\frac{6 \text{ mol } H_2}{1 \text{ mol } B_2H_6}\right)\left(\frac{2.016 \text{ g } H_2}{1 \text{ mol } H_2}\right)$ = 19.15601 = **19.16 g H_2**

3.74 Plan: Write the balanced equation by first writing the formulas for the reactants and products. Convert the mass of phosphorus to moles by dividing by the molar mass, use the mole ratio between phosphorus and chlorine from the balanced chemical equation to obtain moles of chlorine, and finally divide the moles of chlorine by its molar mass to obtain amount in grams.

Solution:

Reactants: formula for phosphorus is given as P_4 and formula for chlorine gas is Cl_2 (chlorine occurs as a diatomic molecule). Product: formula for phosphorus pentachloride (the name indicates one phosphorus atom and five chlorine atoms) is PCl_5.

Equation: $P_4 + Cl_2 \rightarrow PCl_5$

Balancing the equation: $P_4 + 10Cl_2 \rightarrow 4PCl_5$

Moles of P_4 = $(455 \text{ g } P_4)\left(\frac{1 \text{ mol } P_4}{123.88 \text{ g } P_4}\right)$ = 3.67291 mol P_4

Moles of Cl_2 = $(3.67291 \text{ mol } P_4)\left(\frac{10 \text{ mol } Cl_2}{1 \text{ mol } P_4}\right)$ = 36.7291 mol Cl_2

Mass (g) of Cl_2 = $(36.7291 \text{ mol } Cl_2)\left(\frac{70.90 \text{ g } Cl_2}{1 \text{ mol } Cl_2}\right)$ = 2604.09 = **2.60×10^3 g Cl_2**

Combining all steps gives:

Mass (g) of Cl_2 = $(455 \text{ g } P_4)\left(\frac{1 \text{ mol } P_4}{123.88 \text{ g } P_4}\right)\left(\frac{10 \text{ mol } Cl_2}{1 \text{ mol } P_4}\right)\left(\frac{70.90 \text{ g } Cl_2}{1 \text{ mol } Cl_2}\right)$ = 2604.09267 = **2.60×10^3 g Cl_2**

3.76 Plan: Begin by writing the chemical formulas of the reactants and products in each step. Next, balance each of the equations. Combine the equations for the separate steps by adjusting the equations so the intermediate (iodine monochloride) cancels. Finally, change the mass of product from kg to grams to moles by dividing by the molar mass and use the mole ratio between iodine and product to find the moles of iodine. Multiply moles by the molar mass of iodine to obtain mass of iodine.

Solution:

a) *Step 1* $I_2(s) + Cl_2(g) \rightarrow 2ICl(s)$

Step 2 $ICl(s) + Cl_2(g) \rightarrow ICl_3(s)$

b) Multiply the coefficients of the second equation by 2, so that $ICl(s)$, an intermediate product, can be eliminated from the overall equation.

$$I_2(s) + Cl_2(g) \longrightarrow 2ICl(s)$$

$$2ICl(s) + 2Cl_2(g) \longrightarrow 2ICl_3(s)$$

$$I_2(s) + Cl_2(g) + \cancel{2ICl(s)} + 2Cl_2(g) \rightarrow \cancel{2ICl(s)} + 2ICl_3(s)$$

Overall equation: $\mathbf{I_2(s) + 3Cl_2(g) \rightarrow 2ICl_3(s)}$

c) $\text{Mass (g) of } ICl_3 = (2.45 \text{ kg } ICl_3)\left(\frac{10^3 \text{ g}}{1 \text{ kg}}\right) = 2450 \text{ g } ICl_3$

$\text{Moles of } ICl_3 = (2450 \text{ g } ICl_3)\left(\frac{1 \text{ mol } ICl_3}{233.2 \text{ g } ICl_3}\right) = 10.506 \text{ mol } ICl_3$

$\text{Moles of } I_2 = (10.506 \text{ mol } ICl_3)\left(\frac{1 \text{ mol } I_2}{2 \text{ mol } ICl_3}\right) = 5.253 \text{ mol } I_2$

$\text{Mass (g) of } I_2 = (5.253 \text{ mol } I_2)\left(\frac{253.8 \text{ g } I_2}{1 \text{ mol } I_2}\right) = 1333.211 = \mathbf{1.33x10^3 \text{ g } I_2}$

Combining all steps gives:

$\text{Mass (g) of } I_2 = (2.45 \text{ kg } ICl_3)\left(\frac{10^3 \text{ g}}{1 \text{ kg}}\right)\left(\frac{1 \text{ mol } ICl_3}{233.2 \text{ g } ICl_3}\right)\left(\frac{1 \text{ mol } I_2}{2 \text{ mol } ICl_3}\right)\left(\frac{253.8 \text{ g } I_2}{1 \text{ mol } I_2}\right) = 1333.211 = \mathbf{1.33x10^3 \text{ g } I_2}$

3.78 Plan: Convert the given mass of each reactant to moles by dividing by the molar mass of that reactant. Use the mole ratio from the balanced chemical equation to find the moles of CaO formed from each reactant, assuming an excess of the other reactant. The reactant that produces fewer moles of CaO is the limiting reactant. Convert the moles of CaO obtained from the limiting reactant to grams using the molar mass.

Solution:

$2Ca(s) + O_2(g) \rightarrow 2CaO(s)$

a) $\text{Moles of Ca} = (4.20 \text{ g Ca})\left(\frac{1 \text{ mol Ca}}{40.08 \text{ g Ca}}\right) = 0.104790 \text{ mol Ca}$

$\text{Moles of CaO from Ca} = (0.104790 \text{ mol Ca})\left(\frac{2 \text{ mol CaO}}{2 \text{ mol Ca}}\right) = 0.104790 = \mathbf{0.105 \text{ mol CaO}}$

b) $\text{Moles of } O_2 = (2.80 \text{ g } O_2)\left(\frac{1 \text{ mol } O_2}{32.00 \text{ g } O_2}\right) = 0.0875 \text{ mol } O_2$

$\text{Moles of CaO from } O_2 = (0.0875 \text{ mol } O_2)\left(\frac{2 \text{ mol CaO}}{1 \text{ mol } O_2}\right) = 0.17500 = \mathbf{0.175 \text{ mol CaO}}$

c) **Calcium** is the limiting reactant since it will form less calcium oxide.

d) The mass of CaO formed is determined by the limiting reactant, Ca.

$\text{Mass (g) of CaO} = (0.104790 \text{ mol CaO})\left(\frac{56.08 \text{ g CaO}}{1 \text{ mol CaO}}\right) = 5.8766 = \mathbf{5.88 \text{ g CaO}}$

Combining all steps gives:

$\text{Mass (g) of CaO} = (4.20 \text{ g Ca})\left(\frac{1 \text{ mol Ca}}{40.08 \text{ g Ca}}\right)\left(\frac{2 \text{ mol CaO}}{2 \text{ mol Ca}}\right)\left(\frac{56.08 \text{ g CaO}}{1 \text{ mol CaO}}\right) = 5.8766 = \mathbf{5.88 \text{ g CaO}}$

3.80 Plan: First, balance the chemical equation. To determine which reactant is limiting, calculate the amount of HIO_3 formed from each reactant, assuming an excess of the other reactant. The reactant that produces less product is the limiting reagent. Use the limiting reagent and the mole ratio from the balanced chemical equation to determine the amount of HIO_3 formed and the amount of the excess reactant that reacts. The difference between the amount of excess reactant that reacts and the initial amount of reactant supplied gives the amount of excess reactant remaining.

Solution:

The balanced chemical equation for this reaction is:

$$2ICl_3 + 3H_2O \rightarrow ICl + HIO_3 + 5HCl$$

Hint: Balance the equation by starting with oxygen. The other elements are in multiple reactants and/or products and are harder to balance initially.

Finding the moles of HIO_3 from the moles of ICl_3 (if H_2O is limiting):

$$\text{Moles of ICl}_3 = (635 \text{ g ICl}_3)\left(\frac{1 \text{ mol ICl}_3}{233.2 \text{ g ICl}_3}\right) = 2.722985 \text{ mol ICl}_3$$

$$\text{Moles of HIO}_3 \text{ from ICl}_3 = (2.722985 \text{ mol ICl}_3)\left(\frac{1 \text{ mol HIO}_3}{2 \text{ mol ICl}_3}\right) = 1.361492 = 1.36 \text{ mol HIO}_3$$

Finding the moles of HIO_3 from the moles of H_2O (if ICl_3 is limiting):

$$\text{Moles of H}_2\text{O} = (118.5 \text{ g H}_2\text{O})\left(\frac{1 \text{ mol H}_2\text{O}}{18.02 \text{ g H}_2\text{O}}\right) = 6.57603 \text{ mol H}_2\text{O}$$

$$\text{Moles HIO}_3 \text{ from H}_2\text{O} = (6.57603 \text{ mol H}_2\text{O})\left(\frac{1 \text{ mol HIO}_3}{3 \text{ mol H}_2\text{O}}\right) = 2.19201 = 2.19 \text{ mol HIO}_3$$

ICl_3 is the limiting reagent and will produce **1.36 mol HIO_3**.

$$\text{Mass (g) of HIO}_3 = (1.361492 \text{ mol HIO}_3)\left(\frac{175.9 \text{ g HIO}_3}{1 \text{ mol HIO}_3}\right) = 239.486 = \mathbf{239 \text{ g HIO}_3}$$

Combining all steps gives:

$$\text{Mass (g) of HIO}_3 = (635 \text{ g ICl}_3)\left(\frac{1 \text{ mol ICl}_3}{233.2 \text{ g ICl}_3}\right)\left(\frac{1 \text{ mol HIO}_3}{2 \text{ mol ICl}_3}\right)\left(\frac{175.9 \text{ g HIO}_3}{1 \text{ mol HIO}_3}\right) = 239.486 = \mathbf{239 \text{ g HIO}_3}$$

The remaining mass of the excess reagent can be calculated from the amount of H_2O combining with the limiting reagent.

$$\text{Moles of H}_2\text{O required to react with 635 g ICl}_3 = (2.722985 \text{ mol ICl}_3)\left(\frac{3 \text{ mol H}_2\text{O}}{2 \text{ mol ICl}_3}\right) = 4.0844775 \text{ mol H}_2\text{O}$$

$$\text{Mass (g) of H}_2\text{O required to react with 635 g ICl}_3 = (4.0844775 \text{ mol H}_2\text{O})\left(\frac{18.02 \text{ g H}_2\text{O}}{1 \text{ mol H}_2\text{O}}\right)$$

$$= 73.6023 = 73.6 \text{ g H}_2\text{O reacted}$$

Remaining H_2O = 118.5 g – 73.6 g = **44.9 g H_2O**

3.82 Plan: Write the balanced equation; the formula for carbon is C, the formula for oxygen is O_2, and the formula for carbon dioxide is CO_2. To determine which reactant is limiting, calculate the amount of CO_2 formed from each reactant, assuming an excess of the other reactant. The reactant that produces less product is the limiting reagent. Use the limiting reagent and the mole ratio from the balanced chemical equation to determine the amount of CO_2 formed and the amount of the excess reactant that reacts. The difference between the amount of excess reactant that reacts and the initial amount of reactant supplied gives the amount of excess reactant remaining.

Solution:

The balanced equation is: $C(s) + O_2(g) \rightarrow CO_2(g)$

Finding the moles of CO_2 from the moles of carbon (if O_2 is limiting):

$$\text{Moles of CO}_2 \text{ from C} = (0.100 \text{ mol C})\left(\frac{1 \text{ mol CO}_2}{1 \text{ mol C}}\right) = 0.100 \text{ mol CO}_2$$

Finding the moles of CO_2 from the moles of oxygen (if C is limiting):

$$\text{Moles of O}_2 = (8.00 \text{ g O}_2)\left(\frac{1 \text{ mol O}_2}{32.00 \text{ g O}_2}\right) = 0.250 \text{ mol O}_2$$

$$\text{Moles of CO}_2 \text{ from O}_2 = (0.250 \text{ mol O}_2)\left(\frac{1 \text{ mol CO}_2}{1 \text{ mol O}_2}\right) = 0.25000 = 0.250 \text{ mol CO}_2$$

Carbon is the limiting reactant and will be used to determine the amount of CO_2 that will form.

$$\text{Mass (g) of CO}_2 = (0.100 \text{ mol CO}_2)\left(\frac{44.01 \text{ g CO}_2}{1 \text{ mol CO}_2}\right) = 4.401 = \mathbf{4.40 \text{ g CO}_2}$$

Since carbon is limiting, the **O_2 is in excess**. The amount remaining depends on how much combines with the limiting reagent.

$$\text{Moles of O}_2 \text{ required to react with 0.100 mol of C} = (0.100 \text{ mol C})\left(\frac{1 \text{ mol O}_2}{1 \text{ mol C}}\right) = 0.100 \text{ mol O}_2$$

$$\text{Mass (g) of O}_2 \text{ required to react with 0.100 mol of C} = (0.100 \text{ mol O}_2)\left(\frac{32.00 \text{ mol O}_2}{1 \text{ mol O}_2}\right) = 3.20 \text{ g O}_2$$

Remaining O_2 = 8.00 g – 3.20 g = **4.80 g O_2**

3.84 Plan: The question asks for the mass of each substance present at the end of the reaction. "Substance" refers to both reactants and products. Solve this problem using multiple steps. Recognizing that this is a limiting reactant problem, first write a balanced chemical equation. To determine which reactant is limiting, calculate the amount of any product formed from each reactant, assuming an excess of the other reactant. The reactant that produces less product is the limiting reagent. Any product can be used to predict the limiting reactant; in this case, $AlCl_3$ is used. Use the limiting reagent and the mole ratio from the balanced chemical equation to determine the amount of both products formed and the amount of the excess reactant that reacts. The difference between the amount of excess reactant that reacts and the initial amount of reactant supplied gives the amount of excess reactant remaining.

Solution:

The balanced chemical equation is:

$$Al(NO_2)_3(aq) + 3NH_4Cl(aq) \rightarrow AlCl_3(aq) + 3N_2(g) + 6H_2O(l)$$

Now determine the limiting reagent. We will use the moles of $AlCl_3$ produced to determine which is limiting.
Finding the moles of $AlCl_3$ from the moles of $Al(NO_2)_3$ (if NH_4Cl is limiting):

$$\text{Moles of Al(NO}_2)_3 = (72.5 \text{ g Al(NO}_2)_3)\left(\frac{1 \text{ mol Al(NO}_2)_3}{165.01 \text{ g Al(NO}_2)_3}\right) = 0.439367 \text{ mol Al(NO}_2)_3$$

$$\text{Moles of AlCl}_3 \text{ from Al(NO}_2)_3 = (0.439367 \text{ mol Al(NO}_2)_3)\left(\frac{1 \text{ mol AlCl}_3}{1 \text{ mol Al(NO}_2)_3}\right) = 0.439367 = 0.439 \text{ mol AlCl}_3$$

Finding the moles of $AlCl_3$ from the moles of NH_4Cl (if $Al(NO_2)_3$ is limiting):

$$\text{Moles of NH}_4\text{Cl} = (58.6 \text{ g NH}_4\text{Cl})\left(\frac{1 \text{ mol NH}_4\text{Cl}}{53.49 \text{ g NH}_4\text{Cl}}\right) = 1.09553 \text{ mol NH}_4\text{Cl}$$

$$\text{Moles of AlCl}_3 \text{ from NH}_4\text{Cl} = (1.09553 \text{ mol NH}_4\text{Cl})\left(\frac{1 \text{ mol AlCl}_3}{3 \text{ mol NH}_4\text{Cl}}\right) = 0.365177 = 0.365 \text{ mol AlCl}_3$$

Ammonium chloride is the limiting reactant, and it is used for all subsequent calculations.
Mass of substances after the reaction:
$Al(NO_2)_3$:
Mass (g) of $Al(NO_2)_3$ (the excess reactant) required to react with 58.6 g of NH_4Cl =

$$(1.09553 \text{ mol NH}_4\text{Cl})\left(\frac{1 \text{ mol Al(NO}_2)_3}{3 \text{ mol NH}_4\text{Cl}}\right)\left(\frac{165.01 \text{ g Al(NO}_2)_3}{1 \text{ mol Al(NO}_2)_3}\right) = 60.2579 = 60.3 \text{ g Al(NO}_2)_3$$

$Al(NO_2)_3$ remaining: 72.5 g – 60.3 g = **12.2 g $Al(NO_2)_3$**
NH_4Cl: **None left** since it is the limiting reagent.
$AlCl_3$:

$$\text{Mass (g) of AlCl}_3 = (0.365177 \text{ mol AlCl}_3)\left(\frac{133.33 \text{ g AlCl}_3}{1 \text{ mol AlCl}_3}\right) = 48.689 = \mathbf{48.7 \text{ g AlCl}_3}$$

N_2:

$$\text{Mass (g) of N}_2 = (1.09553 \text{ mol NH}_4\text{Cl})\left(\frac{3 \text{ mol N}_2}{3 \text{ mol NH}_4\text{Cl}}\right)\left(\frac{28.02 \text{ g N}_2}{1 \text{ mol N}_2}\right) = 30.697 = \mathbf{30.7 \text{ g N}_2}$$

H_2O:

$$\text{Mass (g) of H}_2\text{O} = (1.09553 \text{ mol NH}_4\text{Cl})\left(\frac{6 \text{ mol H}_2\text{O}}{3 \text{ mol NH}_4\text{Cl}}\right)\left(\frac{18.02 \text{ g H}_2\text{O}}{1 \text{ mol H}_2\text{O}}\right) = 39.483 = \mathbf{39.5 \text{ g H}_2\text{O}}$$

3.86 Plan: Express the yield of each step as a fraction of 1.00; multiply the fraction of the first step by that of the second step and then multiply by 100 to get the overall percent yield.
Solution:
73% = 0.73; 68% = 0.68
(0.73 x 0.68) x 100 = 49.64 = **50.%**

3.88 Plan: Write and balance the chemical equation using the formulas of the substances. Determine the theoretical yield of the reaction from the mass of tungsten(VI) oxide. To do that, convert the mass of tungsten(VI) oxide to moles by dividing by its molar mass and then use the mole ratio between tungsten(VI) oxide and water to determine the moles and then mass of water that should be produced. Use the density of water to determine the actual yield of water in grams. The actual yield divided by the theoretical yield just calculated (with the result multiplied by 100%) gives the percent yield.
Solution:
The balanced chemical equation is:
$WO_3(s) + 3H_2(g) \rightarrow W(s) + 3H_2O(l)$
Determining the theoretical yield of H_2O:

$$\text{Moles of WO}_3 = (45.5 \text{ g WO}_3)\left(\frac{1 \text{ mol WO}_3}{231.9 \text{ g WO}_3}\right) = 0.1962053 \text{ mol WO}_3$$

$$\text{Mass (g) of H}_2\text{O (theoretical yield)} = (0.1962053 \text{ mol WO}_3)\left(\frac{3 \text{ mol H}_2\text{O}}{1 \text{ mol WO}_3}\right)\left(\frac{18.02 \text{ g H}_2\text{O}}{1 \text{ mol H}_2\text{O}}\right) = 10.60686 \text{ g H}_2\text{O}$$

Determining the actual yield of H_2O:

$$\text{Mass (g) of H}_2\text{O (actual yield)} = (9.60 \text{ mL H}_2\text{O})\left(\frac{1.00 \text{ g H}_2\text{O}}{1 \text{ mL H}_2\text{O}}\right) = 9.60 \text{ g H}_2\text{O}$$

$$\%\text{ yield} = \left(\frac{\text{actual Yield}}{\text{theoretical Yield}}\right) \text{x } 100\% = \left(\frac{9.60 \text{ g H}_2\text{O}}{10.60686 \text{ g H}_2\text{O}}\right) \text{x } 100\% = 90.5075 = \mathbf{90.5\%}$$

3.90 Plan: Write the balanced chemical equation. Since quantities of two reactants are given, we must determine which is the limiting reactant. To determine which reactant is limiting, calculate the amount of any product formed from each reactant, assuming an excess of the other reactant. The reactant that produces less product is the limiting reagent. Any product can be used to predict the limiting reactant; in this case, CH_3Cl is used. Only 75.0% of the calculated amounts of products actually form, so the actual yield is 75% of the theoretical yield.

Solution:
The balanced equation is: $CH_4(g) + Cl_2(g) \rightarrow CH_3Cl(g) + HCl(g)$
Determining the limiting reactant:
Finding the moles of CH_3Cl from the moles of CH_4 (if Cl_2 is limiting):

$$\text{Moles of } CH_4 = (20.5 \text{ g } CH_4)\left(\frac{1 \text{ mol } CH_4}{16.04 \text{ g } CH_4}\right) = 1.278055 \text{ mol } CH_4$$

$$\text{Moles of } CH_3Cl \text{ from } CH_4 = (1.278055 \text{ mol } CH_4)\left(\frac{1 \text{ mol } CH_3Cl}{1 \text{ mol } CH_4}\right) = 1.278055 \text{ mol } CH_3Cl$$

Finding the moles of CH_3Cl from the moles of Cl_2 (if CH_4 is limiting):

$$\text{Moles of } Cl_2 = (45.0 \text{ g } Cl_2)\left(\frac{1 \text{ mol } Cl_2}{70.90 \text{ g } Cl_2}\right) = 0.634697 \text{ mol } Cl_2$$

$$\text{Moles of } CH_3Cl \text{ from } Cl_2 = (0.634697 \text{ mol } Cl_2)\left(\frac{1 \text{ mol } CH_3Cl}{1 \text{ mol } Cl_2}\right) = 0.634697 \text{ mol } CH_3Cl$$

Chlorine is the limiting reactant and is used to determine the theoretical yield of CH_3Cl:

$$\text{Mass (g) of } CH_3Cl \text{ (theoretical yield)} = (0.634697 \text{ mol } CH_3Cl)\left(\frac{50.48 \text{ g } CH_3Cl}{1 \text{ mol } CH_3Cl}\right) = 32.0395 \text{ g } CH_3Cl$$

$$\%\text{ yield} = \left(\frac{\text{actual Yield}}{\text{theoretical Yield}}\right) \text{x } 100\%$$

$$\text{Actual yield (g) of } CH_3Cl = \frac{\%\text{ yield}}{100\%}(\text{theoretical yield}) = \frac{75\%}{100\%}(32.0395 \text{ g } CH_3Cl) = 24.02962 = \mathbf{24.0 \text{ g } CH_3Cl}$$

3.92 Plan: Write the balanced equation; the formula for fluorine is F_2, the formula for carbon tetrafluoride is CF_4, and the formula for nitrogen trifluoride is NF_3. To determine which reactant is limiting, calculate the amount of CF_4 formed from each reactant, assuming an excess of the other reactant. The reactant that produces less product is the limiting reagent. Use the limiting reagent and the mole ratio from the balanced chemical equation to determine the mass of CF_4 formed.
Solution:
The balanced chemical equation is:
$(CN)_2(g) + 7F_2(g) \rightarrow 2CF_4(g) + 2NF_3(g)$
Determining the limiting reactant:
Finding the moles of CF_4 from the moles of $(CN)_2$ (if F_2 is limiting):

$$\text{Moles of } CF_4 \text{ from } (CN)_2 = (60.0 \text{ g } (CN)_2)\left(\frac{1 \text{ mol } (CN)_2}{52.04 \text{ g } (CN)_2}\right)\left(\frac{2 \text{ mol } CF_4}{1 \text{ mol } (CN)_2}\right) = 2.30592 \text{ mol } CF_4$$

Finding the moles of CF_4 from the moles of F_2 (if $(CN)_2$ is limiting):

$$\text{Moles of } CF_4 \text{ from } F_2 = (60.0 \text{ g } F_2)\left(\frac{1 \text{ mol } F_2}{38.00 \text{ g } F_2}\right)\left(\frac{2 \text{ mol } CF_4}{7 \text{ mol } F_2}\right) = 0.4511278 \text{ mol } CF_4$$

F_2 is the limiting reactant, and will be used to calculate the amount of CF_4 produced.

$$\text{Mass (g) of } CF_4 = (60.0 \text{ g } F_2)\left(\frac{1 \text{ mol } F_2}{38.00 \text{ g } F_2}\right)\left(\frac{2 \text{ mol } CF_4}{7 \text{ mol } F_2}\right)\left(\frac{88.01 \text{ g } CF_4}{1 \text{ mol } CF_4}\right) = 39.70376 = \mathbf{39.7 \text{ g } CF_4}$$

3.93 Plan: Write and balance the chemical reaction. Remember that both chlorine and oxygen exist as diatomic molecules. Use the mole ratio between oxygen and dichlorine monoxide to find the moles of dichlorine monoxide that reacted. Multiply the amount in moles by Avogadro's number to convert to number of molecules.
Solution:
a) Both oxygen and chlorine are diatomic. **Scene A** best represents the product mixture as there are O_2 and Cl_2 molecules in Scene A. Scene B shows oxygen and chlorine atoms and Scene C shows atoms and molecules. Oxygen and chlorine atoms are NOT products of this reaction.
b) The balanced reaction is $\mathbf{2Cl_2O(g) \rightarrow 2Cl_2(g) + O_2(g)}$.

c) There is a 2:1 mole ratio between Cl_2 and O_2. In Scene A, there are 6 green molecules and 3 red molecules. Since twice as many Cl_2 molecules are produced as there are O_2 molecules produced, the red molecules are the O_2 molecules.

$$\text{Moles of } Cl_2O = (3\ O_2 \text{ molecules})\left(\frac{2\text{ O atoms}}{1\ O_2\text{ molecule}}\right)\left(\frac{0.050\text{ mol O atoms}}{1\text{ O atom}}\right)\left(\frac{1\text{ mol } O_2\text{ molecules}}{2\text{ mol O atoms}}\right)\left(\frac{2\text{ mol } Cl_2O}{1\text{ mol } O_2}\right)$$

$$= 0.30\text{ mol } Cl_2O$$

$$\text{Molecules of } Cl_2O = (0.30\text{ mol } Cl_2O)\left(\frac{6.022\text{x}10^{23}\ Cl_2O\text{ molecules}}{1\text{ mol } Cl_2O}\right) = 1.8066\text{x}10^{23} = \mathbf{1.8x10^{23}\ Cl_2O\ molecules}$$

3.100 Plan: The moles of narceine and the moles of water are required. We can assume any mass of narceine hydrate (we will use 100 g), and use this mass to determine the moles of hydrate. The moles of water in the hydrate is obtained by taking 10.8% of the 100 g mass of hydrate and converting the mass to moles of water. Divide the moles of water by the moles of hydrate to find the value of x.

Solution:

Assuming a 100 g sample of narceine hydrate:

$$\text{Moles of narceine hydrate} = (100\text{ g narceine hydrate})\left(\frac{1\text{ mol narceine hydrate}}{499.52\text{ g narceine hydrate}}\right)$$

$$= 0.20019\text{ mol narceine hydrate}$$

$$\text{Mass (g) of } H_2O = (100\text{ g narceine hydrate})\left(\frac{10.8\%\ H_2O}{100\%\text{ narceine hydrate}}\right) = 10.8\text{ g } H_2O$$

$$\text{Moles of } H_2O = (10.8\text{ g } H_2O)\left(\frac{1\text{ mol } H_2O}{18.02\text{ g } H_2O}\right) = 0.59933\text{ mol } H_2O$$

$$\text{x} = \frac{\text{moles of } H_2O}{\text{moles of hydrate}} = \frac{0.59933\text{ mol}}{0.20019\text{ mol}} = \mathbf{3}$$

Thus, there are three water molecules per mole of hydrate. The formula for narceine hydrate is **narceine•3H₂O**.

3.101 Plan: Determine the formula and the molar mass of each compound. The formula gives the relative numbers of moles of each element present. Multiply the number of moles of each element by its molar mass to find the total mass of element in 1 mole of compound. Mass percent = $\frac{\text{total mass of element}}{\text{molar mass of compound}}(100)$. List the compounds from the highest %H to the lowest.

Solution:

Name	Chemical formula	Molar mass (g/mol)	Mass percent H = $\frac{\text{moles of H x molar mass}}{\text{molar mass of compound}}(100)$
Ethane	C_2H_6	30.07	$\frac{6\text{ mol}(1.008\text{ g/mol})}{30.07\text{ g}}(100) = 20.11\%$ H
Propane	C_3H_8	44.09	$\frac{8\text{ mol}(1.008\text{ g/mol})}{44.09\text{ g}}(100) = 18.29\%$ H
Benzene	C_6H_6	78.11	$\frac{6\text{ mol}(1.008\text{ g/mol})}{78.11\text{ g}}(100) = 7.743\%$ H
Ethanol	C_2H_5OH	46.07	$\frac{6\text{ mol}(1.008\text{ g/mol})}{46.07\text{ g}}(100) = 13.13\%$ H
Cetyl palmitate	$C_{32}H_{64}O_2$	480.83	$\frac{64\text{ mol}(1.008\text{ g/mol})}{480.83\text{ g}}(100) = 13.42\%$ H

The hydrogen percentage decreases in the following order:

Ethane > Propane > Cetyl palmitate > Ethanol > Benzene

3.106 Plan: The key to solving this problem is determining the overall balanced equation. Each individual step must be set up and balanced first. The separate equations can then be combined to get the overall equation. The mass of iron is converted to moles of iron by dividing by the molar mass, and the mole ratio from the balanced equation is used to find the moles and then the mass of CO required to produce that number of moles of iron.

Solution:

a) In the first step, ferric oxide (ferric denotes Fe^{3+}) reacts with carbon monoxide to form Fe_3O_4 and carbon dioxide:

$$3Fe_2O_3(s) + CO(g) \rightarrow 2Fe_3O_4(s) + CO_2(g) \quad (1)$$

In the second step, Fe_3O_4 reacts with more carbon monoxide to form ferrous oxide:

$$Fe_3O_4(s) + CO(g) \rightarrow 3FeO(s) + CO_2(g) \quad (2)$$

In the third step, ferrous oxide reacts with more carbon monoxide to form molten iron:

$$FeO(s) + CO(g) \rightarrow Fe(l) + CO_2(g) \quad (3)$$

Common factors are needed to allow these equations to be combined. The intermediate products are Fe_3O_4 and FeO, so multiply equation (2) by 2 to cancel Fe_3O_4 and equation (3) by 6 to cancel FeO:

$$3Fe_2O_3(s) + CO(g) \rightarrow \cancel{2Fe_3O_4(s)} + CO_2(g)$$
$$\cancel{2Fe_3O_4(s)} + 2CO(g) \rightarrow \cancel{6FeO(s)} + 2CO_2(g)$$
$$\cancel{6FeO(s)} + 6CO(g) \rightarrow 6Fe(l) + 6CO_2(g)$$
$$\overline{3Fe_2O_3(s) + 9CO(g) \rightarrow 6Fe(l) + 9CO_2(g)}$$

Then divide by 3 to obtain the smallest integer coefficients:

$$\mathbf{Fe_2O_3(s) + 3CO(g) \rightarrow 2Fe(s) + 3CO_2(g)}$$

b) A metric ton is equal to 1000 kg.

Converting 45.0 metric tons of Fe to mass in grams:

$$\text{Mass (g) of Fe} = (45.0 \text{ ton Fe})\left(\frac{10^3 \text{ kg}}{1 \text{ ton}}\right)\left(\frac{10^3 \text{ g}}{1 \text{ kg}}\right) = 4.50\text{x}10^7 \text{ g Fe}$$

$$\text{Moles of Fe} = (4.50\text{x}10^7 \text{ g Fe})\left(\frac{1 \text{ mol Fe}}{55.85 \text{ g Fe}}\right) = 8.05730\text{x}10^5 \text{ mol Fe}$$

$$\text{Mass (g) of CO} = (8.05730\text{x}10^5 \text{ mol Fe})\left(\frac{3 \text{ mol CO}}{2 \text{ mol Fe}}\right)\left(\frac{28.01 \text{ g CO}}{1 \text{ mol CO}}\right) = 3.38527\text{x}10^7 = \mathbf{3.39x10^7 \text{ g CO}}$$

3.108 Plan: If 100.0 g of dinitrogen tetroxide reacts with 100.0 g of hydrazine (N_2H_4), what is the theoretical yield of nitrogen if no side reaction takes place? First, we need to identify the limiting reactant. To determine which reactant is limiting, calculate the amount of nitrogen formed from each reactant, assuming an excess of the other reactant. The reactant that produces less product is the limiting reagent. Use the limiting reagent and the mole ratio from the balanced chemical equation to determine the theoretical yield of nitrogen. Then determine the amount of limiting reactant required to produce 10.0 grams of NO. Reduce the amount of limiting reactant by the amount used to produce NO. The reduced amount of limiting reactant is then used to calculate an "actual yield." The "actual" and theoretical yields will give the maximum percent yield.

Solution:

The balanced reaction is $2N_2H_4(l) + N_2O_4(l) \rightarrow 3N_2(g) + 4H_2O(g)$

Determining the limiting reactant:

Finding the moles of N_2 from the amount of N_2O_4 (if N_2H_4 is limiting):

$$\text{Moles of } N_2 \text{ from } N_2O_4 = (100.0 \text{ g } N_2O_4)\left(\frac{1 \text{ mol } N_2O_4}{92.02 \text{ g } N_2O_4}\right)\left(\frac{3 \text{ mol } N_2}{1 \text{ mol } N_2O_4}\right) = 3.26016 \text{ mol } N_2$$

Finding the moles of N_2 from the amount of N_2H_4 (if N_2O_4 is limiting):

$$N_2 \text{ from } N_2H_4 = (100.0 \text{ g } N_2H_4)\left(\frac{1 \text{ mol } N_2H_4}{32.05 \text{ g } N_2H_4}\right)\left(\frac{3 \text{ mol } N_2}{2 \text{ mol } N_2H_4}\right) = 4.68019 \text{ mol } N_2$$

N_2O_4 is the limiting reactant.

$$\text{Theoretical yield of } N_2 = (100.0 \text{ g } N_2O_4)\left(\frac{1 \text{ mol } N_2O_4}{92.02 \text{ g } N_2O_4}\right)\left(\frac{3 \text{ mol } N_2}{1 \text{ mol } N_2O_4}\right)\left(\frac{28.02 \text{ g } N_2}{1 \text{ mol } N_2}\right) = 91.3497 \text{ g } N_2$$

How much of the limiting reactant is used to produce 10.0 g NO?

$N_2H_4(l) + 2N_2O_4(l) \rightarrow 6NO(g) + 2H_2O(g)$

$$\text{Mass (g) of } N_2O_4 \text{ used} = (10.0 \text{ g NO})\left(\frac{1 \text{ mol NO}}{30.01 \text{ g NO}}\right)\left(\frac{2 \text{ mol } N_2O_4}{6 \text{ mol NO}}\right)\left(\frac{92.02 \text{ g } N_2O_4}{1 \text{ mol } N_2O_4}\right)$$

$$= 10.221 \text{ g } N_2O_4$$

Amount of N_2O_4 available to produce N_2 = 100.0 g N_2O_4 – mass of N_2O_4 required to produce 10.0 g NO

= 100.0 g – 10.221 g = 89.779 g N_2O_4

Determine the "actual yield" of N_2 from 89.779 g N_2O_4:

$$\text{“Actual yield” of } N_2 = (89.779 \text{ g } N_2O_4)\left(\frac{1 \text{ mol } N_2O_4}{92.02 \text{ g } N_2O_4}\right)\left(\frac{3 \text{ mol } N_2}{1 \text{ mol } N_2O_4}\right)\left(\frac{28.02 \text{ g } N_2}{1 \text{ mol } N_2}\right)$$

$$= 82.01285 \text{ g } N_2$$

$$\text{Theoretical yield} = \left(\frac{\text{actual yield}}{\text{theoretical yield}}\right)(100) = \left(\frac{82.01285}{91.3497}\right)(100) = 89.7790 = \mathbf{89.8\%}$$

3.110 Plan: Identify the product molecules and write the balanced equation. To determine the limiting reactant for part b), examine the product circle to see which reactant remains in excess and which reactant was totally consumed. For part c), use the mole ratios in the balanced equation to determine the number of moles of product formed by each reactant, assuming the other reactant is in excess. The reactant that produces fewer moles of product is the limiting reactant. Use the mole ratio between the two reactants to determine the moles of excess reactant required to react with the limiting reactant. The difference between the initial moles of excess reactant and the moles required for reaction is the moles of excess reactant that remain.

Solution:

a) The contents of the boxes give:

$AB_2 + B_2 \rightarrow AB_3$

Balancing the reaction gives:

$\mathbf{2AB_2 + B_2 \rightarrow 2AB_3}$

b) Two B_2 molecules remain after reaction so B_2 is in excess. All of the AB_2 molecules have reacted so $\mathbf{AB_2}$ is the limiting reactant.

c) Finding the moles of AB_3 from the moles of AB_2 (if B_2 is limiting):

$$\text{Moles of } AB_3 \text{ from } AB_2 = (5.0 \text{ mol } AB_2)\left(\frac{2 \text{ mol } AB_3}{2 \text{ mol } AB_2}\right) = 5.0 \text{ mol } AB_3$$

Finding the moles of AB_3 from the moles of B_2 (if AB_2 is limiting):

$$\text{Moles of } AB_3 \text{ from } B_2 = (3.0 \text{ mol } B_2)\left(\frac{2 \text{ mol } AB_3}{1 \text{ mol } B_2}\right) = 6.0 \text{ mol } AB_3$$

AB_2 is the limiting reagent and **5.0 mol of AB_3** is formed.

$$\text{d) Moles of } B_2 \text{ that react with 5.0 mol } AB_2 = (5.0 \text{ mol } AB_2)\left(\frac{1 \text{ mol } B_2}{2 \text{ mol } AB_2}\right) = 2.5 \text{ mol } B_2$$

The unreacted B_2 is 3.0 mol – 2.5 mol = **0.5 mol B_2**.

3.111 Plan: Write the formulas in the form $C_xH_yO_z$. Reduce the formulas to obtain the empirical formulas. Add the atomic masses in that empirical formula to obtain the molecular mass.

Solution:

Compound A: $C_4H_{10}O_2 = C_2H_5O$
Compound B: C_2H_4O
Compound C: $C_4H_8O_2 = C_2H_4O$
Compound D: $C_6H_{12}O_3 = C_2H_4O$
Compound E: $C_5H_8O_2$

Compounds **B, C and D** all have the same empirical formula, C_2H_4O. The molecular mass of this formula is (2 x 12.01 g/mol C) + (4 x 1.008 g/mol H) + (1 x 16.00 g/mol O) = **44.05 g/mol.**

3.112 Plan: Write the balanced chemical equation. Since quantities of two reactants are given, we must determine which is the limiting reactant. To determine which reactant is limiting, calculate the amount of product formed from each reactant, assuming an excess of the other reactant. The reactant that produces less product is the limiting reagent. Use the limiting reactant to determine the theoretical yield of product. The actual yield is given. The actual yield divided by the theoretical yield just calculated (with the result multiplied by 100%) gives the percent yield.

Solution:

Determine the balanced chemical equation:

$ZrOCl_2{\bullet}8H_2O(s) + 4H_2C_2O_4{\bullet}2H_2O(s) + 4KOH(aq) \rightarrow K_2Zr(C_2O_4)_3(H_2C_2O_4){\bullet}H_2O(s) + 2KCl(aq) + 20H_2O(l)$

Determining the limiting reactant:

Finding the moles of product from the amount of $ZrOCl_2{\bullet}8H_2O$ (if $H_2C_2O_4{\bullet}2H_2O$ is limiting):

Moles of product from $ZrOCl_2{\bullet}8H_2O$ =

$$(1.68 \text{ g } ZrOCl_2{\bullet}8H_2O)\left(\frac{1 \text{ mol } ZrOCl_2{\bullet}8H_2O}{322.25 \text{ g } ZrOCl_2{\bullet}8H_2O}\right)\left(\frac{1 \text{ mol product}}{1 \text{ mol } ZrOCl_2{\bullet}8H_2O}\right) = 0.00521334 \text{ mol product}$$

Finding the moles of product from the amount of $H_2C_2O_4{\bullet}2H_2O$ (if $ZrOCl_2{\bullet}8H_2O$ is limiting):

Moles of product from $H_2C_2O_4{\bullet}2H_2O$ =

$$(5.20 \text{ g } H_2C_2O_4{\bullet}2H_2O)\left(\frac{1 \text{ mol } H_2C_2O_4{\bullet}H_2O}{126.07 \text{ g } H_2C_2O_4{\bullet}2H_2O}\right)\left(\frac{1 \text{ mol product}}{4 \text{ mol } H_2C_2O_4{\bullet}2H_2O}\right) = 0.0103117 \text{ mol product}$$

It is not necessary to find the moles of product from KOH because KOH is stated to be in excess.

The $ZrOCl_2{\bullet}8H_2O$ is the limiting reactant, and will be used to calculate the theoretical yield:

$$\text{Mass (g) of product} = (0.00521334 \text{ mol product})\left(\frac{541.53 \text{ g product}}{1 \text{ mol product}}\right) = 2.82318 \text{ g product}$$

Calculating the percent yield:

$$\text{Percent yield} = \left(\frac{\text{actual Yield}}{\text{theoretical Yield}}\right) \text{x}100\% = \left(\frac{1.25 \text{ g}}{2.82318 \text{ g}}\right) \text{x } 100\% = 44.276 = \mathbf{44.3\% \text{ yield}}$$

3.121 Plan: Deal with the methane and propane separately, and combine the results. Balanced equations are needed for each hydrocarbon. The total mass and the percentages will give the mass of each hydrocarbon. The mass of each hydrocarbon is changed to moles, and through the balanced chemical equation the amount of CO_2 produced by each gas may be found. Summing the amounts of CO_2 gives the total from the mixture. For part b), let x and 252 – x represent the masses of CH_4 and C_3H_8, respectively.

Solution:

a) The balanced chemical equations are:

Methane: $CH_4(g) + 2O_2(g) \rightarrow CO_2(g) + 2H_2O(l)$

Propane: $C_3H_8(g) + 5O_2(g) \rightarrow 3CO_2(g) + 4H_2O(l)$

Mass (g) of CO_2 from each:

$$\text{Methane: } (200.\text{g Mixture})\left(\frac{25.0\%}{100\%}\right)\left(\frac{1 \text{ mol } CH_4}{16.04 \text{ g } CH_4}\right)\left(\frac{1 \text{ mol } CO_2}{1 \text{ mol } CH_4}\right)\left(\frac{44.01 \text{ g } CO_2}{1 \text{ mol } CO_2}\right) = 137.188 \text{ g } CO_2$$

$$\text{Propane: } (200.\text{g Mixture})\left(\frac{75.0\%}{100\%}\right)\left(\frac{1 \text{ mol } C_3H_8}{44.09 \text{ g } C_3H_8}\right)\left(\frac{3 \text{ mol } CO_2}{1 \text{ mol } C_3H_8}\right)\left(\frac{44.01 \text{ g } CO_2}{1 \text{ mol } CO_2}\right) = 449.183 \text{ g } CO_2$$

Total CO_2 = 137.188 g + 449.183 g = 586.371 = **586 g CO_2**

b) Since the mass of CH_4 + the mass of C_3H_8 = 252 g, let x = mass of CH_4 in the mixture and 252 – x = mass of C_3H_8 in the mixture. Use mole ratios to calculate the amount of CO_2 formed from x amount of CH_4 and the amount of CO_2 formed from 252 – x amount of C_3H_8.

The total mass of CO_2 produced = 748 g.

$$\text{The total moles of } CO_2 \text{ produced} = (748 \text{ g } CO_2)\left(\frac{1 \text{ mol } CO_2}{44.01 \text{ g } CO_2}\right) = 16.996 \text{ mol } CO_2$$

16.996 mol CO_2 =

$$(\text{x g } CH_4)\left(\frac{1 \text{ mol } CH_4}{16.04 \text{ g } CH_4}\right)\left(\frac{1 \text{ mol } CO_2}{1 \text{ mol } CH_4}\right) + (252 - \text{x g } C_3H_8)\left(\frac{1 \text{ mol } C_3H_8}{44.09 \text{ g } C_3H_8}\right)\left(\frac{3 \text{ mol } CO_2}{1 \text{ mol } C_3H_8}\right)$$

$$16.996 \text{ mol } CO_2 = \frac{x}{16.04} \text{ mol } CO_2 + \frac{3(252 - x)}{44.09} \text{ mol } CO_2$$

$$16.996 \text{ mol } CO_2 = \frac{x}{16.04} \text{ mol } CO_2 + \frac{756 - 3x}{44.09} \text{ mol } CO_2$$

$16.996 \text{ mol } CO_2 = 0.06234x \text{ mol } CO_2 + (17.147 - 0.06804x \text{ mol } CO_2)$

$16.996 = 17.147 - 0.0057x$

$x = 26.49 \text{ g } CH_4$ $\qquad 252 - x = 252 \text{ g} - 26.49 \text{ g} = 225.51 \text{ g } C_3H_8$

$$\text{Mass \% } CH_4 = \frac{\text{mass of } CH_4}{\text{mass of mixture}}(100) = \frac{26.49 \text{ g } CH_4}{252 \text{ g mixture}}(100) = \mathbf{10.5\% \ CH_4}$$

$$\text{Mass \% } C_3H_8 = \frac{\text{mass of } C_3H_8}{\text{mass of mixture}}(100) = \frac{225.51 \text{ g } C_3H_8}{252 \text{ g mixture}}(100) = \mathbf{89.5\% \ C_3H_8}$$

3.122 Plan: If we assume a 100-gram sample of fertilizer, then the 30:10:10 percentages become the masses, in grams, of N, P_2O_5, and K_2O. These masses may be changed to moles of substance, and then to moles of each element. To get the desired x:y:1.0 ratio, divide the moles of each element by the moles of potassium.

Solution:

A 100-gram sample of 30:10:10 fertilizer contains 30 g N, 10 g P_2O_5, and 10 g K_2O.

$$\text{Moles of N} = (30 \text{ g N})\left(\frac{1 \text{ mol N}}{14.01 \text{ g N}}\right) = 2.1413 \text{ mol N}$$

$$\text{Moles of P} = (10 \text{ g } P_2O_5)\left(\frac{1 \text{ mol } P_2O_5}{141.94 \text{ g } P_2O_5}\right)\left(\frac{2 \text{ mol P}}{1 \text{ mol } P_2O_5}\right) = 0.14090 \text{ mol P}$$

$$\text{Moles of K} = (10 \text{ g } K_2O)\left(\frac{1 \text{ mol } K_2O}{94.20 \text{ g } K_2O}\right)\left(\frac{2 \text{ mol K}}{1 \text{ mol } K_2O}\right) = 0.21231 \text{ mol K}$$

This gives a N:P:K ratio of 2.1413:0.14090:0.21231

The ratio must be divided by the moles of K and rounded.

$$\frac{2.1413 \text{ mol N}}{0.21231} = 10.086 \qquad \frac{0.14090 \text{ mol P}}{0.21231} = 0.66365 \qquad \frac{0.21231 \text{ mol K}}{0.21231} = 1$$

10.086:0.66365:1.000 or **10:0.66:1.0**

3.127 Plan: Determine the molecular formula from the figure. Once the molecular formula is known, use the periodic table to determine the molar mass. Convert the volume of lemon juice in part b) from qt to mL and use the density to convert from mL to mass in g. Take 6.82% of that mass to find the mass of citric acid and use the molar mass to convert to moles.

Solution:

a) The formula of citric acid obtained by counting the number of carbon atoms, oxygen atoms, and hydrogen atoms is $\mathbf{C_6H_8O_7}$.

Molar mass = (6 x 12.01 g/mol C) + (8 x 1.008 g/mol H) + (7 x 16.00 g/mol O) = **192.12 g/mol**

b) Converting volume of lemon juice in qt to mL:

$$\text{Volume (mL) of lemon juice} = (1.50 \text{ qt})\left(\frac{1 \text{ L}}{1.057 \text{ qt}}\right)\left(\frac{1 \text{ mL}}{10^{-3} \text{ L}}\right) = 1419.111 \text{ mL}$$

Converting volume to mass in grams:

$$\text{Mass (g) of lemon juice} = (1419.111\text{ mL})\left(\frac{1.09\text{ g}}{\text{mL}}\right) = 1546.831\text{ g lemon juice}$$

$$\text{Mass (g) of } C_6H_8O_7 = (1546.831\text{ g lemon juice})\left(\frac{6.82\%\ C_6H_8O_7}{100\%\text{ lemon juice}}\right) = 105.494\text{ g } C_6H_8O_7$$

$$\text{Moles of } C_6H_8O_7 = (105.494\text{ g } C_6H_8O_7)\left(\frac{1\text{ mol } C_6H_8O_7}{192.12\text{ g } C_6H_8O_7}\right) = 0.549104 = \mathbf{0.549\ mol\ C_6H_8O_7}$$

3.128 Plan: Determine the formulas of each reactant and product, then balance the individual equations. Remember that nitrogen and oxygen are diatomic. Combine the three smaller equations to give the overall equation, where some substances serve as intermediates and will cancel. Use the mole ratio between nitrogen and nitric acid in the overall equation to find the moles and then mass of nitric acid produced. The amount of nitrogen in metric tons must be converted to mass in grams to convert the mass of nitrogen to moles.

Solution:

a) Nitrogen and oxygen combine to form nitrogen monoxide:

$$\mathbf{N_2(g) + O_2(g) \rightarrow 2NO(g)}$$

Nitrogen monoxide reacts with oxygen to form nitrogen dioxide:

$$\mathbf{2NO(g) + O_2(g) \rightarrow 2NO_2(g)}$$

Nitrogen dioxide combines with water to form nitric acid and nitrogen monoxide:

$$\mathbf{3NO_2(g) + H_2O(g) \rightarrow 2HNO_3(aq) + NO(g)}$$

b) Combining the reactions may involve adjusting the equations in various ways to cancel out as many materials as possible other than the reactants added and the desired products.

$$2 \times (N_2(g) + O_2(g) \rightarrow 2NO(g)) = \quad 2N_2(g) + 2O_2(g) \rightarrow \cancel{4NO(g)}$$

$$3 \times (2NO(g) + O_2(g) \rightarrow 2NO_2(g)) = \quad \cancel{6NO(g)} + 3O_2(g) \rightarrow \cancel{6NO_2(g)}$$

$$2 \times (3NO_2(g) + H_2O(g) \rightarrow 2HNO_3(aq) + NO(g)) = \quad \cancel{6NO_2(g)} + 2H_2O(g) \rightarrow 4HNO_3(aq) + \cancel{2NO(g)}$$

Multiplying the above equations as shown results in the 6 moles of NO on each side and the 6 moles of NO_2 on each side canceling. Adding the equations gives:

$$\mathbf{2N_2(g) + 5O_2(g) + 2H_2O(g) \rightarrow 4HNO_3(aq)}$$

c) $$\text{Mass (g) of } N_2 = (1350\text{ t } N_2)\left(\frac{10^3\text{ kg}}{1\text{t}}\right)\left(\frac{10^3\text{ g}}{1\text{ kg}}\right) = 1.35\text{x}10^9\text{ g } N_2$$

$$\text{Moles of } N_2 = (1.35\text{x}10^9\text{ g } N_2)\left(\frac{1\text{ mol } N_2}{28.02\text{ g } N_2}\right) = 4.817987\text{x}10^7\text{ mol } N_2$$

$$\text{Mass (g) of } HNO_3 = (4.817987\text{x}10^7\text{ mol } N_2)\left(\frac{4\text{ mol } HNO_3}{2\text{ mol } N_2}\right)\left(\frac{63.02\text{ g } HNO_3}{1\text{ mol } HNO_3}\right) = 6.072591\text{x}10^9\text{ g } HNO_3$$

Metric tons HNO_3 =

$$(6.072591\text{x}10^9\text{ g } HNO_3)\left(\frac{1\text{ kg}}{10^3\text{ g}}\right)\left(\frac{1\text{t}}{10^3\text{ kg}}\right) = 6.072591\text{x}10^3 = \mathbf{6.07x10^3\ metric\ tons\ HNO_3}$$

3.129 Plan: Write and balance the chemical reaction. Use the mole ratio to find the amount of product that should be produced and take 66% of that amount to obtain the actual yield.

Solution:

$2NO(g) + O_2(g) \rightarrow 2NO_2(g)$

With 6 molecules of NO and 3 molecules of O_2 reacting, 6 molecules of NO_2 can be produced.

If the reaction only has a 66% yield, then (0.66)(6) = 4 molecules of NO_2 will be produced. **Circle A** shows the formation of 4 molecules of NO_2. Circle B also shows the formation of 4 molecules of NO_2 but also has 2 unreacted molecules of NO and 1 unreacted molecule of O_2. Since neither reactant is limiting, there will be no unreacted reactant remaining after the reaction is over.

3.131 Plan: Use the mass percent to find the mass of heme in the sample; use the molar mass to convert the mass of heme to moles. Then find the mass of Fe in the sample by using the mole ratio between heme and iron. The mass of hemin is found by using the mole ratio between heme and hemoglobin.

Solution:

a) Mass (g) of heme = $(0.65\text{ g hemoglobin})\left(\frac{6.0\%\text{ heme}}{100\%\text{ hemoglobin}}\right)$ = **0.039 g heme**

b) Moles of heme = $(0.039\text{ g heme})\left(\frac{1\text{ mol heme}}{616.49\text{ g heme}}\right)$ = 6.32614x10^{-5} = **6.3x10^{-5} mol heme**

c) Mass (g) of Fe = $(6.32614\text{x}10^{-5}\text{ mol heme})\left(\frac{1\text{ mol Fe}}{1\text{ mol heme}}\right)\left(\frac{55.85\text{ g Fe}}{1\text{ mol Fe}}\right)$

= 3.5331x10^{-3} = **3.5x10^{-3} g Fe**

d) Mass (g) of hemin = $(6.32614\text{x}10^{-5}\text{ mol heme})\left(\frac{1\text{ mol hemin}}{1\text{ mol heme}}\right)\left(\frac{651.94\text{ g hemin}}{1\text{ mol hemin}}\right)$

= 4.1243x10^{-2} = **4.1x10^{-2} g hemin**

3.133 Plan: Determine the formula and the molar mass of each compound. The formula gives the relative number of moles of nitrogen present. Multiply the number of moles of nitrogen by its molar mass to find the total mass of nitrogen in 1 mole of compound. Mass percent = $\frac{\text{total mass of element}}{\text{molar mass of compound}}(100)$. For part b), convert mass of ornithine to moles, use the mole ratio between ornithine and urea to find the moles of urea, and then use the ratio between moles of urea and nitrogen to find the moles and mass of nitrogen produced.

Solution:

a) Urea: CH_4N_2O, $\mathcal{M}$ = 60.06 g/mol

There are 2 moles of N in 1 mole of CH_4N_2O.

Mass (g) of N = $(2\text{ mol N})\left(\frac{14.01\text{ g N}}{1\text{ mol N}}\right)$ = 28.02 g N

Mass percent = $\frac{\text{total mass N}}{\text{molar mass of compound}}(100) = \frac{28.02\text{ g N}}{60.06\text{ g }CH_4N_2O}(100)$ = 46.6533 = **46.65% N in urea**

Arginine: $C_6H_{15}N_4O_2$, $\mathcal{M}$ = 175.22 g/mol

There are 4 moles of N in 1 mole of $C_6H_{15}N_4O_2$.

Mass (g) of N = $(4\text{ mol N})\left(\frac{14.01\text{ g N}}{1\text{ mol N}}\right)$ = 56.04 g N

Mass percent = $\frac{\text{total mass N}}{\text{molar mass of compound}}(100) = \frac{56.04\text{ g N}}{175.22\text{ g }C_6H_{15}N_4O_2}(100)$

= 31.98265 = **31.98% N in arginine**

Ornithine: $C_5H_{13}N_2O_2$, $\mathcal{M}$ = 133.17 g/mol

There are 2 moles of N in 1 mole of $C_5H_{13}N_2O_2$.

Mass (g) of N = $(2\text{ mol N})\left(\frac{14.01\text{ g N}}{1\text{ mol N}}\right)$ = 28.02 g N

Mass percent = $\frac{\text{total mass N}}{\text{molar mass of compound}}(100) = \frac{28.02\text{ g N}}{133.17\text{ g }C_5H_{13}N_2O_2}(100)$

= 21.04077 = **21.04% N in ornithine**

b) Moles of urea = $(135.2\text{ g }C_5H_{13}N_2O_2)\left(\frac{1\text{ mol }C_5H_{13}N_2O_2}{133.17\text{ g }C_5H_{13}N_2O_2}\right)\left(\frac{1\text{ mol }CH_4N_2O}{1\text{ mol }C_5H_{13}N_2O_2}\right)$ = 1.015244 mol urea

Mass (g) of nitrogen = $(1.015244\text{ mol }CH_4N_2O)\left(\frac{2\text{ mol N}}{1\text{ mol }CH_4N_2O}\right)\left(\frac{14.01\text{ g N}}{1\text{ mol N}}\right)$ = 28.447 = **28.45 g N**

3.135 Plan: Determine the molar mass of each product and use the equation for percent atom economy.
Solution:
Molar masses of product: N_2H_4: 32.05 g/mol NaCl: 58.44 g/mol H_2O: 18.02 g/mol

$$\%\text{ atom economy} = \frac{\text{no. of moles x molar mass of desired products}}{\text{sum of (no. of moles x molar mass) for all products}} \text{ x } 100\%$$

% atom economy =

$$\frac{(1\text{ mol})(\text{molar mass of } N_2H_4)}{(1\text{ mol})(\text{molar mass of } N_2H_4) + (1\text{ mol})(\text{molar mass of NaCl}) + (1\text{ mol})(\text{molar mass of } H_2O)} \text{ x } 100\%$$

$$\frac{(1\text{mol})(32.05\text{ g/mol})}{(1\text{ mol})(32.05\text{ g/mol}) + (1\text{ mol})(58.44\text{ g/mol}) + (1\text{ mol})(18.02\text{ g/mol})} \text{ x } 100\% = 29.5364 = \mathbf{29.54\%\ atom\ economy}$$

3.137 Plan: Convert the mass of ethanol to moles, and use the mole ratio between ethanol and diethyl ether to determine the theoretical yield of diethyl ether. The actual yield divided by the theoretical yield just calculated (with the result multiplied by 100%) gives the percent yield. The difference between the actual and theoretical yields is related to the quantity of ethanol that did not produce diethyl ether, forty-five percent of which produces ethylene instead. Use the mole ratio between ethanol and ethylene to find the mass of ethylene produced by the forty-five percent of ethanol that did not produce diethyl ether.
Solution:
a) The determination of the theoretical yield:
Mass (g) of diethyl ether =

$$(50.0\text{ g } CH_3CH_2OH)\left(\frac{1\text{ mol } CH_3CH_2OH}{46.07\text{ g } CH_3CH_2OH}\right)\left(\frac{1\text{ mol } CH_3CH_2OCH_2CH_3}{2\text{ mol } CH_3CH_2OH}\right)\left(\frac{74.12\text{ g } CH_3CH_2OCH_2CH_3}{1\text{ mol } CH_3CH_2OCH_2CH_3}\right)$$

= 40.2214 g diethyl ether
Determining the percent yield:

$$\text{Percent yield} = \left(\frac{\text{actual Yield}}{\text{theoretical Yield}}\right) \text{ x } 100\% = \left(\frac{35.9\text{ g}}{40.2214\text{ g}}\right) \text{ x } 100\% = 89.2560 = \mathbf{89.3\%\ yield}$$

b) To determine the amount of ethanol not producing diethyl ether, we will use the difference between the theoretical yield and actual yield to determine the amount of diethyl ether that did not form and hence, the amount of ethanol that did not produce the desired product. Forty-five percent of this amount will be used to determine the amount of ethylene formed.
Mass difference = theoretical yield – actual yield = 40.2214 g – 35.9 g = 4.3214 g diethyl ether that did not form
Mass (g) of ethanol not producing diethyl ether =

$$(4.3214\text{ g } CH_3CH_2OCH_2CH_3)\left(\frac{1\text{ mol } CH_3CH_2OCH_2CH_3}{74.12\text{ g } CH_3CH_2OCH_2CH_3}\right)\left(\frac{2\text{ mol} CH_3CH_2OH}{1\text{ mol} CH_3CH_2OCH_2CH_3}\right)\left(\frac{46.07\text{ g } CH_3CH_2OH}{1\text{ mol } CH_3CH_2OH}\right)$$

= 5.37202 g ethanol

$$\text{Mass of ethanol producing ethylene} = (5.37202\text{ g } CH_3CH_2OH)\left(\frac{45.0\%}{100\%}\right) = 2.417409\text{ g ethanol}$$

Mass (g) of ethylene =

$$(2.417409\text{ g } CH_3CH_2OH)\left(\frac{1\text{ mol } CH_3CH_2OH}{46.07\text{ g } CH_3CH_2OH}\right)\left(\frac{1\text{ mol } C_2H_4}{1\text{ mol } CH_3CH_2OH}\right)\left(\frac{28.05\text{ g } C_2H_4}{1\text{ mol } C_2H_4}\right)$$

= 1.47185 = **1.47 g ethylene**

3.139 Plan: For part a), use the given solubility of the salt to find the mass that is soluble in the given volume of water. For part b), convert the mass of dissolved salt in part a) to moles of salt and then to moles of cocaine and then to mass of cocaine. Use the solubility of cocaine to find the volume of water needed to dissolve this mass of cocaine.

Solution:

a) Mass (g) of dissolved salt = $(50.0 \text{ mL } H_2O)\left(\frac{10^{-3} \text{ L } H_2O}{1 \text{ mL } H_2O}\right)\left(\frac{2.50 \text{ kg salt}}{1 \text{ L } H_2O}\right)\left(\frac{10^3 \text{ g}}{1 \text{ kg}}\right)$ = **125 g salt**

b) Moles of dissolved salt = $(125 \text{ g salt})\left(\frac{1 \text{ mol salt}}{339.81 \text{ g salt}}\right)$ = 0.367853 mol salt

Mass (g) cocaine = $(0.367853 \text{ mol salt})\left(\frac{1 \text{ mol cocaine}}{1 \text{ mol salt}}\right)\left(\frac{303.35 \text{ g cocaine}}{1 \text{ mol cocaine}}\right)$ = 111.588 g cocaine

Volume (L) of water needed to dissolve the cocaine = $(111.588 \text{ g cocaine})\left(\frac{1 \text{ L}}{1.70 \text{ g cocaine}}\right)$ = 65.64 L

Additional water needed = total volume needed – original volume of water
= 65.64 L – 0.0500 L = 65.59 = **65.6 L H_2O**

CHAPTER 4 THREE MAJOR CLASSES OF CHEMICAL REACTIONS

FOLLOW–UP PROBLEMS

4.1A Plan: Examine each compound to see what ions, and how many of each, result when the compound is dissolved in water and match one compound's ions to those in the beaker. Use the total moles of particles and the molar ratio in the compound's formula to find moles and then mass of compound.
Solution:

a) $LiBr(s) \xrightarrow{H_2O} Li^+(aq) + Br^-(aq)$

$Cs_2CO_3(s) \xrightarrow{H_2O} 2Cs^+(aq) + CO_3^{2-}(aq)$

$BaCl_2(s) \xrightarrow{H_2O} Ba^{2+}(aq) + 2Cl^-(aq)$

Since the beaker contains +2 ions and twice as many –1 ions, the electrolyte is **$BaCl_2$**.

b) Mass (g) of $BaCl_2$ = $\left(3\ Ba^{2+}\ \text{particles}\right)\left(\frac{0.05\ \text{mol } Ba^{2+}\ \text{ions}}{1\ Ba^{2+}\ \text{particle}}\right)\left(\frac{1\ \text{mol } BaCl_2}{1\ \text{mol } Ba^{2+}\ \text{ions}}\right)\left(\frac{208.2\ \text{g } BaCl_2}{1\ \text{mol } BaCl_2}\right)$

= **31.2 g $BaCl_2$**

4.1B Plan: Write the formula for sodium phosphate and then write a balanced equation showing the ions that result when sodium phosphate is placed in water. Use the balanced equation to determine the number of ions that result when 2 formula units of sodium phosphate are placed in water. The molar ratio from the balanced equation gives the relationship between the moles of sodium phosphate and the moles of ions produced. Use this molar ratio to calculate the moles of ions produced when 0.40 mol of sodium phosphate is placed in water.
Solution:

a) The formula for sodium phosphate is Na_3PO_4. When the compound is placed in water, 4 ions are produced for each formula unit of sodium phosphate: three sodium ions, Na^+, and 1 phosphate ion, PO_4^{3-}.

$Na_3PO_4(s) \xrightarrow{H_2O} 3Na^+(aq) + PO_4^{3-}(aq)$

If two formula units of sodium phosphate are placed in water, twice as many ions should be produced:

$2Na_3PO_4(s) \xrightarrow{H_2O} 6Na^+(aq) + 2PO_4^{3-}(aq)$

Any drawing should include 2 phosphate ions (each with a 3– charge) and 6 sodium ions (each with a 1+ charge).

b) Moles of ions = 0.40 mol Na_3PO_4 $\left(\frac{4\ \text{mol ions}}{1\ \text{mol } Na_3PO_4}\right)$ = **1.6 moles of ions**

4.2A Plan: Write an equation showing the dissociation of one mole of compound into its ions. Use the given information to find the moles of compound; use the molar ratio between moles of compound and moles of ions in the dissociation equation to find moles of ions.
Solution:

a) One mole of $KClO_4$ dissociates to form one mole of potassium ions and one mole of perchlorate ions.

$KClO_4(s) \xrightarrow{H_2O} K^+(aq) + ClO_4^-(aq)$

Therefore, 2 moles of solid $KClO_4$ produce **2 mol of K^+** ions and **2 mol of ClO_4^-** ions.

b) $Mg(C_2H_3O_2)_2(s) \xrightarrow{H_2O} Mg^{2+}(aq) + 2C_2H_3O_2^-(aq)$

First convert grams of $Mg(C_2H_3O_2)_2$ to moles of $Mg(C_2H_3O_2)_2$ and then use molar ratios to determine the moles of each ion produced.

Moles of $Mg(C_2H_3O_2)_2$ = $\left(354\ \text{g } Mg(C_2H_3O_2)_2\right)\left(\frac{1\ \text{mol } Mg(C_2H_3O_2)_2}{142.40\ \text{g } Mg(C_2H_3O_2)_2}\right)$ = 2.48596 mol

The dissolution of 2.48596 mol $Mg(C_2H_3O_2)_2(s)$ produces **2.49 mol Mg^{2+}** and (2 x 2.48596) = **4.97 mol $C_2H_3O_2^-$**

c) $(NH_4)_2CrO_4(s) \xrightarrow{H_2O} 2NH_4^+(aq) + CrO_4^{2-}(aq)$
First convert formula units to moles.

Moles of $(NH_4)_2CrO_4 = \left(1.88 \times 10^{24}\ FU\right)\left(\dfrac{1\ mol\ (NH_4)_2CrO_4}{6.022 \times 10^{23}\ FU}\right) = 3.121886\ mol$

The dissolution of 3.121886 mol $(NH_4)_2CrO_4(s)$ produces (2 x 3.121886) = **6.24 mol NH_4^+** and **3.12 mol CrO_4^{2-}**.

4.2B Plan: Write an equation showing the dissociation of one mole of compound into its ions. Use the given information to find the moles of compound; use the molar ratio between moles of compound and moles of ions in the dissociation equation to find moles of ions.
Solution:
a) One mole of Li_2CO_3 dissociates to form two moles of lithium ions and one mole of carbonate ions.

$$Li_2CO_3(s) \xrightarrow{H_2O} 2Li^+(aq) + CO_3^{2-}(aq)$$

Therefore, 4 moles of solid Li_2CO_3 produce **8 mol of Li^+** ions and **4 mol of CO_3^{2-}** ions.

b) $Fe_2(SO_4)_3(s) \xrightarrow{H_2O} 2Fe^{3+}(aq) + 3SO_4^{2-}(aq)$
First convert grams of $Fe_2(SO_4)_3$ to moles of $Fe_2(SO_4)_3$ and then use molar ratios to determine the moles of each ion produced.

Moles of $Fe_2(SO_4)_3$ = $(112\ g\ Fe_2(SO_4)_3)\left(\dfrac{1\ mol\ Fe_2(SO_4)_3}{399.88\ g\ Fe_2(SO_4)_3}\right) = 0.2801 = 0.280\ mol\ Fe_2(SO_4)_3$

The dissolution of 0.280 mol $Fe_2(SO_4)_3(s)$ produces **0.560 mol Fe^{3+}** (2 x 0.2801) and **0.840 mol SO_4^{2-}** (3 x 0.2801)

c) $Al(NO_3)_3(s) \xrightarrow{H_2O} Al^{3+}(aq) + 3NO_3^-(aq)$
First convert formula units of $Al(NO_3)_3$ to moles of $Al(NO_3)_3$ and then use molar ratios to determine the moles of each ion produced.

Moles of $Al(NO_3)_3$ = $(8.09 \times 10^{22}\ \text{formula units}\ Al(NO_3)_3)\left(\dfrac{1\ mol\ Al(NO_3)_3}{6.022 \times 10^{23}\ \text{formula units}\ Al(NO_3)_3}\right)$

$= 0.1343\ mol\ Al(NO_3)_3$

The dissolution of 0.134 mol $Al(NO_3)_3\ (s)$ produces **0.134 mol Al^{3+}** and **0.403 mol NO_3^-** (3 x 0.1343)

4.3A Plan: Convert the volume from mL to liters. Convert the mass to moles by dividing by the molar mass of KI. Divide the moles by the volume in liters to calculate molarity.
Solution:

Amount (moles) of KI = $6.97\ g\ KI\left(\dfrac{1\ mol\ KI}{166.0\ g\ KI}\right) = 0.0420\ mol\ KI$

$$M = \left(\frac{0.0420\ mol\ KI}{100.\ mL}\right)\left(\frac{1000\ mL}{1\ L}\right) = \mathbf{0.420}\ \boldsymbol{M}$$

4.3B Plan: Convert the volume from mL to liters. Convert the mass to moles by first converting mg to g and then dividing by the molar mass of $NaNO_3$. Divide the moles by the volume in liters to calculate molarity.
Solution:

Amount (moles) of $NaNO_3$ = $175\ mg\ NaNO_3\left(\dfrac{1\ g}{1000\ mg}\right)\left(\dfrac{1\ mol\ NaNO_3}{85.00\ g\ NaNO_3}\right) = 0.00206\ mol\ NaNO_3$

$$M = \left(\frac{0.00206\ mol\ NaNO_3}{15.0\ mL}\right)\left(\frac{1000\ mL}{1\ L}\right) = \mathbf{0.137}\ \boldsymbol{M}$$

4.4A Plan: Divide the mass of sucrose by its molar mass to change the grams to moles. Divide the moles of sucrose by the molarity to obtain the volume of solution.

Solution:
Volume (L) of solution =

$$(135\text{ g } C_{12}H_{22}O_{11})\left(\frac{1\text{ mol } C_{12}H_{22}O_{11}}{342.30\text{ g } C_{12}H_{22}O_{11}}\right)\left(\frac{1\text{ L}}{3.30\text{ mol } C_{12}H_{22}O_{11}}\right) = 0.11951 = \mathbf{0.120\ L}$$

Road map:

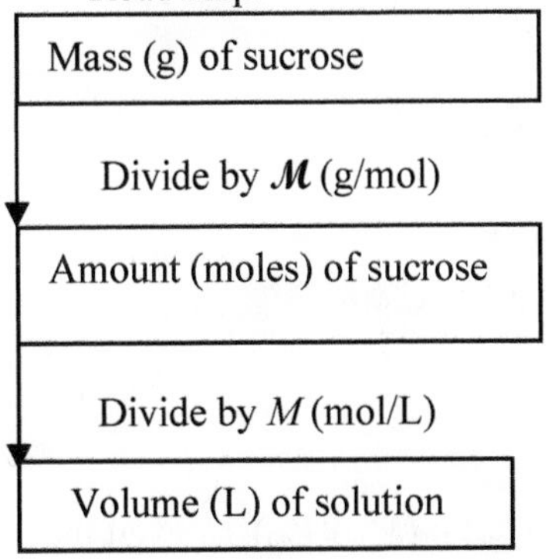

Mass (g) of sucrose

↓ Divide by $\mathcal{M}$ (g/mol)

Amount (moles) of sucrose

↓ Divide by M (mol/L)

Volume (L) of solution

4.4B Plan: Convert the volume from mL to L; then multiply by the molarity of the solution to obtain the moles of H_2SO_4.
Solution:

$$\text{Amount (mol) of } H_2SO_4 = 40.5\text{ mL } H_2SO_4\left(\frac{1\text{ L}}{1000\text{ mL}}\right)\left(\frac{0.128\text{ mol } H_2SO_4}{1\text{ L}}\right) = \mathbf{0.00518\ mol\ H_2SO_4}$$

Road map:

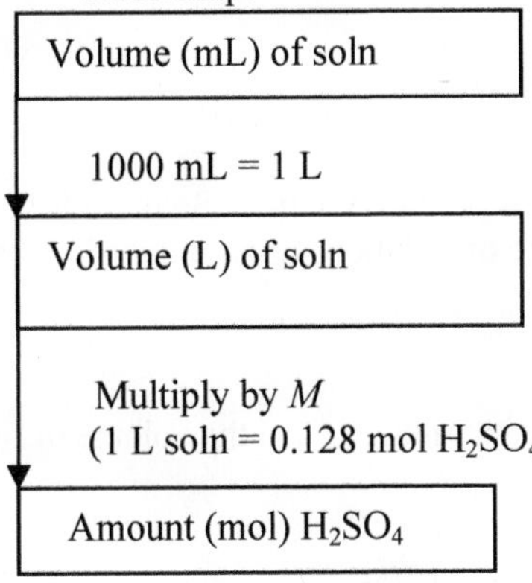

Volume (mL) of soln

↓ 1000 mL = 1 L

Volume (L) of soln

↓ Multiply by M
(1 L soln = 0.128 mol H_2SO_4)

Amount (mol) H_2SO_4

4.5A Plan: Multiply the volume and molarity to calculate the number of moles of sodium phosphate in the solution. Write the formula of sodium phosphate. Determine the number of each type of ion that is included in each formula unit. Use this information to determine the amount of each type of ion in the described solution.
Solution:

$$\text{Amount (mol) of } Na_3PO_4 = 1.32\text{ L}\left(\frac{0.55\text{ mol } Na_3PO_4}{1\text{ L}}\right) = 0.7260 = 0.73\text{ mol } Na_3PO_4$$

In each formula unit of Na_3PO_4, there are 3 Na^+ ions and 1 PO_4^{3-} ion.

$$\text{Amount (mol) of } Na^+ = 0.73\text{ mol } Na_3PO_4\left(\frac{3\text{ mol } Na^+}{1\text{ mol } Na_3PO_4}\right) = \mathbf{2.2\ mol\ Na^+}$$

$$\text{Amount (mol) of } PO_4^{3-} = 0.73\text{ mol } Na_3PO_4\left(\frac{1\text{ mol } PO_4^{3-}}{1\text{ mol } Na_3PO_4}\right) = \mathbf{0.73\ mol\ PO_4^{3-}}$$

4.5B Plan: Write the formula of aluminum sulfate. Determine the number of aluminum ions in each formula unit. Calculate the number of aluminum ions in the sample of aluminum sulfate. Convert the volume from mL to L. Divide the number of moles of aluminum ion by the volume in L to calculate the molarity of the solution.
Solution:
In each formula unit of $Al_2(SO_4)_3$, there are 2 Al^{3+} ions.

$$\text{Amount (mol) of } Al^{3+} = 1.25 \text{ mol } Al_2(SO_4)_3 \left(\frac{2 \text{ mol } Al^{3+}}{1 \text{ mol } Al_2(SO_4)_3}\right) = 2.50 \text{ mol } Al^{3+}$$

$$M = \left(\frac{2.50 \text{ mol } Al^{3+}}{875 \text{ mL}}\right)\left(\frac{1000 \text{ mL}}{1 \text{ L}}\right) = \mathbf{2.86}\ \boldsymbol{M}$$

4.6A Plan: Determine the new volume from the dilution equation $(M_{conc})(V_{conc}) = (M_{dil})(V_{dil})$.
Solution:

$$V_{dil} = \frac{M_{conc}V_{conc}}{M_{dil}} = \frac{(4.50\ M)(60.0 \text{ mL})}{(1.25\ M)} = \mathbf{216 \text{ mL}}$$

4.6B Plan: Determine the new concentration from the dilution equation $(M_{conc})(V_{conc}) = (M_{dil})(V_{dil})$. Convert the molarity (mol/L) to g/mL in two steps (one step is moles to grams, and the other step is L to mL).
Solution:

$$M_{dil} = \frac{M_{conc}V_{conc}}{V_{dil}} = \frac{(7.50\ M)(25.0 \text{ m}^3)}{500. \text{m}^3} = 0.375\ M$$

$$\text{Concentration (g/mL)} = \left(\frac{0.375 \text{ mol } H_2SO_4}{1 \text{ L}}\right)\left(\frac{98.08 \text{ g } H_2SO_4}{1 \text{ mol } H_2SO_4}\right)\left(\frac{10^{-3} \text{ L}}{1 \text{ mL}}\right)$$

$$= 0.036780 = \mathbf{3.68x10^{-2} \text{ g/mL}} \text{ solution}$$

4.7A Plan: Count the number of particles in each solution per unit volume.
Solution:
Solution A has 6 particles per unit volume while Solution B has 12 particles per unit volume. Solution B is more concentrated than Solution A. To obtain Solution B, the total volume of Solution A was reduced by half:

$$V_{conc} = \frac{N_{dil}V_{dil}}{N_{conc}} = \frac{(6 \text{ particles})(1.0 \text{ mL})}{(12 \text{ particles})} = 0.50 \text{ mL}$$

Solution C has 4 particles and is thus more dilute than Solution A. To obtain Solution C, ½ the volume of solvent must be added for every volume of Solution A:

$$V_{dil} = \frac{N_{conc}V_{conc}}{N_{dil}} = \frac{(6 \text{ particles})(1.0 \text{ mL})}{(4 \text{ particles})} = 1.5 \text{ mL}$$

4.7B Plan: Count the number of particles in each solution per unit volume. Determine the final volume of the solution. Use the dilution equation, $(N_{conc})(V_{conc}) = (N_{dil})(V_{dil})$, to determine the number of particles that will be present when 300. mL of solvent is added to the 100. mL of solution represented in circle A. (Because M is directly proportional to the number of particles in a given solution, we can replace the molarity terms in the dilution equation with terms representing the number of particles.)
Solution:
There are 12 particles in circle A, 3 particles in circle B, 4 particles in circle C, and 6 particles in circle D. The concentrated solution (circle A) has a volume of 100. mL. 300. mL of solvent are added, so the volume of the diluted solution is 400. mL.

$$N_{dil} = \frac{N_{conc}V_{conc}}{V_{dil}} = \frac{(12 \text{ particles})(100.0 \text{ mL})}{(400. \text{ mL})} = 3 \text{ particles}$$

There are 3 particles in circle B, so **circle B** represents the diluted solution.

4.8A Plan: Determine the ions present in each substance on the reactant side and write new cation-anion combinations. Use Table 4.1 to determine if either of the combinations of ions is not soluble. If a precipitate forms there will be a reaction and chemical equations may be written. The molecular equation simply includes the formulas of the substances and balancing. In the total ionic equation, all soluble substances are written as separate ions. The net ionic equation comes from the total ionic equation by eliminating all substances appearing in identical form (spectator ions) on each side of the reaction arrow.

<u>Solution:</u>

a) The resulting ion combinations that are possible are iron(III) phosphate and cesium chloride. According to Table 4.1, iron(III) phosphate is insoluble, so a reaction occurs. We see that cesium chloride is soluble.

Total ionic equation:

$$Fe^{3+}(aq) + 3Cl^-(aq) + 3Cs^+(aq) + PO_4^{3-}(aq) \rightarrow FePO_4(s) + 3Cl^-(aq) + 3Cs^+(aq)$$

Net ionic equation:

$$Fe^{3+}(aq) + PO_4^{3-}(aq) \rightarrow FePO_4(s)$$

b) The resulting ion combinations that are possible are sodium nitrate (soluble) and cadmium hydroxide (insoluble). A reaction occurs.

Total ionic equation:

$$2Na^+(aq) + 2OH^-(aq) + Cd^{2+}(aq) + 2NO_3^-(aq) \rightarrow Cd(OH)_2(s) + 2Na^+(aq) + 2NO_3^-(aq)$$

Note: The coefficients for Na^+ and OH^- are necessary to balance the reaction and must be included.

Net ionic equation:

$$Cd^{2+}(aq) + 2OH^-(aq) \rightarrow Cd(OH)_2(s)$$

c) The resulting ion combinations that are possible are magnesium acetate (soluble) and potassium bromide (soluble). No reaction occurs.

4.8B <u>Plan:</u> Determine the ions present in each substance on the reactant side and write new cation-anion combinations. Use Table 4.1 to determine if either of the combinations of ions is not soluble. If a precipitate forms there will be a reaction and chemical equations may be written. The molecular equation simply includes the formulas of the substances and balancing. In the total ionic equation, all soluble substances are written as separate ions. The net ionic equation comes from the total ionic equation by eliminating all substances appearing in identical form (spectator ions) on each side of the reaction arrow.

<u>Solution:</u>

a) The resulting ion combinations that are possible are silver chloride (insoluble, an exception) and barium nitrate (soluble). A reaction occurs.

Total ionic equation:

$$2Ag^+(aq) + 2NO_3^-(aq) + Ba^{2+}(aq) + 2Cl^-(aq) \rightarrow 2AgCl(s) + Ba^{2+}(aq) + 2NO_3^-(aq)$$

Net ionic equation:

$$Ag^+(aq) + Cl^-(aq) \rightarrow AgCl(s)$$

b) The resulting ion combinations that are possible are ammonium sulfide (soluble) and potassium carbonate (soluble). No reaction occurs.

c) The resulting ion combinations that are possible are lead(II) sulfate (insoluble, an exception) and nickel(II) nitrate (soluble). A reaction occurs.

Total ionic equation:

$$Ni^{2+}(aq) + SO_4^{2-}(aq) + Pb^{2+}(aq) + 2NO_3^-(aq) \rightarrow PbSO_4(s) + Ni^{2+}(aq) + 2NO_3^-(aq)$$

Net ionic equation:

$$Pb^{2+}(aq) + SO_4^{2-}(aq) \rightarrow PbSO_4\ (s)$$

4.9A <u>Plan:</u> Look at the ions (number and charge) produced when each of the given compounds dissolves in water and find the match to the ions shown in the beaker. Once the ions in each beaker are known, write new cation-anion combinations and use Table 4.1 to determine if any of the combination of ions is not soluble. If a precipitate forms there will be a reaction and chemical equations may be written. The molecular equation simply includes the formulas of the substances and must be balanced. In the total ionic equation, all soluble substances are written as separate ions. The net ionic equation comes from the total ionic equation by eliminating all substances appearing in identical form (spectator ions) on each side of the reaction arrow.

<u>Solution:</u>

a) Beaker A has four ions with a +2 charge and eight ions with a –1 charge. The beaker contains dissolved $\mathbf{Zn(NO_3)_2}$ which dissolves to produce Zn^{2+} and NO_3^- ions in a 1:2 ratio. The compound $PbCl_2$ also has a +2 ion and –1 ion in a 1:2 ratio but $PbCl_2$ is insoluble so ions would not result from this compound.

b) Beaker B has three ions with a +2 charge and six ions with a –1 charge. The beaker contains dissolved **$Ba(OH)_2$** which dissolves to produce Ba^{2+} and OH^- ions in a 1:2 ratio. $Cd(OH)_2$ also has a +2 ion and a –1 ion in a 1:2 ratio but $Cd(OH)_2$ is insoluble so ions would not result from this compound.
c) The resulting ion combinations that are possible are zinc hydroxide (insoluble) and barium nitrate (soluble). The precipitate formed is **$Zn(OH)_2$**. The spectator ions are **Ba^{2+} and NO_3^-**.
Balanced molecular equation: $Zn(NO_3)_2(aq) + Ba(OH)_2(aq) \rightarrow Zn(OH)_2(s) + Ba(NO_3)_2(aq)$
Total ionic equation:
$Zn^{2+}(aq) + 2NO_3^-(aq) + Ba^{2+}(aq) + 2OH^-(aq) \rightarrow Zn(OH)_2(s) + Ba^{2+}(aq) + 2NO_3^-(aq)$
Net ionic equation:

$$Zn^{2+}(aq) + 2OH^-(aq) \rightarrow Zn(OH)_2(s)$$

d) Since there are only six OH^- ions and four Zn^{2+} ions, the OH^- is the limiting reactant.

$$\text{Mass of } Zn(OH)_2 = (6\ OH^-\ \text{ions}) \left(\frac{0.050\ \text{mol}\ OH^-}{1\ OH^-\ \text{particle}}\right) \left(\frac{1\ \text{mol}\ Zn(OH)_2}{2\ \text{mol}\ OH^-}\right) \left(\frac{99.40\ \text{g}\ Zn(OH)_2}{1\ \text{mol}\ Zn(OH)_2}\right)$$

$= 14.9100 =$ **15 g $Zn(OH)_2$**

4.9B Plan: Look at the ions (number and charge) produced when each of the given compounds dissolves in water and find the match to the ions shown in the beaker. Once the ions in each beaker are known, write new cation-anion combinations and use Table 4.1 to determine if any of the combination of ions is not soluble. If a precipitate forms there will be a reaction and chemical equations may be written. The molecular equation simply includes the formulas of the substances and must be balanced. In the total ionic equation, all soluble substances are written as separate ions. The net ionic equation comes from the total ionic equation by eliminating all substances appearing in identical form (spectator ions) on each side of the reaction arrow.
Solution:
a) Beaker A has eight ions with a +1 charge and four ions with a –2 charge. The beaker contains dissolved **Li_2CO_3** which dissolves to produce Li^+ and CO_3^{2-} ions in a 2:1 ratio. The compound Ag_2SO_4 also has a +1 ion and –2 ion in a 2:1 ratio but Ag_2SO_4 is insoluble so ions would not result from this compound.
b) Beaker B has three ions with a +2 charge and six ions with a –1 charge. The beaker contains dissolved **$CaCl_2$** which dissolves to produce Ca^{2+} and Cl^- ions in a 1:2 ratio. $Ni(OH)_2$ also has a +2 ion and a –1 ion in a 1:2 ratio but $Cd(OH)_2$ is insoluble so ions would not result from this compound.
c) The resulting ion combinations that are possible are calcium carbonate (insoluble) and lithium chloride (soluble). The precipitate formed is **$CaCO_3$**. The spectator ions are **Li^+ and Cl^-**.
Balanced molecular equation: $Li_2CO_3(aq) + CaCl_2(aq) \rightarrow CaCO_3(s) + 2LiCl(aq)$
Total ionic equation:

$$2Li^+(aq) + CO_3^{2-}(aq) + Ca^{2+}(aq) + 2Cl^-(aq) \rightarrow CaCO_3(s) + 2Li^+(aq) + 2Cl^-(aq)$$

Net ionic equation:

$$Ca^{2+}(aq) + CO_3^{2-}(aq) \rightarrow CaCO_3(s)$$

d) Since there are only four CO_3^{2-} ions and three Ca^{2+} ions, the Ca^{2+} is the limiting reactant.

$$\text{Mass of } CaCO_3 = (3\ Ca^{2+}\ \text{ions}) \left(\frac{0.20\ \text{mol}\ Ca^{2+}}{1\ Ca^{2+}\ \text{particle}}\right) \left(\frac{1\ \text{mol}\ CaCO_3}{1\ \text{mol}\ Ca^{2+}}\right) \left(\frac{100.09\ \text{g}\ CaCO_3}{1\ \text{mol}\ CaCO_3}\right) = 60.0540 = \mathbf{60.\ g\ CaCO_3}$$

4.10A Plan: We are given the molarity and volume of calcium chloride solution, and we must find the volume of sodium phosphate solution that will react with this amount of calcium chloride. After writing the balanced equation, we find the amount (mol) of calcium chloride from its molarity and volume and use the molar ratio to find the amount (mol) of sodium phosphate required to react with the calcium chloride. Finally, we use the molarity of the sodium phosphate solution to convert the amount (mol) of sodium phosphate to volume (L).
Solution:
The balanced equation is: $3CaCl_2(aq) + 2Na_3PO_4(aq) \rightarrow Ca_3(PO_4)_2(s) + 6NaCl(aq)$
Finding the volume (L) of Na_3PO_4 needed to react with the $CaCl_2$:

$$\text{Volume (L) of } Na_3PO_4 = 0.300\ \text{L}\ CaCl_2 \left(\frac{0.175\ \text{moles}\ CaCl_2}{1\ \text{L}}\right) \left(\frac{2\ \text{mol}\ Na_3PO_4}{3\ \text{mol}\ CaCl_2}\right) \left(\frac{1\ \text{L}}{0.260\ \text{mol}\ Na_3PO_4}\right)$$

$= 0.1346 =$ **0.135 L Na_3PO_4**

4.10B Plan: We are given the mass of silver chloride produced in the reaction of silver nitrate and sodium chloride, and we must find the molarity of the silver nitrate solution. After writing the balanced equation, we find the amount (mol) of silver nitrate that produces the precipitate by dividing the mass of silver chloride produced by its molar mass and then using the molar ratios from the balanced equation. Then we calculate the molarity by dividing the moles of silver nitrate by the volume of the solution (in L).

Solution:

The balanced equation is: $AgNO_3(aq) + NaCl(aq) \rightarrow AgCl(s) + NaNO_3(aq)$

Amount (mol) of $AgNO_3 = 0.148 \text{ g AgCl}\left(\frac{1 \text{ mol AgCl}}{143.4 \text{ g AgCl}}\right)\left(\frac{1 \text{ mol } AgNO_3}{1 \text{ mol AgCl}}\right) = 0.001032 = 1.03\text{x}10^{-3} \text{ mol } AgNO_3$

Molarity (M) of $AgNO_3 = \left(\frac{1.03 \text{ x } 10^{-3} \text{mol } AgNO_3}{45.0 \text{ mL}}\right)\left(\frac{1000 \text{ mL}}{1 \text{ L}}\right) = \mathbf{2.29 \text{ x } 10^{-2}}\ \boldsymbol{M}$

4.11A Plan: Multiply the volume in liters of each solution by its molarity to obtain the moles of each reactant. Write a balanced equation. Use molar ratios from the balanced equation to determine the moles of lead(II) chloride that may be produced from each reactant. The reactant that generates the smaller number of moles is limiting. Change the moles of lead(II) chloride from the limiting reactant to the grams of product using the molar mass of lead(II) chloride.

Solution:

(a)The balanced equation is:

$$Pb(C_2H_3O_2)_2(aq) + 2NaCl(aq) \rightarrow PbCl_2(s) + 2NaC_2H_3O_2(aq)$$

Moles of $Pb(C_2H_3O_2)_2 = (268 \text{ mL})\left(\frac{10^{-3} \text{L}}{1 \text{ mL}}\right)\left(\frac{1.50 \text{ mol } Pb(C_2H_3O_2)_2}{1 \text{ L}}\right) = 0.402 \text{ mol } Pb(C_2H_3O_2)_2$

Moles of NaCl $= (130 \text{ mL})\left(\frac{10^{-3} \text{L}}{1 \text{ mL}}\right)\left(\frac{3.40 \text{ mol NaCl}}{1 \text{ L}}\right) = 0.442 \text{ mol NaCl}$

Moles of $PbCl_2$ from $Pb(C_2H_3O_2)_2 = (0.402 \text{ mol } Pb(C_2H_3O_2)_2)\left(\frac{1 \text{ mol } PbCl_2}{1 \text{ mol } Pb(C_2H_3O_2)_2}\right)$

$= 0.402 \text{ mol } PbCl_2$

Moles of $PbCl_2$ from NaCl $= (0.442 \text{ mol NaCl})\left(\frac{1 \text{ mol } PbCl_2}{2 \text{ mol NaCl}}\right) = 0.221 \text{ mol } PbCl_2$

The NaCl is limiting. The mass of $PbCl_2$ may now be determined using the molar mass.

Mass (g) of $PbCl_2 = (0.221 \text{ mol } PbCl_2)\left(\frac{278.1 \text{ g } PbCl_2}{1 \text{ mol } PbCl_2}\right) = 61.4601 = \mathbf{61.5 \text{ g } PbCl_2}$

(b) Ac is used to represent $C_2H_3O_2$:

Amount (mol)	$Pb(Ac)_2$	+	2NaCl	$\rightarrow$	$PbCl_2$	+	2NaAc
Initial	0.402		0.442		0		0
Change	– 0.221		– 0.442		+0.221		+0.442
Final	0.181		0		0.221		0.442

4.11B Plan: Write a balanced equation. Multiply the volume in liters of each solution by its molarity to obtain the moles of each reactant. Use molar ratios from the balanced equation and the molar mass of iron(III) hydroxide to determine the mass (g) of iron(III) hydroxide that may be produced from each reactant. The smaller mass is the amount of product actually made.

Solution:

(a)The balanced equation is: $FeCl_3(aq) + 3NaOH(aq) \rightarrow 3NaCl(aq) + Fe(OH)_3(s)$

Mass(g) of $Fe(OH)_3$ produced from $FeCl_3$ =

$$155 \text{ mL } FeCl_3\left(\frac{1 \text{ L}}{1000 \text{ mL}}\right)\left(\frac{0.250 \text{ mol } FeCl_3}{1 \text{ L}}\right)\left(\frac{1 \text{ mol mol } Fe(OH)_3}{1 \text{ mol } FeCl_3}\right)\left(\frac{106.87 \text{ g } Fe(OH)_3}{1 \text{ mol mol } Fe(OH)_3}\right) = 4.14 \text{ g } Fe(OH)_3$$

Mass(g) of $Fe(OH)_3$ produced from NaOH =

$$215 \text{ mL NaOH}\left(\frac{1 \text{ L}}{1000 \text{ mL}}\right)\left(\frac{0.300 \text{ mol NaOH}}{1 \text{ L}}\right)\left(\frac{1 \text{ mol mol } Fe(OH)_3}{3 \text{ mol NaOH}}\right)\left(\frac{106.87 \text{ g } Fe(OH)_3}{1 \text{ mol mol } Fe(OH)_3}\right) = 2.30 \text{ g } Fe(OH)_3$$

NaOH produces the smaller amount of product, so it is the limiting reagent and **2.30 g** of $Fe(OH)_3$ are produced.

(b) To complete the reaction table, we need the moles of $FeCl_3$ and NaOH that react. Remember that NaOH is the limiting reagent and will be consumed in this reaction.
Amount (mol) of $FeCl_3$ =

$$155\ \text{mL FeCl}_3 \left(\frac{1\ \text{L}}{1000\ \text{mL}}\right)\left(\frac{0.250\ \text{mol FeCl}_3}{1\ \text{L}}\right) = 0.0388\ \text{mol FeCl}_3$$

Amount (mol) of NaOH =

$$215\ \text{mL NaOH} \left(\frac{1\ \text{L}}{1000\ \text{mL}}\right)\left(\frac{0.300\ \text{mol NaOH}}{1\ \text{L}}\right) = 0.0645\ \text{mol NaOH}$$

Amount (mol)	$FeCl_3$	+	3NaOH	→	3NaCl	+	$Fe(OH)_3$
Initial	0.0388		0.0645		0		0
Change	− 0.0215		−0.0645		+0.0645		+0.0215
Final	0.0173		0		0.0645		0.0215

4.12A Plan: Convert the given volume from mL to L and multiply by the molarity (mol/L) to find moles of KOH. Each mole of the strong base KOH will produce one mole of hydroxide ions. Finally, multiply the amount (mol) of hydroxide ions by Avogadro's number to calculate the number of hydroxide ions produced.
Solution:

$$\text{KOH}(s) \xrightarrow{H_2O} \text{K}^+(aq) + \text{OH}^-(aq)$$

$$\text{No. of OH}^- \text{ ions} = 451\ \text{mL NaOH}\left(\frac{1\ \text{L}}{1000\ \text{mL}}\right)\left(\frac{1.20\ \text{mole KOH}}{1\ \text{L}}\right)\left(\frac{1\ \text{mol OH}^-}{1\ \text{mole KOH}}\right)\left(\frac{6.022 \times 10^{23}\ \text{OH}^-\ \text{ions}}{1\ \text{mole OH}^-}\right)$$
$$= 3.2591 \times 10^{23} = \mathbf{3.26 \times 10^{23}\ OH^-\ ions}$$

4.12B Plan: Convert the given volume from mL to L and multiply by the molarity (mol/L) to find moles of HCl. Each mole of the strong acid HCl will produce one mole of hydrogen ions. Finally, multiply the amount (mol) of hydrogen ions by Avogadro's number to calculate the number of hydrogen ions produced.
Solution:

$$\text{HCl}(g) \xrightarrow{H_2O} \text{H}^+(aq) + \text{Cl}^-(aq)$$

$$\text{No. of H}^+ \text{ ions} = 65.5\ \text{mL HCl}\left(\frac{1\ \text{L}}{1000\ \text{mL}}\right)\left(\frac{0.722\ \text{mole HCl}}{1\ \text{L}}\right)\left(\frac{1\ \text{mol H}^+}{1\ \text{mole HCl}}\right)\left(\frac{6.022 \times 10^{23}\ \text{H}^+\ \text{ions}}{1\ \text{mole H}^+}\right)$$
$$= 2.8479 \times 10^{22} = \mathbf{2.85 \times 10^{22}\ H^+\ ions}$$

4.13A Plan: According to Table 4.2, both reactants are strong and therefore completely dissociate in water. Thus, the key reaction is the formation of water. The other product of the reaction is soluble.
Solution:
Molecular equation: $2HNO_3(aq) + Ca(OH)_2(aq) \rightarrow Ca(NO_3)_2(aq) + 2H_2O(l)$
Total ionic equation:
$2H^+(aq) + 2NO_3^-(aq) + Ca^{2+}(aq) + 2OH^-(aq) \rightarrow Ca^{2+}(aq) + 2NO_3^-(aq) + 2H_2O(l)$
Net ionic equation: $2H^+(aq) + 2OH^-(aq) \rightarrow 2H_2O(l)$ which simplifies to $\mathbf{H^+(aq) + OH^-(aq) \rightarrow H_2O(l)}$

4.13B Plan: According to Table 4.2, both reactants are strong and therefore completely dissociate in water. Thus, the key reaction is the formation of water. The other product of the reaction is soluble.
Solution:
Molecular equation: $HI(aq) + LiOH(aq) \rightarrow LiI(aq) + H_2O(l)$
Total ionic equation: $H^+(aq) + I^-(aq) + Li^+(aq) + OH^-(aq) \rightarrow Li^+(aq) + I^-(aq) + H_2O(l)$
Net ionic equation: $\mathbf{H^+(aq) + OH^-(aq) \rightarrow H_2O(l)}$

4.14A Plan: The reactants are a weak acid and a strong base. The acidic species is H^+ and a proton is transferred to OH^- from the acid. The only spectator ion is the cation of the base.

Solution:
Molecular equation: $2HNO_2(aq)$ + $Sr(OH)_2(aq) \rightarrow Sr(NO_2)_2(aq)$ + $2H_2O(l)$Ionic equation: $2HNO_2(aq)$ + $Sr^{2+}(aq)$ + $2OH^-(aq) \rightarrow$ $Sr^{2+}(aq)$ + $2NO_2^-(aq) + 2H_2O(l)$
Net ionic equation: $2HNO_2(aq)$ + $2OH^-(aq) \rightarrow$ $2NO_2^-(aq) + 2H_2O(l)$
or **$HNO_2(aq)$ + $OH^-(aq) \rightarrow$ $NO_2^-(aq) + H_2O(l)$**

$HNO_2(aq)$ + $OH^-(aq) \longrightarrow$ $NO_2^-(aq) + H_2O(l)$
The salt is **$Sr(NO_2)_2$, strontium nitrite**, and the spectator ion is **Sr^{2+}**.

4.14B Plan: The reactants are a strong acid and the salt of a weak base. The acidic species is H_3O^+ and a proton is transferred to the weak base HCO_3^- to form H_2CO_3, which then decomposes to form CO_2 and water.
Solution:
Molecular equation:
$2HBr(aq)$ + $Ca(HCO_3)_2(aq) \rightarrow CaBr_2(aq)$ + $2H_2CO_3(aq)$
Ionic equation:
$2H_3O^+(aq)$ + $2Br^-(aq) + Ca^{2+}(aq)$ + $2HCO_3^-(aq) \rightarrow$ $2CO_2(g)$ + $4H_2O(l)$ + $2Br^-(aq)$ + $Ca^{2+}(aq)$
Net ionic equation:
$2H_3O^+(aq)$ + $2HCO_3^-(aq) \rightarrow 2CO_2(g)$ + $4H_2O(l)$ or **$H_3O^+(aq)$ + $HCO_3^-(aq) \rightarrow CO_2(g)$ + $2H_2O(l)$**

$H_3O^+(aq)$ + $HCO_3^-(aq) \longrightarrow$ $CO_2(g) + 2H_2O(l)$
The salt is **$CaBr_2$, calcium bromide.**

4.15A Plan: Write a balanced equation. Determine the moles of HCl by multiplying its molarity by its volume, and, through the balanced chemical equation and the molar mass of aluminum hydroxide, determine the mass of aluminum hydroxide required for the reaction.
Solution:
The balanced equation is: $Al(OH)_3(s) + 3HCl(aq) \rightarrow AlCl_3(aq) + 3H_2O(l)$

$$\text{Mass(g) of } Al(OH)_3 = 3.4 \times 10^{-2} \text{ L HCl} \left(\frac{0.10 \text{ mol HCl}}{1 \text{ L}}\right)\left(\frac{1 \text{ mol } Al(OH)_3}{3 \text{ mol HCl}}\right)\left(\frac{78.00 \text{ g } Al(OH)_3}{1 \text{ mol } Al(OH)_3}\right)$$
$$= 0.08840 = \mathbf{0.088 \text{ g } Al(OH)_3}$$

4.15B Plan: Write a balanced equation. Determine the moles of NaOH by multiplying its molarity by its volume, and, through the balanced chemical equation and the molar mass of acetylsalicylic acid, determine the mass of acetylsalicylic acid in the tablet.
Solution:
The balanced equation is: $HC_9H_7O_4(aq) + NaOH(aq) \rightarrow NaC_9H_7O_4(aq) + H_2O(l)$

$$\text{Mass(g) of } HC_9H_7O_4 = 14.10 \text{ mL NaOH} \left(\frac{1 \text{ L}}{1000 \text{ mL}}\right)\left(\frac{0.128 \text{ mol NaOH}}{1 \text{ L}}\right)\left(\frac{1 \text{ mol } HC_9H_7O_4}{1 \text{ mol NaOH}}\right)\left(\frac{180.15 \text{ g } HC_9H_7O_4}{1 \text{ mol } HC_9H_7O_4}\right)$$
$$= 0.3251 = \mathbf{0.325 \text{ g } HC_9H_7O_4}$$

4.16A Plan: Write a balanced chemical equation. Determine the moles of HCl by multiplying its molarity by its volume, and, through the balanced chemical equation, determine the moles of $Ba(OH)_2$ required for the reaction. The amount of base in moles is divided by its molarity to find the volume.
Solution:
The molarity of the HCl solution is 0.1016 *M*. However, the molar ratio is not 1:1 as in the example problem. According to the balanced equation, the ratio is 2 moles of acid per 1 mole of base:
$2HCl(aq) + Ba(OH)_2(aq) \rightarrow BaCl_2(aq) + 2H_2O(l)$

$$\text{Volume (L) of } Ba(OH)_2 = (50.00 \text{ mL})\left(\frac{10^{-3} \text{L}}{1 \text{ mL}}\right)\left(\frac{0.1016 \text{ mol HCl}}{\text{L}}\right)\left(\frac{1 \text{ mol } Ba(OH)_2}{2 \text{ mol HCl}}\right)\left(\frac{\text{L}}{0.1292 \text{ mol } Ba(OH)_2}\right)$$
$$= 0.0196594 = \mathbf{0.01966 \text{ L } Ba(OH)_2 \text{ solution}}$$

4.16B Plan: Write a balanced chemical equation. Determine the moles of H_2SO_4 by multiplying its molarity by its volume, and, through the balanced chemical equation, determine the moles of KOH required for the reaction. The amount of base in moles is divided by its volume (in L) to find the molarity.
Solution:
The balanced equation is: $2KOH(aq) + H_2SO_4(aq) \rightarrow K_2SO_4(aq) + 2H_2O(l)$

Amount (mol) of KOH = 20.00 mL H_2SO_4 $\left(\frac{1\ L}{1000\ mL}\right)\left(\frac{0.2452\ mol\ H_2SO_4}{1\ L}\right)\left(\frac{2\ mol\ KOH}{1\ mol\ H_2SO_4}\right)$ = 0.009808 mol KOH

Molarity = $\left(\frac{0.009808\ mol\ KOH}{18.15\ mL}\right)\left(\frac{1000\ mL}{1\ L}\right)$ = **0.5404 *M***

4.17A Plan: Apply Table 4.4 to the compounds. Do not forget that the sum of the O.N.'s (oxidation numbers) for a compound must sum to zero, and for a polyatomic ion, the sum must equal the charge on the ion.
Solution:
a) **Sc = +3 O = –2** In most compounds, oxygen has a –2 O.N., so oxygen is often a good starting point. If each oxygen atom has a –2 O.N., then each scandium must have a +3 oxidation state so that the sum of O.N.'s equals zero: 2(+3) + 3(–2) = 0.
b) **Ga = +3 Cl = –1** In most compounds, chlorine has a –1 O.N., so chlorine is a good starting point. If each chlorine atom has a –1 O.N., then the gallium must have a +3 oxidation state so that the sum of O.N.'s equals zero: 1(+3) + 3(–1) = 0.
c) **H = +1 P = +5 O = –2** The hydrogen phosphate ion is HPO_4^{2-}. Again, oxygen has a –2 O.N. Hydrogen has a +1 O.N. because it is combined with nonmetals. The sum of the O.N.'s must equal the ionic charge, so the following algebraic equation can be solved for P: 1(+1) + 1(P) + 4(–2) = –2; O.N. for P = +5.
d) **I = +3 F = –1** The formula of iodine trifluoride is IF_3. In all compounds, fluorine has a –1 O.N., so fluorine is often a good starting point. If each fluorine atom has a –1 O.N., then the iodine must have a +3 oxidation state so that the sum of O.N.'s equal zero: 1(+3) + 3(–1) = 0.

4.17B Plan: Apply Table 4.4 to the compounds. Do not forget that the sum of the O.N.'s (oxidation numbers) for a compound must sum to zero, and for a polyatomic ion, the sum must equal the charge on the ion.
Solution:
a) **K = +1 C = +4 O = –2** In all compounds, potassium has a +1 O.N, and in most compounds, oxygen has a –2 O.N. If each potassium has a +1 O.N. and each oxygen has a –2 O.N., carbon must have a +4 oxidation state so that the sum of the O.N.'s equals zero: 2(+1) + 1(+4) + 3(–2) = 0.
b) **N = –3 H = +1** When it is combined with a nonmetal, like N, hydrogen has a +1 O.N. If hydrogen has a +1 O.N., nitrogen must have a –3 O.N. so the sum of the O.N.'s equals +1, the charge on the polyatomic ion: 1(–3) + 4(+1) = +1.
c) **Ca = +2 P = –3** Calcium, a group 2A metal, has a +2 O.N. in all compounds. If calcium has a +2 O.N., the phosphorus must have a –3 O.N. so the sum of the O.N.'s equals zero: 3(+2) + 2(–3) = 0.
d) **S = +4 Cl = –1** Chlorine, a group 7A nonmetal, has a –1 O.N. when it is in combination with any nonmetal except O or other halogens lower in the group. If chlorine has an O.N. of –1, the sulfur must have an O.N. of +4 so that the sum of the O.N.'s equals zero: 1(+4) + 4(–1) = 0.

4.18A Plan: Apply Table 4.4 to determine the oxidation numbers for all the compounds in the reaction. Do not forget that the sum of the O.N.'s (oxidation numbers) for a compound must sum to zero, and for a polyatomic ion, the sum must equal the charge on the ion. After determining oxidation numbers for all atoms in the reaction, identify the atoms for which the oxidation numbers have changed from the left hand side of the equation to the right hand side of the equation. If the oxidation number of a particular atom increases, that atom has been oxidized, and the compound, element, or ion containing that atom on the reactant side of the equation is the reducing agent. If the oxidation number of a particular atom decreases, that atom has been reduced, and the compound, element, or ion containing that atom on the reactant side of the equation is the oxidizing agent.
Solution:
a) Oxidation numbers in NCl_3: N = +3, Cl = –1
Oxidation numbers in H_2O: H = +1, O = –2
Oxidation numbers in NH_3: N = –3, H = +1
Oxidation numbers in HOCl: H = +1, O = –2, Cl = +1

The oxidation number of nitrogen decreases from +3 to –3, so N is reduced and **NCl_3 is the oxidizing agent.** The oxidation number of chlorine increases from –1 to +1, so Cl is oxidized and **NCl_3 is also the reducing agent.**
b) Oxidation numbers in $AgNO_3$: N = +1, N = +5, O = –2
Oxidation numbers in NH_4I: N = –3, H = +1, I = –1
Oxidation numbers in AgI: Ag = +1, I = –1
Oxidation numbers in NH_4NO_3: N (in NH_4^+) = –3, H = +1, N (in NO_3^-) = +5, O = –2
None of the oxidation numbers change, so **this is not an oxidation-reduction reaction.**
c) Oxidation numbers in H_2S: H = +1, S = –2
Oxidation numbers in O_2: O = 0
Oxidation numbers in SO_2: S = +4, O = –2
Oxidation numbers in H_2O: H = +1, O = –2
The oxidation number of oxygen decreases from 0 to –2, so O is reduced and **O_2 is the oxidizing agent.** The oxidation number of sulfur increases from –2 to +4, so S is oxidized and **H_2S is the reducing agent.**

4.18B Plan: Apply Table 4.4 to determine the oxidation numbers for all the compounds in the reaction. Do not forget that the sum of the O.N.'s (oxidation numbers) for a compound must sum to zero, and for a polyatomic ion, the sum must equal the charge on the ion. After determining oxidation numbers for all atoms in the reaction, identify the atoms for which the oxidation numbers have changed from the left hand side of the equation to the right hand side of the equation. If the oxidation number of a particular atom increases, that atom has been oxidized, and the compound, element, or ion containing that atom on the reactant side of the equation is the reducing agent. If the oxidation number of a particular atom decreases, that atom has been reduced, and the compound, element, or ion containing that atom on the reactant side of the equation is the oxidizing agent.
Solution:
a) Oxidation numbers in SiO_2: Si = +4, O = –2
Oxidation numbers in HF: H = +1, F = –1
Oxidation numbers in SiF_4: Si = +4, F = –1
Oxidation numbers in H_2O: H = +1, O = –2
None of the oxidation numbers change, so **this is not an oxidation-reduction reaction.**
b) Oxidation numbers in C_2H_6: C = –3, H = +1
Oxidation numbers in O_2: O = 0
Oxidation numbers in CO_2: C = +4, O = –2
Oxidation numbers in H_2O: H = +1, O = –2
The oxidation number of oxygen decreases from 0 to –2, so O is reduced and **O_2 is the oxidizing agent.** The oxidation number of carbon increases from –3 to +4, so C is oxidized and **C_2H_6 is the reducing agent.**
c) Oxidation numbers in CO: C = +2, O = –2
Oxidation numbers in I_2O_5: I = +5, O = –2
Oxidation numbers in I_2: I = 0
Oxidation numbers in CO_2: C = +4, O = –2
The oxidation number of iodine decreases from +5 to 0, so I is reduced and **I_2O_5 is the oxidizing agent.** The oxidation number of carbon increases from +2 to +4, so C is oxidized and **CO is the reducing agent.**

4.19A Plan: Write a balanced reaction. Find moles of $KMnO_4$ by multiplying its volume and molarity and determine the moles of Ca^{2+} in the sample using the molar ratio from the reaction. Divide moles of Ca^{2+} by the volume of the milk sample to obtain molarity. In part (b), moles of Ca^{2+} will be converted to grams.
Solution:

$$2KMnO_4(aq) + 5CaC_2O_4(s) + 8H_2SO_4(aq) \rightarrow 2MnSO_4(aq) + K_2SO_4(aq) + 5CaSO_4(s) + 10CO_2(g) + 8H_2O(l)$$

$$\text{Moles of } KMnO_4 = (6.53 \text{ mL})\left(\frac{10^{-3} \text{ L}}{1 \text{ mL}}\right)\left(\frac{4.56 \times 10^{-3} \text{ mol } KMnO_4}{1 \text{ L}}\right)$$

$$= 2.97768 \times 10^{-5} \text{ mol } KMnO_4$$

$$\text{Molarity of } Ca^{2+} = \left(2.97768 \times 10^{-5} \text{ mol } KMnO_4\right)\left(\frac{5 \text{ mol } CaC_2O_4}{2 \text{ mol } KMnO_4}\right)\left(\frac{1 \text{ mol } Ca^{2+}}{1 \text{ mol } CaC_2O_4}\right)\left(\frac{1}{2.50 \text{ mL}}\right)\left(\frac{1 \text{ mL}}{10^{-3} \text{ L}}\right)$$

$$= 2.97768 \times 10^{-2} = 2.98 \times 10^{-2} \text{ mol/L} = \mathbf{2.98 \times 10^{-2}}\ \boldsymbol{M}\ \mathbf{Ca^{2+}}$$

b) Concentration (g/L) = $\left(\frac{2.97768 \times 10^{-2} \text{ mol } Ca^{2+}}{L}\right)\left(\frac{40.08 \text{ g } Ca^{2+}}{1 \text{ mol } Ca^{2+}}\right)$ = 1.193454 = **1.19 g/L**

This concentration is consistent with the typical value in milk.

4.19B Plan: Find moles of $K_2Cr_2O_7$ by multiplying its volume and molarity, and determine the moles of Fe^{2+} in the sample using the molar ratio from the reaction provided in the problem statement (remember that the Fe^{2+} is part of the $FeSO_4$ compound and that there is one Fe^{2+} ion for every formula unit of $FeSO_4$). Divide moles of Fe^{2+} by the volume of the $FeSO_4$ solution to obtain molarity. In part (b), convert the moles of Fe^{2+} to grams. Then divide the mass of iron ion by the total mass of the ore and multiply by 100% to find the mass percent of iron in the ore.

Solution:

a) The balanced equation (provided in the problem statement) is:

$6FeSO_4(aq) + K_2Cr_2O_7(aq) + 7H_2SO_4(aq) \rightarrow 3Fe_2(SO_4)_3(aq) + Cr_2(SO_4)_3(aq) + 7H_2O(l) + K_2SO_4(aq)$

Amount (mol) of Fe^{2+} = 21.85 mL $K_2Cr_2O_7$ $\left(\frac{1 \text{ L}}{1000 \text{ mL}}\right)\left(\frac{0.250 \text{ mol } K_2Cr_2O_7}{1 \text{ L}}\right)\left(\frac{6 \text{ mole } FeSO_4}{1 \text{ mol } K_2Cr_2O_7}\right)\left(\frac{1 \text{ mol } Fe^{2+}}{1 \text{ mol } FeSO_4}\right)$

= 0.0328 mol Fe^{2+}

Molarity of Fe^{2+} = $\left(\frac{0.0328 \text{ mol } Fe^{2+}}{30.0 \text{ mL}}\right)\left(\frac{1000 \text{ mL}}{1 \text{ L}}\right)$ = 1.0933 = **1.09 *M***

b) Mass (g) of iron = 0.0328 mol Fe^{2+} $\left(\frac{1 \text{ mol Fe}}{1 \text{ mol } Fe^{2+}}\right)\left(\frac{55.85 \text{ g Fe}}{1 \text{ mol Fe}}\right)$ = 1.8319 = 1.83 g Fe

Mass % of iron in sample = $\left(\frac{1.83 \text{ g Fe}}{2.58 \text{ g ore}}\right)$(100%) = 70.9302 = **70.9%**

4.20A Plan: To classify a reaction, compare the number of reactants used versus the number of products formed. Also examine the changes, if any, in the oxidation numbers. Recall the definitions of each type of reaction:

Combination: $X + Y \rightarrow Z$; Decomposition: $Z \rightarrow X + Y$

Single displacement: $X + YZ \rightarrow XZ + Y$

Solution:

a) **Combination**; $S_8(s) + 16F_2(g) \rightarrow 8SF_4(g)$

O.N.: S = 0 F = 0 S = +4
F = –1

Sulfur changes from 0 to +4 oxidation state; it is oxidized and **S_8 is the reducing agent.**
Fluorine changes from 0 to –1 oxidation state; it is reduced and **F_2 is the oxidizing agent.**

b) **Displacement**; $2CsI(aq) + Cl_2(aq) \rightarrow 2CsCl(aq) + I_2(aq)$

O.N.: Cs = +1 Cl = 0 Cs = +1 I = 0
I = –1 Cl = –1

Total ionic eqn: $2Cs^+(aq) + 2I^-(aq) + Cl_2(aq) \rightarrow 2Cs^+(aq) + 2Cl^-(aq) + I_2(aq)$

Net ionic eqn: $2I^-(aq) + Cl_2(aq) \rightarrow 2Cl^-(aq) + I_2(aq)$

Iodine changes from –1 to 0 oxidation state; it is oxidized and **CsI is the reducing agent.** Chlorine changes from 0 to –1 oxidation state; it is reduced and **Cl_2 is the oxidizing agent.**

c) **Displacement**; $3Ni(NO_3)_2(aq) + 2Cr(s) \rightarrow 2Cr(NO_3)_3(aq) + 3Ni(s)$

O.N.: Ni = +2 Cr = 0 Cr = +3 Ni = 0
N = +5 N = +5
O = –2 O = –2

Total ionic eqn: $3Ni^{+2}(aq) + 6NO_3^-(aq) + 2Cr(s) \rightarrow 2Cr^{+3}(aq) + 6NO_3^-(aq) + 3Ni(s)$

Net ionic eqn: $3Ni^{+2}(aq) + 2Cr(s) \rightarrow 2Cr^{+3}(aq) + 3Ni(s)$

Nickel changes from +2 to 0 oxidation state; it is reduced and **$Ni(NO_3)_2$ is the oxidizing agent.**
Chromium changes from 0 to +3 oxidation state; it is oxidized and **Cr is the reducing agent.**

4.20B Plan: To classify a reaction, compare the number of reactants used versus the number of products formed. Also examine the changes, if any, in the oxidation numbers. Recall the definitions of each type of reaction:

Combination: $X + Y \rightarrow Z$; Decomposition: $Z \rightarrow X + Y$

Single displacement: $X + YZ \rightarrow XZ + Y$

Solution:

a) **Displacement**; $Co(s) + 2HCl(aq) \rightarrow CoCl_2(aq) + H_2(g)$ (molecular equation)

O.N.: Co = 0 H = +1, Cl = –1 Co = +2, Cl = –1 H = 0

$Co(s) + 2H^+(aq) + 2Cl^-(aq) \rightarrow Co^{2+}(aq) + 2Cl^-(aq) + H_2(g)$ (total ionic equation)

$Co(s) + 2H^+(aq) \rightarrow Co^{2+}(aq) + H_2(g)$ (net ionic equation)

Cobalt changes from 0 to +2 oxidation state; it is oxidized and **Co is the reducing agent.** Hydrogen changes from +1 to 0 oxidation state; it is reduced and **HCl is the oxidizing agent.**

b) **Combination**; $2CO(g) + O_2(g) \rightarrow 2CO_2(g)$

O.N.: C = +2, O = –2 O = 0 C = +4, O = –2

Carbon changes from +2 to +4 oxidation state; it is oxidized and **CO is the reducing agent.** Oxygen changes from 0 to –2 oxidation state; it is reduced and **O_2 is the oxidizing agent.**

c) **Decomposition**; $2N_2O_5(s) \rightarrow 4NO_2(g) + O_2(g)$

O.N.: N = +5 N = +4 O = 0

O = –2 O = –2

Nitrogen changes from +5 to +4 oxidation state; it is reduced and **N_2O_5 is the oxidizing agent.** Oxygen changes from –2 to 0 oxidation state; it is oxidized and **N_2O_5 is also the reducing agent.**

END–OF–CHAPTER PROBLEMS

4.2 Plan: Review the discussion on water soluble compounds.

Solution:

Ionic and polar covalent compounds are most likely to be soluble in water. Because water is polar, the partial charges in its molecules are able to interact with the charges, either ionic or dipole-induced, in other substances.

4.3 Plan: Solutions that conduct an electric current contain electrolytes.

Solution:

Ions must be present in an aqueous solution for it to conduct an electric current. Ions come from ionic compounds or from other electrolytes such as acids and bases.

4.6 Plan: Write the formula for magnesium nitrate and note the ratio of magnesium ions to nitrate ions.

Solution:

Upon dissolving the salt in water, magnesium nitrate, $Mg(NO_3)_2$, would dissociate to form one Mg^{2+} ion for every two NO_3^- ions, thus forming twice as many nitrate ions. **Scene B** best represents a volume of magnesium nitrate solution. Only Scene B has twice as many nitrate ions (red circles) as magnesium ions (blue circles).

4.13 Plan: Remember that molarity is moles of solute/volume of solution.

Solution:

Volumes may **not** be additive when two different solutions are mixed, so the final volume may be slightly different from 1000.0 mL. The correct method would state, "Take 100.0 mL of the 10.0 *M* solution and add water until the total volume is 1000 mL."

4.14 Plan: Compounds that are soluble in water tend to be ionic compounds or covalent compounds that have polar bonds. Many ionic compounds are soluble in water because the attractive force between the oppositely charged ions in an ionic compound are replaced with an attractive force between the polar water molecule and the ions when the compound is dissolved in water. Covalent compounds with polar bonds are often soluble in water since the polar bonds of the covalent compound interact with those in water.

Solution:

a) Benzene, a covalent compound, is likely to be **insoluble** in water because it is nonpolar and water is polar.

b) Sodium hydroxide (NaOH) is an ionic compound and is therefore likely to be **soluble** in water.

c) Ethanol (CH_3CH_2OH) will likely be **soluble** in water because it contains a polar –OH bond like water.

d) Potassium acetate ($KC_2H_3O_2$) is an ionic compound and will likely be **soluble** in water.

4.16 Plan: Substances whose aqueous solutions conduct an electric current are electrolytes such as ionic compounds, acids, and bases.

Solution:
a) Cesium bromide, CsBr, is a soluble ionic compound, and a solution of this salt in water contains Cs^+ and Br^- ions. Its solution **conducts** an electric current.
b) HI is a strong acid that dissociates completely in water. Its aqueous solution contains H^+ and I^- ions, so it **conducts** an electric current.

4.18 Plan: To determine the total moles of ions released, write an equation that shows the compound dissociating into ions with the correct molar ratios. Convert mass and formula units to moles of compound and use the molar ratio to convert moles of compound to moles of ions.
Solution:
a) Each mole of NH_4Cl dissolves in water to form 1 mole of NH_4^+ ions and 1 mole of Cl^- ions, or a total of 2 moles of ions: $NH_4Cl(s) \rightarrow NH_4^+(aq) + Cl^-(aq)$.

$$\text{Moles of ions} = (0.32 \text{ mol NH}_4\text{Cl})\left(\frac{2 \text{ mol ions}}{1 \text{ mol NH}_4\text{Cl}}\right) = \mathbf{0.64 \text{ mol of ions}}$$

b) Each mole of $Ba(OH)_2•8H_2O$ forms 1 mole of Ba^{2+} ions and 2 moles of OH^- ions, or a total of 3 moles of ions: $Ba(OH)_2•8H_2O(s) \rightarrow Ba^{2+}(aq) + 2OH^-(aq)$. The waters of hydration become part of the larger bulk of water.
Convert mass to moles using the molar mass.

$$\text{Moles of ions} = (25.4 \text{ g Ba(OH)}_2\text{•8H}_2\text{O})\left(\frac{1 \text{ mol Ba(OH)}_2\text{•8H}_2\text{O}}{315.4 \text{ g Ba(OH)}_2\text{•8H}_2\text{O}}\right)\left(\frac{3 \text{ mol ions}}{1 \text{ mol Ba(OH)}_2\text{•8H}_2\text{O}}\right)$$

$$= 0.2415980 = \mathbf{0.242 \text{ mol of ions}}$$

c) Each mole of LiCl produces 2 moles of ions (1 mole of Li^+ ions and 1 mole of Cl^- ions): $LiCl(s) \rightarrow Li^+(aq) + Cl^-(aq)$. Recall that a mole contains $6.022x10^{23}$ entities, so a mole of LiCl contains $6.022x10^{23}$ units of LiCl, more easily expressed as formula units.

$$\text{Moles of ions} = (3.55\text{x}10^{19} \text{ FU LiCl})\left(\frac{1 \text{ mol LiCl}}{6.022\text{x}10^{23} \text{FU LiCl}}\right)\left(\frac{2 \text{ mol ions}}{1 \text{ mol LiCl}}\right)$$

$$= 1.17901\text{x}10^{-4} = \mathbf{1.18x10^{-4} \text{ mol of ions}}$$

4.20 Plan: To determine the total moles of ions released, write an equation that shows the compound dissociating into ions with the correct molar ratios. Convert mass and formula units to moles of compound and use the molar ratio to convert moles of compound to moles of ions.
Solution:
a) Each mole of K_3PO_4 forms 3 moles of K^+ ions and 1 mole of PO_4^{3-} ions, or a total of 4 moles of ions: $K_3PO_4(s) \rightarrow 3K^+(aq) + PO_4^{3-}(aq)$

$$\text{Moles of ions} = (0.75 \text{ mol K}_3\text{PO}_4)\left(\frac{4 \text{ mol ions}}{1 \text{ mol K}_3\text{PO}_4}\right) = \mathbf{3.0 \text{ mol of ions}}.$$

b) Each mole of $NiBr_2•3H_2O$ forms 1mole of Ni^{2+} ions and 2 moles of Br^- ions, or a total of 3 moles of ions: $NiBr_2•3H_2O(s) \rightarrow Ni^{2+}(aq) + 2Br^-(aq)$. The waters of hydration become part of the larger bulk of water. Convert mass to moles using the molar mass.

$$\text{Moles of ions} = (6.88 \text{ x } 10^{-3} \text{ g NiBr}_2\text{•3H}_2\text{O})\left(\frac{1 \text{ mol NiBr}_2\text{•3H}_2\text{O}}{272.54 \text{ g NiBr}_2\text{•3H}_2\text{O}}\right)\left(\frac{3 \text{ mol ions}}{1 \text{ mol NiBr}_2\text{•3H}_2\text{O}}\right)$$

$$= 7.5732\text{x}10^{-5} = \mathbf{7.57x10^{-5} \text{ mol of ions}}$$

c) Each mole of $FeCl_3$ forms 1mole of Fe^{3+} ions and 3 moles of Cl^- ions, or a total of 4 moles of ions: $FeCl_3(s) \rightarrow Fe^{3+}(aq) + 3Cl^-(aq)$. Recall that a mole contains $6.022x10^{23}$ entities, so a mole of $FeCl_3$ contains $6.022x10^{23}$ units of $FeCl_3$, more easily expressed as formula units.

$$\text{Moles of ions} = (2.23\text{x}10^{22} \text{ FU FeCl}_3)\left(\frac{1 \text{ mol FeCl}_3}{6.022\text{x}10^{23} \text{FU FeCl}_3}\right)\left(\frac{4 \text{ mol ions}}{1 \text{ mol FeCl}_3}\right)$$

$$= 0.148124 = \mathbf{0.148 \text{ mol of ions}}$$

4.22 Plan: In all cases, use the known quantities and the definition of molarity $\left(M = \frac{\text{moles solute}}{\text{L of solution}}\right)$ to find the unknown quantity. Volume must be expressed in liters. The molar mass is used to convert moles to grams. The chemical formulas must be written to determine the molar mass. (a) You will need to convert milliliters to liters, multiply by the molarity to find moles, and convert moles to mass in grams. (b) Convert mass of solute to moles and volume from mL to liters. Divide the moles by the volume. (c) Multiply the molarity by the volume.

Solution:

a) Calculating moles of solute in solution:

$$\text{Moles of } Ca(C_2H_3O_2)_2 = (185.8 \text{ mL})\left(\frac{10^{-3}\text{ L}}{1 \text{ mL}}\right)\left(\frac{0.267 \text{ mol } Ca(C_2H_3O_2)_2}{1 \text{ L}}\right) = 0.0496086 \text{ mol } Ca(C_2H_3O_2)_2$$

Converting from moles of solute to grams:

$$\text{Mass (g) of } Ca(C_2H_3O_2)_2 = (0.0496086 \text{ mol } Ca(C_2H_3O_2)_2)\left(\frac{158.17 \text{ g } Ca(C_2H_3O_2)_2}{1 \text{ mol } Ca(C_2H_3O_2)_2}\right)$$

$$= 7.84659 = \mathbf{7.85\ g\ Ca(C_2H_3O_2)_2}$$

b) Converting grams of solute to moles:

$$\text{Moles of KI} = (21.1 \text{ g KI})\left(\frac{1 \text{ mol KI}}{166.0 \text{ g KI}}\right) = 0.127108 \text{ moles KI}$$

$$\text{Volume (L)} = (500.\text{ mL})\left(\frac{10^{-3}\text{ L}}{1 \text{ mL}}\right) = 0.500 \text{ L}$$

$$\text{Molarity of KI} = \frac{0.127108 \text{ mol KI}}{0.500 \text{ L}} = 0.254216 = \mathbf{0.254}\ \boldsymbol{M}\ \mathbf{KI}$$

c) $\text{Moles of NaCN} = (145.6 \text{ L})\left(\frac{0.850 \text{ mol NaCN}}{1 \text{ L}}\right) = 123.76 = \mathbf{124\ mol\ NaCN}$

4.24 Plan: In all cases, use the known quantities and the definition of molarity $\left(M = \frac{\text{moles solute}}{\text{L of solution}}\right)$ to find the unknown quantity. Volume must be expressed in liters. The molar mass is used to convert moles to grams. The chemical formulas must be written to determine the molar mass. (a) Convert volume in milliliters to liters, multiply the volume by the molarity to obtain moles of solute, and convert moles to mass in grams. (b) The simplest way will be to convert the milligrams to millimoles. Molarity may not only be expressed as moles/L, but also as mmoles/mL. (c) Convert the milliliters to liters and find the moles of solute and moles of ions by multiplying the volume and molarity. Use Avogadro's number to determine the number of ions present.

Solution:

a) Calculating moles of solute in solution:

$$\text{Moles of } K_2SO_4 = (475 \text{ mL})\left(\frac{10^{-3}\text{ L}}{1 \text{ mL}}\right)\left(\frac{5.62 \times 10^{-2} \text{ mol } K_2SO_4}{\text{L}}\right) = 0.026695 \text{ mol } K_2SO_4$$

Converting moles of solute to mass:

$$\text{Mass (g) of } K_2SO_4 = (0.026695 \text{ mol } K_2SO_4)\left(\frac{174.26 \text{ g } K_2SO_4}{1 \text{ mol } K_2SO_4}\right) = 4.6519 = \mathbf{4.65\ g\ K_2SO_4}$$

b) Calculating mmoles of solute:

$$\text{Mmoles of } CaCl_2 = \left(\frac{7.25 \text{ mg } CaCl_2}{1 \text{ mL}}\right)\left(\frac{1 \text{ mmol } CaCl_2}{110.98 \text{ mg } CaCl_2}\right) = 0.065327 \text{ mmoles } CaCl_2$$

Calculating molarity:

$$\text{Molarity of } CaCl_2 = \left(\frac{0.065327 \text{ mmol } CaCl_2}{1 \text{ mL}}\right) = 0.065327 = \mathbf{0.0653}\ \boldsymbol{M}\ \mathbf{CaCl_2}$$

If you believe that molarity must be moles/liters then the calculation becomes:

$$\text{Molarity of } CaCl_2 = \left(\frac{7.25 \text{ mg } CaCl_2}{1 \text{ mL}}\right)\left(\frac{10^{-3} \text{ g}}{1 \text{ mg}}\right)\left(\frac{1 \text{ mL}}{10^{-3} \text{ L}}\right)\left(\frac{1 \text{ mol } CaCl_2}{110.98 \text{ g } CaCl_2}\right) = 0.065327 = \mathbf{0.0653} \; \boldsymbol{M} \; \mathbf{CaCl_2}$$

Notice that the two central terms cancel each other.

c) Converting volume in L to mL:

$$\text{Volume (L)} = (1 \text{ mL})\left(\frac{10^{-3} \text{ L}}{1 \text{ mL}}\right) = 0.001 \text{ L}$$

Calculating moles of solute and moles of ions:

$$\text{Moles of } MgBr_2 = (0.001 \text{ L})\left(\frac{0.184 \text{ mol } MgBr_2}{1 \text{ L}}\right) = 1.84\text{x}10^{-4} \text{ mol } MgBr_2$$

$$\text{Moles of } Mg^{2+} \text{ ions} = (1.84 \text{ x } 10^{-4} \text{ mol } MgBr_2)\left(\frac{1 \text{ mol } Mg^{2+}}{1 \text{ mol } MgBr_2}\right) = 1.84\text{x}10^{-4} \text{ mol } Mg^{2+} \text{ ions}$$

$$\text{Number of } Mg^{2+} \text{ ions} = (1.84\text{x}10^{-4} \; Mg^{2+} \text{ ions})\left(\frac{6.022\text{x}10^{23} \; Mg^{2+} \text{ ions}}{1 \text{ mol } Mg^{2+} \text{ ions}}\right)$$

$$= 1.1080\text{x}10^{20} = \mathbf{1.11x10^{20} \; Mg^{2+} \; ions}$$

4.26 Plan: To determine the total moles of ions released, write an equation that shows the compound dissociating into ions with the correct molar ratios. Convert the information given to moles of compound and use the molar ratio to convert moles of compound to moles of ions. Avogadro's number is used to convert moles of ions to numbers of ions.

Solution:

a) Each mole of $AlCl_3$ forms 1mole of Al^{3+} ions and 3 moles of Cl^- ions: $AlCl_3(s) \rightarrow Al^{3+}(aq) + 3Cl^-(aq)$.
Molarity and volume must be converted to moles of $AlCl_3$.

$$\text{Moles of } AlCl_3 = (130. \text{ mL})\left(\frac{10^{-3} \text{ L}}{1 \text{ mL}}\right)\left(\frac{0.45 \text{ mol } AlCl_3}{\text{L}}\right) = 0.0585 \text{ mol } AlCl_3$$

$$\text{Moles of } Al^{3+} = (0.0585 \text{ mol } AlCl_3)\left(\frac{1 \text{ mol } Al^{3+}}{1 \text{ mol } AlCl_3}\right) = 0.0585 = \mathbf{0.058 \; mol \; Al^{3+}}$$

$$\text{Number of } Al^{3+} \text{ ions} = (0.0585 \text{ mol } Al^{3+})\left(\frac{6.022\text{x}10^{23} \; Al^{3+}}{1 \text{ mol } Al^{3+}}\right) = 3.52287\text{x } 10^{22} = \mathbf{3.5x10^{22} \; Al^{3+} \; ions}$$

$$\text{Moles of } Cl^- = (0.0585 \text{ mol } AlCl_3)\left(\frac{3 \text{ mol } Cl^-}{1 \text{ mol } AlCl_3}\right) = 0.1755 = \mathbf{0.18 \; mol \; Cl^-}$$

$$\text{Number of } Cl^- \text{ ions} = (0.1755 \text{ mol } Cl^-)\left(\frac{6.022\text{x}10^{23} \; Cl^-}{1 \text{ mol } Cl^-}\right) = 1.05686\text{x}10^{23} = \mathbf{1.1x10^{23} \; Cl^- \; ions}$$

b) Each mole of Li_2SO_4 forms 2 moles of Li^+ ions and 1 mole of SO_4^{2-} ions: $Li_2SO_4(s) \rightarrow 2Li^+(aq) + SO_4^{2-}(aq)$.

$$\text{Moles of } Li_2SO_4 = (9.80 \text{ mL})\left(\frac{10^{-3} \text{ L}}{1 \text{ mL}}\right)\left(\frac{2.59 \text{ g } Li_2SO_4}{1 \text{ L}}\right)\left(\frac{1 \text{ mol } Li_2SO_4}{109.94 \text{ g } Li_2SO_4}\right) = 2.3087\text{x}10^{-4} \text{ mol } Li_2SO_4$$

$$\text{Moles of } Li^+ = (2.3087\text{x}10^{-4} \text{ mol } Li_2SO_4)\left(\frac{2 \text{ mol } Li^+}{1 \text{ mol } Li_2SO_4}\right) = 4.6174\text{x}10^{-4} = \mathbf{4.62x10^{-4} \; mol \; Li^+}$$

$$\text{Number of } Li^+ \text{ ions} = (4.6174\text{x}10^{-4} \text{ mol } Li^+)\left(\frac{6.022 \text{ x } 10^{23} \; Li^+}{1 \text{ mol } Li^+}\right) = 2.7806\text{x}10^{20} = \mathbf{2.78x10^{20} \; Li^+ \; ions}$$

$$\text{Moles of } SO_4^{2-} = \left(2.3087\text{x}10^{-4} \text{ mol } Li_2SO_4\right)\left(\frac{1 \text{ mol } SO_4^{2-}}{1 \text{ mol } Li_2SO_4}\right) = 2.3087\text{x}10^{-4} = \mathbf{2.31x10^{-4}\ mol\ SO_4^{2-}}$$

$$\text{Number of } SO_4^{2-} \text{ ions} = \left(2.3087\text{x}10^{-4} \text{ mol } SO_4^{2-}\right)\left(\frac{6.022 \text{ x } 10^{23}\ SO_4^{2-}}{1 \text{ mol } SO_4^{2-}}\right)$$

$$= 1.39030\text{x}10^{20} = \mathbf{1.39x10^{20}\ SO_4^{2-}\ ions}$$

c) Each mole of KBr forms 1 mole of K^+ ions and 1 mole of Br^- ions: $KBr(s) \rightarrow K^+(aq) + Br^-(aq)$.

$$\text{Moles of KBr} = (245 \text{ mL})\left(\frac{10^{-3} \text{ L}}{1 \text{ mL}}\right)\left(\frac{3.68\text{x}10^{22} \text{ FU KBr}}{\text{L}}\right)\left(\frac{1 \text{ mol KBr}}{6.022\text{x}10^{23} \text{ FU KBr}}\right) = 0.01497 \text{ mol KBr}$$

$$\text{Moles of } K^+ = (0.01497 \text{ mol KBr})\left(\frac{1 \text{ mol } K^+}{1 \text{ mol KBr}}\right) = 0.01497 = \mathbf{1.50x10^{-2}\ mol\ K^+}$$

$$\text{Number of } K^+ \text{ ions} = \left(0.01497 \text{ mol } K^+\right)\left(\frac{6.022\text{x}10^{23}\ K^+}{1 \text{ mol } K^+}\right) = 9.016\text{x}10^{21} = \mathbf{9.02x10^{21}\ K^+\ ions}$$

$$\text{Moles of } Br^- = (0.01497 \text{ mol KBr})\left(\frac{1 \text{ mol } Br^-}{1 \text{ mol KBr}}\right) = 0.01497 = \mathbf{1.50x10^{-2}\ mol\ Br^-}$$

$$\text{Number of } Br^- \text{ ions} = \left(0.01497 \text{ mol } Br^-\right)\left(\frac{6.022\text{x}10^{23}\ Br^-}{1 \text{ mol } Br^-}\right) = 9.016\text{x}10^{21} = \mathbf{9.02x10^{21}\ Br^-\ ions}$$

4.28 Plan: These are dilution problems. Dilution problems can be solved by converting to moles and using the new volume; however, it is much easier to use $M_1V_1 = M_2V_2$. The dilution equation does not require a volume in liters; it only requires that the volume units match. In part c), it is necessary to find the moles of sodium ions in each separate solution, add these two mole amounts, and divide by the total volume of the two solutions.

Solution:

a) $M_1 = 0.250\ M$ KCl $\quad V_1 = 37.00$ mL $\quad M_2 = ?$ $\quad V_2 = 150.00$ mL

$M_1V_1 = M_2V_2$

$$M_2 = \frac{M_1 \text{ x } V_1}{V_2} = \frac{(0.250\ M)(37.00 \text{ mL})}{150.0 \text{ mL}} = 0.061667 = \mathbf{0.0617\ \mathit{M}\ KCl}$$

b) $M_1 = 0.0706\ M\ (NH_4)_2SO_4$ $\quad V_1 = 25.71$ mL $\quad M_2 = ?$ $\quad V_2 = 500.00$ mL

$M_1V_1 = M_2V_2$

$$M_2 = \frac{M_1 \text{ x } V_1}{V_2} = \frac{(0.0706\ M)(25.71 \text{ mL})}{500.0 \text{ mL}} = 0.003630 = \mathbf{0.00363\ \mathit{M}\ (NH_4)_2SO_4}$$

$$\text{c) Moles of } Na^+ \text{ from NaCl solution} = (3.58 \text{ mL})\left(\frac{10^{-3} \text{ L}}{1 \text{ mL}}\right)\left(\frac{0.348 \text{ mol NaCl}}{1 \text{ L}}\right)\left(\frac{1 \text{ mol } Na^+}{1 \text{ mol NaCl}}\right)$$

$$= 0.00124584 \text{ mol } Na^+$$

$$\text{Moles of } Na^+ \text{ from } Na_2SO_4 \text{ solution} = (500. \text{ mL})\left(\frac{10^{-3} \text{ L}}{1 \text{ mL}}\right)\left(\frac{6.81\text{x}10^{-2} \text{ mol } Na_2SO_4}{1 \text{ L}}\right)\left(\frac{2 \text{ mol } Na^+}{1 \text{ mol } Na_2SO_4}\right)$$

$$= 0.0681 \text{ mol } Na^+$$

Total moles of Na^+ ions = 0.00124584 mol Na^+ ions + 0.0681 mol Na^+ ions = 0.06934584 mol Na^+ ions

Total volume = 3.58 mL + 500. mL = 503.58 mL = 0.50358 L

$$\text{Molarity of } Na^+ = \frac{\text{total moles } Na^+ \text{ ions}}{\text{total volume}} = \frac{0.06934584 \text{ mol } Na^+ \text{ ions}}{0.50358 \text{ L}} = 0.1377057 = \mathbf{0.138\ \mathit{M}\ Na^+\ ions}$$

4.30 Plan: Use the density of the solution to find the mass of 1 L of solution. Volume in liters must be converted to volume in mL. The 70.0% by mass translates to 70.0 g solute/100 g solution and is used to find the mass of HNO_3 in 1 L of solution. Convert mass of HNO_3 to moles to obtain moles/L, molarity.

Solution:

a) Mass (g) of 1 L of solution = $(1 \text{ L solution})\left(\frac{1 \text{ mL}}{10^{-3} \text{ L}}\right)\left(\frac{1.41 \text{ g solution}}{1 \text{ mL}}\right)$ = 1410 g solution

Mass (g) of HNO_3 in 1 L of solution = $(1410 \text{ g solution})\left(\frac{70.0 \text{ g } HNO_3}{100 \text{ g solution}}\right)$ = **987 g HNO_3/L**

b) Moles of HNO_3 = $(987 \text{ g } HNO_3)\left(\frac{1 \text{ mol } HNO_3}{63.02 \text{ g } HNO_3}\right)$ = 15.6617 mol HNO_3

Molarity of HNO_3 = $\left(\frac{15.6617 \text{ mol } HNO_3}{1 \text{ L solution}}\right)$ = 15.6617 = **15.7 *M* HNO_3**

4.33 Plan: The first part of the problem is a simple dilution problem ($M_1V_1 = M_2V_2$). The volume in units of gallons can be used. In part b), convert mass of HCl to moles and use the molarity to find the volume that contains that number of moles.

Solution:

a) $M_1 = 11.7\ M$ $\quad V_1 = ?$ $\quad M_2 = 3.5\ M$ $\quad V_2 = 3.0$ gal

$$V_1 = \frac{M_2 \text{ x } V_2}{M_1} = \frac{(3.5\ M)(3.0 \text{ gal})}{11.7\ M} = 0.897436 \text{ gal}$$

Instructions: Be sure to wear goggles to protect your eyes! Pour approximately 2.0 gal of water into the container. Add slowly and with mixing 0.90 gal of 11.7 *M* HCl into the water. Dilute to 3.0 gal with water.

b) Converting from mass of HCl to moles of HCl:

Moles of HCl = $(9.66 \text{ g HCl})\left(\frac{1 \text{ mol HCl}}{36.46 \text{ g HCl}}\right)$ = 0.264948 mol HCl

Converting from moles of HCl to volume:

Volume (mL) of solution = $(0.264948 \text{ mol HCl})\left(\frac{1 \text{ L}}{11.7 \text{ mol HCl}}\right)\left(\frac{1 \text{ mL}}{10^{-3} \text{ L}}\right)$

= 22.64513 = **22.6 mL muriatic acid solution**

4.36 Plan: Review the definition of spectator ions.

Solution:

Ions in solution that do not participate in the reaction do not appear in a net ionic equation. These spectator ions remain as dissolved ions throughout the reaction. These ions are only present to balance charge.

4.40 Plan: Use the solubility rules to predict the products of this reaction. Ions not involved in the precipitate are spectator ions and are not included in the net ionic equation.

Solution:

Assuming that the left beaker is $AgNO_3$ (because it has gray Ag^+ ions) and the right must be NaCl, then the NO_3^- is blue, the Na^+ is brown, and the Cl^- is green. (Cl^- must be green since it is present with Ag^+ in the precipitate in the beaker on the right.)

Molecular equation: $AgNO_3(aq) + NaCl(aq) \rightarrow AgCl(s) + NaNO_3(aq)$

Total ionic equation: $Ag^+(aq) + NO_3^-(aq) + Na^+(aq) + Cl^-(aq) \rightarrow AgCl(s) + Na^+(aq) + NO_3^-(aq)$

Net ionic equation: $Ag^+(aq) + Cl^-(aq) \rightarrow AgCl(s)$

4.41 Plan: Write the new cation-anion combinations as the products of the reaction and use the solubility rules to determine if any of the new combinations are insoluble. The total ionic equation shows all soluble ionic substances dissociated into ions. The spectator ions are the ions that are present in the soluble ionic compound. The spectator ions are omitted from the net ionic equation.

Solution:

a) Molecular: $Hg_2(NO_3)_2(aq) + 2KI(aq) \rightarrow Hg_2I_2(s) + 2KNO_3(aq)$

Total ionic: $Hg_2^{2+}(aq) + 2NO_3^-(aq) + 2K^+(aq) + 2I^-(aq) \rightarrow Hg_2I_2(s) + 2K^+(aq) + 2NO_3^-(aq)$

Net ionic: $Hg_2^{2+}(aq) + 2I^-(aq) \rightarrow Hg_2I_2(s)$
Spectator ions are K^+ and NO_3^-.

b) Molecular: $FeSO_4(aq) + Sr(OH)_2(aq) \rightarrow Fe(OH)_2(s) + SrSO_4(s)$
Total ionic: $Fe^{2+}(aq) + SO_4^{2-}(aq) + Sr^{2+}(aq) + 2OH^-(aq) \rightarrow Fe(OH)_2(s) + SrSO_4(s)$
Net ionic: This is the same as the total ionic equation because there are no spectator ions.

4.43 Plan: A precipitate forms if reactant ions can form combinations that are insoluble, as determined by the solubility rules in Table 4.1. Create cation-anion combinations other than the original reactants and determine if they are insoluble. Any ions not involved in a precipitate are spectator ions and are omitted from the net ionic equation.
Solution:
a) $NaNO_3(aq) + CuSO_4(aq) \rightarrow Na_2SO_4(aq) + Cu(NO_3)_2(aq)$
No precipitate will form. The ions Na^+ and SO_4^{2-} will not form an insoluble salt according to the first solubility rule which states that all common compounds of Group 1A ions are soluble. The ions Cu^{2+} and NO_3^- will not form an insoluble salt according to the solubility rule #2: All common nitrates are soluble. There is no reaction.
b) A precipitate will form because silver ions, Ag^+, and bromide ions, Br^-, will combine to form a solid salt, silver bromide, AgBr. The ammonium and nitrate ions do not form a precipitate.
Molecular: $NH_4Br(aq) + AgNO_3(aq) \rightarrow AgBr(s) + NH_4NO_3(aq)$
Total ionic: $NH_4^+(aq) + Br^-(aq) + Ag^+(aq) + NO_3^-(aq) \rightarrow AgBr(s) + NH_4^+(aq) + NO_3^-(aq)$
Net ionic: $Ag^+(aq) + Br^-(aq) \rightarrow AgBr(s)$

4.45 Plan: A precipitate forms if reactant ions can form combinations that are insoluble, as determined by the solubility rules in Table 4.1. Create cation-anion combinations other than the original reactants and determine if they are insoluble. Any ions not involved in a precipitate are spectator ions and are omitted from the net ionic equation.
Solution:
a) New cation-anion combinations are potassium nitrate (KNO_3) and iron(III) chloride ($FeCl_3$). The solubility rules state that all common nitrates and chlorides (with some exceptions) are soluble, so no precipitate forms.
$3KCl(aq) + Fe(NO_3)_3(aq) \rightarrow 3KNO_3(aq) + FeCl_3(aq)$
b) New cation-anion combinations are ammonium chloride and barium sulfate. The solubility rules state that most chlorides are soluble; however, another rule states that sulfate compounds containing barium are insoluble. Barium sulfate is a precipitate and its formula is $BaSO_4$.
Molecular: $(NH_4)_2SO_4(aq) + BaCl_2(aq) \rightarrow BaSO_4(s) + 2NH_4Cl(aq)$
Total ionic: $2NH_4^+(aq) + SO_4^{2-}(aq) + Ba^{2+}(aq) + 2Cl^-(aq) \rightarrow BaSO_4(s) + 2NH_4^+(aq) + 2Cl^-(aq)$
Net ionic: $Ba^{2+}(aq) + SO_4^{2-}(aq) \rightarrow BaSO_4(s)$

4.47 Plan: Write a balanced equation for the chemical reaction described in the problem. By applying the solubility rules to the two possible products ($NaNO_3$ and PbI_2), determine that PbI_2 is the precipitate. By using molar relationships, determine how many moles of $Pb(NO_3)_2$ are required to produce 0.628 g of PbI_2. The molarity is calculated by dividing moles of $Pb(NO_3)_2$ by its volume in liters.
Solution:
The reaction is: $Pb(NO_3)_2(aq) + 2NaI(aq) \rightarrow PbI_2(s) + 2NaNO_3(aq)$.

$$\text{Moles of } Pb(NO_3)_2 = (0.628\text{ g } PbI_2)\left(\frac{1\text{ mol } PbI_2}{461.0\text{ g } PbI_2}\right)\left(\frac{1\text{ mol } Pb(NO_3)_2}{1\text{ mol } PbI_2}\right) = 0.001362256\text{ mol } Pb(NO_3)_2$$

Moles of Pb^{2+} = moles of $Pb(NO_3)_2$ = 0.001362256 mol Pb^{2+}

$$\text{Molarity of } Pb^{2+} = \frac{\text{moles } Pb^{2+}}{\text{volume of } Pb^{2+}} = \frac{0.001362256\text{ mol}}{38.5\text{ mL}}\left(\frac{1\text{ mL}}{10^{-3}\text{ L}}\right) = 0.035383 = \mathbf{0.0354}\ \boldsymbol{M}\ \mathbf{Pb^{2+}}$$

4.49 Plan: The first step is to write and balance the chemical equation for the reaction. Multiply the molarity and volume of each of the reactants to determine the moles of each. To determine which reactant is limiting, calculate the amount of barium sulfate formed from each reactant, assuming an excess of the other reactant. The reactant that produces less product is the limiting reagent. Use the limiting reagent and the mole ratio from the balanced chemical equation to determine the mass of barium sulfate formed.
Solution:
The balanced chemical equation is:
$BaCl_2(aq) + Na_2SO_4(aq) \rightarrow BaSO_4(s) + 2NaCl(aq)$

$$\text{Moles of BaCl}_2 = (35.0\text{ mL})\left(\frac{10^{-3}\text{ L}}{1\text{ mL}}\right)\left(\frac{0.160\text{ mol BaCl}_2}{1\text{ L}}\right) = 0.00560\text{ mol BaCl}_2$$

Finding the moles of $BaSO_4$ from the moles of $BaCl_2$ (if Na_2SO_4 is in excess):

$$\text{Moles of BaSO}_4\text{ from BaCl}_2 = (0.00560\text{ moL BaCl}_2)\left(\frac{1\text{ mol BaSO}_4}{1\text{ mol BaCl}_2}\right) = 0.00560\text{ mol BaSO}_4$$

$$\text{Moles of Na}_2\text{SO}_4 = (58.0\text{ mL})\left(\frac{10^{-3}\text{ L}}{1\text{ mL}}\right)\left(\frac{0.065\text{ mol Na}_2\text{SO}_4}{1\text{ L}}\right) = 0.00377\text{ mol Na}_2\text{SO}_4$$

Finding the moles of $BaSO_4$ from the moles of Na_2SO_4 (if $BaCl_2$ is in excess):

$$\text{Moles BaSO}_4\text{ from Na}_2\text{SO}_4 = (0.00377\text{ moL Na}_2\text{SO}_4)\left(\frac{1\text{ mol BaSO}_4}{1\text{ mol Na}_2\text{SO}_4}\right) = 0.00377\text{ mol BaSO}_4$$

Sodium sulfate is the limiting reactant.
Converting from moles of $BaSO_4$ to mass:

$$\text{Mass (g) of BaSO}_4 = (0.0377\text{ moL BaSO}_4)\left(\frac{233.4\text{ g BaSO}_4}{1\text{ mol BaSO}_4}\right) = 0.879918 = \mathbf{0.88\text{ g BaSO}_4}$$

4.51 Plan: A precipitate forms if reactant ions can form combinations that are insoluble, as determined by the solubility rules in Table 4.1. Create cation-anion combinations other than the original reactants and determine if they are insoluble. Any ions not involved in a precipitate are spectator ions and are omitted from the net ionic equation. Use the molar ratio in the balanced net ionic equation to calculate the mass of product.
Solution:
a) The yellow spheres cannot be ClO_4^- or NO_3^- as these ions form only soluble compounds. So the yellow sphere must be SO_4^{2-}. The only sulfate compounds possible that would be insoluble are Ag_2SO_4 and $PbSO_4$. The precipitate has a 1:1 ratio between its ions. Ag_2SO_4 has a 2:1 ratio between its ions. Therefore the blue spheres are Pb^{2+} and the yellow spheres are SO_4^{2-}. The precipitate is thus **$PbSO_4$**.
b) The net ionic equation is $Pb^{2+}(aq) + SO_4^{2-}(aq) \rightarrow PbSO_4(s)$.

$$\text{c) Mass (g) of PbSO}_4 = (10\text{ Pb}^{2+}\text{ spheres})\left(\frac{5.0\text{x}10^{-4}\text{ mol Pb}^{2+}}{1\text{ Pb}^{2+}\text{ sphere}}\right)\left(\frac{1\text{ mol PbSO}_4}{1\text{ mol Pb}^{2+}}\right)\left(\frac{303.3\text{ g PbSO}_4}{1\text{ mol PbSO}_4}\right)$$

$$= 1.5165 = \mathbf{1.5\text{ g PbSO}_4}$$

4.53 Plan: Multiply the molarity of the $CaCl_2$ solution by its volume in liters to determine the number of moles of $CaCl_2$ reacted. Write the precipitation reaction using M to represent the alkali metal. Use the moles of $CaCl_2$ reacted and the molar ratio in the balanced equation to find the moles of alkali metal carbonate. Divide the mass of that carbonate by the moles to obtain the molar mass of the carbonate. Subtract the mass of CO_3 from the molar mass to obtain the molar mass of the alkali metal, which can be used to identify the alkali metal and the formula and name of the compound.
Solution:
The reaction is: $M_2CO_3(aq) + CaCl_2(aq) \rightarrow CaCO_3(s) + 2MCl(aq)$.
Since the alkali metal M forms a +1 ion and carbonate is a –2 ion, the formula is M_2CO_3.

$$\text{Moles of CaCl}_2 = (31.10\text{ mL})\left(\frac{10^{-3}\text{ L}}{1\text{ mL}}\right)\left(\frac{0.350\text{ mol CaCl}_2}{1\text{ L}}\right) = 0.010885\text{ mol CaCl}_2$$

$$\text{Moles of M}_2\text{CO}_3 = (0.010885\text{ mol CaCl}_2)\left(\frac{1\text{ mol M}_2\text{CO}_3}{1\text{ mol CaCl}_2}\right) = 0.010885\text{ mol M}_2\text{CO}_3$$

$$\text{Molar mass (g/mol) of M}_2\text{CO}_3 = \frac{\text{mass of M}_2\text{CO}_3}{\text{moles of M}_2\text{CO}_3} = \frac{1.50\text{ g}}{0.010885\text{ mol}} = 137.804\text{ g/mol}$$

$$\text{Molar mass (g/mol) of M}_2 = \text{molar mass of M}_2\text{CO}_3 - \text{molar mass of CO}_3$$
$$= 137.804\text{ g/mol} - 60.01\text{ g/mol} = 77.79\text{ g/mol}$$

Molar mass (g/mol) of M = 77.79 g/mol/2 = 38.895 g/mol = 38.9 g/mol
This molar mass is closest to that of potassium; the formula of the compound is **K_2CO_3, potassium carbonate.**

4.55 Plan: Write a balanced equation for the reaction. Find the moles of $AgNO_3$ by multiplying the molarity and volume of the $AgNO_3$ solution; use the molar ratio in the balanced equation to find the moles of Cl^- present in the 25.00 mL sample. Then, convert moles of Cl^- into grams, and convert the sample volume into grams using the given density. The mass percent of Cl^- is found by dividing the mass of Cl^- by the mass of the sample volume and multiplying by 100.
Solution:
The balanced equation is $AgNO_3(aq) + Cl^-(aq) \rightarrow AgCl(s) + NO_3^-(aq)$.

$$\text{Moles of } AgNO_3 = (53.63 \text{ mL})\left(\frac{10^{-3}\text{ L}}{1 \text{ mL}}\right)\left(\frac{0.2970 \text{ mol } AgNO_3}{\text{L}}\right) = 0.01592811 \text{ mol } AgNO_3$$

$$\text{Mass (g) of } Cl^- = (0.01592811 \text{ mol } AgNO_3)\left(\frac{1 \text{ mol } Cl^-}{1 \text{ mol } AgNO_3}\right)\left(\frac{35.45 \text{ g Cl}}{1 \text{ mol } Cl^-}\right) = 0.56465 \text{ g } Cl^-$$

$$\text{Mass (g) of seawater sample} = (25.00 \text{ mL})\left(\frac{1.024 \text{ g}}{\text{mL}}\right) = 25.60 \text{ g sample}$$

$$\text{Mass \% } Cl^- = \frac{\text{mass } Cl^-}{\text{mass sample}} \times 100\% = \frac{0.56465 \text{ g } Cl^-}{25.60 \text{ g sample}} \times 100\% = 2.20566 = \mathbf{2.206\%\ Cl^-}$$

4.61 Plan: Formation of a gaseous product or a precipitate drives a reaction to completion.
Solution:
a) The formation of a gas, $SO_2(g)$, and formation of water drive this reaction to completion, because both products remove reactants from solution.
b) The formation of a precipitate, $Ba_3(PO_4)_2(s)$, will cause this reaction to go to completion. This reaction is one between an acid and a base, so the formation of water molecules through the combination of H^+ and OH^- ions also drives the reaction.

4.63 Plan: The acids in this problem are all strong acids, so you can assume that all acid molecules dissociate completely to yield H^+ ions and associated anions. One mole of $HClO_4$, HNO_3, and HCl each produce one mole of H^+ upon dissociation, so moles H^+ = moles acid. Calculate the moles of acid by multiplying the molarity (moles/L) by the volume in liters.
Solution:
a) $HClO_4(aq) \rightarrow H^+(aq) + ClO_4^-(aq)$

$$\text{Moles } H^+ = \text{mol } HClO_4 = (1.40 \text{ L})\left(\frac{0.25 \text{ mol}}{1 \text{ L}}\right) = \mathbf{0.35\ mol\ H^+}$$

b) $HNO_3(aq) \rightarrow H^+(aq) + NO_3^-(aq)$

$$\text{Moles } H^+ = \text{mol } HNO_3 = (6.8 \text{ mL})\left(\frac{10^{-3}\text{ L}}{1 \text{ mL}}\right)\left(\frac{0.92 \text{ mol}}{1 \text{ L}}\right) = 6.256\text{x}10^{-3} = \mathbf{6.3x10^{-3}\ mol\ H^+}$$

c) $HCl(aq) \rightarrow H^+(aq) + Cl^-(aq)$

$$\text{Moles } H^+ = \text{mol HCl} = (2.6 \text{ L})\left(\frac{0.085 \text{ mol}}{1 \text{ L}}\right) = 0.221 = \mathbf{0.22\ mol\ H^+}$$

4.65 Plan: Remember that strong acids and bases can be written as ions in the total ionic equation but weak acids and bases cannot be written as ions. Omit spectator ions from the net ionic equation.
Solution:
a) KOH is a strong base and HBr is a strong acid; both may be written in dissociated form. KBr is a soluble compound since all Group 1A(1) compounds are soluble.
Molecular equation: $KOH(aq) + HBr(aq) \rightarrow KBr(aq) + H_2O(l)$
Total ionic equation: $K^+(aq) + OH^-(aq) + H^+(aq) + Br^-(aq) \rightarrow K^+(aq) + Br^-(aq) + H_2O(l)$

Net ionic equation: $OH^-(aq) + H^+(aq) \rightarrow H_2O(l)$
The spectator ions are $K^+(aq)$ and $Br^-(aq)$.
b) NH_3 is a weak base and is written in the molecular form. HCl is a strong acid and is written in the dissociated form (as ions). NH_4Cl is a soluble compound, because all ammonium compounds are soluble.
Molecular equation: $NH_3(aq) + HCl(aq) \rightarrow NH_4Cl(aq)$
Total ionic equation: $NH_3(aq) + H^+(aq) + Cl^-(aq) \rightarrow NH_4^+(aq) + Cl^-(aq)$
Net ionic equation: $NH_3(aq) + H^+(aq) \rightarrow NH_4^+(aq)$
Cl^- is the only spectator ion.

4.67 Plan: Write an acid-base reaction between $CaCO_3$ and HCl. Remember that HCl is a strong acid.
Solution:
Calcium carbonate dissolves in HCl(*aq*) because the carbonate ion, a base, reacts with the acid to form H_2CO_3 which decomposes into $CO_2(g)$ and $H_2O(l)$.

$$CaCO_3(s) + 2HCl(aq) \rightarrow CaCl_2(aq) + H_2CO_3(aq)$$

Total ionic equation:

$$CaCO_3(s) + 2H^+(aq) + 2Cl^-(aq) \rightarrow Ca^{2+}(aq) + 2Cl^-(aq) + H_2O(l) + CO_2(g)$$

Net ionic equation:

$$CaCO_3(s) + 2H^+(aq) \rightarrow Ca^{2+}(aq) + H_2O(l) + CO_2(g)$$

4.69 Plan: Convert the mass of calcium carbonate to moles, and use the mole ratio in the balanced chemical equation to find the moles of hydrochloric acid required to react with these moles of calcium carbonate. Use the molarity of HCl to find the volume that contains this number of moles.
Solution:
$2HCl(aq) + CaCO_3(s) \rightarrow CaCl_2(aq) + CO_2(g) + H_2O(l)$
Converting from grams of $CaCO_3$ to moles:

$$\text{Moles of } CaCO_3 = (16.2\text{ g } CaCO_3)\left(\frac{1\text{ mol } CaCO_3}{100.09\text{ g } CaCO_3}\right) = 0.161854\text{ mol } CaCO_3$$

Converting from moles of $CaCO_3$ to moles of HCl:

$$\text{Moles of HCl} = (0.161854\text{ mol } CaCO_3)\left(\frac{2\text{ mol HCl}}{1\text{ mol } CaCO_3}\right) = 0.323708\text{ mol HCl}$$

Converting from moles of HCl to volume:

$$\text{Volume (mL) of HCl} = (0.323708\text{ mol HCl})\left(\frac{1\text{ L}}{0.383\text{ mol HCl}}\right)\left(\frac{1\text{ mL}}{10^{-3}\text{ L}}\right) = 845.1906 = \mathbf{845\text{ mL HCl solution}}$$

4.71 Plan: Write a balanced equation. Find the moles of KOH from the molarity and volume information and use the molar ratio in the balanced equation to find the moles of acid present. Divide the moles of acid by its volume to determine the molarity.
Solution:
The reaction is: $KOH(aq) + CH_3COOH(aq) \rightarrow CH_3COOK(aq) + H_2O(l)$

$$\text{Moles of KOH} = (25.98\text{ mL})\left(\frac{10^{-3}\text{ L}}{1\text{ mL}}\right)\left(\frac{0.1180\text{ mol KOH}}{\text{L}}\right) = 0.00306564\text{ mol KOH}$$

$$\text{Moles of } CH_3COOH = (0.00306564\text{ mol KOH})\left(\frac{1\text{mol } CH_3COOH}{1\text{ mol KOH}}\right) = 0.00306564\text{ mol } CH_3COOH$$

$$\text{Molarity of } CH_3COOH = \left(\frac{0.00306564\text{ mol } CH_3COOH}{52.50\text{ mL}}\right)\left(\frac{1\text{ mL}}{10^{-3}\text{ L}}\right) = 0.05839314 = \mathbf{0.05839\ \mathit{M}\ CH_3COOH}$$

4.82 Plan: An oxidizing agent gains electrons and therefore has an atom whose oxidation number decreases during the reaction. Use the Rules for Assigning an Oxidation Number to assign S in H_2SO_4 an O.N. and see if this oxidation number changes during the reaction. An acid transfers a proton during reaction.

Solution:
a) In H_2SO_4, hydrogen has an O.N. of +1, for a total of +2; oxygen has an O.N. of –2 for a total of –8. The S has an O.N. of +6. In SO_2, the O.N. of oxygen is –2 for a total of –4 and S has an O.N. of +4. So the S has been reduced from +6 to +4 and is an **oxidizing agent**. Iodine is oxidized during the reaction.
b) The oxidation number of S is +6 in H_2SO_4; in $BaSO_4$, Ba has an O.N. of +2, the four oxygen atoms have a total O.N. of –8, and S is again +6. Since the oxidation number of S (or any of the other atoms) did not change, this is not a redox reaction. H_2SO_4 transfers a proton to F^- to produce HF, so it acts as an **acid**.

4.84 Plan: Consult the Rules for Assigning an Oxidation Number. The sum of the O.N. values for the atoms in a molecule equals zero, while the sum of the O.N. values for the atoms in an ion equals the ion's charge.
Solution:
a) CF_2Cl_2. The rules dictate that F and Cl each have an O.N. of –1; two F and two Cl yield a sum of –4, so the O.N. of C must be +4. **C = +4**
b) $Na_2C_2O_4$. The rule dictates that Na [Group 1A(1)] has a +1 O.N.; rule 5 dictates that O has a –2 O.N.; two Na and four O yield a sum of –6 [2(+1) + 4(–2)]. Therefore, the total of the O.N.s on the two C atoms is +6 and each C is +3. **C = +3**
c) HCO_3^-. H is combined with nonmetals and has an O.N. of +1; O has an O.N. of –2 and three O have a sum of –6. To have an overall oxidation state equal to –1, C must be +4 because (+1) + (+4) + (–6) = –1. **C = +4**
d) C_2H_6. Each H has an O.N. of +1; six H gives +6. The sum of O.N.s for the two C atoms must be –6, so each C is –3. **C = –3**

4.86 Plan: Consult the Rules for Assigning an Oxidation Number. The sum of the O.N. values for the atoms in a molecule equals zero, while the sum of the O.N. values for the atoms in an ion equals the ion's charge.
Solution:
a) NH_2OH. Hydrogen has an O.N. of +1, for a total of +3 for the three hydrogen atoms. Oxygen has an O.N. of –2. The O.N. of N must be –1 since [(–1) + (+3) + (–2)] = 0. **N = –1**
b) N_2F_4. The O.N. of each fluorine is –1 for a total of –4; the sum of the O.N.s for the two N atoms must be +4, so each N has an O.N. of +2. **N = +2**
c) NH_4^+. The O.N. of each hydrogen is +1 for a total of +4; the O.N. of nitrogen must be –3 since the overall sum of the O.N.s must be +1: [(–3) + (+4)] = +1 **N = –3**
d) HNO_2. The O.N. of hydrogen is +1 and that of each oxygen is –2 for a total of –4 from the oxygens. The O.N. of nitrogen must be +3 since [(+1) + (+3) + (–4)] = 0. **N = +3**

4.88 Plan: Consult the Rules for Assigning an Oxidation Number. The sum of the O.N. values for the atoms in a molecule equals zero, while the sum of the O.N. values for the atoms in an ion equals the ion's charge.
Solution:
a) AsH_3. H is combined with a nonmetal, so its O.N. is +1 (Rule 3). Three H atoms have a sum of +3. To have a sum of 0 for the molecule, As has an O.N. of –3. **As = –3**
b) $H_2AsO_4^-$. The O.N. of H in this compound is +1, for a total of +2. The O.N. of each oxygen is –2, for a total of –8. As has an O.N. of **+5** since [(+2) + (+5) + (–8)] = –1, the charge of the ion. **As = +5**
c) $AsCl_3$. Each chlorine has an O.N. of –1, for a total of –3. The O.N. of As is +3. **As = +3**

4.90 Plan: Consult the Rules for Assigning an Oxidation Number. The sum of the O.N. values for the atoms in a molecule equals zero, while the sum of the O.N. values for the atoms in an ion equals the ion's charge.
Solution:
a) MnO_4^{2-}. The O.N. of each oxygen is –2, for a total of –8; the O.N. of Mn must be +6 since [(+6) + (–8)] = –2, the charge of the ion. **Mn = +6**
b) Mn_2O_3. The O.N. of each oxygen is –2, for a total of –6; the sum of the O.N.s of the two Mn atoms must be +6. The O.N. of each manganese is +3. **Mn = +3**
c) $KMnO_4$. The O.N. of potassium is +1 and the O.N. of each oxygen is –2, for a total of –8. The O.N. of Mn is +7 since [(+1) + (+7) + (–8)] = 0. **Mn = +7**

4.92 Plan: First, assign oxidation numbers to all atoms following the rules. The reactant that is the reducing agent contains an atom that is oxidized (O.N. increases from the left side to the right side of the equation). The reactant that is the oxidizing agent contains an atom that is reduced (O.N. decreases from the left side to the right side of the equation). Recognize that the agent is the compound that contains the atom that is oxidized or reduced, not just the atom itself.

Solution:

a) +2 +6 –8   –8   –4   +2

+1 +3 –2   +7 –2   +1   +2   +4 –2   +1 –2

$5H_2C_2O_4(aq) + 2MnO_4^-(aq) + 6H^+(aq) \rightarrow 2Mn^{2+}(aq) + 10CO_2(g) + 8H_2O(l)$

Mn in MnO_4^- changes from +7 to +2 (reduction). Therefore, **MnO_4^- is the oxidizing agent.** C in $H_2C_2O_4$ changes from +3 to +4 (oxidation), so **$H_2C_2O_4$ is the reducing agent.**

b) –6   +2

0   +1   +5 –2   +2   +2 –2   +1 –2

$3Cu(s) + 8H^+(aq) + 2NO_3^-(aq) \rightarrow 3Cu^{2+}(aq) + 2NO(g) + 4H_2O(l)$

Cu changes from 0 to +2 (is oxidized) and **Cu is the reducing agent.** N changes from +5 (in NO_3^-) to +2 (in NO) and is reduced, so **NO_3^- is the oxidizing agent.**

4.94 Plan: First, assign oxidation numbers to all atoms following the rules. The reactant that is the reducing agent contains an atom that is oxidized (O.N. increases from the left side to the right side of the equation). The reactant that is the oxidizing agent contains an atom that is reduced (O.N. decreases from the left side to the right side of the equation). Recognize that the agent is the compound that contains the atom that is oxidized or reduced, not just the atom itself.

Solution:

a)   –6   –6   –4   +2

+1   –1   0   +5 –2   +4 –1   +4 –2   +1 –2

$8H^+(aq) + 6Cl^-(aq) + Sn(s) + 4NO_3^-(aq) \rightarrow SnCl_6^{2-}(aq) + 4NO_2(g) + 4H_2O(l)$

Nitrogen changes from an O.N. of +5 in NO_3^- to +4 in NO_2 (is reduced) so **NO_3^- is the oxidizing agent.** Sn changes from an O.N. of 0 to an O.N. of +4 in $SnCl_6^{2-}$ (is oxidized) so **Sn is the reducing agent.**

b) –8   +2

+7 –2   –1   +1   0   +2   +1 –2

$2MnO_4^-(aq) + 10Cl^-(aq) + 16H^+(aq) \rightarrow 5Cl_2(g) + 2Mn^{2+}(aq) + 8H_2O(l)$

Manganese changes from an O.N. of +7 in MnO_4^- to an O.N. of +2 in Mn^{2+} (is reduced) so **MnO_4^- is the oxidizing** agent. Chlorine changes its O.N. from –1 in Cl^- to 0 as the element Cl_2 (is oxidized) so **Cl^- is the reducing agent.**

4.96 Plan: Find the moles of MnO_4^- from the molarity and volume information. Use the molar ratio in the balanced equation to find the moles of H_2O_2. Multiply the moles of H_2O_2 by its molar mass to determine the mass of H_2O_2 present. Mass percent is calculated by dividing the mass of H_2O_2 by the mass of the sample and multiplying by 100. Assign oxidation numbers to all atoms following the rules. The reactant that is the reducing agent contains an atom that is oxidized (O.N. increases from the left side to the right side of the equation).

Solution:

a) Moles of $MnO_4^- = (43.2\text{ mL})\left(\frac{10^{-3}\text{ L}}{1\text{ mL}}\right)\left(\frac{0.105\text{ mol }MnO_4^-}{\text{L}}\right) = 4.536\text{x}10^{-3} = \mathbf{4.54x10^{-3}\ mol\ MnO_4^-}$

b) Moles of $H_2O_2 = (4.536\text{x}10^{-3}\ MnO_4^-)\left(\frac{5\text{ mol }H_2O_2}{2\text{ mol }MnO_4^-}\right) = 0.01134 = \mathbf{0.0113\ mol\ H_2O_2}$

c) Mass (g) of $H_2O_2 = (0.01134\text{ mol }H_2O_2)\left(\frac{34.02\text{ g }H_2O_2}{1\text{ mol }H_2O_2}\right) = 0.3857868 = \mathbf{0.386\ g\ H_2O_2}$

d) Mass percent of $H_2O_2 = \frac{\text{mass of }H_2O_2}{\text{mass of sample}}(100) = \frac{0.3857868\text{ g }H_2O_2}{14.8\text{ g sample}}(100) = 2.606668 = \mathbf{2.61\%\ H_2O_2}$

e) –8   +2 –2   +2

+7 –2   +1 –1   +1   0   +2   +1 –2

$2MnO_4^-(aq) + 5H_2O_2(aq) + 6H^+(aq) \rightarrow 5O_2(g) + 2Mn^{2+}(aq) + 8H_2O(l)$

The O.N. of oxygen increases from –1 in H_2O_2 to 0 in O_2 and is therefore oxidized while the O.N. of Mn decreases from +7 in MnO_4^- to +2 in Mn^{2+} and is reduced. **H_2O_2** is the reducing agent.

4.102 Plan: Recall that two reactants are combined to form one product in a combination reaction. A reaction is a redox reaction only if the oxidation numbers of some atoms change during the reaction.

Solution:

A common example of a combination/redox reaction is the combination of a metal and nonmetal to form an ionic salt, such as $2Mg(s) + O_2(g) \rightarrow 2MgO(s)$ in which magnesium is oxidized and oxygen is reduced. A common example of a combination/non-redox reaction is the combination of a metal oxide and water to form an acid, such as: $CaO(s) + H_2O(l) \rightarrow Ca(OH)_2(aq)$.

4.103 Plan: In a combination reaction, two or more reactants form one product. In a decomposition reaction, one reactant forms two or more products. In a displacement reaction, atoms or ions exchange places. Balance the reactions by inspection.

Solution:

a) $Ca(s) + 2H_2O(l) \rightarrow Ca(OH)_2(aq) + H_2(g)$

Displacement: one Ca atom displaces 2 H atoms.

b) $2NaNO_3(s) \rightarrow 2NaNO_2(s) + O_2(g)$

Decomposition: one reactant breaks into two products.

c) $C_2H_2(g) + 2H_2(g) \rightarrow C_2H_6(g)$

Combination: two reactants combine to form one product.

4.105 Plan: In a combination reaction, two or more reactants form one product. In a decomposition reaction, one reactant forms two or more products. In a displacement reaction, atoms or ions exchange places. Balance the reactions by inspection.

Solution:

a) $2Sb(s) + 3Cl_2(g) \rightarrow 2SbCl_3(s)$

Combination: two reactants combine to form one product.

b) $2AsH_3(g) \rightarrow 2As(s) + 3H_2(g)$

Decomposition: one reactant breaks into two products.

c) $Zn(s) + Fe(NO_3)_2(aq) \rightarrow Zn(NO_3)_2(aq) + Fe(s)$

Displacement: one Zn displaces one Fe atom.

4.107 Plan: In a combination reaction, two or more reactants form one product. Two elements as reactants often results in a combination reaction. In a decomposition reaction, one reactant forms two or more products; one reactant only often indicates a decomposition reaction. In a displacement reaction, atoms or ions exchange places. An element and a compound as reactants often indicate a displacement reaction. Balance the reactions by inspection.

Solution:

a) The combination between a metal and a nonmetal gives a binary ionic compound.

$$Sr(s) + Br_2(l) \rightarrow SrBr_2(s)$$

b) Many metal oxides release oxygen gas upon thermal decomposition.

$$2Ag_2O(s) \xrightarrow{\Delta} 4Ag(s) + O_2(g)$$

c) This is a displacement reaction. Mn is a more reactive metal and displaces Cu^{2+} from solution.

$$Mn(s) + Cu(NO_3)_2(aq) \rightarrow Mn(NO_3)_2(aq) + Cu(s)$$

4.109 Plan: In a combination reaction, two or more reactants form one product. Two elements as reactants often results in a combination reaction. In a decomposition reaction, one reactant forms two or more products; one reactant only often indicates a decomposition reaction. In a displacement reaction, atoms or ions exchange places. An element and a compound as reactants often indicate a displacement reaction. Balance the reactions by inspection.

Solution:

a) The combination of two nonmetals gives a covalent compound.

$$N_2(g) + 3H_2(g) \rightarrow 2NH_3(g)$$

b) Some compounds undergo thermal decomposition to simpler substances.

$$2NaClO_3(s) \xrightarrow{\Delta} 2NaCl(s) + 3O_2(g)$$

c) This is a displacement reaction. Active metals like Ba can displace hydrogen from water.

$$Ba(s) + 2H_2O(l) \rightarrow Ba(OH)_2(aq) + H_2(g)$$

4.111 Plan: In a combination reaction, two or more reactants form one product. Two elements as reactants often results in a combination reaction. In a decomposition reaction, one reactant forms two or more products; one reactant only often indicates a decomposition reaction. In a displacement reaction, atoms or ions exchange places. An element and a compound as reactants often indicate a displacement reaction. Balance the reactions by inspection.

Solution:

a) Cs, a metal, and I_2, a nonmetal, combine to form the binary ionic compound, CsI.

$$2Cs(s) + I_2(s) \rightarrow 2CsI(s)$$

b) Al is a stronger reducing agent than Mn and is able to displace Mn from solution, i.e., cause the reduction from $Mn^{2+}(aq)$ to $Mn^0(s)$.

$$2Al(s) + 3MnSO_4(aq) \rightarrow Al_2(SO_4)_3(aq) + 3Mn(s)$$

c) This is a combination reaction in which sulfur dioxide, SO_2, a nonmetal oxide, combines with oxygen, O_2, to form the higher oxide, SO_3.

$$2SO_2(g) + O_2(g) \xrightarrow{\Delta} 2SO_3(g)$$

It is not clear from the problem, but energy must be added to force this reaction to proceed.

d) Butane is a four carbon hydrocarbon with the formula C_4H_{10}. It burns in the presence of oxygen, O_2, to form carbon dioxide gas and water vapor. Although this is a redox reaction that could be balanced using the oxidation number method, it is easier to balance by considering only atoms on either side of the equation. First, balance carbon and hydrogen (because they only appear in one species on each side of the equation), and then balance oxygen.

$$2C_4H_{10}(g) + 13O_2(g) \rightarrow 8CO_2(g) + 10H_2O(g)$$

e) Total ionic equation in which soluble species are shown dissociated into ions:

$$2Al(s) + 3Mn^{2+}(aq) + 3SO_4^{2-}(aq) \rightarrow 2Al^{3+}(aq) + 3SO_4^{2-}(aq) + 3Mn(s)$$

Net ionic equation in which the spectator ions are omitted:

$$2Al(s) + 3Mn^{2+}(aq) \rightarrow 2Al^{3+}(aq) + 3Mn(s)$$

Note that the molar coefficients are not simplified because the number of electrons lost (6 e^-) must equal the electrons gained (6 e^-).

4.113 Plan: Write a balanced equation that shows the decomposition of HgO to its elements. Convert the mass of HgO to moles and use the molar ratio from the balanced equation to find the moles and then the mass of O_2. Perform the same calculation to find the mass of the other product.

Solution:

a) The balanced chemical equation is $2HgO(s) \xrightarrow{\Delta} 2Hg(l) + O_2(g)$.

$$\text{Moles of HgO} = (4.27 \text{ kg HgO})\left(\frac{10^3 \text{ g}}{1 \text{ kg}}\right)\left(\frac{1 \text{ mol HgO}}{216.6 \text{ g HgO}}\right) = 19.71376 \text{ mol HgO}$$

$$\text{Moles of } O_2 = (19.71376 \text{ mol HgO})\left(\frac{1 \text{ mol } O_2}{2 \text{ mol HgO}}\right) = 9.85688 \text{ mol } O_2$$

$$\text{Mass (g) of } O_2 = (9.85688 \text{ mol } O_2)\left(\frac{32.00 \text{ g } O_2}{1 \text{ mol } O_2}\right) = 315.420 = \mathbf{315 \text{ g } O_2}$$

b) The other product is **mercury**.

$$\text{Moles of Hg} = (19.71376 \text{ mol HgO})\left(\frac{2 \text{ mol Hg}}{2 \text{ mol HgO}}\right) = 19.71376 \text{ mol Hg}$$

$$\text{Mass (kg) Hg} = (19.71376 \text{ mol Hg})\left(\frac{200.6 \text{ g Hg}}{1 \text{ mol Hg}}\right)\left(\frac{1 \text{ kg}}{10^3 \text{ g}}\right) = 3.95458 = \mathbf{3.95 \text{ kg Hg}}$$

4.115 Plan: To determine the reactant in excess, write the balanced equation (metal + $O_2 \rightarrow$ metal oxide), convert reactant masses to moles, and use molar ratios to see which reactant makes the smaller ("limiting") amount of product. Use the limiting reactant to calculate the amount of product formed. Use the molar ratio to find the amount of excess reactant required to react with the limiting reactant; the amount of excess reactant that remains is the initial amount of excess reactant minus the amount required for the reaction.

Solution:
The balanced equation is $4Li(s) + O_2(g) \rightarrow 2Li_2O(s)$.

a) Moles of Li_2O if Li limiting $= (1.62 \text{ g Li})\left(\frac{1 \text{ mol Li}}{6.941 \text{ g Li}}\right)\left(\frac{2 \text{ mol } Li_2O}{4 \text{ mol Li}}\right) = 0.1166979 \text{ mol } Li_2O$

Moles of Li_2O if O_2 limiting $= (6.50 \text{ g } O_2)\left(\frac{1 \text{ mol } O_2}{32.00 \text{ g } O_2}\right)\left(\frac{2 \text{ mol } Li_2O}{1 \text{ mol } O_2}\right) = 0.40625 \text{ mol } Li_2O$

Li is the limiting reactant since it produces the smaller amount of product; **O_2 is in excess.**
b) Using Li as the limiting reagent, 0.1166979 = **0.117 mol Li_2O** is formed.
c) Li is limiting, thus there will be none remaining (**0 g Li**).

Mass (g) of $Li_2O = (0.1166979 \text{ mol } Li_2O)\left(\frac{29.88 \text{ g } Li_2O}{1 \text{ mol } Li_2O}\right) = 3.4869 = \mathbf{3.49 \text{ g } Li_2O}$

Mass (g) of O_2 reacted $= (1.62 \text{ g Li})\left(\frac{1 \text{ mol Li}}{6.941 \text{ g Li}}\right)\left(\frac{1 \text{ mol } O_2}{4 \text{ mol Li}}\right)\left(\frac{32.00 \text{ g } O_2}{1 \text{ mol } O_2}\right) = 1.867166 \text{ g } O_2$

Remaining O_2 = initial amount – amount reacted = 6.50 g O_2 – 1.867166 g O_2 = 4.632834 = **4.63 g O_2**

4.117 Plan: Since mass must be conserved, the original amount of mixture – amount of residue = mass of oxygen produced. Write a balanced equation and use molar ratios to convert from the mass of oxygen produced to the amount of $KClO_3$ reacted. Mass percent is calculated by dividing the mass of $KClO_3$ by the mass of the sample and multiplying by 100.
Solution:

$2KClO_3(s) \xrightarrow{\Delta} 2KCl(s) + 3O_2(g)$

Mass (g) of O_2 produced = mass of mixture – mass of residue = 0.950 g – 0.700 g = 0.250 g O_2

Mass (g) of $KClO_3 = (0.250 \text{ g } O_2)\left(\frac{1 \text{ mol } O_2}{32.00 \text{ g } O_2}\right)\left(\frac{2 \text{ mol } KClO_3}{3 \text{ mol } O_2}\right)\left(\frac{122.55 \text{ g } KClO_3}{1 \text{ mol } KClO_3}\right) = 0.63828125 \text{ g } KClO_3$

Mass % $KClO_3 = \frac{\text{mass of } KClO_3}{\text{mass of sample}}(100\%) = \frac{0.63828125 \text{ g } KClO_3}{0.950 \text{ g sample}}(100\%) = 67.1875 = \mathbf{67.2\% \ KClO_3}$

4.119 Plan: Write the balanced equation for the displacement reaction, convert reactant masses to moles, and use molar ratios to see which reactant makes the smaller ("limiting") amount of product. Use the limiting reactant to calculate the amount of product formed.
Solution:
The balanced reaction is $2Al(s) + Fe_2O_3(s) \rightarrow 2Fe(l) + Al_2O_3(s)$.

Moles of Fe if Al is limiting $= (1.50 \text{ kg Al})\left(\frac{10^3 \text{ g}}{1 \text{ kg}}\right)\left(\frac{1 \text{ mol Al}}{26.98 \text{ g Al}}\right)\left(\frac{2 \text{ mol Fe}}{2 \text{ mol Al}}\right) = 55.59674 \text{ mol Fe}$

Moles of Fe if Fe_2O_3 is limiting $= (25.0 \text{ mol } Fe_2O_3)\left(\frac{2 \text{ mol Fe}}{1 \text{ mol } Fe_2O_3}\right) = 50.0 \text{ mol Fe}$

Fe_2O_3 is the limiting reactant since it produces the smaller amount of Fe; 50.0 moles of Fe forms.

Mass (g) of Fe $= (50.0 \text{ mol Fe})\left(\frac{55.85 \text{ g Fe}}{1 \text{ mol Fe}}\right) = 2792.5 = \mathbf{2790 \text{ g Fe} = 2.79 \text{ kg Fe}}$

4.120 Plan: In ionic compounds, iron has two common oxidation states, +2 and +3. First, write the balanced equations for the formation and decomposition of compound A. Then, determine which reactant is limiting by converting reactant masses to moles, and using molar ratios to see which reactant makes the smaller ("limiting") amount of product. From the amount of the limiting reactant calculate how much compound B will form.

Solution:

Compound A is iron chloride with iron in the higher, +3, oxidation state. Thus, the formula for compound A is $FeCl_3$ and the correct name is iron(III) chloride. The balanced equation for formation of $FeCl_3$ is:

$$2Fe(s) + 3Cl_2(g) \rightarrow 2FeCl_3(s)$$

To find out whether 50.6 g Fe or 83.8 g Cl_2 limits the amount of product, calculate the number of moles of iron(III) chloride that could form based on each reactant.

$$\text{Moles of } FeCl_3 \text{ if Fe is limiting} = (50.6 \text{ g Fe})\left(\frac{1 \text{ mol Fe}}{55.85 \text{ g Fe}}\right)\left(\frac{2 \text{ mol } FeCl_3}{2 \text{ mol Fe}}\right) = 0.905998 \text{ mol } FeCl_3$$

$$\text{Moles of } FeCl_3 \text{ if } Cl_2 \text{ is limiting} = (83.8 \text{ g } Cl_2)\left(\frac{1 \text{ mol } Cl_2}{70.90 \text{ g } Cl_2}\right)\left(\frac{2 \text{ mol } FeCl_3}{3 \text{ mol } Cl_2}\right) = 0.787964 \text{ mol } FeCl_3$$

Since fewer moles of $FeCl_3$ are produced from the available amount of chlorine, the chlorine is the limiting reactant, producing 0.787964 mol of $FeCl_3$. The $FeCl_3$ decomposes to $FeCl_2$ with iron in the +2 oxidation state. $FeCl_2$ is compound B. The balanced equation for the decomposition of $FeCl_3$ is:

$$2FeCl_3(s) \rightarrow 2FeCl_2(s) + Cl_2(g)$$

$$\text{Mass (g) of } FeCl_2 = (0.787964 \text{ mol } FeCl_3)\left(\frac{2 \text{ mol } FeCl_2}{2 \text{ mol } FeCl_3}\right)\left(\frac{126.75 \text{ g } FeCl_2}{1 \text{ mol } FeCl_2}\right) = 99.874 = \mathbf{99.9 \text{ g } FeCl_2}$$

4.125 Plan: Review the concept of dynamic equilibrium.

Solution:

$$2NO(g) + Br_2(g) \leftrightarrow 2NOBr(g)$$

On a molecular scale, chemical reactions are dynamic. If NO and Br_2 are placed in a container, molecules of NO and molecules of Br_2 will react to form NOBr. Some of the NOBr molecules will decompose and the resulting NO and Br_2 molecules will recombine with different NO and Br_2 molecules to form more NOBr. In this sense, the reaction is dynamic because the original NO and Br_2 pairings do not remain permanently attached to each other. Eventually, the rate of the forward reaction (combination of NO and Br_2) will equal the rate of the reverse reaction (decomposition of NOBr) at which point the reaction is said to have reached equilibrium. If you could take "snapshot" pictures of the molecules at equilibrium, you would see a constant number of reactant (NO, Br_2) and product molecules (NOBr), but the pairings would not stay the same.

4.127 Plan: Ferrous ion is Fe^{2+}. Write a reaction to show the conversion of Fe to Fe^{2+}. Convert the mass of Fe in a 125-g serving to the mass of Fe in a 737-g sample. Use molar mass to convert mass of Fe to moles of Fe and use Avogadro's number to convert moles of Fe to moles of ions.

Solution:

a) Fe oxidizes to Fe^{2+} with a loss of 2 electrons. The H^+ in the acidic food is reduced to H_2 with a gain of 2 electrons. The balanced reaction is:

$$Fe(s) + 2H^+(aq) \rightarrow Fe^{2+}(aq) + H_2(g)$$

O.N.: 0 +1 +2 0

$$\text{b) Mass (g) of Fe in the jar of tomato sauce} = (737 \text{ g sauce})\left(\frac{49 \text{ mg Fe}}{125 \text{ g sauce}}\right)\left(\frac{10^{-3} \text{ g}}{1 \text{ mg}}\right) = 0.288904 \text{ g Fe}$$

$$\text{Number of } Fe^{2+} \text{ ions} = (0.288904 \text{ g Fe})\left(\frac{1 \text{ mol Fe}}{55.85 \text{ g Fe}}\right)\left(\frac{1 \text{ mol } Fe^{2+}}{1 \text{ mol Fe}}\right)\left(\frac{6.022 \times 10^{23} \ Fe^{2+} \text{ions}}{1 \text{ mol } Fe^{2+}}\right)$$

$$= 3.11509 \times 10^{21} = \mathbf{3.1 \times 10^{21} \ Fe^{2+} \text{ ions}} \text{ per jar of sauce}$$

4.129 Plan: Convert the mass of glucose to moles and use the molar ratios from the balanced equation to find the moles of ethanol and CO_2. The amount of ethanol is converted from moles to grams using its molar mass. The amount of CO_2 is converted from moles to volume in liters using the conversion factor given.

Solution:

$$\text{Moles of } C_2H_5OH = (100. \text{ g } C_6H_{12}O_6)\left(\frac{1 \text{ mol } C_6H_{12}O_6}{180.16 \text{ g } C_6H_{12}O_6}\right)\left(\frac{2 \text{ mol } C_2H_5OH}{1 \text{ mol } C_6H_{12}O_6}\right) = 1.11012 \text{ mol } C_2H_5OH$$

$$\text{Mass (g) of } C_2H_5OH = (1.11012 \text{ mol } C_2H_5OH)\left(\frac{46.07 \text{ g } C_2H_5OH}{1 \text{ mol } C_2H_5OH}\right) = 51.143 = \mathbf{51.1 \text{ g } C_2H_5OH}$$

$$\text{Moles of } CO_2 = (100. \text{ g } C_6H_{12}O_6)\left(\frac{1 \text{ mol } C_6H_{12}O_6}{180.16 \text{ g } C_6H_{12}O_6}\right)\left(\frac{2 \text{ mol } CO_2}{1 \text{ mol } C_6H_{12}O_6}\right) = 1.11012 \text{ mol } CO_2$$

$$\text{Volume (L) of } CO_2 = (1.11012 \text{ mol } CO_2)\left(\frac{22.4 \text{ L } CO_2}{1 \text{ mol } CO_2}\right) = 24.8667 = \mathbf{24.9 \text{ L } CO_2}$$

4.131 Plan: Remember that spectator ions are omitted from net ionic equations. Assign oxidation numbers to all atoms in the titration reaction, following the rules. The reactant that is the reducing agent contains an atom that is oxidized (O.N. increases from the left side to the right side of the equation). The reactant that is the oxidizing agent contains an atom that is reduced (O.N. decreases from the left side to the right side of the equation). Find the number of moles of $KMnO_4$ from the molarity and volume and use molar ratios in the balanced equations to find the moles and then mass of $CaCl_2$. Mass percent is calculated by dividing the mass of $CaCl_2$ by the mass of the sample and multiplying by 100.

Solution:

a) The reaction is: $Na_2C_2O_4(aq) + CaCl_2(aq) \rightarrow CaC_2O_4(s) + 2NaCl(aq)$

The total ionic equation in which soluble substances are dissociated into ions is:

$$2Na^+(aq) + C_2O_4^{2-}(aq) + Ca^{2+}(aq) + 2Cl^-(aq) \rightarrow CaC_2O_4(s) + 2Na^+(aq) + 2Cl^-(aq)$$

Omitting Na^+ and Cl^- as spectator ions gives the net ionic equation:

$$\mathbf{Ca^{2+}(aq) + C_2O_4^{2-}(aq) \rightarrow CaC_2O_4(s)}$$

b) You may recognize this reaction as a redox titration, because the permanganate ion, MnO_4^-, is a common oxidizing agent. The MnO_4^- oxidizes the oxalate ion, $C_2O_4^{2-}$ to CO_2. Mn changes from +7 to +2 (reduction) and C changes from +3 to +4 (oxidation). The equation that describes this process is:

$$H_2C_2O_4(aq) + K^+(aq) + MnO_4^-(aq) \rightarrow Mn^{2+}(aq) + CO_2(g) + K^+(aq)$$

$H_2C_2O_4$ is a weak acid, so it cannot be written in a fully dissociated form. $KMnO_4$ is a soluble salt, so it can be written in its dissociated form. $K^+(aq)$ is omitted in the net ionic equation because it is a spectator ion. We will balance the equation using the oxidation number method. First assign oxidation numbers to all elements in the reaction:

$$\begin{array}{cccc} +2\ +6\ -8 & -8 & & -4 \\ +1\ +3\ -2 & +7\ -2 & +2 & +4\ -2 \\ H_2C_2O_4(aq) + & MnO_4^-(aq) \rightarrow & Mn^{2+}(aq) + & 2CO_2(g) \end{array}$$

Identify the oxidized and reduced species and multiply one or both species by the appropriate factors to make the electrons lost equal the electrons gained. Each C in $H_2C_2O_4$ increases in O.N. from +3 to +4 for a total gain of 2 electrons. Mn in MnO_4^- decreases in O.N. from +7 to +2 for a loss of 5 electrons. Multiply C by 5 and Mn by 2 to get an electron loss = electron gain of 10 electrons.

$$5H_2C_2O_4(aq) + 2MnO_4^-(aq) \rightarrow 2Mn^{2+}(aq) + 10CO_2(g)$$

Adding water and $H^+(aq)$ to finish balancing the equation is appropriate since the reaction takes place in acidic medium. Add $8H_2O(l)$ to right side of equation to balance the oxygen and then add $6H^+(aq)$ to the left to balance hydrogen.

$$\mathbf{5H_2C_2O_4(aq) + 2MnO_4^-(aq) + 6H^+(aq) \rightarrow 10CO_2(g) + 2Mn^{2+}(aq) + 8H_2O(l)}$$

c) Mn in MnO_4^- decreases in O.N. from +7 to +2 and is reduced. **$KMnO_4$** is the oxidizing agent.

d) C in $H_2C_2O_4$ increases in O.N. from +3 to +4 and is oxidized. **$H_2C_2O_4$** is the reducing agent.

e) The balanced equations provide the accurate molar ratios between species.

$$\text{Moles of } MnO_4^- = (37.68 \text{ mL})\left(\frac{10^{-3} \text{ L}}{1 \text{ mL}}\right)\left(\frac{0.1019 \text{ mol } KMnO_4}{1 \text{ L}}\right) = 0.0038396 \text{ mol } MnO_4^-$$

$$\text{Moles of } H_2C_2O_4 = (0.0038396 \text{ mol } MnO_4^-)\left(\frac{5 \text{ mol } H_2C_2O_4}{2 \text{ mol } MnO_4^-}\right) = 0.009599 \text{ mol } H_2C_2O_4$$

$$\text{Mass (g) } CaCl_2 = (0.009599 \text{ mol } H_2C_2O_4)\left(\frac{1 \text{ mol } CaCl_2}{1 \text{ mol } H_2C_2O_4}\right)\left(\frac{110.98 \text{ g } CaCl_2}{1 \text{ mol } CaCl_2}\right) = 1.06530 \text{ g } CaCl_2$$

$$\text{Mass percent CaCl}_2 = \frac{\text{mass of CaCl}_2}{\text{mass of sample}}(100) = \frac{1.06530 \text{ g CaCl}_2}{1.9348 \text{ g mixture}}(100) = 55.05995 = \mathbf{55.06\% \ CaCl_2}$$

4.134 Plan: Write a balanced equation for the reaction. This is an acid-base reaction between HCl and the base CO_3^{2-} to form H_2CO_3 which then decomposes into CO_2 and H_2O. Find the moles of HCl from the molarity and volume information and use the molar ratio in the balanced equation to find the moles and mass of dolomite. To find mass %, divide the mass of dolomite by the mass of soil and multiply by 100.

Solution:

The balanced equation for this reaction is:

$$CaMg(CO_3)_2(s) + 4HCl(aq) \rightarrow Ca^{2+}(aq) + Mg^{2+}(aq) + 2H_2O(l) + 2CO_2(g) + 4Cl^-(aq)$$

$$\text{Moles of HCl} = (33.56 \text{ mL})\left(\frac{10^{-3} \text{ L}}{1 \text{ mL}}\right)\left(\frac{0.2516 \text{ mol HCl}}{1 \text{ L}}\right) = 0.0084437 \text{ mol HCl}$$

$$\text{Mass CaMg(CO}_3)_2 = (0.0084437 \text{ mol HCl})\left(\frac{1 \text{ mol CaMg(CO}_3)_2}{4 \text{ mol HCl}}\right)\left(\frac{184.41 \text{ g CaMg(CO}_3)_2}{1 \text{ mol CaMg(CO}_3)_2}\right)$$

$$= 0.389276 \text{ g CaMg(CO}_3)_2$$

$$\text{Mass percent CaMg(CO}_3)_2 = \frac{\text{mass CaMg(CO}_3)_2}{\text{mass soil}}(100) = \frac{0.389276 \text{ g CaMg(CO}_3)_2}{13.86 \text{ g soil}}(100)$$

$$= 2.80863 = \mathbf{2.809\% \ CaMg(CO_3)_2}$$

4.136 Plan: For part a), assign oxidation numbers to each element; the oxidizing agent has an atom whose oxidation number decreases while the reducing agent has an atom whose oxidation number increases. For part b), use the molar ratios, beginning with step 3, to find the moles of NO_2, then moles of NO, then moles of NH_3 required to produce the given mass of HNO_3.

Solution:

a) *Step 1*

```
 +3                              +2
-3 +1       0         +2 -2      +1 -2
4NH3(g) + 5O2(g) → 4NO(g) + 6H2O(l)
```

$4NH_3(g) + 5O_2(g) \rightarrow 4NO(g) + 6H_2O(l)$

N is oxidized from –3 in NH_3 to +2 in NO; O is reduced from 0 in O_2 to to –2 in NO.

Oxidizing agent = O_2 **Reducing agent = NH_3**

Step 2

```
                   -4
+2 -2     0       +4 -2
2NO(g) + O2(g) → 2NO2(g)
```

$2NO(g) + O_2(g) \rightarrow 2NO_2(g)$

N is oxidized from +2 in NO to +4 in NO_2; O is reduced from 0 in O_2 to –2 in NO_2.

Oxidizing agent = O_2 **Reducing agent = NO**

Step 3

```
 -4       +2              -6
+4 -2     +1 -2         +1+5 -2     +2 -2
3NO2(g) + H2O(l) → 2HNO3(l) + NO(g)
```

$3NO_2(g) + H_2O(l) \rightarrow 2HNO_3(l) + NO(g)$

N is oxidized from +4 in NO_2 to +5 in HNO_3; N is reduced from +4 in NO_2 to +2 in NO.

Oxidizing agent = NO_2 **Reducing agent = NO_2**

$$\text{b) Moles of NO}_2 = (3.0\text{x}10^4 \text{ kg HNO}_3)\left(\frac{10^3 \text{ g}}{1 \text{ kg}}\right)\left(\frac{1 \text{ mol HNO}_3}{63.02 \text{ g HNO}_3}\right)\left(\frac{3 \text{ mol NO}_2}{2 \text{ mol HNO}_3}\right) = 7.14059\text{x}10^5 \text{ mol NO}_2$$

$$\text{Moles of NO} = (7.14059\text{x}10^5 \text{ mol NO}_2)\left(\frac{2 \text{ mol NO}}{2 \text{ mol NO}_2}\right) = 7.14059\text{x}10^5 \text{ mol NO}$$

$$\text{Moles of NH}_3 = (7.14059\text{x}10^5 \text{ mol NO})\left(\frac{4 \text{ mol NH}_3}{4 \text{ mol NO}}\right) = 7.14059\text{x}10^5 \text{ mol NH}_3$$

$$\text{Mass (kg) of NH}_3 = \left(7.14059\text{x}10^5 \text{ mol NH}_3\right)\left(\frac{17.03 \text{ g NH}_3}{1 \text{ mol NH}_3}\right)\left(\frac{1 \text{ kg}}{10^3 \text{ g}}\right) = 1.21604\text{x}10^4 = \mathbf{1.2x10^4 \text{ kg NH}_3}$$

4.139 Plan: Write a balanced equation and use the molar ratio between Na_2O_2 and CO_2 to convert the amount of Na_2O_2 given to the amount of CO_2 that reacts with that amount. Convert that amount of CO_2 to liters of air.
Solution:
The reaction is: $2Na_2O_2(s) + 2CO_2(g) \rightarrow 2Na_2CO_3(s) + O_2(g)$.

$$\text{Mass (g) of CO}_2 = \left(80.0 \text{ g Na}_2\text{O}_2\right)\left(\frac{1 \text{ mol Na}_2\text{O}_2}{77.98 \text{ g Na}_2\text{O}_2}\right)\left(\frac{2 \text{ mol CO}_2}{2 \text{ mol Na}_2\text{O}_2}\right)\left(\frac{44.01 \text{ g CO}_2}{1 \text{ mol CO}_2}\right) = 45.1500 \text{ g CO}_2$$

$$\text{Volume (L) of air} = \left(45.150 \text{ g CO}_2\right)\left(\frac{\text{L air}}{0.0720 \text{ g CO}_2}\right) = 627.08 = \mathbf{627 \text{ L air}}$$

4.141 Plan: Use the mass percents to find the mass of each component needed for 1.00 kg of glass. Write balanced reactions for the decomposition of sodium carbonate and calcium carbonate to produce an oxide and CO_2. Use the molar ratios in these reactions to find the moles and mass of each carbonate required to produce the amount of oxide in the glass sample.
Solution:
A 1.00-kg piece of glass of composition 75% SiO_2, 15% Na_2O, and 10% CaO would contain:

$$\text{Mass (kg) of SiO}_2 = \left(1.00 \text{ kg glass}\right)\left(\frac{75\% \text{ SiO}_2}{100\% \text{ glass}}\right) = \mathbf{0.75 \text{ kg SiO}_2}$$

$$\text{Mass (kg) of Na}_2\text{O} = \left(1.00 \text{ kg glass}\right)\left(\frac{15\% \text{ Na}_2\text{O}}{100\% \text{ glass}}\right) = 0.15 \text{ kg Na}_2\text{O}$$

$$\text{Mass (kg) of CaO} = \left(1.00 \text{ kg glass}\right)\left(\frac{10.\% \text{ CaO}}{100\% \text{ glass}}\right) = 0.10 \text{ kg CaO}$$

In this example, the SiO_2 is added directly while the sodium oxide comes from decomposition of sodium carbonate and the calcium oxide from decomposition of calcium carbonate:

$Na_2CO_3(s) \rightarrow Na_2O(s) + CO_2(g)$

$CaCO_3(s) \rightarrow CaO(s) + CO_2(g)$

Mass (kg) of Na_2CO_3 =

$$\left(0.15 \text{ kg Na}_2\text{O}\right)\left(\frac{10^3 \text{ g}}{1 \text{ kg}}\right)\left(\frac{1 \text{ mol Na}_2\text{O}}{61.98 \text{ g Na}_2\text{O}}\right)\left(\frac{1 \text{ mol Na}_2\text{CO}_3}{1 \text{ mol Na}_2\text{O}}\right)\left(\frac{105.99 \text{ g Na}_2\text{CO}_3}{1 \text{ mol Na}_2\text{CO}_3}\right)\left(\frac{1 \text{ kg}}{10^3 \text{ g}}\right)$$

$$= 0.25651 = \mathbf{0.26 \text{ kg Na}_2\text{CO}_3}$$

$$\text{Mass (kg) of CaCO}_3 = \left(0.10 \text{ kg CaO}\right)\left(\frac{10^3 \text{ g}}{1 \text{ kg}}\right)\left(\frac{1 \text{ mol CaO}}{56.08 \text{ g CaO}}\right)\left(\frac{1 \text{ mol CaCO}_3}{1 \text{ mol CaO}}\right)\left(\frac{100.09 \text{ g CaCO}_3}{1 \text{ mol CaCO}_3}\right)\left(\frac{1 \text{ kg}}{10^3 \text{ g}}\right)$$

$$= 0.178477 = \mathbf{0.18 \text{ kg CaCO}_3}$$

4.144 Plan: Write balanced reactions and use molar ratios to find the moles of product. To find mass %, divide the mass of thyroxine by the mass of extract and multiply by 100.
Solution:
a) There is not enough information to write complete chemical equations, but the following equations can be written:

$C_{15}H_{11}I_4NO_4(s) + Na_2CO_3(s) \rightarrow 4I^-(aq)$ + other products

$I^-(aq) + Br_2(l) + HCl(aq) \rightarrow IO_3^-(aq)$ + other products

$$\text{Moles of IO}_3^- = \left(1 \text{ mol C}_{15}\text{H}_{11}\text{I}_4\text{NO}_4\right)\left(\frac{4 \text{ mol I}^-}{1 \text{ mol C}_{15}\text{H}_{11}\text{I}_4\text{NO}_4}\right)\left(\frac{1 \text{ mol IO}_3^-}{1 \text{ mol I}^-}\right) = \mathbf{4 \text{ moles IO}_3^- \text{ are produced}}$$

b) +5 −2 +1 −1 0 +1 −2

$IO_3^-(aq) + H^+(aq) + I^-(aq) \rightarrow I_2(aq) + H_2O(l)$

This is a difficult equation to balance because the iodine species are both reducing and oxidizing. The O.N. of iodine decreases from +5 in IO_3^- to 0 in I_2 and so gains 5 electrons; the O.N. of iodine increases from −1 in I^- to 0 in I_2 and so loses 1 electron. Start balancing the equation by placing a coefficient of 5 in front of $I^-(aq)$, so the electrons lost equal the electrons gained. Do not place a 5 in front of $I_2(aq)$, because not all of the $I_2(aq)$ comes from oxidation of $I^-(aq)$. Some of the $I_2(aq)$ comes from the reduction of $IO_3^-(aq)$. Place a coefficient of 3 in front of $I_2(aq)$ to correctly balance iodine:

$IO_3^-(aq) + H^+(aq) + 5I^-(aq) \rightarrow 3I_2(aq) + H_2O(l)$

The reaction is now balanced from a redox standpoint, so finish balancing the reaction by balancing the oxygen and hydrogen.

$IO_3^-(aq) + 6H^+(aq) + 5I^-(aq) \rightarrow 3I_2(aq) + 3H_2O(l)$

IO_3^- is the oxidizing agent, and **I^- is the reducing agent.**

$$\text{Moles of } I_2 \text{ produced per mole of thyroxine} = (1 \text{ mol } C_{15}H_{11}I_4NO_4)\left(\frac{4 \text{ mol } IO_3^-}{1 \text{ mol } C_{15}H_{11}I_4NO_4}\right)\left(\frac{3 \text{ mol } I_2}{1 \text{ mol } IO_3^-}\right)$$

= **12 moles of I_2 are produced per mole of thyroxine**

c) Using Thy to represent thyroxine:

The balanced equation for this reaction is $I_2(aq) + 2S_2O_3^{2-}(aq) \rightarrow 2I^-(aq) + S_4O_6^{2-}(aq)$.

$$\text{Moles of } S_2O_3^{2-} = (17.23 \text{ mL})\left(\frac{10^{-3} \text{ L}}{1 \text{ mL}}\right)\left(\frac{0.1000 \text{ mol } S_2O_3^{2-}}{\text{L}}\right) = 0.001723 \text{ mol } S_2O_3^{2-}$$

$$\text{Moles of Thy} = (0.001723 \text{ mol } S_2O_3^{2-})\left(\frac{1 \text{ mol } I_2}{2 \text{ mol } S_2O_3^{2-}}\right)\left(\frac{1 \text{ mol Thy}}{12 \text{ mol } I_2}\right) = 7.179167\text{x}10^{-5} \text{ mol Thy}$$

$$\text{Mass (g) of Thy} = (7.179167\text{x}10^{-5} \text{ mol Thy})\left(\frac{776.8 \text{ g Thy}}{1 \text{ mol Thy}}\right) = 0.055767769 \text{ g Thy}$$

$$\text{Mass \% Thy} = \frac{\text{mass of Thy}}{\text{mass of extract}}(100) = \frac{0.055767769 \text{ g Thy}}{0.4332 \text{ g}}(100) = 12.8734 = \mathbf{12.87\% \ thyroxine}$$

4.147 Plan: Balance the equation to obtain the correct molar ratios. Use the mass percents to find the mass of each reactant in a 1.00 g sample, convert the mass of each reactant to moles, and use the molar ratios to find the limiting reactant and the amount of CO_2 produced. Convert moles of CO_2 produced to volume using the given conversion factor.

Solution:

a) Here is a suggested method for balancing the equation.

— Since PO_4^{2-} remains as a unit on both sides of the equation, treat it as a unit when balancing.

— On first inspection, one can see that Na needs to be balanced by adding a "2" in front of $NaHCO_3$. This then affects the balance of C, so add a "2" in front of CO_2.

— Hydrogen is not balanced, so change the coefficient of water to "2," as this will have the least impact on the other species.

— Verify that the other species are balanced.

$$Ca(H_2PO_4)_2(s) + 2NaHCO_3(s) \xrightarrow{\Delta} 2CO_2(g) + 2H_2O(g) + CaHPO_4(s) + Na_2HPO_4(s)$$

Determine whether $Ca(H_2PO_4)_2$ or $NaHCO_3$ limits the production of CO_2. In each case calculate the moles of CO_2 that might form.

$$\text{Mass (g) of } NaHCO_3 = (1.00 \text{ g})\left(\frac{31.0\%}{100\%}\right) = 0.31 \text{ g } NaHCO_3$$

$$\text{Mass (g) of } Ca(H_2PO_4)_2 = (1.00 \text{ g})\left(\frac{35.0\%}{100\%}\right) = 0.35 \text{ g } Ca(H_2PO_4)_2$$

$$\text{Moles of } CO_2 \text{ if } NaHCO_3 \text{ is limiting} = (0.31 \text{ g } NaHCO_3)\left(\frac{1 \text{ mol } NaHCO_3}{84.01 \text{ g } NaHCO_3}\right)\left(\frac{2 \text{ mol } CO_2}{2 \text{ mol } NaHCO_3}\right)$$

$$= 3.690\text{x}10^{-3} \text{ mol } CO_2$$

$$\text{Moles of } CO_2 \text{ if } Ca(H_2PO_4)_2 \text{ is limiting} = (0.35\text{g } Ca(H_2PO_4)_2)\left(\frac{1 \text{ mol } Ca(H_2PO_4)_2}{234.05 \text{ g } Ca(H_2PO_4)_2}\right)\left(\frac{2 \text{ mol } CO_2}{1 \text{ mol } Ca(H_2PO_4)_2}\right)$$

$$= 2.9908\text{x}10^{-3} \text{ mol } CO_2$$

Since $Ca(H_2PO_4)_2$ produces the smaller amount of product, it is the limiting reactant and **$3.0\text{x}10^{-3}$ mol CO_2** will be produced.

b) $$\text{Volume (L) of } CO_2 = (2.9908\text{x}10^{-3} \text{ mol } CO_2)\left(\frac{37.0 \text{ L}}{1 \text{ mol } CO_2}\right) = 0.1106596 = \mathbf{0.11 \text{ L } CO_2}$$

4.149 Plan: To determine the empirical formula, find the moles of each element present and divide by the smallest number of moles to get the smallest ratio of atoms. To find the molecular formula, divide the molar mass by the mass of the empirical formula to find the factor by which to multiple the empirical formula. Write the balanced acid-base reaction for part c) and use the molar ratio in that reaction to find the mass of bismuth(III) hydroxide.

Solution:

a) Determine the moles of each element present. The sample was burned in an unknown amount of O_2, therefore, the moles of oxygen must be found by a different method.

$$\text{Moles of C} = (0.1880 \text{ g } CO_2)\left(\frac{1 \text{ mol } CO_2}{44.01 \text{ g } CO_2}\right)\left(\frac{1 \text{ mol C}}{1 \text{ mol } CO_2}\right) = 4.271756\text{x}10^{-3} \text{ mol C}$$

$$\text{Moles of H} = (0.02750 \text{ g } H_2O)\left(\frac{1 \text{ mol } H_2O}{18.02 \text{ g } H_2O}\right)\left(\frac{2 \text{ mol H}}{1 \text{ mol } H_2O}\right) = 3.052164\text{x}10^{-3} \text{ mol H}$$

$$\text{Moles of Bi} = (0.1422 \text{ g } Bi_2O_3)\left(\frac{1 \text{ mol } Bi_2O_3}{466.0 \text{ g } Bi_2O_3}\right)\left(\frac{2 \text{ mol Bi}}{1 \text{ mol } Bi_2O_3}\right) = 6.103004\text{x}10^{-4} \text{ mol Bi}$$

Subtracting the mass of each element present from the mass of the sample will give the mass of oxygen originally present in the sample. This mass is used to find the moles of oxygen.

$$\text{Mass (g) of C} = (4.271756\text{x}10^{-3} \text{ mol C})\left(\frac{12.01 \text{ g C}}{1 \text{ mol C}}\right) = 0.0513038 \text{ g C}$$

$$\text{Mass (g) of H} = (3.052164\text{x}10^{-3} \text{ mol H})\left(\frac{1.008 \text{ g H}}{1 \text{ mol H}}\right) = 0.0030766 \text{ g H}$$

$$\text{Mass (g) of Bi} = (6.103004\text{x}10^{-4} \text{ mol Bi})\left(\frac{209.0 \text{ g Bi}}{1 \text{ mol Bi}}\right) = 0.127553 \text{ g Bi}$$

Mass (g) of O = mass of sample – (mass C + mass H + mass Bi)
= 0.22105 g sample – (0.0513038 g C + 0.0030766 g H + 0.127553 g Bi) = 0.0391166 g O

$$\text{Moles of O} = (0.0391166\text{g O})\left(\frac{1\text{mol O}}{16.00\text{g O}}\right) = 2.44482\text{x}10^{-4} \text{ mol O}$$

Divide each of the moles by the smallest value (moles Bi).

$$C = \frac{4.271756\text{x}10^{-3}}{6.103004\text{x}10^{-4}} = 7 \qquad H = \frac{3.052164\text{x}10^{-3}}{6.103004\text{x}10^{-4}} = 5$$

$$O = \frac{2.4448\text{x}10^{-3}}{6.103004\text{x}10^{-4}} = 4 \qquad Bi = \frac{6.103004\text{x}10^{-4}}{6.103004\text{x}10^{-4}} = 1$$

Empirical formula = $\mathbf{C_7H_5O_4Bi}$

b) The empirical formula mass is 362 g/mol. Therefore, there are 1086/362 = 3 empirical formula units per molecular formula making the molecular formula = 3 x $C_7H_5O_4Bi$ = $\mathbf{C_{21}H_{15}O_{12}Bi_3}$.

c) $Bi(OH)_3(s) + 3HC_7H_5O_3(aq) \rightarrow Bi(C_7H_5O_3)_3(s) + 3H_2O(l)$

d) Moles of $C_{21}H_{15}O_{12}Bi_3$ = $\left(0.600 \text{ mg } C_{21}H_{15}O_{12}Bi_3\right)\left(\frac{10^{-3} \text{ g}}{1 \text{ mg}}\right)\left(\frac{1 \text{ mol } C_{21}H_{15}O_{12}Bi_3}{1086 \text{ g } C_{21}H_{15}O_{12}Bi_3}\right)$

$= 5.52486\text{x}10^{-4}$ mol $C_{21}H_{15}O_{12}Bi_3$

Mass (mg) of $Bi(OH)_3$ =

$$\left(5.52486\text{x}10^{-7} \text{ mol } C_{21}H_{15}O_{12}Bi_3\right)\left(\frac{3 \text{ mol Bi}}{1 \text{ mol } C_{21}H_{15}O_{12}Bi_3}\right)\left(\frac{1 \text{ mol Bi(OH)}_3}{1 \text{ mol Bi}}\right)\left(\frac{260.0 \text{ g Bi(OH)}_3}{1 \text{ mol Bi(OH)}_3}\right)\left(\frac{1 \text{ mg}}{10^{-3} \text{ g}}\right)\left(\frac{100\%}{88.0\%}\right)$$

$= 0.48970 =$ **0.490 mg $Bi(OH)_3$**

4.151 Plan: Write balanced equations. Use the density to convert volume of fuel to mass of fuel and then use the molar ratios to convert mass of each fuel to the mass of oxygen required for the reaction. Use the conversion factor given to convert mass of oxygen to volume of oxygen.

Solution:

a) Complete combustion of hydrocarbons involves heating the hydrocarbon in the presence of oxygen to produce carbon dioxide and water.

Ethanol: $C_2H_5OH(l) + 3O_2(g) \rightarrow 2CO_2(g) + 3H_2O(l)$

Gasoline: $2C_8H_{18}(l) + 25O_2(g) \rightarrow 16CO_2(g) + 18H_2O(g)$

b) The mass of each fuel must be found:

Mass (g) of gasoline = $\left(1.00 \text{ L}\right)\left(\frac{90\%}{100\%}\right)\left(\frac{1 \text{ mL}}{10^{-3} \text{ L}}\right)\left(\frac{0.742 \text{ g}}{1 \text{ mL}}\right) = 667.8$ g gasoline

Mass (g) of ethanol = $\left(1.00 \text{ L}\right)\left(\frac{10\%}{100\%}\right)\left(\frac{1 \text{ mL}}{10^{-3} \text{ L}}\right)\left(\frac{0.789 \text{ g}}{1 \text{ mL}}\right) = 78.9$ g ethanol

Mass (g) of O_2 to react with gasoline = $\left(667.8 \text{ g } C_8H_{18}\right)\left(\frac{1 \text{ mol } C_8H_{18}}{114.22 \text{ g } C_8H_{18}}\right)\left(\frac{25 \text{ mol } O_2}{2 \text{ mol } C_8H_{18}}\right)\left(\frac{32.00 \text{ g } O_2}{1 \text{ mol } O_2}\right)$

$= 2338.64$ g O_2

Mass (g) of O_2 to react with ethanol = $\left(78.9 \text{ g } C_2H_5OH\right)\left(\frac{1 \text{ mol } C_2H_5OH}{46.07 \text{ g } C_2H_5OH}\right)\left(\frac{3 \text{ mol } O_2}{1 \text{ mol } C_2H_5OH}\right)\left(\frac{32.00 \text{ g } O_2}{1 \text{ mol } O_2}\right)$

$= 164.41$ g O_2

Total mass (g) of O_2 = 2338.64 g O_2 + 164.41 g O_2 = 2503.05 = **$2.50\text{x}10^3$ g O_2**

c) Volume (L) of O_2 = $\left(2503.05 \text{ g } O_2\right)\left(\frac{1 \text{ mol } O_2}{32.00 \text{ g } O_2}\right)\left(\frac{22.4 \text{ L}}{1 \text{ mol } O_2}\right) = 1752.135 =$ **$1.75\text{x}10^3$ L O_2**

d) Volume (L) of air = $\left(1752.135 \text{ L } O_2\right)\left(\frac{100\%}{20.9\%}\right) = 8383.42 =$ **$8.38\text{x}10^3$ L air**

4.153 Plan: From the molarity and volume of the base NaOH, find the moles of NaOH and use the molar ratios from the two balanced equations to convert the moles of NaOH to moles of HBr to moles of vitamin C. Use the molar mass of vitamin C to convert moles to grams.

Solution:

Moles of NaOH = $\left(43.20 \text{ mL NaOH}\right)\left(\frac{10^{-3} \text{ L}}{1 \text{ mL}}\right)\left(\frac{0.1350 \text{ mol NaOH}}{1 \text{ L}}\right) = 0.005832$ mol NaOH

Mass (g) of vitamin C = $\left(0.005832 \text{ mol NaOH}\right)\left(\frac{1 \text{ mol HBr}}{1 \text{ mol NaOH}}\right)\left(\frac{1 \text{ mol } C_6H_8O_6}{2 \text{ mol HBr}}\right)\left(\frac{176.12 \text{ g } C_6H_8O_6}{1 \text{ mol } C_6H_8O_6}\right)\left(\frac{1 \text{ mg}}{10^{-3} \text{ g}}\right)$

$= 513.5659 = 513.6$ mg $C_6H_8O_6$

Yes, the tablets have the quantity advertised.

CHAPTER 5 GASES AND THE KINETIC-MOLECULAR THEORY

FOLLOW–UP PROBLEMS

5.1A Plan: Use the equation for gas pressure in an open-end manometer to calculate the pressure of the gas. Use conversion factors to convert pressure in mmHg to units of torr, pascals, and lb/in^2.

Solution:

Because $P_{gas} < P_{atm}$, $P_{gas} = P_{atm} - \Delta h$

P_{gas} = 753.6 mm Hg – 174.0 mm Hg = 579.6 mm Hg

$$\text{Pressure (torr)} = (579.6\ \text{mm Hg})\left(\frac{1\ \text{torr}}{1\ \text{mm Hg}}\right) = \mathbf{579.6\ torr}$$

$$\text{Pressure (Pa)} = (579.6\ \text{mm Hg})\left(\frac{1\ \text{atm}}{760\ \text{mm Hg}}\right)\left(\frac{1.01325 \times 10^5\ \text{Pa}}{1\text{atm}}\right)$$

$$= 7.727364 \times 10^4 = \mathbf{7.727 \times 10^4\ Pa}$$

$$\text{Pressure (lb/in}^2) = (579.6\ \text{mm Hg})\left(\frac{1\ \text{atm}}{760\ \text{mm Hg}}\right)\left(\frac{14.7\ \text{lb/in}^2}{1\ \text{atm}}\right) = 11.21068 = \mathbf{11.2\ lb/in^2}$$

5.1B Plan: Convert the atmospheric pressure to torr. Use the equation for gas pressure in an open-end manometer to calculate the pressure of the gas. Use conversion factors to convert pressure in torr to units of mmHg, pascals, and lb/in^2.

Solution:

Because $P_{gas} > P_{atm}$, $P_{gas} = P_{atm} + \Delta h$

$$P_{gas} = (0.9475\ \text{atm})\left(\frac{760\ \text{torr}}{1\ \text{atm}}\right) + 25.8\ \text{torr} = 745.9\ \text{torr}$$

$$\text{Pressure (mmHg)} = (745.9\ \text{torr})\left(\frac{1\ \text{mmHg}}{1\ \text{torr}}\right) = \mathbf{745.9\ mmHg}$$

$$\text{Pressure (Pa)} = (745.9\ \text{mmHg})\left(\frac{1\ \text{atm}}{760\ \text{mmHg}}\right)\left(\frac{1.01325 \times 10^5\ \text{Pa}}{1\ \text{atm}}\right) = \mathbf{9.945 \times 10^4\ Pa}$$

$$\text{Pressure (lb/in}^2) = (745.9\ \text{mmHg})\left(\frac{1\ \text{atm}}{760\ \text{mmHg}}\right)\left(\frac{14.7\ \text{lb/in}^2}{1\ \text{atm}}\right) = \mathbf{14.4\ lb/in^2}$$

5.2A Plan: Given in the problem is an initial volume, initial pressure, and final volume for the argon gas. The final pressure is to be calculated. The temperature and amount of gas are fixed. Rearrange the ideal gas law to the appropriate form and solve for P_2. Once solved for, P_2 must be converted from atm units to kPa units.

Solution:

P_1 = 0.871 atm; V_1 = 105 mL

P_2 = unknown V_2 = 352 mL

$$\frac{P_1V_1}{n_1T_1} = \frac{P_2V_2}{n_2T_2} \qquad \text{At fixed } n \text{ and } T\text{:}$$

$$P_1V_1 = P_2V_2$$

$$P_2\ (\text{atm}) = \frac{P_1V_1}{V_2} = \frac{(0.871\ \text{atm})(105\ \text{mL})}{(352\ \text{mL})} = 0.260\ \text{atm}$$

$$P_2\ (\text{kPa}) = (0.260\ \text{atm})\left(\frac{101.325\ \text{kPa}}{1\ \text{atm}}\right) = \mathbf{26.3\ kPa}$$

5.2B Plan: Given in the problem is an initial volume, initial pressure, and final pressure for the oxygen gas. The final volume is to be calculated. The temperature and amount of gas are fixed. Convert the final pressure to atm units. Rearrange the ideal gas law to the appropriate form and solve for V_2.

Solution:

P_1 = 122 atm; V_1 = 651 L

P_2 = 745 mmHg V_2 = unknown

$$\frac{P_1V_1}{n_1T_1} = \frac{P_2V_2}{n_2T_2}$$ At fixed n and T:

$$P_1V_1 = P_2V_2$$

$$P_2\text{ (atm)} = (745\text{ mmHg})\left(\frac{1\text{ atm}}{760\text{ mmHg}}\right) = 0.980\text{ atm}$$

$$V_2\text{ (atm)} = \frac{P_1V_1}{P_2} = \frac{(122\text{ atm})(651\text{ L})}{(0.980\text{ atm})} = \mathbf{8.10 \times 10^4\ L}$$

5.3A Plan: Convert the temperatures to kelvin units and the initial pressure to units of torr. Examine the ideal gas law, noting the fixed variables and those variables that change. R is always constant so $\frac{P_1V_1}{n_1T_1} = \frac{P_2V_2}{n_2T_2}$. In this problem, P and T are changing, while n and V remain fixed.

Solution:

T_1 = 23°C T_2 = 100°C

P_1 = 0.991 atm P_2 = unknown

n and V remain constant

Converting T_1 from °C to K: 23 °C + 273.15 = 296 K

Converting T_2 from °C to K: 100°C + 273.15 = 373 K

$$P_1\text{ (torr)} = (0.991\text{ atm})\left(\frac{760\text{ torr}}{1\text{ atm}}\right) = 753\text{ torr}$$

Arranging the ideal gas law and solving for P_2:

$$\frac{P_1\cancel{V_1}}{\cancel{n_1}T_1} = \frac{P_2\cancel{V_2}}{\cancel{n_2}T_2} \quad \text{or} \quad \frac{P_1}{T_1} = \frac{P_2}{T_2}$$

$$P_2\text{ (torr)} = P_1\frac{T_2}{T_1} = (753\text{ torr})\left(\frac{373\text{ K}}{296\text{ K}}\right) = \mathbf{949\ torr}$$

Because the pressure in the tank (949 torr) is less than the pressure at which the safety valve will open (1.00×10^3 torr), **the safety valve will not open.**

5.3B Plan: This is Charles's law: at constant pressure and with a fixed amount of gas, the volume of a gas is directly proportional to the absolute temperature of the gas. The temperature must be lowered to reduce the volume of a gas. Arrange the ideal gas law, solving for T_2 at fixed n and P. Temperature must be converted to kelvin units.

Solution:

V_1 = 32.5 L V_2 = 28.6 L

T_1 = 40°C (convert to K) T_2 = unknown

n and P remain constant

Converting T from °C to K: T_1 = 40 °C + 273 = 313K

Arranging the ideal gas law and solving for T_2:

$$\frac{\cancel{P_1}V_1}{\cancel{n_1}T_1} = \frac{\cancel{P_2}V_2}{\cancel{n_2}T_2} \quad \text{or} \quad \frac{V_1}{T_1} = \frac{V_2}{T_2}$$

$$T_2 = T_1\frac{V_2}{V_1} = (313\text{ K})\left(\frac{28.6\text{ L}}{32.5\text{ L}}\right) = 275\text{ K} - 273.15 = \mathbf{2°C}$$

5.4A Plan: In this problem, the amount of gas is decreasing. Since the container is rigid, the volume of the gas will not change with the decrease in moles of gas. The temperature is also constant. So, the only change will be that the pressure of the gas will decrease since fewer moles of gas will be present after removal of the 5.0 g of ethylene. Rearrange the ideal gas law to the appropriate form and solve for P_2. Since the ratio of moles of ethylene is equal to the ratio of grams of ethylene, there is no need to convert the grams to moles. (This is illustrated in the solution by listing the molar mass conversion twice.)

Solution:

$P_1 = 793$ torr; $P_2 = ?$ mass$_1 = 35.0$ g; mass$_2 = 35.0 - 5.0 = 30.0$ g

$$\frac{P_1V_1}{n_1T_1} = \frac{P_2V_2}{n_2T_2} \quad \text{At fixed } V \text{ and } T\text{:}$$

$$\frac{P_1}{n_1} = \frac{P_2}{n_2}$$

$$P_2 = \frac{P_1n_2}{n_1} = (793 \text{ torr})\frac{(30.0 \text{ g C}_2\text{H}_4)\left(\frac{1 \text{ mol C}_2\text{H}_4}{28.05 \text{ g C}_2\text{H}_4}\right)}{(35.0 \text{ g C}_2\text{H}_4)\left(\frac{1 \text{ mol C}_2\text{H}_4}{28.05 \text{ g C}_2\text{H}_4}\right)} = 679.714 = \mathbf{680.\ torr}$$

5.4B Plan: Examine the ideal gas law, noting the fixed variables and those variables that change. R is always constant so $\frac{P_1V_1}{n_1T_1} = \frac{P_2V_2}{n_2T_2}$. In this problem, n and V are changing, while P and T remain fixed.

Solution:

$m_1 = 1.26$ g N_2 $m_2 = 1.26$ g N_2 + 1.26 g He
$V_1 = 1.12$ L V_2 = unknown
P and T remain constant

Converting m_1 (mass) to n_1 (moles): $(1.26 \text{ g N}_2)\left(\frac{1 \text{ mol N}_2}{28.02 \text{ g N}_2}\right) = 0.0450 \text{ mol N}_2 = n_1$

Converting m_2 (mass) to n_2 (moles): $0.0450 \text{ mol N}_2 + (1.26 \text{ g He})\left(\frac{1 \text{ mol He}}{4.003 \text{ g He}}\right)$

$= 0.0450 \text{ mol N}_2 + 0.315 \text{ mol He} = 0.360 \text{ mol gas} = n_2$

Arranging the ideal gas law and solving for V_2:

$$\frac{\cancel{P_1}V_1}{n_1\cancel{T_1}} = \frac{\cancel{P_2}V_2}{n_2\cancel{T_2}} \quad \text{or} \quad \frac{V_1}{n_1} = \frac{V_2}{n_2}$$

$$V_2 = V_1\frac{n_2}{n_1} = (1.12 \text{ L})\left(\frac{0.360 \text{ mol}}{0.0450 \text{ mol}}\right) = \mathbf{8.96\ L}$$

5.5A Plan: Convert the temperatures to kelvin. Examine the ideal gas law, noting the fixed variables and those variables that change. R is always constant so $\frac{P_1V_1}{n_1T_1} = \frac{P_2V_2}{n_2T_2}$. In this problem, P, V, and T are changing, while n remains fixed.

Solution:

$T_1 = 23°C$ $T_2 = 18°C$
$P_1 = 755$ mmHg P_2 = unknown
$V_1 = 2.55$ L $V_2 = 4.10$ L
n remains constant

Converting T_1 from °C to K: 23°C + 273.15 = 296 K

Converting T_2 from °C to K: 18°C + 273.15 = 291 K

Arranging the ideal gas law and solving for P_2:

$$\frac{P_1V_1}{\cancel{n_1}T_1} = \frac{P_2V_2}{\cancel{n_2}T_2} \quad \text{or} \quad \frac{P_1V_1}{T_1} = \frac{P_2V_2}{T_2}$$

$$P_2\,(\text{mmHg}) = P_1\frac{V_1T_2}{V_2T_1} = (755\ \text{mmHg})\left(\frac{(2.55\ \text{L})(291\ \text{K})}{(4.10\ \text{L})(296\ \text{K})}\right) = \mathbf{462\ mmHg}$$

5.5B Plan: Convert the temperatures to kelvin. Examine the ideal gas law, noting the fixed variables and those variables that change. R is always constant so $\frac{P_1V_1}{n_1T_1} = \frac{P_2V_2}{n_2T_2}$. In this problem, P, V, and T are changing, while n remains fixed.

Solution:

$T_1 = 28°C$ $\quad$ $T_2 = 21°C$

$P_1 = 0.980$ atm $\quad$ $P_2 = 1.40$ atm

$V_1 = 2.2$ L $\quad$ $V_2 =$ unknown

n remains constant

Converting T_1 from °C to K: 28°C + 273.15 = 301 K

Converting T_2 from °C to K: 21°C + 273.15 = 294 K

Arranging the ideal gas law and solving for V_2:

$$\frac{P_1V_1}{\cancel{n_1}T_1} = \frac{P_2V_2}{\cancel{n_2}T_2} \quad \text{or} \quad \frac{P_1V_1}{T_1} = \frac{P_2V_2}{T_2}$$

$$V_2\,(\text{L}) = V_1\frac{P_1T_2}{P_2T_1} = (2.2\ \text{L})\left(\frac{(0.980\ \text{atm})(294\ \text{K})}{(1.40\ \text{atm})(301\ \text{K})}\right) = \mathbf{1.5\ L}$$

5.6A Plan: From Sample Problem 5.6 the temperature of 21°C and volume of 438 L are given. The pressure is 1.37 atm and the unknown is the moles of oxygen gas. Use the ideal gas equation $PV = nRT$ to calculate the number of moles of gas. Multiply moles by molar mass to obtain mass.

Solution:

$PV = nRT$

$$n = \frac{PV}{RT} = \frac{(1.37\ \text{atm})(438\ \text{L})}{\left(\frac{0.0821\ \text{atm} \bullet \text{L}}{\text{mol} \bullet \text{K}}\right)((273.15 + 21)\text{K})} = 24.9\ \text{mol}\ O_2$$

$$\text{Mass (g) of } O_2 = (24.9\ \text{mol}\ O_2)\left(\frac{32.00\ \text{g}\ O_2}{1\ \text{mol}\ O_2}\right) = 796.8 = \mathbf{797\ g\ O_2}$$

5.6B Plan: Convert the mass of helium to moles, the temperature to kelvin units, and the pressure to atm units. Use the ideal gas equation $PV = nRT$ to calculate the volume of the gas.

Solution:

$P = 731$ mmHg $\quad$ $V =$ unknown

$m = 3950$ kg He $\quad$ $T = 20°C$

Converting m (mass) to n (moles): $(3950\ \text{kg He})\left(\frac{1000\ \text{g}}{1\ \text{kg}}\right)\left(\frac{1\ \text{mol He}}{4.003\ \text{g He}}\right) = 9.87 \times 10^5\ \text{mol} = n$

Converting T from °C to K: 20°C + 273.15 = 293 K

Converting P from mmHg to atm: $(731\ \text{mmHg})\left(\frac{1\ \text{atm}}{760\ \text{mmHg}}\right) = 0.962\ \text{atm}$

$PV = nRT$

$$V = \frac{nRT}{P} = \frac{(9.87 \times 10^5\ \text{mol})\left(0.0821\ \frac{\text{atm} \bullet \text{L}}{\text{mol} \bullet \text{K}}\right)(293\ \text{K})}{(0.962\ \text{atm})} = \mathbf{2.47 \times 10^7\ L}$$

5.7A Plan: Balance the chemical equation. The pressure is constant and, according to the picture, the volume approximately doubles. The volume change may be due to the temperature and/or a change in moles. Examine the balanced reaction for a possible change in number of moles. Rearrange the ideal gas law to the appropriate form and solve for the variable that changes.

Solution:

The balanced chemical equation must be 2CD → $C_2 + D_2$

Thus, the number of moles of gas does not change (2 moles both before and after the reaction). Only the temperature remains as a variable to cause the volume change. Let V_1 = the initial volume and $2V_1$ = the final volume V_2.

$T_1 = (-73 + 273.15)\ \text{K} = 200.15\ \text{K}$

$$\frac{P_1V_1}{n_1T_1} = \frac{P_2V_2}{n_2T_2} \qquad \text{At fixed } n \text{ and } P:$$

$$\frac{V_1}{T_1} = \frac{V_2}{T_2}$$

$$T_2 = \frac{V_2T_1}{V_1} = \frac{(2V_1)(200.15\ \text{K})}{(V_1)} = 400.30\ \text{K} - 273.15 = 127.15 = \mathbf{127°C}$$

5.7B Plan: The pressure is constant and, according to the picture, the volume approximately decreases by a factor of 2 (the final volume is approximately one half the original volume). The volume change may be due to the temperature change and/or a change in moles. Consider the change in temperature. Examine the balanced reactions for a possible change in number of moles. Think about the relationships between the variables in the ideal gas law in order to determine the effect of temperature and moles on gas volume.

Solution:

Converting T_1 from °C to K: 199°C + 273.15 = 472 K

Converting T_2 from °C to K: –155°C + 273.15 = 118 K

According to the ideal gas law, temperature and volume are directly proportional. The temperature decreases by a factor of 4, which should cause the volume to also decrease by a factor of 4. Because the volume only decreases by a factor of 2, the number of moles of gas must have *increased* by a factor of 2 (moles of gas and volume are also directly proportional).

1/4 (decrease in V from the decrease in T) x 2 (increase in V from the increase in n)

= 1/2 (a decrease in V by a factor of 2)

Thus, we need to find a reaction in which the number of moles of gas increases by a factor of 2.

In equation (1), 3 moles of gas yield 2 moles of gas.
In equation (2), 2 moles of gas yield 4 moles of gas.
In equation (3), 1 mole of gas yields 3 moles of gas.
In equation (4), 2 moles of gas yield 2 moles of gas.

Because the number of moles of gas doubles in **equation (2)**, that equation best describes the reaction in the figure in this problem.

5.8A Plan: Density of a gas can be calculated using a version of the ideal gas equation, $d = \frac{P\mathcal{M}}{RT}$. Two calculations are required, one with T = 0°C = 273 K and P = 380 torr and the other at STP which is defined as T = 273 K and P = 1 atm.

Solution:

Density at T = 273 K and P = 380 torr:

$$d = \frac{(380\ \text{torr})(44.01\ \text{g/mol})}{\left(\frac{0.0821\ \text{atm} \bullet \text{L}}{\text{mol} \bullet \text{K}}\right)(273\ \text{K})}\left(\frac{1\ \text{atm}}{760\ \text{torr}}\right) = 0.981783 = \mathbf{0.982\ g/L}$$

Density at T = 273 K and P = 1 atm (Note: The 1 atm is an exact number and does not affect the significant figures in the answer.):

$$d = \frac{(1\text{ atm})(44.01\text{ g/mol})}{\left(\frac{0.0821\text{ atm}\cdot\text{L}}{\text{mol}\cdot\text{K}}\right)(273\text{ K})} = 1.9638566 = \mathbf{1.96\ g/L}$$

The density of a gas increases proportionally to the increase in pressure.

5.8B Plan: Density of a gas can be calculated using a version of the ideal gas equation, $d = \frac{P\mathcal{M}}{RT}$

Solution:
Density of NO_2 at $T = 297$ K (24°C + 273.15) and $P = 0.950$ atm:

$$d = \frac{(0.950\text{ atm})(46.01\text{ g/mol})}{\left(0.0821\ \frac{\text{atm}\cdot\text{L}}{\text{mol}\cdot\text{K}}\right)(297\text{ K})} = 1.7926 = \mathbf{1.79\ g/L}$$

Nitrogen dioxide is **more dense** than dry air at the same conditions (density of dry air = 1.13 g/L).

5.9A Plan: Calculate the mass of the gas by subtracting the mass of the empty flask from the mass of the flask containing the condensed gas. The volume, pressure, and temperature of the gas are known. The relationship $d = \frac{P\mathcal{M}}{RT}$ is rearranged to give $\mathcal{M} = \frac{dRT}{P}$ or $\mathcal{M} = \frac{mRT}{PV}$

Solution:
Mass (g) of gas = mass of flask + vapor – mass of flask = 68.697 – 68.322 = 0.375 g
$T = 95.0°\text{C} + 273 = 368$ K

$$P = (740.\text{ torr})\left(\frac{1\text{ atm}}{760\text{ torr}}\right) = 0.973684\text{ atm}$$

V = 149 mL = 0.149 L

$$\mathcal{M} = \frac{mRT}{PV} = \frac{(0.375\text{ g})\left(\frac{0.0821\text{ atm}\cdot\text{L}}{\text{mol}\cdot\text{K}}\right)(368\text{ K})}{(0.973684\text{ atm})(0.149\text{ L})} = 78.094 = \mathbf{78.1\ g}$$

5.9B Plan: Calculate the mass of the gas by subtracting the mass of the empty glass bulb from the mass of the bulb containing the gas. The volume, pressure, and temperature of the gas are known. The relationship $d = \frac{P\mathcal{M}}{RT}$ is rearranged to give $\mathcal{M} = \frac{dRT}{P}$ or $\mathcal{M} = \frac{mRT}{PV}$. Use the molar mass of the gas to determine its identity.

Solution:
Mass (g) of gas = mass of bulb + gas – mass of bulb = 82.786 – 82.561 = 0.225 g
$T = 22°\text{C} + 273.15 = 295$ K

$$P = (733\text{ mmHg})\left(\frac{1\text{ atm}}{760\text{ mmHg}}\right) = 0.965\text{ atm}$$

V = 350. mL = 0.350 L

$$\mathcal{M} = \frac{mRT}{PV} = \frac{(0.225\text{ g})\left(0.0821\ \frac{\text{atm}\cdot\text{L}}{\text{mol}\cdot\text{K}}\right)(295\text{ K})}{(0.965\text{ atm})(0.350\text{ L})} = 16.1\text{ g/mol}$$

Methane has a molar mass of 16.04 g/mol. Nitrogen monoxide has a molar mass of 30.01 g/mol. The gas that has a molar mass that matches the calculated value is **methane**.

5.10A Plan: Calculate the number of moles of each gas present and then the mole fraction of each gas. The partial pressure of each gas equals the mole fraction times the total pressure. Total pressure equals 1 atm since the problem specifies STP. This pressure is an exact number, and will not affect the significant figures in the answer

Solution:

$$\text{Moles of He} = (5.50\text{ g He})\left(\frac{1\text{ mol He}}{4.003\text{ g He}}\right) = 1.373970\text{ mol He}$$

$$\text{Moles of Ne} = (15.0 \text{ g Ne})\left(\frac{1 \text{ mol Ne}}{20.18 \text{ g Ne}}\right) = 0.743310 \text{ mol Ne}$$

$$\text{Moles of Kr} = (35.0 \text{ g Kr})\left(\frac{1 \text{ mol Kr}}{83.80 \text{ g Kr}}\right) = 0.417661 \text{ mol Ke}$$

Total number of moles of gas = 1.373970 + 0.743310 + 0.417661 = 2.534941 mol

$P_A = X_A \text{ x } P_{total}$

$$P_{He} = \left(\frac{1.37397 \text{ mol He}}{2.534941 \text{ mol}}\right)(1 \text{ atm}) = 0.54201 = \mathbf{0.542\ atm\ He}$$

$$P_{Ne} = \left(\frac{0.74331 \text{ mol Ne}}{2.534941 \text{ mol}}\right)(1 \text{ atm}) = 0.29323 = \mathbf{0.293\ atm\ Ne}$$

$$P_{Kr} = \left(\frac{0.41766 \text{ mol Kr}}{2.534941 \text{ mol}}\right)(1 \text{ atm}) = 0.16476 = \mathbf{0.165\ atm\ Kr}$$

5.10B Plan: Use the formula $P_A = X_A \text{ x } P_{total}$ to calculate the mole fraction of He. Multiply the mole fraction by 100% to calculate the mole percent of He.

Solution:

$P_{He} = X_{He} \text{ x } P_{total}$

$$\text{Mole percent He} = X_{He}(100\%) = \left(\frac{P_{He}}{P_{total}}\right)(100\%) = \left(\frac{143 \text{ atm}}{204 \text{ atm}}\right)(100\%) = \mathbf{70.1\%}$$

5.11A Plan: The gas collected over the water will consist of H_2 and H_2O gas molecules. The partial pressure of the water can be found from the vapor pressure of water at the given temperature given in the text. Subtracting this partial pressure of water from total pressure gives the partial pressure of hydrogen gas collected over the water. Calculate the moles of hydrogen gas using the ideal gas equation. The mass of hydrogen can then be calculated by converting the moles of hydrogen from the ideal gas equation to grams.

Solution:

From the table in the text, the partial pressure of water is 13.6 torr at 16°C.

$P = 752 \text{ torr} - 13.6 \text{ torr} = 738.4 = \mathbf{738\ torr\ H_2}$

The unrounded partial pressure (738.4 torr) will be used to avoid rounding error.

$$\text{Moles of hydrogen} = n = \frac{PV}{RT} = \frac{(738.4 \text{ torr})(1495 \text{ mL})}{\left(0.0821 \frac{\text{atm} \bullet \text{L}}{\text{mol} \bullet \text{K}}\right)((273.15 + 16)\text{K})}\left(\frac{1 \text{ atm}}{760 \text{ torr}}\right)\left(\frac{10^{-3} \text{L}}{1 \text{ mL}}\right)$$

$$= 0.061186 \text{ mol } H_2$$

$$\text{Mass (g) of hydrogen} = (0.061186 \text{ mol } H_2)\left(\frac{2.016 \text{ g } H_2}{1 \text{ mol } H_2}\right) = 0.123351 = \mathbf{0.123\ g\ H_2}$$

5.11B Plan: The gas collected over the water will consist O_2 and H_2O gas molecules. The partial pressure of the water can be found from the vapor pressure of water at the given temperature given in the text. Subtracting this partial pressure of water from total pressure gives the partial pressure of oxygen gas collected over the water. Calculate the moles of oxygen gas using the ideal gas equation. The mass of oxygen can then be calculated by converting the moles of oxygen from the ideal gas equation to grams.

Solution:

From the table in the text, the partial pressure of water is 17.5 torr at 20°C.

$P = 748 \text{ torr} - 17.5 \text{ torr} = 730.5 = \mathbf{730.\ torr\ O_2}$

$$\text{Moles of oxygen} = n = \frac{PV}{RT} = \frac{(730. \text{ torr})(307 \text{ mL})}{\left(0.0821 \frac{\text{atm} \bullet \text{L}}{\text{mol} \bullet \text{K}}\right)(293 \text{ K})}\left(\frac{1 \text{ atm}}{760 \text{ torr}}\right)\left(\frac{1 \text{ L}}{1000 \text{ mL}}\right)$$

$$= 0.012258 \text{ mol } O_2$$

$$\text{Mass (g) of oxygen} = (0.012258 \text{ mol } O_2)\left(\frac{32.00 \text{ g } O_2}{1 \text{ mol } O_2}\right) = 0.3923 = \mathbf{0.392\ g\ O_2}$$

5.12A Plan: Write a balanced equation for the reaction. Calculate the moles of HCl(g) from the starting amount of sodium chloride using the stoichiometric ratio from the balanced equation. Find the volume of the HCl(g) from the molar volume at STP.

Solution:

The balanced equation is $H_2SO_4(aq) + 2NaCl(aq) \rightarrow Na_2SO_4(aq) + 2HCl(g)$.

$$\text{Moles of HCl} = (0.117 \text{ kg NaCl})\left(\frac{10^3 \text{ g}}{1 \text{ kg}}\right)\left(\frac{1 \text{ mol NaCl}}{58.44 \text{ g NaCl}}\right)\left(\frac{2 \text{ mol HCl}}{2 \text{ mol NaCl}}\right) = 2.00205 \text{ mol HCl}$$

$$\text{Volume (mL) of HCl} = (2.00205 \text{ mol HCl})\left(\frac{22.4 \text{ L}}{1 \text{ mol HCl}}\right)\left(\frac{1 \text{ mL}}{10^{-3} \text{ L}}\right)$$

$$= 4.4846 \times 10^4 = \mathbf{4.48 \times 10^4 \text{ mL HCl}}$$

5.12B Plan: Write a balanced equation for the reaction. Use the ideal gas law to calculate the moles of $CO_2(g)$ scrubbed. Use the molar ratios from the balanced equation to calculate the moles of lithium hydroxide needed to scrub that amount of CO_2. Finally, use the molar mass of lithium hydroxide to calculate the mass of lithium hydroxide required.

Solution:

The balanced equation is $2LiOH(s) + CO_2(g) \rightarrow Li_2CO_3(s) + H_2O(l)$.

$$\text{Amount (mol) of } CO_2 \text{ scrubbed} = n = \frac{PV}{RT} = \frac{(0.942 \text{ atm})(215 \text{ L})}{\left(0.0821 \frac{\text{atm} \bullet \text{L}}{\text{mol} \bullet \text{K}}\right)(296 \text{ K})} = 8.3340 = 8.33 \text{ mol } CO_2$$

$$\text{Mass (g) of LiOH} = 8.33 \text{ mol } CO_2 \left(\frac{2 \text{ mol LiOH}}{1 \text{ mol } CO_2}\right)\left(\frac{23.95 \text{ g LiOH}}{1 \text{ mol LiOH}}\right) = 399.0070 = \mathbf{399 \text{ g LiOH}}$$

5.13A Plan: Balance the equation for the reaction. Determine the limiting reactant by finding the moles of each reactant from the ideal gas equation, and comparing the values. Calculate the moles of remaining excess reactant. This is the only gas left in the flask, so it is used to calculate the pressure inside the flask.

Solution:

The balanced equation is $NH_3(g) + HCl(g) \rightarrow NH_4Cl(s)$.

The stoichiometric ratio of NH_3 to HCl is 1:1, so the reactant present in the lower quantity of moles is the limiting reactant.

$$\text{Moles of ammonia} = \frac{PV}{RT} = \frac{(0.452 \text{ atm})(10.0 \text{ L})}{\left(\frac{0.0821 \text{ atm} \bullet \text{L}}{\text{mol} \bullet \text{K}}\right)((273.15 + 22)\text{K})} = 0.18653 \text{ mol } NH_3$$

$$\text{Moles of hydrogen chloride} = \frac{PV}{RT} = \frac{(7.50 \text{ atm})(155 \text{ mL})}{\left(\frac{0.0821 \text{ atm} \bullet \text{L}}{\text{mol} \bullet \text{K}}\right)(271 \text{ K})}\left(\frac{10^{-3} \text{ L}}{1 \text{ mL}}\right) = 0.052249 \text{ mol HCl}$$

The HCl is limiting so the moles of ammonia gas left after the reaction would be $0.18653 - 0.052249 = 0.134281$ mol NH_3.

$$\text{Pressure (atm) of ammonia} = \frac{nRT}{V} = \frac{(0.134281 \text{ mol})\left(\frac{0.0821 \text{ atm} \bullet \text{L}}{\text{mol} \bullet \text{K}}\right)((273.15 + 22)\text{K})}{(10.0 \text{ L})}$$

$$= 0.325387 = \mathbf{0.325 \text{ atm } NH_3}$$

5.13B Plan: Balance the equation for the reaction. Use the ideal gas law to calculate the moles of fluorine that react. Determine the limiting reactant by determining the moles of product that can be produced from each of the reactants and comparing the values. Use the moles of IF_5 produced and the ideal gas law to calculate the volume of gas produced.

Solution:

The balanced equation is $I_2(s) + 5F_2(g) \rightarrow 2IF_5(g)$.

Amount (mol) of F_2 that reacts $= n = \dfrac{PV}{RT} = \dfrac{(0.974 \text{ atm})(2.48 \text{ L})}{\left(0.0821 \frac{\text{atm} \cdot \text{L}}{\text{mol} \cdot \text{K}}\right)(291 \text{ K})} = 0.1011 = 0.101 \text{ mol } F_2$

Amount (mol) of IF_5 produced from $F_2 = 0.101 \text{ mol } F_2 \left(\dfrac{2 \text{ mol } IF_5}{5 \text{ mol } F_2}\right) = 0.0404 \text{ mol } IF_5$

Amount (mol) of IF_5 produced from $I_2 = 4.16 \text{ g } I_2 \left(\dfrac{1 \text{ mol } I_2}{253.8 \text{ g } I_2}\right)\left(\dfrac{2 \text{ mol } IF_5}{1 \text{ mol } I_2}\right) = 0.0328 \text{ mol } IF_5$

Because a smaller number of moles is produced from the I_2, I_2 is limiting and 0.0328 mol of IF_5 are produced.

Volume (L) of $IF_5 = \dfrac{nRT}{P} = \dfrac{(0.0328 \text{ mol})\left(0.0821 \frac{\text{atm} \cdot \text{L}}{\text{mol} \cdot \text{K}}\right)(378 \text{ K})}{(0.935 \text{ atm})} = 1.08867 = \mathbf{1.09\ L}$

5.14A Plan: Graham's law can be used to solve for the effusion rate of the ethane since the rate and molar mass of helium are known, along with the molar mass of ethane. In the same way that running slower increases the time to go from one point to another, so the rate of effusion decreases as the time increases. The rate can be expressed as 1/time.

Solution:

$$\frac{\text{Rate He}}{\text{Rate } C_2H_6} = \sqrt{\frac{\mathcal{M}_{C_2H_6}}{\mathcal{M}_{He}}}$$

$$\frac{\left(\dfrac{0.010 \text{ mol He}}{1.25 \text{ min}}\right)}{\left(\dfrac{0.010 \text{ mol } C_2H_6}{t_{C_2H_6}}\right)} = \sqrt{\frac{(30.07 \text{ g/mol})}{(4.003 \text{ g/mol})}}$$

$0.800\, t = 2.74078$

$t = 3.42597 = \mathbf{3.43\ min}$

5.14B Plan: Graham's law can be used to solve for the molar mass of the unknown gas since the rates of both gases and the molar mass of argon are known. Rate can be expressed as the volume of gas that effuses per unit time.

Solution:

Rate of Ar = 13.8 mL/time

Rate of unknown gas = 7.23 mL/time

Mass of Ar = 39.95 g/mol

$$\frac{\text{Rate of Ar}}{\text{Rate of unknown gas}} = \left(\sqrt{\frac{\mathcal{M}_{\text{unknown gas}}}{\mathcal{M}_{Ar}}}\right)$$

$$\left(\frac{\text{Rate of Ar}}{\text{Rate of unknown gas}}\right)^2 = \left(\frac{\mathcal{M}_{\text{unknown gas}}}{\mathcal{M}_{Ar}}\right)$$

$$\mathcal{M}_{\text{unknown gas}} = (\mathcal{M}_{Ar})\left(\frac{\text{Rate of Ar}}{\text{Rate of unknown gas}}\right)^2$$

$$\mathcal{M}_{\text{unknown gas}} = (39.95 \text{ g/mol})\left(\frac{13.8 \text{ mL/time}}{7.23 \text{ mL/time}}\right)^2 = \mathbf{146\ g/mol}$$

CHEMICAL CONNECTIONS BOXED READING PROBLEMS

B5.1 Plan: Examine the change in density of the atmosphere as altitude changes.
Solution:
The density of the atmosphere decreases with increasing altitude. High density causes more drag on the aircraft. At high altitudes, low density means that there are relatively few gas particles present to collide with the aircraft.

B5.2 Plan: The conditions that result in deviations from ideal behavior are high pressure and low temperature. At high pressure, the volume of the gas decreases, the distance between particles decreases, and attractive forces between gas particles have a greater effect. A low temperature slows the gas particles, also increasing the affect of attractive forces between particles.
Solution:
Since the pressure on Saturn is significantly higher and the temperature significantly lower than that on Venus, atmospheric gases would deviate more from ideal gas behavior on **Saturn**.

B5.3 Plan: To find the volume percent of argon, multiply its mole fraction by 100. The partial pressure of argon gas can be found by using the relationship $P_{Ar} = X_{Ar} \times P_{total}$. The mole fraction of argon is given in Table B5.1.
Solution:
Volume percent = mole fraction x 100 = 0.00934 x 100 = **0.934 %**
The total pressure at sea level is 1.00 atm = 760 torr.
$P_{Ar} = X_{Ar} \times P_{total}$ = 0.00934 x 760 torr = 7.0984 = **7.10 torr**

B5.4 Plan: To find the moles of gas, convert the mass of the atmosphere from t to g and divide by the molar mass of air. Knowing the moles of air, the volume can be calculated at the specified pressure and temperature by using the ideal gas law.
Solution:

a) Moles of gas $= \left(5.14\text{x}10^{15}\ \text{t}\right)\left(\frac{1000\ \text{kg}}{1\ \text{t}}\right)\left(\frac{1000\ \text{g}}{1\ \text{kg}}\right)\left(\frac{1\ \text{mol}}{28.8\ \text{g}}\right)$

$= 1.78472\text{x}10^{20} = \mathbf{1.78x10^{20}\ mol}$

b) $PV = nRT$

$$V = \frac{nRT}{P} = \frac{\left(1.78472\times10^{20}\ \text{mol}\right)\left(0.0821\frac{\text{L•atm}}{\text{mol•K}}\right)\left((273+25)\ \text{K}\right)}{(1\ \text{atm})} = 4.36646\text{x}10^{21} = \mathbf{4\ x\ 10^{21}\ L}$$

END–OF–CHAPTER PROBLEMS

5.1 Plan: Review the behavior of the gas phase vs. the liquid phase.
Solution:
a) The volume of the liquid remains constant, but the volume of the gas increases to the volume of the larger container.
b) The volume of the container holding the gas sample increases when heated, but the volume of the container holding the liquid sample remains essentially constant when heated.
c) The volume of the liquid remains essentially constant, but the volume of the gas is reduced.

5.6 Plan: The ratio of the heights of columns of mercury and water are inversely proportional to the ratio of the densities of the two liquids. Convert the height in mm to height in cm.
Solution:

$$\frac{h_{H_2O}}{h_{Hg}} = \frac{d_{Hg}}{d_{H_2O}}$$

$$h_{H_2O} = \frac{d_{Hg}}{d_{H_2O}} \text{ x } h_{Hg} = \left(\frac{13.5 \text{ g/mL}}{1.00 \text{ g/mL}}\right)(730 \text{ mmHg})\left(\frac{10^{-3} \text{ m}}{1 \text{ mm}}\right)\left(\frac{1 \text{ cm}}{10^{-2} \text{ m}}\right) = 985.5 = \mathbf{990 \text{ cm } H_2O}$$

5.8 Plan: Use the conversion factors between pressure units:
1 atm = 760 mmHg = 760 torr = 101.325 kPa = 1.01325 bar
Solution:

a) Converting from atm to mmHg: $P(\text{mmHg}) = (0.745 \text{ atm})\left(\frac{760 \text{ mmHg}}{1 \text{ atm}}\right) = 566.2 = \mathbf{566 \text{ mmHg}}$

b) Converting from torr to bar: $P(\text{bar}) = (992 \text{ torr})\left(\frac{1.01325 \text{ bar}}{760 \text{ torr}}\right) = 1.32256 = \mathbf{1.32 \text{ bar}}$

c) Converting from kPa to atm: $P(\text{atm}) = (365 \text{ kPa})\left(\frac{1 \text{ atm}}{101.325 \text{ kPa}}\right) = 3.60227 = \mathbf{3.60 \text{ atm}}$

d) Converting from mmHg to kPa: $P(\text{kPa}) = (804 \text{ mmHg})\left(\frac{101.325 \text{ kPa}}{760 \text{ mmHg}}\right) = 107.191 = \mathbf{107 \text{ kPa}}$

5.10 Plan: This is an open-end manometer. Since the height of the mercury column in contact with the gas is higher than the column in contact with the air, the gas is exerting less pressure on the mercury than the air. Therefore the pressure corresponding to the height difference (Δh) between the two arms is subtracted from the atmospheric pressure. Since the height difference is in units of cm and the barometric pressure is given in units of torr, cm must be converted to mm and then torr before the subtraction is performed. The overall pressure is then given in units of atm.
Solution:

$$(2.35 \text{ cm})\left(\frac{10^{-2} \text{ m}}{1 \text{ cm}}\right)\left(\frac{1 \text{ mm}}{10^{-3} \text{ m}}\right)\left(\frac{1 \text{ torr}}{1 \text{ mmHg}}\right) = 23.5 \text{ torr}$$

738.5 torr – 23.5 torr = 715.0 torr

$$P(\text{atm}) = (715.0 \text{ torr})\left(\frac{1 \text{ atm}}{760 \text{ torr}}\right) = 0.940789 = \mathbf{0.9408 \text{ atm}}$$

5.12 Plan: This is a closed-end manometer. The difference in the height of the Hg (Δh) equals the gas pressure. The height difference is given in units of m and must be converted to mmHg and then to atm.
Solution:

$$P(\text{atm}) = (0.734 \text{ mHg})\left(\frac{1 \text{ mmHg}}{10^{-3} \text{ mHg}}\right)\left(\frac{1 \text{ atm}}{760 \text{ mmHg}}\right) = 0.965789 = \mathbf{0.966 \text{ atm}}$$

5.18 Plan: Examine the ideal gas law; volume and temperature are constant and pressure and moles are variable.
Solution:

$PV = nRT$ $\quad P = n\frac{RT}{V}$ $\quad R$, T, and V are constant

$P = n$ x constant
At constant temperature and volume, the pressure of the gas is directly proportional to the amount of gas in moles.

5.20 Plan: Use the relationship $\frac{P_1V_1}{n_1T_1} = \frac{P_2V_2}{n_2T_2}$ or $V_2 = \frac{P_1V_1n_2T_2}{P_2n_1T_1}$.

Solution:
a) As the pressure on a fixed amount of gas (n is fixed) increases at constant temperature (T is fixed), the molecules move closer together, decreasing the volume. When the pressure is tripled, the **volume decreases to one-third of the original volume** at constant temperature (Boyle's law).

$$V_2 = \frac{P_1V_1n_2T_2}{P_2n_1T_1} = \frac{(P_1)(V_1)(1)(1)}{(3P_1)(1)(1)} \qquad V_2 = \tfrac{1}{3}V_1$$

b) As the temperature of a fixed amount of gas (n is fixed) increases at constant pressure (P is fixed), the gas molecules gain kinetic energy. With higher energy, the gas molecules collide with the walls of the container with greater force, which increases the size (volume) of the container. If the temperature is increased by a factor of 3.0 (at constant pressure) then the **volume will increase by a factor of 3.0** (Charles's law).

$$V_2 = \frac{P_1V_1n_2T_2}{P_2n_1T_1} = \frac{(1)(V_1)(1)(3T_1)}{(1)(1)(T_1)} \qquad V_2 = 3V_1$$

c) As the number of molecules of gas increases at constant pressure and temperature (P and T are fixed), the force they exert on the container increases. This results in an increase in the volume of the container. Adding 3 moles of gas to 1 mole increases the number of moles by a factor of 4, thus the **volume increases by a factor of 4**(Avogadro's law).

$$V_2 = \frac{P_1V_1n_2T_2}{P_2n_1T_1} = \frac{(1)(V_1)(4n_1)(1)}{(1)(n_1)(1)} \qquad V_2 = 4V_1$$

5.22 Plan: Use the relationship $\frac{P_1V_1}{T_1} = \frac{P_2V_2}{T_2}$ or $V_2 = \frac{P_1V_1T_2}{P_2T_1}$. R and n are fixed.

Solution:

a) The temperature is decreased by a factor of 2, so **the volume is decreased by a factor of 2** (Charles's law).

$$V_2 = \frac{P_1V_1T_2}{P_2T_1} = \frac{(1)(V_1)(400\text{ K})}{(1)(800\text{ K})} \qquad V_2 = \tfrac{1}{2}V_1$$

b) $T_1 = 250°\text{C} + 273 = 523\text{ K}$ $\qquad$ $T_2 = 500°\text{C} + 273 = 773\text{ K}$

The temperature increases by a factor of 773/523 = 1.48, so **the volume is increased by a factor of 1.48** (Charles's law).

$$V_2 = \frac{P_1V_1T_2}{P_2T_1} = \frac{(1)(V_1)(773\text{ K})}{(1)(523\text{ K})} \qquad V_2 = 1.48V_1$$

c) The pressure is increased by a factor of 3, so **the volume decreases by a factor of 3** (Boyle's law).

$$V_2 = \frac{P_1V_1T_2}{P_2T_1} = \frac{(2\text{ atm})(V_1)(1)}{(6\text{ atm})(1)} \qquad V_2 = \tfrac{1}{3}V_1$$

5.24 Plan: Examine the ideal gas law, noting the fixed variables and those variables that change. R is always constant so $\frac{P_1V_1}{n_1T_1} = \frac{P_2V_2}{n_2T_2}$. In this problem, P and V are changing, while n and T remain fixed.

Solution:

$V_1 = 1.61$ L $\qquad$ V_2 = unknown

$P_1 = 734$ torr $\qquad$ $P_2 = 0.844$ atm

n and T remain constant

Converting P_1 from torr to atm: $(734\text{ torr})\left(\frac{1\text{ atm}}{760\text{ torr}}\right) = 0.966\text{ atm}$

Arranging the ideal gas law and solving for V_2:

$$\frac{P_1V_1}{\cancel{n_1T_1}} = \frac{P_2V_2}{\cancel{n_2T_2}} \quad \text{or} \quad P_1V_1 = P_2V_2$$

$$V_2 = V_1\frac{P_1}{P_2} = (1.61\text{ L})\left(\frac{0.966\text{ atm}}{0.844\text{ atm}}\right) = \mathbf{1.84\text{ L}}$$

5.26 Plan: This is Charles's law: at constant pressure and with a fixed amount of gas, the volume of a gas is directly proportional to the absolute temperature of the gas. The temperature must be lowered to reduce the volume of a gas. Arrange the ideal gas law, solving for T_2 at fixed n and P. Temperature must be converted to kelvin.

Solution:

$V_1 = 9.10$ L $V_2 = 2.50$ L

$T_1 = 198°C$ (convert to K) T_2 = unknown

n and P remain constant

Converting T from °C to K: $T_1 = 198°C + 273 = 471K$

Arranging the ideal gas law and solving for T_2:

$$\frac{\cancel{P_1}V_1}{\cancel{n_1}T_1} = \frac{\cancel{P_2}V_2}{\cancel{n_2}T_2} \quad \text{or} \quad \frac{V_1}{T_1} = \frac{V_2}{T_2}$$

$$T_2 = T_1\frac{V_2}{V_1} = 471\text{ K}\left(\frac{2.50\text{ L}}{9.10\text{ L}}\right) = 129.396\text{ K} - 273 = -143.604 = \mathbf{-144°C}$$

5.28 Plan: Examine the ideal gas law, noting the fixed variables and those variables that change. R is always constant so $\frac{P_1V_1}{n_1T_1} = \frac{P_2V_2}{n_2T_2}$. In this problem, P and T are changing, while n and V remain fixed.

Solution:

$T_1 = 25°C$ $T_2 = 195°C$

$P_1 = 177$ atm P_2 = unknown

n and V remain constant

Converting T_1 from°C to K: 25°C + 273.15 = 298 K

Converting T_2 from °C to K: 195°C + 273.15 = 468 K

Arranging the ideal gas law and solving for P_2:

$$\frac{P_1\cancel{V_1}}{\cancel{n_1}T_1} = \frac{P_2\cancel{V_2}}{\cancel{n_2}T_2} \quad \text{or} \quad \frac{P_1}{T_1} = \frac{P_2}{T_2}$$

$$P_2 = P_1\frac{T_2}{T_1} = (177\text{ atm})\left(\frac{468\text{ K}}{298\text{ K}}\right) = \mathbf{278\ atm}$$

5.30 Plan: Examine the ideal gas law, noting the fixed variables and those variables that change. R is always constant so $\frac{P_1V_1}{n_1T_1} = \frac{P_2V_2}{n_2T_2}$. In this problem, n and V are changing, while P and T remain fixed.

Solution:

$m_1 = 1.92$ g He $m_2 = 1.92\text{ g} - 0.850\text{ g} = 1.07$ g He

$V_1 = 12.5$ L V_2 = unknown

P and T remain constant

Converting m_1 (mass) to n_1 (moles): $(1.92\text{ g He})\left(\frac{1\text{ mol He}}{4.003\text{ g He}}\right) = 0.480\text{ mol He} = n_1$

Converting m_2 (mass) to n_2 (moles): $(1.07\text{ g He})\left(\frac{1\text{ mol He}}{4.003\text{ g He}}\right) = 0.267\text{ mol He} = n_2$

Arranging the ideal gas law and solving for V_2:

$$\frac{\cancel{P_1}V_1}{n_1\cancel{T_1}} = \frac{\cancel{P_2}V_2}{n_2\cancel{T_2}} \quad \text{or} \quad \frac{V_1}{n_1} = \frac{V_2}{n_2}$$

$$V_2 = V_1\frac{n_2}{n_1} = (12.5\text{ L})\left(\frac{0.267\text{ mol He}}{0.480\text{ mol He}}\right) = \mathbf{6.95\ L}$$

5.32 Plan: Since the volume, temperature, and pressure of the gas are changing, use the combined gas law. Arrange the ideal gas law, solving for V_2 at fixed n. STP is 0°C (273 K) and 1 atm (101.325 kPa)

Solution:

$P_1 = 153.3$ kPa $P_2 = 101.325$ kPa

$V_1 = 25.5$ L V_2 = unknown

$T_1 = 298$ K $T_2 = 273$ K

n remains constant

Arranging the ideal gas law and solving for V_2:

$$\frac{P_1V_1}{\cancel{n_1}T_1} = \frac{P_2V_2}{\cancel{n_2}T_2} \quad \text{or} \quad \frac{P_1V_1}{T_1} = \frac{P_2V_2}{T_2}$$

$$V_2 = V_1\left(\frac{T_2}{T_1}\right)\left(\frac{P_1}{P_2}\right) = (25.5\ \text{L})\left(\frac{273\ \text{K}}{298\ \text{K}}\right)\left(\frac{153.3\ \text{kPa}}{101.325\ \text{kPa}}\right) = 35.3437 = \mathbf{35.3\ L}$$

5.34 Plan: Given the volume, pressure, and temperature of a gas, the number of moles of the gas can be calculated using the ideal gas law, solving for n. The gas constant, $R = 0.0821$ L•atm/mol•K, gives pressure in atmospheres and temperature in Kelvin. The given pressure in torr must be converted to atmospheres and the temperature converted to kelvins.

Solution:

$P = 328$ torr (convert to atm) $V = 5.0$ L

$T = 37°$C $n =$ unknown

Converting P from torr to atm: $P = (328\ \text{torr})\left(\frac{1\ \text{atm}}{760\ \text{torr}}\right) = 0.43158\ \text{atm}$

Converting T from °C to K: $T = 37°\text{C} + 273 = 310\ \text{K}$

$PV = nRT$

Solving for n:

$$n = \frac{PV}{RT} = \frac{(0.43158\ \text{atm})(5.0\ \text{L})}{\left(0.0821\frac{\text{L•atm}}{\text{mol•K}}\right)(310\ \text{K})} = 0.08479 = \mathbf{0.085\ mol\ chlorine}$$

5.36 Plan: Solve the ideal gas law for moles and convert to mass using the molar mass of ClF_3. The gas constant, $R = 0.0821$ L•atm/mol•K, gives volume in liters, pressure in atmospheres, and temperature in Kelvin so volume must be converted to L, pressure to atm, and temperature to K.

Solution:

$V = 357$ mL $T = 45°$C

$P = 699$ mmHg $n =$ unknown

Converting V from mL to L: $V = (357\ \text{mL})\left(\frac{10^{-3}\ \text{L}}{1\ \text{mL}}\right) = 0.357\ \text{L}$

Converting T from °C to K: $T = 45°\text{C} + 273 = 318\ \text{K}$

Converting P from mmHg to atm: $P = (699\ \text{mmHg})\left(\frac{1\ \text{atm}}{760\ \text{mmHg}}\right) = 0.91974\ \text{atm}$

$PV = nRT$

Solving for n:

$$n = \frac{PV}{RT} = \frac{(0.91974\ \text{atm})(0.357\ \text{L})}{\left(0.0821\frac{\text{L•atm}}{\text{mol•K}}\right)(318\ \text{K})} = 0.01258\ \text{mol ClF}_3$$

$$\text{Mass ClF}_3 = (0.01258\ \text{mol ClF}_3)\left(\frac{92.45\ \text{g ClF}_3}{1\ \text{mol ClF}_3}\right) = 1.163021 = \mathbf{1.16\ g\ ClF_3}$$

5.39 Plan: Assuming that while rising in the atmosphere the balloon will neither gain nor lose gas molecules, the number of moles of gas calculated at sea level will be the same as the number of moles of gas at the higher altitude (n is fixed). Volume, temperature, and pressure of the gas are changing. Arrange the ideal gas law, solving for V_2 at fixed n. Given the sea-level conditions of volume, pressure, and temperature, and the temperature and pressure at the higher altitude for the gas in the balloon, we can set up an equation to solve for the volume at the higher altitude. Comparing the calculated volume to the given maximum volume of 835 L will tell us if the balloon has reached its maximum volume at this altitude. Temperature must be converted to kelvins and pressure in torr must be converted to atm for unit agreement.

Solution:

$P_1 = 745$ torr $P_2 = 0.066$ atm
$V_1 = 65$ L V_2 = unknown
$T_1 = 25°C + 273 = 298$ K $T_2 = -5°C + 273 = 268$ K
n remains constant

Converting P from torr to atm: $P = (745 \text{ torr})\left(\frac{1 \text{ atm}}{760 \text{ torr}}\right) = 0.98026 \text{ atm}$

Arranging the ideal gas law and solving for V_2:

$$\frac{P_1V_1}{\cancel{n_1}T_1} = \frac{P_2V_2}{\cancel{n_2}T_2} \quad \text{or} \quad \frac{P_1V_1}{T_1} = \frac{P_2V_2}{T_2}$$

$$V_2 = V_1\left(\frac{T_2}{T_1}\right)\left(\frac{P_1}{P_2}\right) = (65 \text{ L})\left(\frac{268 \text{ K}}{298 \text{ K}}\right)\left(\frac{0.98026 \text{ atm}}{0.066 \text{ atm}}\right) = 868.219 = \mathbf{870 \text{ L}}$$

The calculated volume of the gas at the higher altitude is more than the maximum volume of the balloon. **Yes**, the balloon will reach its maximum volume.

Check: Should we expect that the volume of the gas in the balloon should increase? At the higher altitude, the pressure decreases; this increases the volume of the gas. At the higher altitude, the temperature decreases, this decreases the volume of the gas. Which of these will dominate? The pressure decreases by a factor of 0.98/0.066 = 15. If we label the initial volume V_1, then the resulting volume is $15V_1$. The temperature decreases by a factor of 298/268 = 1.1, so the resulting volume is $V_1/1.1$ or $0.91V_1$. The increase in volume due to the change in pressure is greater than the decrease in volume due to change in temperature, so the volume of gas at the higher altitude should be greater than the volume at sea level.

5.41 The molar mass of H_2 is less than the average molar mass of air (mostly N_2, O_2, and Ar), so air is denser. To collect a beaker of $H_2(g)$, **invert** the beaker so that the air will be replaced by the lighter H_2. The molar mass of CO_2 is greater than the average molar mass of air, so $CO_2(g)$ is more dense. Collect the CO_2 holding the beaker **upright**, so the lighter air will be displaced out the top of the beaker.

5.45 Plan: Rearrange the ideal gas law to calculate the density of xenon from its molar mass at STP. Standard temperature is 0°C (273 K) and standard pressure is 1 atm. Do not forget that the pressure at STP is exact and will not affect the significant figures.

Solution:

$P = 1$ atm $T = 273$ K
$\mathcal{M}$ of Xe = 131.3 g/mol d = unknown
$PV = nRT$

Rearranging to solve for density:

$$d = \frac{P\mathcal{M}}{RT} = \frac{(1 \text{ atm})(131.3 \text{ g/mol})}{\left(0.0821 \frac{\text{L•atm}}{\text{mol•K}}\right)(273 \text{ K})} = 5.8581 = \mathbf{5.86 \text{ g/L}}$$

5.47 Plan: Solve the ideal gas law for moles. Convert moles to mass using the molar mass of AsH_3 and divide this mass by the volume to obtain density in g/L. Standard temperature is 0°C (273 K) and standard pressure is 1 atm. Do not forget that the pressure at STP is exact and will not affect the significant figures.

Solution:

$V = 0.0400$ L $T = 0°C + 273 = 273$ K
$P = 1$ atm n = unknown
$\mathcal{M}$ of AsH_3 = 77.94 g/mol
$PV = nRT$

Solving for n:

$$n = \frac{PV}{RT} = \frac{(1 \text{ atm})(0.0400 \text{ L})}{\left(0.0821 \frac{\text{L•atm}}{\text{mol•K}}\right)(273 \text{ K})} = 1.78465\text{x}10^{-3} = \mathbf{1.78x10^{-3} \text{ mol } AsH_3}$$

Converting moles of AsH_3 to mass of AsH_3:

$$\text{Mass (g) of AsH}_3 = \left(1.78465\text{x}10^{-3}\ \text{mol AsH}_3\right)\left(\frac{77.94\ \text{g AsH}_3}{1\ \text{mol AsH}_3}\right) = 0.1391\ \text{g AsH}_3$$

$$d = \frac{\text{mass}}{\text{volume}} = \frac{(0.1391\ \text{g})}{(0.0400\ \text{L})} = 3.4775 = \mathbf{3.48\ g/L}$$

5.49 Plan: Rearrange the formula $PV = (m/\mathcal{M})RT$ to solve for molar mass. Convert the mass in ng to g and volume in μL to L. Temperature must be in Kelvin and pressure in atm.

Solution:

$V = 0.206$ μL $\quad T = 45°\text{C} + 273 = 318$ K

$P = 380$ torr $\quad m = 206$ ng

$\mathcal{M}$ = unknown

Converting P from torr to atm: $\quad P = (380\ \text{torr})\left(\frac{1\ \text{atm}}{760\ \text{torr}}\right) = 0.510526\ \text{atm}$

Converting V from μL to L: $\quad V = (0.206\ \mu\text{L})\left(\frac{10^{-6}\ \text{L}}{1\ \mu\text{L}}\right) = 2.06\text{x}10^{-7}\ \text{L}$

Converting m from ng to g: $\quad m = (206\ \text{ng})\left(\frac{10^{-9}\ \text{g}}{1\ \text{ng}}\right) = 2.06\text{x}10^{-7}\ \text{g}$

$$PV = \left(\frac{m}{\mathcal{M}}\right)RT$$

Solving for molar mass, $\mathcal{M}$:

$$\mathcal{M} = \frac{mRT}{PV} = \frac{\left(2.06\text{x}10^{-7}\ \text{g}\right)\left(0.0821\ \frac{\text{L•atm}}{\text{mol•K}}\right)(318\ \text{K})}{(0.510526\ \text{atm})\left(2.06\text{x}10^{-7}\ \text{L}\right)} = 51.1390 = \mathbf{51.1\ g/mol}$$

5.51 Plan: Use the ideal gas law to determine the number of moles of Ar and of O_2. The gases are combined ($n_{\text{total}} = n_{\text{Ar}} + n_{O_2}$) into a 400 mL flask ($V$) at 27°C ($T$). Use the ideal gas law again to determine the total pressure from n_{total}, V, and T. Pressure must be in units of atm, volume in units of L and temperature in K.

Solution:

For Ar:

$V = 0.600$ L $\quad T = 227°\text{C} + 273 = 500.$ K

$P = 1.20$ atm $\quad n$ = unknown

$PV = nRT$

Solving for n:

$$n = \frac{PV}{RT} = \frac{(1.20\ \text{atm})(0.600\ \text{L})}{\left(0.0821\frac{\text{L•atm}}{\text{mol•K}}\right)(500.\ \text{K})} = 0.017539586\ \text{mol Ar}$$

For O_2:

$V = 0.200$ L $\quad T = 127°\text{C} + 273 = 400.$ K

$P = 501$ torr $\quad n$ = unknown

Converting P from torr to atm: $\quad P = (501\ \text{torr})\left(\frac{1\ \text{atm}}{760\ \text{torr}}\right) = 0.6592105\ \text{atm}$

$PV = nRT$

Solving for n:

$$n = \frac{PV}{RT} = \frac{(0.6592105\ \text{atm})(0.200\ \text{L})}{\left(0.0821\frac{\text{L•atm}}{\text{mol•K}}\right)(400.\ \text{K})} = 0.004014680\ \text{mol O}_2$$

$n_{total} = n_{Ar} + n_{O_2} = 0.017539586 \text{ mol} + 0.004014680 \text{ mol} = 0.021554266 \text{ mol}$

For the mixture of Ar and O_2:

$V = 400$ mL $T = 27°C + 273 = 300.$ K

P = unknownn $n = 0.021554265$ mol

Converting V from mL to L: $V = (400 \text{ mL})\left(\frac{10^{-3} \text{ L}}{1 \text{ mL}}\right) = 0.400 \text{ L}$

$PV = nRT$

Solving for P:

$$P_{mixture} = \frac{nRT}{V} = \frac{(0.021554266 \text{ mol})\left(0.0821 \frac{\text{L•atm}}{\text{mol•K}}\right)(300 \text{ K})}{(0.400 \text{ L})} = 1.32720 = \mathbf{1.33 \text{ atm}}$$

5.53 Plan: Use the ideal gas law, solving for n to find the moles of O_2. Use the molar ratio from the balanced equation to determine the moles (and then mass) of phosphorus that will react with the oxygen. Standard temperature is 0°C (273 K) and standard pressure is 1 atm.

Solution:

$V = 35.5$ L $T = 0°C + 273 = 273$ K

$P = 1$ atm n = unknown

$PV = nRT$

Solving for n:

$$n = \frac{PV}{RT} = \frac{(1 \text{ atm})(35.5 \text{ L})}{\left(0.0821 \frac{\text{L•atm}}{\text{mol•K}}\right)(273 \text{ K})} = 1.583881 \text{ mol } O_2$$

$P_4(s) + 5O_2(g) \rightarrow P_4O_{10}(s)$

$$\text{Mass } P_4 = (1.583881 \text{ mol } O_2)\left(\frac{1 \text{ mol } P_4}{5 \text{ mol } O_2}\right)\left(\frac{123.88 \text{ g } P_4}{1 \text{ mol } P_4}\right) = 39.24224 = \mathbf{39.2 \text{ g } P_4}$$

5.55 Plan: Since the amounts of two reactants are given, this is a limiting reactant problem. To find the mass of PH_3, write the balanced equation and use molar ratios to find the number of moles of PH_3 produced by each reactant. The smaller number of moles of product indicates the limiting reagent. Solve for moles of H_2 using the ideal gas law.

Solution:

Moles of hydrogen:

$V = 83.0$ L $T = 0°C + 273 = 273$ K

$P = 1$ atm n = unknown

$PV = nRT$

Solving for n:

$$n = \frac{PV}{RT} = \frac{(1 \text{ atm})(83.0 \text{ L})}{\left(0.0821 \frac{\text{L•atm}}{\text{mol•K}}\right)(273 \text{ K})} = 3.7031584 \text{ mol } H_2$$

$P_4(s) + 6H_2(g) \rightarrow 4PH_3(g)$

$$PH_3 \text{ from } P_4 = (37.5 \text{ g } P_4)\left(\frac{1 \text{ mol } P_4}{123.88 \text{ g } P_4}\right)\left(\frac{4 \text{ mol } PH_3}{1 \text{ mol } P_4}\right) = 1.21085 \text{ mol } PH_3$$

$$PH_3 \text{ from } H_2 = (3.7031584 \text{ mol } H_2)\left(\frac{4 \text{ mol } PH_3}{6 \text{ mol } H_2}\right) = 2.4687723 \text{ mol } PH_3$$

P_4 is the limiting reactant because it forms less PH_3.

$$\text{Mass } PH_3 = (37.5 \text{ g } P_4)\left(\frac{1 \text{ mol } P_4}{123.88 \text{ g } P_4}\right)\left(\frac{4 \text{ mol } PH_3}{1 \text{ mol } P_4}\right)\left(\frac{33.99 \text{ g } PH_3}{1 \text{ mol } PH_3}\right) = 41.15676 = \mathbf{41.2 \text{ g } PH_3}$$

5.57 Plan: First, write the balanced equation. The moles of hydrogen produced can be calculated from the ideal gas law. The problem specifies that the hydrogen gas is collected over water, so the partial pressure of water vapor must be subtracted from the overall pressure given. Table 5.2 reports pressure at 26°C (25.2 torr) and 28°C (28.3 torr), so take the average of the two values to obtain the partial pressure of water at 27°C. Volume must be in units of liters, pressure in atm, and temperature in kelvins. Once the moles of hydrogen produced are known, the molar ratio from the balanced equation is used to determine the moles of aluminum that reacted.

Solution:

$V = 35.8$ mL $\quad T = 27°C + 273 = 300$ K

$P_{total} = 751$ mmHg $\quad n =$ unknown

$P_{water\ vapor} = (28.3 + 25.2)$ torr/2 = 26.75 torr = 26.75 mmHg

$P_{hydrogen} = P_{total} - P_{water\ vapor} = 751$ mmHg – 26.75 mmHg = 724.25 mmHg

Converting P from mmHg to atm: $P = (724.25\ \text{mmHg})\left(\frac{1\ \text{atm}}{760\ \text{mmHg}}\right) = 0.952960526\ \text{atm}$

Converting V from mL to L: $V = (35.8\ \text{mL})\left(\frac{10^{-3}\ \text{L}}{1\ \text{mL}}\right) = 0.0358\ \text{L}$

$PV = nRT$

Solving for n:

$$n = \frac{PV}{RT} = \frac{(0.952960526\ \text{atm})(0.0358\ \text{L})}{\left(0.0821\frac{\text{L•atm}}{\text{mol•K}}\right)(300.\ \text{K})} = 0.0013851395\ \text{mol H}_2$$

$$2Al(s) + 6HCl(aq) \rightarrow 2AlCl_3(aq) + 3H_2(g)$$

$$\text{Mass (g) of Al} = (0.0013851395\ \text{mol H}_2)\left(\frac{2\ \text{mol Al}}{3\ \text{mol H}_2}\right)\left(\frac{26.98\ \text{g Al}}{1\ \text{mol Al}}\right) = 0.024914 = \mathbf{0.0249\ g\ Al}$$

5.61 Plan: The problem gives the mass, volume, temperature, and pressure of a gas; rearrange the formula $PV = (m/\mathcal{M})RT$ to solve for the molar mass of the gas. Temperature must be in Kelvin and pressure in atm. The problem also states that the gas is a hydrocarbon, which by, definition, contains only carbon and hydrogen atoms. We are also told that each molecule of the gas contains five carbon atoms so we can use this information and the calculated molar mass to find out how many hydrogen atoms are present and the formula of the compound.

Solution:

$V = 0.204$ L $\quad T = 101°C + 273 = 374$ K

$P = 767$ torr $\quad m = 0.482$ g

$\mathcal{M} =$ unknown

Converting P from torr to atm: $P = (767\ \text{torr})\left(\frac{1\ \text{atm}}{760\ \text{torr}}\right) = 1.009210526\ \text{atm}$

$$PV = \left(\frac{m}{\mathcal{M}}\right)RT$$

Solving for molar mass, $\mathcal{M}$:

$$\mathcal{M} = \frac{mRT}{PV} = \frac{(0.482\ \text{g})\left(0.0821\frac{\text{L•atm}}{\text{mol•K}}\right)(374\ \text{K})}{(1.009210526\ \text{atm})(0.204\ \text{L})} = 71.8869\ \text{g/mol (unrounded)}$$

The mass of the five carbon atoms accounts for [5(12 g/mol)] = 60 g/mol; thus, the hydrogen atoms must make up the difference (72 – 60) = 12 g/mol. A value of 12 g/mol corresponds to 12 H atoms. (Since fractional atoms are not possible, rounding is acceptable.) Therefore, the molecular formula is $\mathbf{C_5H_{12}}$.

5.63 Plan: Since you have the pressure, volume, and temperature, use the ideal gas law to solve for n, the total moles of gas. Pressure must be in units of atmospheres and temperature in units of kelvins. The partial pressure of SO_2 can be found by multiplying the total pressure by the volume fraction of SO_2.

Solution:

a) $V = 21$ L $\quad\quad T = 45°C + 273 = 318$ K

$P = 850$ torr $\quad\quad n =$ unknown

Converting P from torr to atm: $\quad P = (850 \text{ torr})\left(\frac{1 \text{ atm}}{760 \text{ torr}}\right) = 1.118421053$ atm

$PV = nRT$

Moles of gas $= n = \frac{PV}{RT} = \frac{(1.118421053 \text{ atm})(21 \text{ L})}{\left(0.0821 \frac{\text{L•atm}}{\text{mol•K}}\right)(318 \text{ K})} = 0.89961 = \mathbf{0.90\ mol\ gas}$

b) The equation $P_{SO_2} = X_{SO_2} \text{ x } P_{total}$ can be used to find partial pressure. The information given in ppm is a way of expressing the proportion, or fraction, of SO_2 present in the mixture. Since n is directly proportional to V, the *volume* fraction can be used in place of the *mole* fraction, X_{SO_2}. There are $7.95\text{x}10^3$ parts SO_2 in a million parts of mixture, so volume fraction = $(7.95\text{x}10^3/1\text{x}10^6) = 7.95\text{x}10^{-3}$.

P_{D_2} = volume fraction x $P_{total} = (7.95\text{x}10^{-3})$ (850. torr) = 6.7575 = **6.76 torr**

5.64 Plan: First, write the balanced equation. Convert mass of P_4S_3 to moles and use the molar ratio from the balanced equation to find the moles of SO_2 gas produced. Use the ideal gas law to find the volume of that amount of SO_2. Pressure must be in units of atm and temperature in kelvins.

Solution:

$$P_4S_3(s) + 8O_2(g) \rightarrow P_4O_{10}(s) + 3SO_2(g)$$

Moles SO_2 = $(0.800 \text{ g } P_4S_3)\left(\frac{1 \text{ mol } P_4S_3}{220.06 \text{ g } P_4S_3}\right)\left(\frac{3 \text{ mol } SO_2}{1 \text{ mol } P_4S_3}\right) = 0.010906 \text{ mol } SO_2$

Finding the volume of SO_2:

$V =$ unknown $\quad\quad T = 32°C + 273 = 305$ K

$P = 725$ torr $\quad\quad n = 0.010905$ mol

Converting P from torr to atm: $\quad P = (725 \text{ torr})\left(\frac{1 \text{ atm}}{760 \text{ torr}}\right) = 0.953947368$ atm

$PV = nRT$

Solving for V:

$$V = \frac{nRT}{P} = \frac{(0.010906 \text{ mol})\left(0.0821 \frac{\text{L•atm}}{\text{mol•K}}\right)(305 \text{ K})}{(0.953947368 \text{ atm})} = 0.28627543 \text{ L}$$

Converting V from L to mL:

$V = (0.28627543 \text{ L})\left(\frac{1 \text{ mL}}{10^{-3} \text{ L}}\right) = 286.275 = \mathbf{286\ mL\ SO_2}$

5.66 Plan: First, write the balanced equation. Given the amount of xenon hexafluoride that reacts, we can find the number of moles of silicon tetrafluoride gas formed by using the molar ratio in the balanced equation. Then, using the ideal gas law with the moles of gas, the temperature, and the volume, we can calculate the pressure of the silicon tetrafluoride gas. Temperature must be in units of kelvins.

Solution:

$$2XeF_6(s) + SiO_2(s) \rightarrow 2XeOF_4(l) + SiF_4(g)$$

Moles $SiF_4 = n = (2.00 \text{ g } XeF_6)\left(\frac{1 \text{ mol } XeF_6}{245.3 \text{ g } XeF_6}\right)\left(\frac{1 \text{ mol } SiF_4}{2 \text{ mol } XeF_6}\right) = 0.0040766 \text{ mol } SiF_4$

Finding the pressure of SiF_4:

$V = 1.00$ L $\quad\quad T = 25°C + 273 = 298$ K

$P =$ unknown $\quad\quad n = 0.0040766$ mol

$PV = nRT$

Solving for P:

$$\text{Pressure SiF}_4 = P = \frac{nRT}{V} = \frac{(0.0040766 \text{ mol SiF}_4)\left(0.0821 \frac{\text{L•atm}}{\text{mol•K}}\right)(298 \text{ K})}{1.00 \text{ L}} = 0.099737 = \mathbf{0.0997\ atm\ SiF_4}$$

5.71 At STP (or any identical temperature and pressure), the volume occupied by a mole of any gas will be identical. One mole of krypton has the same number of particles as one mole of helium and, at the same temperature, all of the gas particles have the same average kinetic energy, resulting in the same pressure and volume.

5.74 Plan: The molar masses of the three gases are 2.016 for H_2 (Flask A), 4.003 for He (Flask B), and 16.04 for CH_4 (Flask C). Since hydrogen has the smallest molar mass of the three gases, 4 g of H_2 will contain more gas molecules (about 2 mole's worth) than 4 g of He or 4 g of CH_4. Since helium has a smaller molar mass than methane, 4 g of He will contain more gas molecules (about 1 mole's worth) than 4 g of CH_4 (about 0.25 mole's worth).

Solution:

a) $\mathbf{P_A > P_B > P_C}$ The pressure of a gas is proportional to the number of gas molecules ($\underline{P}V = \underline{n}RT$). So, the gas sample with more gas molecules will have a greater pressure.

b) $\boldsymbol{E_A = E_B = E_C}$ Average kinetic energy depends only on temperature. The temperature of each gas sample is 273 K, so they all have the same average kinetic energy.

c) $\mathbf{rate_A > rate_B > rate_C}$ When comparing the speed of two gas molecules, the one with the lower mass travels faster.

d) **total** $\boldsymbol{E_A}$ **> total** $\boldsymbol{E_B}$ **> total** $\boldsymbol{E_C}$ Since the average kinetic energy for each gas is the same (part b) of this problem), the total kinetic energy would equal the average times the number of molecules. Since the hydrogen flask contains the most molecules, its total kinetic energy will be the greatest.

e) $\boldsymbol{d_A = d_B = d_C}$ Under the conditions stated in this problem, each sample has the same volume, 5 L, and the same mass, 4 g. Thus, the density of each is 4 g/5 L = 0.8 g/L.

f) **Collision frequency (A) > collision frequency (B) > collision frequency (C)** The number of collisions depends on both the speed and the distance between gas molecules. Since hydrogen is the lightest molecule it has the greatest speed and the 5 L flask of hydrogen also contains the most molecules, so collisions will occur more frequently between hydrogen molecules than between helium molecules. By the same reasoning, collisions will occur more frequently between helium molecules than between methane molecules.

5.75 Plan: To find the ratio of effusion rates, calculate the inverse of the ratio of the square roots of the molar masses (Graham's law).

Solution:

$$\frac{\text{Rate H}_2}{\text{Rate UF}_6} = \sqrt{\frac{\text{molar mass UF}_6}{\text{molar mass H}_2}} = \sqrt{\frac{352.0 \text{ g/mol}}{2.016 \text{ g/mol}}} = 13.2137 = \mathbf{13.21}$$

5.77 Plan: Recall that the heavier the gas, the slower the molecular speed. The molar mass of Ar is 39.95 g/mol while the molar mass of He is 4.003 g/mol.

Solution:

a) The gases have the same average kinetic energy because they are at the same temperature. The heavier Ar atoms are moving more slowly than the lighter He atoms to maintain the same average kinetic energy. Therefore, **Curve 1** with the lower average molecular speed, better represents the behavior of Ar.

b) A gas that has a slower molecular speed would effuse more slowly, so **Curve 1** is the better choice.

c) Fluorine gas exists as a diatomic molecule, F_2, with $\mathcal{M}$= 38.00 g/mol. Therefore, F_2 is much closer in mass to Ar (39.95 g/mol) than He (4.003 g/mol), so **Curve 1** more closely represents the behavior of F_2.

5.79 Plan: To find the ratio of effusion rates, calculate the inverse of the ratio of the square roots of the molar masses (Graham's law). Then use the ratio of effusion rates to find the time for the F_2 effusion. Effusion rate and time required for the effusion are inversely proportional.

Solution:

$\mathcal{M}$ of He = 4.003 g/mol $\qquad$ $\mathcal{M}$ of F_2 = 38.00 g/mol

$$\frac{\text{Rate He}}{\text{Rate F}_2} = \sqrt{\frac{\text{molar mass F}_2}{\text{molar mass He}}} = \sqrt{\frac{38.00\text{ g/mol}}{4.003\text{ g/mol}}} = 3.08105 \text{ (unrounded)}$$

$$\frac{\text{Rate He}}{\text{Rate F}_2} = \frac{\text{time F}_2}{\text{time He}} \qquad \frac{3.08105}{1.00} = \frac{\text{time F}_2}{4.85\text{ min He}} \qquad \text{Time F}_2 = 14.9431 = \mathbf{14.9\ min}$$

5.81 Plan: White phosphorus is a molecular form of the element phosphorus consisting of some number, x, of phosphorus atoms; the number of atoms in a molecule determines the molar mass of the phosphorus molecule. Use the relative rates of effusion of white phosphorus and neon (Graham's law) to determine the molar mass of white phosphorus. From the molar mass of white phosphorus, determine the number of phosphorus atoms, x, in one molecule of white phosphorus.

Solution:

$\mathcal{M}$ of Ne = 20.18 g/mol

$$\frac{\text{Rate P}_x}{\text{Rate Ne}} = 0.404 = \sqrt{\frac{\text{molar mass Ne}}{\text{molar mass P}_x}}$$

$$0.404 = \sqrt{\frac{20.18\text{ g/mol}}{\text{molar mass P}_x}}$$

$$(0.404)^2 = \frac{20.18\text{ g/mol}}{\text{molar mass P}_x}$$

$$0.163216 = \frac{20.18\text{ g/mol}}{\text{molar mass P}_x}$$

Molar mass P_x = 123.6398 g/mol

$$\left(\frac{123.6398\text{ g}}{\text{mol P}_x}\right)\left(\frac{1\text{ mol P}}{30.97\text{ g P}}\right) = 3.992244 = 4\text{ mol P/mol P}_x \text{ or 4 atoms P/molecule P}_x$$

Thus, **4 atoms per molecule**, so $P_x = P_4$.

5.84 Interparticle attractions cause the real pressure to be *less than* ideal pressure, so it causes a **negative** deviation. The size of the interparticle attraction is related to the constant *a*. According to Table 5.4, $a_{N_2} = 1.39$, $a_{Kr} = 2.32$, and $a_{CO_2} = 3.59$. Therefore, CO_2 experiences a greater negative deviation in pressure than the other two gases: $\mathbf{N_2 < Kr < CO_2}$.

5.86 Nitrogen gas behaves more ideally at **1 atm** than at 500 atm because at lower pressures the gas molecules are farther apart. An ideal gas is defined as consisting of gas molecules that act independently of the other gas molecules. When gas molecules are far apart they act more ideally, because intermolecular attractions are less important and the volume of the molecules is a smaller fraction of the container volume.

5.89 Plan: Use the ideal gas law to find the number of moles of O_2. Moles of O_2 is divided by 4 to find moles of Hb since O_2 combines with Hb in a 4:1 ratio. Divide the given mass of Hb by the number of moles of Hb to obtain molar mass, g/mol. Temperature must be in units of kelvins, pressure in atm, and volume in L.

Solution:

V = 1.53 mL $\qquad$ T = 37°C + 273 = 310 K

P = 743 torr $\qquad$ n = unknown

Converting V from mL to L: $\quad V = (1.53\text{ mL})\left(\frac{10^{-3}\text{ L}}{1\text{ mL}}\right) = 1.53\text{x}10^{-3}\text{ L}$

Converting P from torr to atm: $\quad P = (743\text{ torr})\left(\frac{1\text{ atm}}{760\text{ torr}}\right) = 0.977631578\text{ atm}$

$PV = nRT$

Solving for n:

$$\text{Moles of } O_2 = n = \frac{PV}{RT} = \frac{(0.977631578 \text{ atm})(1.53\text{x}10^{-3} \text{ L})}{\left(0.0821 \frac{\text{L•atm}}{\text{mol•K}}\right)(310 \text{ K})} = 5.87708\text{x}10^{-5} \text{ mol } O_2$$

$$\text{Moles Hb} = \left(5.87708\text{x}10^{-5} \text{ mol } O_2\right)\left(\frac{1 \text{ mol Hb}}{4 \text{ mol } O_2}\right) = 1.46927\text{x}10^{-5} \text{ mol Hb (unrounded)}$$

$$\text{Molar mass hemoglobin} = \frac{1.00 \text{ g Hb}}{1.46927\text{x}10^{-5} \text{ Hb}} = 6.806098\text{x}10^{4} = \mathbf{6.81x10^4\ g/mol}$$

5.92 Plan: Convert the mass of Cl_2 to moles and use the ideal gas law and van der Waals equation to find the pressure of the gas.

Solution:

a) Moles Cl_2: $\left(0.5950 \text{ kg } Cl_2\right)\left(\frac{10^3 \text{ g}}{1 \text{ kg}}\right)\left(\frac{1 \text{ mol } Cl_2}{70.90 \text{ g } Cl_2}\right) = 8.3921016 \text{ mol}$

$V = 15.50$ L
$n = 8.3921016$ mol
$T = 225°C + 273 = 498$ K
P = unknown

Ideal gas law: $PV = nRT$

Solving for P:

$$P_{IGL} = \frac{nRT}{V} = \frac{(8.3921016 \text{mol})\left(0.0821 \frac{\text{L•atm}}{\text{mol•K}}\right)(498 \text{ K})}{15.50 \text{ L}} = 22.1366 = \mathbf{22.1\ atm}$$

b) van der Waals equation: $\left(P + \frac{n^2 a}{V^2}\right)(V - nb) = nRT$

Solving for P:

$P_{VDW} = \frac{nRT}{V - nb} - \frac{n^2 a}{V^2}$ From Table 5.4: $a = 6.49 \frac{\text{atm•L}^2}{\text{mol}^2}$; $b = 0.0562 \frac{\text{L}}{\text{mol}}$

n = 8.3921016 mol from part a)

$$P_{VDW} = \frac{(8.3921016 \text{ mol } Cl_2)\left(0.0821 \frac{\text{L•atm}}{\text{mol•K}}\right)(498 \text{ K})}{15.50 \text{ L} - (8.3921016 \text{ mol } Cl_2)\left(0.0562 \frac{\text{L}}{\text{mol}}\right)} - \frac{(8.3921016 \text{ mol } Cl_2)^2\left(6.49 \frac{\text{atm•L}^2}{\text{mol}^2}\right)}{(15.50 \text{ L})^2}$$

$= 20.928855 = \mathbf{20.9\ atm}$

5.96 Plan: Partial pressures and mole fractions are calculated from Dalton's law of partial pressures: $P_A = X_A \text{ x } P_{total}$. Remember that 1 atm = 760 torr. Solve the ideal gas law for moles and then convert to molecules using Avogadro's number to calculate the number of O_2 molecules in the volume of an average breath.

Solution:

a) Convert each mole percent to a mole fraction by dividing by 100%. P_{total} = 1 atm = 760 torr

$P_{Nitrogen} = X_{Nitrogen} \text{ x } P_{total} = 0.786 \text{ x } 760 \text{ torr} = 597.36 = \mathbf{597\ torr\ N_2}$

$P_{Oxygen} = X_{Oxygen} \text{ x } P_{total} = 0.209 \text{ x } 760 \text{ torr} = 158.84 = \mathbf{159\ torr\ O_2}$

$P_{Carbon\ Dioxide} = X_{Carbon\ Dioxide} \text{ x } P_{total} = 0.0004 \text{ x } 760 \text{ torr} = 0.304 = \mathbf{0.3\ torr\ CO_2}$

$P_{Water} = X_{Water} \text{ x } P_{total} = 0.0046 \text{ x } 760 \text{ torr} = 3.496 = \mathbf{3.5\ torr\ H_2O}$

b) Mole fractions can be calculated by rearranging Dalton's law of partial pressures:

$X_A = \frac{P_A}{P_{total}}$ and multiply by 100 to express mole fraction as percent

P_{total} = 1 atm = 760 torr

$$X_{\text{Nitrogen}} = \frac{569 \text{ torr}}{760 \text{ torr}} \text{ x } 100\% = 74.8684 = \mathbf{74.9 \text{ mol\% } N_2}$$

$$X_{\text{Oxygen}} = \frac{104 \text{ torr}}{760 \text{ torr}} \text{ x } 100\% = 13.6842 = \mathbf{13.7 \text{ mol\% } O_2}$$

$$X_{\text{Carbon Dioxide}} = \frac{40 \text{ torr}}{760 \text{ torr}} \text{ x } 100\% = 5.263 = \mathbf{5.3 \text{ mol\% } CO_2}$$

$$X_{\text{Water}} = \frac{47 \text{ torr}}{760 \text{ torr}} \text{ x } 100\% = 6.1842 = \mathbf{6.2 \text{ mol\% } H_2O}$$

c) $V = 0.50$ L $\quad T = 37°\text{C} + 273 = 310$ K
$P = 104$ torr $\quad n =$ unknown

Converting P from torr to atm: $\quad P = (104 \text{ torr})\left(\frac{1 \text{ atm}}{760 \text{ torr}}\right) = 0.136842105 \text{ atm}$

$PV = nRT$
Solving for n:

$$n = \frac{PV}{RT} = \frac{(0.136842105 \text{ atm})(0.50 \text{ L})}{\left(0.0821\frac{\text{L•atm}}{\text{mol•K}}\right)(310 \text{ K})} = 0.0026883 \text{ mol } O_2$$

$$\text{Molecules of } O_2 = (0.0026883 \text{ mol } O_2)\left(\frac{6.022\text{x}10^{23} \text{ molecules } O_2}{1 \text{ mol } O_2}\right)$$

$$= 1.6189\text{x}10^{21} = \mathbf{1.6x10^{21} \text{ molecules } O_2}$$

5.98 Plan: For part a), since the volume, temperature, and pressure of the gas are changing, use the combined gas law. For part b), use the ideal gas law to solve for moles of air and then moles of N_2.
Solution:
a) $P_1 = 1450.$ mmHg $\quad P_2 = 1$ atm
$V_1 = 208$ mL $\quad V_2 =$ unknown
$T_1 = 286$ K $\quad T_2 = 298$ K

Converting P_1 from mmHg to atm: $P_1 = (1450. \text{ mmHg})\left(\frac{1 \text{ atm}}{760 \text{ mmHg}}\right) = 1.9079 \text{ atm}$

Arranging the ideal gas law and solving for V_2:

$$\frac{P_1V_1}{T_1} = \frac{P_2V_2}{T_2}$$

$$V_2 = V_1\left(\frac{T_2}{T_1}\right)\left(\frac{P_1}{P_2}\right) = (208 \text{ L})\left(\frac{298 \text{ K}}{286 \text{ K}}\right)\left(\frac{1.9079 \text{ atm}}{1 \text{ atm}}\right) = 413.494 \text{ mL} = \mathbf{4x10^2 \text{ mL}}$$

b) $V = 208$ mL $\quad T = 286$ K
$P = 1450$ mmHg $= 1.9079$ atm $\quad n =$ unknown

Converting V from mL to L: $\quad V = (208 \text{ mL})\left(\frac{10^{-3} \text{ L}}{1 \text{ mL}}\right) = 0.208 \text{ L}$

$PV = nRT$
Solving for n:

$$\text{Moles of air} = n = \frac{PV}{RT} = \frac{(1.9079 \text{ atm})(0.208 \text{ L})}{\left(0.0821\frac{\text{L•atm}}{\text{mol•K}}\right)(286 \text{ K})} = 0.016901 \text{ mol air}$$

$$\text{Mole of } N_2 = (0.016901 \text{ mol})\left(\frac{77\% \ N_2}{100\%}\right) = 0.01301 = \mathbf{0.013 \text{ mol } N_2}$$

5.99 Plan: The amounts of both reactants are given, so the first step is to identify the limiting reactant. Write the balanced equation and use molar ratios to find the number of moles of NO_2 produced by each reactant. The smaller number of moles of product indicates the limiting reagent. Solve for volume of NO_2 using the ideal gas law.
Solution:
$Cu(s) + 4HNO_3(aq) \rightarrow Cu(NO_3)_2(aq) + 2NO_2(g) + 2H_2O(l)$

$$\text{Moles } NO_2 \text{ from Cu} = \left(4.95\ \text{cm}^3\right)\left(\frac{8.95\ \text{g Cu}}{\text{cm}^3}\right)\left(\frac{1\ \text{mol Cu}}{63.55\ \text{g Cu}}\right)\left(\frac{2\ \text{mol } NO_2}{1\ \text{mol Cu}}\right) = 1.394256\ \text{mol } NO_2$$

$$\text{Moles } NO_2 \text{ from } HNO_3 = \left(230.0\ \text{mL}\right)\left(\frac{68.0\%\ HNO_3}{100\%}\right)\left(\frac{1\ \text{cm}^3}{1\ \text{mL}}\right)\left(\frac{1.42\ \text{g}}{\text{cm}^3}\right)\left(\frac{1\ \text{mol } HNO_3}{63.02\ \text{g}}\right)\left(\frac{2\ \text{mol } NO_2}{4\ \text{mol } HNO_3}\right)$$

$$= 1.7620\ \text{mol } NO_2$$

Since less product can be made from the copper, it is the limiting reactant and excess nitric acid will be left after the reaction goes to completion. Use the calculated number of moles of NO_2 and the given temperature and pressure in the ideal gas law to find the volume of nitrogen dioxide produced. Note that nitrogen dioxide is the only gas involved in the reaction.

V = unknown　　　　$T = 28.2°C + 273.2 = 301.4$ K
P = 735 torr　　　　n = 1.394256 mol NO_2

Converting P from torr to atm: $P = \left(735\ \text{torr}\right)\left(\frac{1\ \text{atm}}{760\ \text{torr}}\right) = 0.967105\ \text{atm}$

$PV = nRT$
Solving for V:

$$V = \frac{nRT}{P} = \frac{\left(1.394256\ \text{mol}\right)\left(0.0821\frac{\text{L•atm}}{\text{mol•K}}\right)\left(301.4\ \text{K}\right)}{\left(0.967105\ \text{atm}\right)} = 35.67429 = \mathbf{35.7\ L\ NO_2}$$

5.104 Plan: The empirical formula for aluminum chloride is $AlCl_3$ (Al^{3+} and Cl^-). The empirical formula mass is (133.33 g/mol). Calculate the molar mass of the gaseous species from the ratio of effusion rates (Graham's law). This molar mass, divided by the empirical weight, should give a whole-number multiple that will yield the molecular formula.
Solution:

$$\frac{\text{Rate unknown}}{\text{Rate He}} = 0.122 = \sqrt{\frac{\text{molar mass He}}{\text{molar mass unknown}}}$$

$$0.122 = \sqrt{\frac{4.003\ \text{g/mol}}{\text{molar mass unknown}}}$$

$$0.014884 = \frac{4.003\ \text{g/mol}}{\text{molar mass unknown}}$$

Molar mass unknown = 268.9465 g/mol
The whole-number multiple is 268.9465/133.33, which is about 2. Therefore, the molecular formula of the gaseous species is 2 x ($AlCl_3$) = $\mathbf{Al_2Cl_6}$.

5.106 Plan: First, write the balanced equation for the reaction: $2SO_2 + O_2 \rightarrow 2SO_3$. The total number of moles of gas will change as the reaction occurs since 3 moles of reactant gas forms 2 moles of product gas. From the volume, temperature, and pressures given, we can calculate the number of moles of gas before and after the reaction using the ideal gas law. For each mole of SO_3 formed, the total number of moles of gas decreases by 1/2 mole. Thus, twice the decrease in moles of gas equals the moles of SO_3 formed.
Solution:
Moles of gas before and after reaction:
V = 2.00 L　　　　T = 800. K
P_{total} = 1.90 atm　　　　n = unknown
$PV = nRT$

$$\text{Initial moles} = n = \frac{PV}{RT} = \frac{(1.90\ \text{atm})(2.00\ \text{L})}{\left(0.0821\frac{\text{L•atm}}{\text{mol•K}}\right)(800.\ \text{K})} = 0.05785627\ \text{mol}$$

$$\text{Final moles} = n = \frac{PV}{RT} = \frac{(1.65\ \text{atm})(2.00\ \text{L})}{\left(0.0821\frac{\text{L•atm}}{\text{mol•K}}\right)(800.\ \text{K})} = 0.050243605\ \text{mol}$$

Moles of SO_3 produced = 2 x decrease in the total number of moles
= 2 x (0.05785627 mol – 0.050243605 mol)
= 0.01522533 = **1.52x10^{-2} mol**

Check: If the starting amount is 0.0578 total moles of SO_2 and O_2, then x + y = 0.0578 mol, where x = mol of SO_2 and y = mol of O_2. After the reaction:
(x – z) + (y – 0.5z) + z = 0.0502 mol
Where z = mol of SO_3 formed = mol of SO_2 reacted = 2(mol of O_2 reacted).
Subtracting the two equations gives:
x – (x – z) + y – (y – 0.5z) – z = 0.0578 – 0.0502
z = 0.0152 mol SO_3
The approach of setting up two equations and solving them gives the same result as above.

5.110 Plan: First, write the balanced equation. The moles of CO that react in part a) can be calculated from the ideal gas law. Volume must be in units of L, pressure in atm, and temperature in kelvins. Once the moles of CO that react are known, the molar ratio from the balanced equation is used to determine the mass of nickel that will react with the CO. For part b), assume the volume is 1 m^3. Use the ideal gas law to solve for moles of $Ni(CO)_4$, which equals the moles of Ni, and convert moles to grams using the molar mass. For part c), the mass of Ni obtained from 1 m^3 (part b)) can be used to calculate the amount of CO released. Use the ideal gas law to calculate the volume of CO. The vapor pressure of water at 35°C (42.2 torr) must be subtracted from the overall pressure (see Table 5.2).

Solution:

a) $Ni(s) + 4CO(g) \rightarrow Ni(CO)_4(g)$

$V = 3.55\ m^3$ $\quad T = 50°C + 273 = 323\ K$

$P = 100.7\ kPa$ $\quad n$ = unknown

Converting V from m^3 to L: $\quad V = (3.55\ m^3)\left(\frac{1\ L}{10^{-3}\ m^3}\right) = 3550\ L$

Converting P from kPa to atm: $\quad P = (100.7\ kPa)\left(\frac{1\ atm}{101.325\ kPa}\right) = 0.993831729\ atm$

$PV = nRT$

Solving for n:

$$\text{Moles of CO} = n = \frac{PV}{RT} = \frac{(0.993831729\ \text{atm})(3550\ \text{L})}{\left(0.0821\frac{\text{L•atm}}{\text{mol•K}}\right)(323\ \text{K})} = 133.044073\ \text{mol CO}$$

$$\text{Mass Ni} = (133.044073\ \text{mol CO})\left(\frac{1\ \text{mol Ni}}{4\ \text{mol CO}}\right)\left(\frac{58.69\ \text{g Ni}}{1\ \text{mol Ni}}\right) = 1952.089 = \mathbf{1.95x10^3\ g\ Ni}$$

b) $Ni(s) + 4\ CO(g) \rightarrow Ni(CO)_4(g)$

$V = 1\ m^3$ $\quad T = 155°C + 273 = 428\ K$

$P = 21\ atm$ $\quad n$ = unknown

Converting V from m^3 to L: $\quad V = (1\ m^3)\left(\frac{1\ L}{10^{-3}\ m^3}\right) = 1000\ L$

$PV = nRT$

Solving for n:

$$\text{Moles of Ni(CO)}_4 = n = \frac{PV}{RT} = \frac{(21\text{ atm})(1000\text{ L})}{\left(0.0821\frac{\text{L•atm}}{\text{mol•K}}\right)(428\text{ K})} = 597.62997\text{ mol Ni(CO)}_4$$

$$\text{Mass Ni} = (597.62997\text{ mol Ni(CO)}_4)\left(\frac{1\text{ mol Ni}}{1\text{ mol Ni(CO)}_4}\right)\left(\frac{58.69\text{ g Ni}}{1\text{ mol Ni}}\right)$$

$= 3.50749\text{x}10^4 =$ **$3.5\text{x}10^4$ g Ni**

The pressure limits the significant figures.

c) $$\text{Moles CO} = (3.50749\text{x}10^4\text{ g Ni})\left(\frac{1\text{ mol Ni}}{58.69\text{ g Ni}}\right)\left(\frac{4\text{ mol CO}}{1\text{ mol Ni}}\right) = 2390.51968\text{ mol CO}$$

Finding the volume of CO:

V = unknown

$T = 35°\text{C} + 273 = 308$ K

$P_{\text{total}} = 769$ torr

$n = 2390.51968$ mol

$P_{\text{water vapor}} = 42.2$ torr

$P_{\text{CO}} = P_{\text{total}} - P_{\text{water vapor}} = 769\text{ torr} - 42.2\text{ torr} = 726.8\text{ torr}$

Converting P from torr to atm: $$P = (726.8\text{ torr})\left(\frac{1\text{ atm}}{760\text{ torr}}\right) = 0.956315789\text{ atm}$$

$PV = nRT$

Solving for V:

$$V = \frac{nRT}{P} = \frac{(2390.51968\text{ mol})\left(0.0821\frac{\text{L•atm}}{\text{mol•K}}\right)(308\text{ K})}{(0.956315789\text{ atm})} = 63209.86614\text{ L CO}$$

Converting V from L to m^3: $$V = (63209.86614\text{ L})\left(\frac{10^{-3}\text{ m}^3}{1\text{ L}}\right) = 63.209866 = \mathbf{63\text{ m}^3\text{ CO}}$$

The answer is limited to two significant figures because the mass of Ni comes from part b).

5.112 a) A preliminary equation for this reaction is $4C_xH_yN_z + nO_2 \rightarrow 4CO_2 + 2N_2 + 10H_2O$.
Since the organic compound does not contain oxygen, the only source of oxygen as a reactant is oxygen gas. To form 4 volumes of CO_2 would require 4 volumes of O_2 and to form 10 volumes of H_2O would require 5 volumes of O_2. Thus, 9 **volumes of O_2** was required.
b) Since the volume of a gas is proportional to the number of moles of the gas we can equate volume and moles. From a volume ratio of $4CO_2$:$2N_2$:$10H_2O$ we deduce a mole ratio of 4C:4N:20H or 1C:1N:5H for an empirical formula of **CH_5N**.

5.115 Plan: To find the factor by which a diver's lungs would expand, find the factor by which P changes from 125 ft to the surface, and apply Boyle's law. To find that factor, calculate P_{seawater} at 125 ft by converting the given depth from ft-seawater to mmHg to atm and adding the surface pressure (1.00 atm).
Solution:

$$P(\text{H}_2\text{O}) = (125\text{ ft})\left(\frac{12\text{ in}}{1\text{ ft}}\right)\left(\frac{2.54\text{ cm}}{1\text{ in}}\right)\left(\frac{10^{-2}\text{ m}}{1\text{ cm}}\right)\left(\frac{1\text{ mm}}{10^{-3}\text{ m}}\right) = 3.81\text{x}10^4\text{ mmH}_2\text{O}$$

$$P(\text{Hg}):\ \frac{h_{\text{H}_2\text{O}}}{h_{\text{Hg}}} = \frac{d_{\text{Hg}}}{d_{\text{H}_2\text{O}}} \qquad \frac{3.81\text{x}10^4\text{ mmH}_2\text{O}}{h_{\text{Hg}}} = \frac{13.5\text{ g/mL}}{1.04\text{ g/mL}} \qquad h_{\text{Hg}} = 2935.1111\text{ mmHg}$$

$$P(\text{Hg}) = (2935.11111\text{ mmHg})\left(\frac{1\text{ atm}}{760\text{ mm Hg}}\right) = 3.861988\text{ atm (unrounded)}$$

$P_{\text{total}} = (1.00\text{ atm}) + (3.861988\text{ atm}) = 4.861988\text{ atm}$ (unrounded)

Use Boyle's law to find the volume change of the diver's lungs:

$P_1V_1 = P_2V_2$

$$\frac{V_2}{V_1} = \frac{P_1}{P_2} \qquad \frac{V_2}{V_1} = \frac{4.861988 \text{ atm}}{1 \text{ atm}} = \mathbf{4.86}$$

To find the depth to which the diver could ascend safely, use the given safe expansion factor (1.5) and the pressure at 125 ft, P_{125}, to find the safest ascended pressure, P_{safe}.

$P_{125}/P_{safe} = 1.5$

$P_{safe} = P_{125}/1.5 = (4.861988 \text{ atm})/1.5 = 3.241325 \text{ atm}$ (unrounded)

Convert the pressure in atm to pressure in ft of seawater using the conversion factors above. Subtract this distance from the initial depth to find how far the diver could ascend.

$$h(\text{Hg}): \ (4.861988 - 3.241325 \text{ atm})\left(\frac{760 \text{ mmHg}}{1 \text{ atm}}\right) = 1231.7039 \text{ mmHg}$$

$$\frac{h_{H_2O}}{h_{Hg}} = \frac{d_{Hg}}{d_{H_2O}} \qquad \frac{h_{H_2O}}{1231.7039 \text{ mmHg}} = \frac{13.5 \text{ g/mL}}{1.04 \text{ g/mL}} \qquad h_{H_2O} = 15988.464 \text{ mm}$$

$$(15988.464 \text{ mmH}_2\text{O})\left(\frac{10^{-3} \text{ m}}{1 \text{ mm}}\right)\left(\frac{1.094 \text{ yd}}{1 \text{ m}}\right)\left(\frac{3 \text{ ft}}{1 \text{ yd}}\right) = 52.4741 \text{ ft}$$

Therefore, the diver can safely ascend 52.5 ft to a depth of (125 – 52.4741) = 72.5259 = **73 ft.**

5.117 Plan: First, write the balanced equation. According to the description in the problem, a given volume of peroxide solution (0.100 L) will release a certain number of "volumes of oxygen gas" (20). Assume that 20 is exact. A 0.100 L solution will produce (20 x 0.100 L) = 2.00 L O_2 gas. Use the ideal gas law to convert this volume of O_2 gas to moles of O_2 gas and convert to moles and then mass of H_2O_2 using the molar ratio in the balanced equation.

Solution:

$$2H_2O_2(aq) \rightarrow 2H_2O(l) + O_2(g)$$

$V = 2.00$ L $\qquad T = 0°C + 273 = 273$ K

$P = 1$ atm $\qquad n =$ unknown

$PV = nRT$

Solving for n:

$$\text{Moles of } O_2 = n = \frac{PV}{RT} = \frac{(1 \text{ atm})(2.00 \text{ L})}{\left(0.0821 \frac{\text{L•atm}}{\text{mol•K}}\right)(273 \text{ K})} = 8.92327\text{x}10^{-2} \text{ mol } O_2$$

$$\text{Mass } H_2O_2 = (8.92327\text{x}10^{-2} \text{ mol } O_2)\left(\frac{2 \text{ mol } H_2O_2}{1 \text{ mol } O_2}\right)\left(\frac{34.02 \text{ g } H_2O_2}{1 \text{ mol } H_2O_2}\right) = 6.071395 = \mathbf{6.07 \text{ g } H_2O_2}$$

5.122 Plan: The diagram below describes the two Hg height levels within the barometer. First, find the pressure of the N_2. The P_{N_2} is directly related to the change in column height of Hg. Then find the volume occupied by the N_2. The volume of the space occupied by the $N_2(g)$ is calculated from the length and cross-sectional area of the barometer. To find the mass of N_2, use these values of P and V (T is given) in the ideal gas law to find moles which is converted to mass using the molar mass of nitrogen.

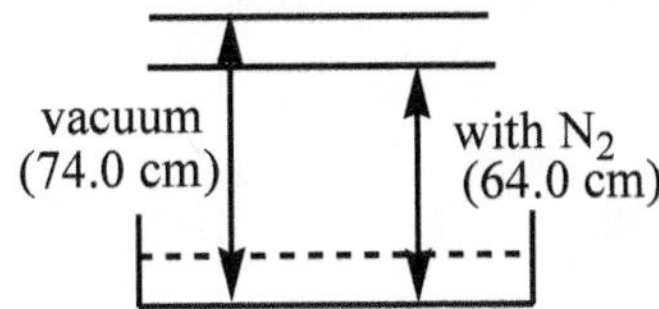

Solution:

$$\text{Pressure of the nitrogen} = (74.0 \text{ cm} - 64.0 \text{ cm})\left(\frac{10^{-2} \text{ m}}{1 \text{ cm}}\right)\left(\frac{1 \text{ mm}}{10^{-3} \text{ m}}\right)\left(\frac{1 \text{ atm}}{760 \text{ atm}}\right) = 0.1315789 \text{ atm}$$

$$\text{Volume of the nitrogen} = (1.00 \text{ x } 10^2 \text{ cm} - 64.0 \text{ cm})(1.20 \text{ cm}^2)\left(\frac{1 \text{ mL}}{1 \text{ cm}^3}\right)\left(\frac{10^{-3} \text{ L}}{1 \text{ mL}}\right) = 0.0432 \text{ L}$$

$V = 0.0432$ L $\quad\quad\quad\quad$ $T = 24°C + 273 = 297$ K
$P = 0.1315789$ atm $\quad\quad\quad\quad$ n = unknown
$PV = nRT$
Solving for n:

$$\text{Moles of N}_2 = n = \frac{PV}{RT} = \frac{(0.1315789 \text{ atm})(0.0432 \text{ L})}{\left(0.0821 \frac{\text{L•atm}}{\text{mol•K}}\right)(297 \text{ K})} = 2.331151\text{x}10^{-4} \text{ mol N}_2$$

$$\text{Mass of N}_2 = \left(2.331151\text{x}10^{-4} \text{ mol N}_2\right)\left(\frac{28.02 \text{ g N}_2}{1 \text{ mol N}_2}\right) = 6.5319\text{x}10^{-3} = \mathbf{6.53x10^{-3}\ g\ N_2}$$

5.126 Plan: Deviations from ideal gas behavior are due to attractive forces between particles which reduce the pressure of the real gas and due to the size of the particle which affects the volume. Compare the size and/or attractive forces between the substances. The greater the size and/or the stronger the attractive forces, the greater the deviation from ideal gas behavior.
Solution:
a) **Xenon** would show greater deviation from ideal behavior than argon since xenon is a larger atom than argon. The electron cloud of Xe is more easily distorted so intermolecular attractions are greater. Xe's larger size also means that the volume the gas occupies becomes a greater proportion of the container's volume at high pressures.
b) **Water vapor** would show greater deviation from ideal behavior than neon gas since the attractive forces between water molecules are greater than the attractive forces between neon atoms. We know the attractive forces are greater for water molecules because it remains a liquid at a higher temperature than neon (water is a liquid at room temperature while neon is a gas at room temperature).
c) **Mercury vapor** would show greater deviation from ideal behavior than radon gas since the attractive forces between mercury atoms is greater than that between radon atoms. We know that the attractive forces for mercury are greater because it is a liquid at room temperature while radon is a gas.
d) **Water** is a liquid at room temperature; methane is a gas at room temperature. Therefore, water molecules have stronger attractive forces than methane molecules and should deviate from ideal behavior to a greater extent than methane molecules.

5.130 Plan: V and T are not given, so the ideal gas law cannot be used. The total pressure of the mixture is given. Use $P_A = X_A \text{ x } P_{total}$ to find the mole fraction of each gas and then the mass fraction. The total mass of the two gases is 35.0 g.
Solution:

$$P_{total} = P_{krypton} + P_{carbon\ dioxide} = 0.708 \text{ atm}$$

The NaOH absorbed the CO_2 leaving the Kr, thus $P_{krypton} = 0.250$ atm.

$$P_{carbon\ dioxide} = P_{total} - P_{krypton} = 0.708 \text{ atm} - 0.250 \text{ atm} = 0.458 \text{ atm}$$

Determining mole fractions: $P_A = X_A \text{ x } P_{total}$

$$\text{Carbon dioxide: } X = \frac{P_{CO_2}}{P_{total}} = \frac{0.458 \text{ atm}}{0.708 \text{ atm}} = 0.64689$$

$$\text{Krypton: } X = \frac{P_{Kr}}{P_{total}} = \frac{0.250 \text{ atm}}{0.708 \text{ atm}} = 0.353107$$

$$\text{Relative mass fraction} = \left[\frac{(0.353107)\left(\frac{83.80 \text{ g Kr}}{\text{mol}}\right)}{(0.64689)\left(\frac{44.01 \text{ g CO}_2}{\text{mol}}\right)}\right] = 1.039366$$

35.0 g = x g CO_2 + (1.039366 x) g Kr
35.0 g = 2.039366 x
Grams CO_2 = x = (35.0 g)/(2.039366) = 17.16219581 = **17.2 g CO_2**
Grams Kr = 35.0 g – 17.162 g CO_2 = 17.83780419 = **17.8 g Kr**

5.136 Plan: Use the equation for root mean speed (u_{rms}). Molar mass values must be in units of kg/mol and temperature in kelvins.
Solution:

$$u_{rms} = \sqrt{\frac{3\ RT}{\mathcal{M}}}$$

$$u_{rms}\ \text{Ne} = \sqrt{\frac{3(8.314\ \text{J/mol•K})(370\ \text{K})}{(20.18\ \text{g/mol})}\left(\frac{10^3\ \text{g}}{\text{kg}}\right)\left(\frac{\text{kg•m}^2/\text{s}^2}{\text{J}}\right)} = 676.24788 = \mathbf{676\ m/s\ Ne}$$

$$u_{rms}\ \text{Ar} = \sqrt{\frac{3(8.314\ \text{J/mol•K})(370\ \text{K})}{(39.95\ \text{g/mol})}\left(\frac{10^3\ \text{g}}{\text{kg}}\right)\left(\frac{\text{kg•m}^2/\text{s}^2}{\text{J}}\right)} = 480.6269 = \mathbf{481\ m/s\ Ar}$$

$$u_{rms}\ \text{He} = \sqrt{\frac{3(8.314\ \text{J/mol•K})(370\ \text{K})}{(4.003\ \text{g/mol})}\left(\frac{10^3\ \text{g}}{\text{kg}}\right)\left(\frac{\text{kg•m}^2/\text{s}^2}{\text{J}}\right)} = 1518.356 = \mathbf{1.52x10^3\ m/s\ He}$$

5.138 Plan: For part a), the number of moles of water vapor can be found using the ideal gas law. Convert moles of water to mass using the molar mass and adjust to the 1.6% water content of the kernel. For part b), use the ideal gas law to find the volume of water vapor at the stated set of condition.
Solution:

a) Volume of water in kernel = $(0.25\ \text{mL kernel})\left(\frac{75\%\ H_2O}{100\ \%\ \text{kernel}}\right) = 0.1875\ \text{mL} = 1.875\text{x}10^{-4}\ \text{L}$

$V = 1.875\text{x}10^{-4}$ L $T = 170°\text{C} + 273.2 = 443$ K
$P = 9.0$ atm n = unknown
$PV = nRT$
Solving for n:

$$\text{Moles of } H_2O = n = \frac{PV}{RT} = \frac{(9.0\ \text{atm})(1.875\ 10^{-4}\ \text{L})}{\left(0.0821\frac{\text{L•atm}}{\text{mol•K}}\right)(443\ \text{K})} = 4.639775\text{x}10^{-5}\ \text{mol}$$

$$\text{Mass (g) of} = (4.639775\text{x}10^{-5}\ \text{mol}\ H_2O)\left(\frac{18.02\ \text{g}\ H_2O}{1\ \text{mol}\ H_2O}\right)\left(\frac{100\%}{1.6\%}\right) = 0.052255 = \mathbf{0.052\ g}$$

b) V = unknown $T = 25°\text{C} + 273 = 298$ K
$P = 1.00$ atm $n = 4.639775\text{x}10^{-5}$ mol
$PV = nRT$
Solving for V:

$$V = \frac{nRT}{P} = \frac{(4.639775\text{x}10^{-4}\ \text{mol})\left(0.0821\frac{\text{L•atm}}{\text{mol•K}}\right)(298\ \text{K})}{(1.00\ \text{atm})} = 0.00113516\ \text{L} = 1.13516\ \text{mL} = \mathbf{1.1\ mL}$$

5.145 Plan: For part a), convert mass of glucose to moles and use the molar ratio from the balanced equation to find the moles of CO_2 gas produced. Use the ideal gas law to find the volume of that amount of CO_2. Pressure must be in units of atm and temperature in kelvins. For part b), use the molar ratios in the balanced equation to calculate the moles of each gas and then use Dalton's law of partial pressures to determine the pressure of each gas.
Solution:
a) $C_6H_{12}O_6(s) + 6O_2(g) \rightarrow 6CO_2(g) + 6H_2O(g)$

$$\text{Moles } CO_2\text{:}\ (20.0\ \text{g}\ C_6H_{12}O_6)\left(\frac{1\ \text{mol}\ C_6H_{12}O_6}{180.16\ \text{g}\ C_6H_{12}O_6}\right)\left(\frac{6\ \text{mol}\ CO_2}{1\ \text{mol}\ C_6H_{12}O_6}\right) = 0.666075\ \text{mol}\ CO_2$$

Finding the volume of CO_2:
V = unknown $T = 37°\text{C} + 273 = 310$ K
$P = 780.$ torr $n = 0.666075$ mol

Converting P from torr to atm: $P = (780.\text{ torr})\left(\frac{1\text{ atm}}{760\text{ torr}}\right) = 1.0263158\text{ atm}$

$PV = nRT$
Solving for V:

$$V = \frac{nRT}{P} = \frac{(0.666075\text{ mol})\left(0.0821\frac{\text{L•atm}}{\text{mol•K}}\right)(310\text{ K})}{(1.0263158\text{ atm})} = 16.5176 = \mathbf{16.5\text{ L }CO_2}$$

This solution assumes that partial pressure of O_2 does not interfere with the reaction conditions.

b) Moles CO_2 = moles O_2 $= (10.0\text{ g }C_6H_{12}O_6)\left(\frac{1\text{ mol }C_6H_{12}O_6}{180.16\text{ g }C_6H_{12}O_6}\right)\left(\frac{6\text{ mol}}{1\text{ mol }C_6H_{12}O_6}\right)$

$= 0.333037\text{ mol }CO_2 = \text{mol }O_2$

At 37°C, the vapor pressure of water is 48.8 torr. No matter how much water is produced, the partial pressure of H_2O will still be 48.8 torr. The remaining pressure, 780 torr – 48.8 torr = 731.2 torr is the sum of partial pressures for O_2 and CO_2. Since the mole fractions of O_2 and CO_2 are equal, their pressures must be equal, and must be one-half of 731.2 torr.

$\mathbf{P_{water} = 48.8\text{ torr}}$

(731.2 torr)/2 = 365.6 = **3.7x10^2 torr** $\mathbf{P_{oxygen} = P_{carbon\ dioxide}}$

5.150 Plan: To find the number of steps through the membrane, calculate the molar masses to find the ratio of effusion rates. This ratio is the enrichment factor for each step.

Solution:

$$\frac{\text{Rate}_{^{235}UF_6}}{\text{Rate}_{^{238}UF_6}} = \sqrt{\frac{\text{molar mass }^{238}UF_6}{\text{molar mass }^{235}UF_6}} = \sqrt{\frac{352.04\text{ g/mol}}{349.03\text{ g/mol}}}$$

$= 1.004302694$ enrichment factor

Therefore, the abundance of $^{235}UF_6$ after one membrane is 0.72% x 1.004302694
Abundance of $^{235}UF_6$ after "N" membranes = 0.72% x $(1.004302694)^N$
Desired abundance of $^{235}UF_6$ = 3.0% = 0.72% x $(1.004302694)^N$
Solving for N:
3.0% = 0.72% x $(1.004302694)^N$
4.16667 = $(1.004302694)^N$
ln 4.16667 = ln $(1.004302694)^N$
ln 4.16667 = N x ln (1.004302694)
N = (ln 4.16667)/(ln 1.004302694)
N = 1.4271164/0.004293464 = 332.39277 = **332 steps**

5.152 Plan: The amount of each gas that leaks from the balloon is proportional to its effusion rate. Using 35% as the rate for H_2, the rate for O_2 can be determined from Graham's law.

Solution:

$$\frac{\text{Rate }O_2}{\text{Rate }H_2} = \sqrt{\frac{\text{molar mass }H_2}{\text{molar mass }O_2}} = \sqrt{\frac{2.016\text{ g/mol}}{32.00\text{ g/mol}}} = \frac{\text{rate }O_2}{35}$$

$$0.250998008 = \frac{\text{rate }O_2}{35}$$

Rate O_2 = 8.78493
Amount of H_2 that leaks = 35%; 100–35 = 65% H_2 remains
Amount of O_2 that leaks = 8.78493%; 100–8.78493 = 91.21507% O_2 remains

$$\frac{O_2}{H_2} = \frac{91.21507}{65} = 1.40331 = \mathbf{1.4}$$

5.156 Plan: Since the amounts of two reactants are given, this is a limiting reactant problem. Write the balanced equation and use molar ratios to find the number of moles of IF_7 produced by each reactant. The mass of I_2 is converted to moles using its molar mass and the moles of F_2 is found using the ideal gas law. The smaller number of moles of product indicates the limiting reagent. Determine the moles of excess reactant gas and the moles of product gas and use the ideal gas law to solve for the total pressure.

Solution:

Moles of F_2:

$V = 2.50$ L $T = 250.$ K

$P = 350.$ torr $n =$ unknown

Converting P from torr to atm: $P = (350.\ \text{torr})\left(\frac{1\ \text{atm}}{760\ \text{torr}}\right) = 0.460526315\ \text{atm}$

$PV = nRT$

Solving for n:

$$n = \frac{PV}{RT} = \frac{(0.460526315\ \text{atm})(2.50\ \text{L})}{\left(0.0821\frac{\text{L}\bullet\text{atm}}{\text{mol}\bullet\text{K}}\right)(250.\ \text{K})} = 0.056093339\ \text{mol}\ F_2$$

$$7F_2(g) + I_2(s) \rightarrow 2IF_7(g)$$

Moles IF_7 from F_2 = $(0.056093339\ \text{mol}\ F_2)\left(\frac{2\ \text{mol}\ IF_7}{7\ \text{mol}\ F_2}\right) = 0.016026668\ \text{mol}\ IF_7$ (unrounded)

Moles IF_7 from I_2 = $(2.50\ \text{g}\ I_2)\left(\frac{1\ \text{mol}\ I_2}{253.8\ \text{g}\ I_2}\right)\left(\frac{2\ \text{mol}\ IF_7}{1\ \text{mol}\ I_2}\right) = 0.019700551\ \text{mol}\ IF_7$ (unrounded)

F_2 is limiting. All of the F_2 is consumed.

Mole I_2 remaining = original amount of moles of I_2 – number of I_2 moles reacting with F_2

Mole I_2 remaining = $(2.50\ \text{g}\ I_2)\left(\frac{1\ \text{mol}\ I_2}{253.8\ \text{g}\ I_2}\right) - (0.056093339\ \text{mol}\ F_2)\left(\frac{1\ \text{mol}\ I_2}{7\ \text{mol}\ F_2}\right) = 1.83694\text{x}10^{-3}\ \text{mol}\ I_2$

Total moles of gas = (0 mol F_2) + (0.016026668 mol IF_7) + ($1.83694\text{x}10^{-3}$ mol I_2)
= 0.0178636 mol gas

$V = 2.50$ L $T = 550.$ K

$P =$ unknown $n = 0.0178636$ mol

$PV = nRT$

Solving for P:

$$P\ (\text{atm}) = \frac{nRT}{V} = \frac{(0.0178636\ \text{mol})\left(0.0821\frac{\text{L}\bullet\text{atm}}{\text{mol}\bullet\text{K}}\right)(550.\ \text{K})}{2.50\ \text{L}} = 0.322652\ \text{atm}$$

P (torr) = $(0.322652\ \text{atm})\left(\frac{760\ \text{torr}}{1\ \text{atm}}\right) = 245.21552 =$ **245 torr**

P_{iodine} (torr) = $X_{\text{iodine}}\ P_{\text{total}}$ = [($1.83694\text{x}10^{-3}$ mol I_2)/(0.0178636 mol)] (245.21552 torr) = 25.215869 = **25.2 torr**

CHAPTER 6 THERMOCHEMISTRY: ENERGY FLOW AND CHEMICAL CHANGE

FOLLOW–UP PROBLEMS

6.1A Plan: The system is the liquid. Since the system absorbs heat from the surroundings, the system gains heat and q is positive. Because the system does work, w is negative. Use the equation $\Delta E = q + w$ to calculate ΔE. Convert ΔE to kJ.
Solution:
ΔE (kJ) $= q + w = +13.5$ kJ $+ -1.8$ kJ $= 11.7$ kJ
ΔE (J) $= 11.7\ \text{kJ}\left(\frac{1000\ \text{J}}{1\ \text{kJ}}\right) = \mathbf{1.17 \times 10^4\ J}$

6.1B Plan: The system is the reactant and products of the reaction. Since heat is absorbed by the surroundings, the system releases heat and q is negative. Because work is done on the system, w is positive. Use the equation $\Delta E = q + w$ to calculate ΔE. Both kcal and Btu must be converted to kJ.
Solution:
$$q = (-26.0\ \text{kcal})\left(\frac{4.184\ \text{kJ}}{1\ \text{kcal}}\right) = -108.784\ \text{kJ}$$
$$w = (+15.0\ \text{Btu})\left(\frac{1.055\ \text{kJ}}{1\ \text{Btu}}\right) = 15.825\ \text{kJ}$$
$\Delta E = q + w = -108.784$ kJ $+ 15.825$ kJ $= -92.959 =$ **– 93 kJ**

6.2A Plan: Convert the pressure from torr to atm units. Subtract the initial V from the final V to find ΔV. Use $w = -P\Delta V$ to calculate w in atm•L. Convert the answer from atm•L to J.
Solution:
$V_{\text{initial}} = 5.68$ L
$V_{\text{final}} = 2.35$ L
$P = 732$ torr
Converting P from torr to atm: $(732\ \text{torr})\left(\frac{1\ \text{atm}}{760\ \text{torr}}\right) = 0.9632 = 0.963\ \text{atm}$
w (atm•L) $= -P\Delta V = -(0.963\ \text{atm})(2.35\ \text{L} - 5.68\ \text{L}) = 3.2068 = 3.21$ atm•L
w (J) $= (3.21\ \text{atm•L})\left(\frac{101.3\ \text{J}}{1\ \text{atm•L}}\right) =$ **325 J**

6.2B Plan: Subtract the initial V from the final V to find ΔV. Use $w = -P\Delta V$ to calculate w in atm•L. Convert the answer from atm•L to J.
Solution:
$V_{\text{initial}} = 10.5$ L
$V_{\text{final}} = 16.3$ L
$P = 5.5$ atm
w (atm•L) $= -P\Delta V = -(5.5\ \text{atm})(16.3\ \text{L} - 10.5\ \text{L}) = -31.90 = -32$ atm•L
w (J) $= (-32\ \text{atm•L})\left(\frac{101.3\ \text{J}}{1\ \text{atm•L}}\right) =$ **-3.2×10^3 J**

6.3A Plan: Since heat is released in this reaction, the reaction is **exothermic** ($\Delta H < 0$) and the reactants are above the products in an enthalpy diagram.

Solution:

Enthalpy, H

$C_3H_5(NO_3)_3(l)$

$\Delta H = -5.72 \times 10^3$ kJ

$3\ CO_2(g) + 5/2\ H_2O(g) + 1/4\ O_2(g) + 3/2\ N_2(g)$

6.3B Plan: Since heat is absorbed in this reaction, the reaction is **endothermic** ($\Delta H > 0$) and the reactants are below the products in an enthalpy diagram.
Solution:

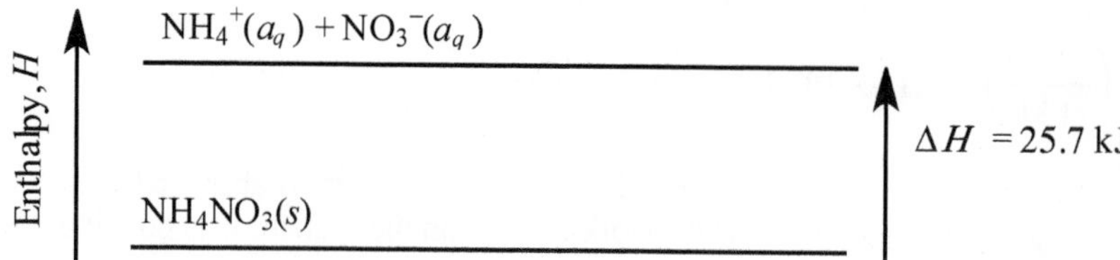

6.4A Plan: Heat is added to the aluminum foil, so q will be positive. The heat is calculated using the equation $q = c \times \text{mass} \times \Delta T$. Table 6.2 lists the specific heat of aluminum as 0.900 J/g•K.
Solution:

$$\Delta T = 375°C - 18\ °C = (357°C)\left(\frac{\text{change in 1 K}}{\text{change in 1 degree C}}\right) = 357\ K$$

$$q = c \times \text{mass} \times \Delta T = (0.900\ J/g•K)\ (7.65\ g)\ (357\ K) = \mathbf{2.46 \times 10^3\ J}$$

6.4B Plan: Heat is transferred away from the ethylene glycol as it cools so q will be negative. The heat released is calculated using the equation $q = c \times \text{mass} \times \Delta T$. Table 6.2 lists the specific heat of ethylene glycol as 2.42 J/g•K. The volume of ethylene glycol is converted to mass in grams by using the density.
Solution:

$$\Delta T = 25.0°C - 37.0°C = (-12.0°C)\left(\frac{\text{change in 1 K}}{\text{change in 1 degree C}}\right) = -12.0\ K$$

$$\text{Mass (g) of ethylene glycol} = (5.50\ L)\left(\frac{1\ mL}{10^{-3}\ L}\right)\left(\frac{1.11\ g}{mL}\right) = 6105 = 6.10 \times 10^3\ g$$

$$q = c \times \text{mass} \times \Delta T = (2.42\ J/g•K)\ (6.10 \times 10^3\ g)\ (-12.0\ K)\left(\frac{1\ kJ}{1000\ J}\right) = -177.1440 = \mathbf{-177\ kJ}$$

6.5A Plan: The heat absorbed by the water can be calculated with the equation $c \times \text{mass} \times \Delta T$; the heat absorbed by the water equals the heat lost by the hot metal. Since the mass and temperature change of the metal is known, the specific heat capacity can be calculated and used to identify the metal.
Solution:

$$\Delta T_{H_2O} = T_{final} - T_{initial} = 27.25°C - 25.55°C = (1.70°C)\left(\frac{\text{change in 1 K}}{\text{change in 1 degree C}}\right) = 1.70\ K$$

$$\Delta T_{metal} = T_{final} - T_{initial} = 27.25°C - 65.00°C = (-37.75°C)\left(\frac{\text{change in 1 K}}{\text{change in 1 degree C}}\right) = -37.75\ K$$

$$q_{H_2O} = -q_{metal}$$

$$-c_{H_2O} \times \text{mass}_{H_2O} \times \Delta T_{H_2O} = c_{metal} \times \text{mass}_{metal} \times \Delta T_{metal}$$

$$-c_{metal} = -\frac{c_{H_2O} \times \text{mass}_{H_2O} \times \Delta T_{H_2O}}{\text{mass}_{metal} \times \Delta T_{metal}} = -\frac{(4.184\ J/g•K)(25.00\ g)(1.70\ K)}{(12.18\ g)(-37.75\ K)} = 0.386738 = 0.387\ J/g•K$$

From Table 6.2, the metal with this value of specific heat is **copper**.

6.5B Plan: The heat absorbed by the titanium metal can be calculated with the equation c x mass x ΔT; the heat absorbed by the metal equals the heat lost by the water. Since the mass and temperature change of the water is known, along with the specific heat and final temperature of the titanium, initial temperature of the metal can be calculated.

Solution:

$$\Delta T_{H_2O} = T_{final} - T_{initial} = 49.30°C - 50.00°C = (-0.70°C)\left(\frac{\text{change in 1 K}}{\text{change in 1 degree C}}\right) = -0.70 \text{ K}$$

Converting T_{final} from °C to K = 49.30°C + 273.15 = 322.45 K

$$\Delta T_{metal} = T_{final} - T_{initial} = 322.45 \text{ K} - T_{initial}$$

$$-q_{H_2O} = q_{metal}$$

$$-c_{H_2O} \text{ x mass}_{H_2O} \text{ x } \Delta T_{H_2O} = c_{metal} \text{ x mass}_{metal} \text{ x } \Delta T_{metal}$$

$$\Delta T_{metal} = \frac{-c_{H_2O} \text{ x mass}_{H_2O} \text{ x } \Delta T_{H_2O}}{c_{metal} \text{ x mass}_{metal}} = \frac{-(4.184 \text{ J/g}\cdot\text{K})(75.0 \text{ g})(-0.70 \text{ K})}{(0.228 \text{ J/g}\cdot\text{K})(33.2 \text{ g})} = 29.0187 = 29.0 \text{ K}$$

ΔT_{metal} = 29.0187 K = 322.45 K – $T_{initial}$ (using unrounded numbers to avoid rounding errors)

$T_{initial}$ = 293.4313 K – 273.15 = 20.2813 = **20.3°C**

6.6A Plan: First write the balanced molecular, total ionic and net ionic equations for the acid-base reaction. To find q_{soln}, we use the equation $q = c$ x mass x ΔT, so we need the mass of solution, the change in temperature, and the specific heat capacity. We know the solutions' volumes (25.0 mL and 50.0 mL), so we find their masses with the given density (1.00 g/mL). Then, to find q_{soln}, we multiply the total mass by the given c (4.184 J/g•K) and the change in T, which we find from $T_{final} - T_{initial}$. The heat of reaction (q_{rxn}) is the negative of the heat of solution (q_{soln}).

Solution:

a) The balanced molecular equation is: **$HNO_3(aq) + KOH(aq) \rightarrow KNO_3(aq) + H_2O(l)$**

The total ionic equation is: $H^+(aq) + NO_3^-(aq) + K^+(aq) + OH^-(aq) \rightarrow K^+(aq) + NO_3^-(aq) + H_2O(l)$

The net ionic equation is: **$H^+(aq) + OH^-(aq) \rightarrow H_2O(l)$**

b) Total mass (g) of solution = (25.0 mL + 50.0 mL) x 1.00 g/mL = 75.0 g

$$\Delta T = 27.05°C - 21.50°C = (5.15°C)\left(\frac{\text{change in 1 K}}{\text{change in 1 degree C}}\right) = 5.15 \text{ K}$$

q_{soln} (J) = c_{soln} x $mass_{soln}$ x ΔT_{soln} = (4.184 J/g•K)(75.0 g)(5.15 K) = 1620 J

$$q_{soln} \text{ (kJ)} = 1620 \text{ J}\left(\frac{1 \text{ kJ}}{1000 \text{ J}}\right) = 1.62 \text{ kJ}$$

$q_{rxn} = -q_{soln}$ so q_{rxn} = **–1.62 kJ**

6.6B Plan: Write a balanced equation. Multiply the volume by the molarity of each reactant solution to find moles of each reactant. Use the molar ratios in the balanced reaction to find the moles of water produced from each reactant; the smaller amount gives the limiting reactant and the actual moles of water produced. Divide the heat evolved by the moles of water produced to obtain the enthalpy in kJ/mol. Since q_{soln} is positive, the solution absorbed heat that was released by the reaction; q_{rxn} and ΔH are negative.

Solution:

$$Ba(OH)_2(aq) + 2HCl(aq) \rightarrow 2H_2O(l) + BaCl_2(aq)$$

$$\text{Moles of } Ba(OH)_2 = (50.0 \text{ mL})\left(\frac{10^{-3} \text{ L}}{1 \text{ mL}}\right)\left(\frac{0.500 \text{ mol } Ba(OH)_2}{1 \text{ L}}\right) = 0.0250 \text{ mol } Ba(OH)_2$$

$$\text{Moles of HCl} = (50.0 \text{ mL})\left(\frac{10^{-3} \text{ L}}{1 \text{ mL}}\right)\left(\frac{0.500 \text{ mol HCl}}{1 \text{ L}}\right) = 0.0250 \text{ mol HCl}$$

$$\text{Moles of } H_2O \text{ from } Ba(OH)_2 = (0.0250 \text{ mol } Ba(OH)_2)\left(\frac{2 \text{ mol } H_2O}{1 \text{ mol } Ba(OH)_2}\right) = 0.0500 \text{ mol } H_2O$$

$$\text{Moles of } H_2O \text{ from HCl} = (0.0250 \text{ mol HCl})\left(\frac{2 \text{ mol } H_2O}{2 \text{ mol HCl}}\right) = 0.0250 \text{ mol } H_2O$$

HCl is the limiting reactant; 0.0250 mol of H_2O is produced.

$$\Delta H\text{ (kJ/mol)} = \frac{q}{\text{moles of H}_2\text{O produced}} = \frac{-1.386\text{ kJ}}{0.0250\text{ mol}} = -55.44 = \mathbf{-55.4\ kJ/mol}$$

6.7A Plan: The bomb calorimeter gains heat from the combustion of graphite, so $-q_{graphite} = q_{calorimeter}$. Convert the mass of graphite from grams to moles and use the given kJ/mol to find $q_{graphite}$. The heat lost by graphite equals the heat gained by the calorimeter, or ΔT multiplied by $C_{calorimeter}$.
Solution:

$$\text{Moles of graphite} = (0.8650\text{ g C})\left(\frac{1\text{ mol C}}{12.01\text{ g C}}\right) = 0.0720233\text{ mol C}$$

$$q_{graphite} = (0.0720233\text{ mol C})\left(\frac{-393.5\text{ kJ}}{1\text{ mol C}}\right) = -28.3412\text{ kJ/mol}$$

$$-q_{graphite} = C_{calorimeter}\Delta T_{calorimeter}$$
$$28.3412\text{ kJ/mol} = C_{calorimeter}(2.613\text{ K})$$
$$C_{calorimeter} = 10.84623 = \mathbf{10.85\ kJ/K}$$

6.7B Plan: The bomb calorimeter gains heat from the combustion of acetylene, so $-q_{rxn} = q_{calorimeter}$. Use the given heat capacity from Follow-up Problem 6.7A to find q_{rxn}: the amount of heat lost by the reaction of acetylene equals the amount of heat gained by the calorimeter, or ΔT multiplied by $C_{calorimeter}$. Divide the heat produced by the combustion of acetylene (in kJ) by the moles of acetylene to obtain the enthalpy in kJ/mol.
Solution:

$$\Delta T = (11.50°\text{C})\left(\frac{\text{change in 1 K}}{\text{change in 1 degree C}}\right) = 11.50\text{ K}$$

$$-q_{rxn} = q_{calorimeter} = (c_{calorimeter})(\Delta T)$$
$$-q_{rxn} = (10.85\text{ kJ/K})\ (11.50\text{ K}) = 124.8\text{ kJ}$$
$$q_{rxn} = -124.8\text{ kJ}$$

$$\text{Moles of acetylene} = (2.50\text{ g C}_2\text{H}_2)\left(\frac{1\text{ mol C}_2\text{H}_2}{26.04\text{ g C}_2\text{H}_2}\right) = 0.0960\text{ mol C}_2\text{H}_2$$

$$\Delta H\text{ (kJ/mol)} = \frac{q}{\text{moles of acetylene}} = \frac{-124.8\text{ kJ}}{0.0960\text{ moles}} = -1300 = \mathbf{-1.30\ x\ 10^3\ kJ/mol}$$

6.8A Plan: To find the heat required, write a balanced thermochemical equation and use appropriate molar ratios to solve for the required heat.
Solution:

$C_2H_4(g) + H_2(g) \rightarrow C_2H_6(g)$ $\Delta H = -137$ kJ

$$\text{Heat (kJ)} = (15.0\text{ kg C}_2\text{H}_6)\left(\frac{10^3\text{g}}{1\text{ kg}}\right)\left(\frac{1\text{ mol C}_2\text{H}_6}{30.07\text{ g C}_2\text{H}_6}\right)\left(\frac{-137\text{ kJ}}{1\text{ mol C}_2\text{H}_6}\right)$$
$$= -6.83405\text{ x }10^4 = \mathbf{-6.83\ x\ 10^4\ kJ}$$

6.8B Plan: Write a balanced thermochemical equation and use appropriate molar ratios to solve for the required heat.
Solution:

$N_2(g) + O_2(g) \rightarrow 2NO(g)$ $\Delta H = +180.58$ kJ

$$\text{Heat (kJ)} = (3.50\text{ t NO})\left(\frac{10^3\text{ kg}}{1\text{ t}}\right)\left(\frac{1000\text{ g}}{1\text{ kg}}\right)\left(\frac{1\text{ mol NO}}{30.01\text{ g NO}}\right)\left(\frac{+180.58\text{ kJ}}{2\text{ mol NO}}\right) = \mathbf{1.05\ x\ 10^7\ kJ}$$

6.9A Plan: Manipulate the two equations so that their sum will result in the overall equation. Reverse the first equation (and change the sign of ΔH); reverse the second equation and multiply the coefficients (and ΔH) by two.

Solution:

$$\cancel{2NO(g)} + 3/2O_2(g) \rightarrow N_2O_5(s) \qquad \Delta H = -(223.7\text{ kJ}) = -223.7\text{ kJ}$$
$$2NO_2(g) \rightarrow \cancel{2NO(g)} + O_2(g) \qquad \Delta H = -2(-57.1\text{ kJ}) = 114.2\text{ kJ}$$
$$\text{Total: } 2NO_2(g) + 1/2O_2(g) \rightarrow N_2O_5(s) \qquad \Delta H = \mathbf{-109.5\text{ kJ}}$$

6.9B Plan: Manipulate the three equations so that their sum will result in the overall equation. Reverse the first equation (and change the sign of ΔH) and multiply the coefficients (and ΔH) by 1/2. Multiply the coefficients of the second equation (and ΔH) by 1/2. Reverse the third equation (and change the sign of ΔH).
Solution:

$$\cancel{NH_3(g)} \rightarrow \cancel{1/2N_2(g)} + \cancel{3/2H_2(g)} \qquad \Delta H = -1/2(-91.8\text{ kJ}) = 45.9\text{ kJ}$$
$$\cancel{1/2N_2(g)} + \cancel{2}1/2H_2(g) + 1/2Cl_2(g) \rightarrow \cancel{NH_4Cl(s)} \qquad \Delta H = 1/2(-628.8\text{ kJ}) = -314.4\text{ kJ}$$
$$\cancel{NH_4Cl(s)} \rightarrow \cancel{NH_3(g)} + HCl(g) \qquad \Delta H = -(-176.2\text{ kJ}) = 176.2\text{ kJ}$$
$$\text{Total: } 1/2H_2(g) + 1/2Cl_2(g) \rightarrow HCl(g) \qquad \Delta H = \mathbf{-92.3\text{ kJ}}$$

6.10A Plan: Write the elements as reactants (each in its standard state), and place one mole of the substance formed on the product side. Balance the equation with the following differences from "normal" balancing — only one mole of the desired product can be on the right hand side of the arrow (and nothing else), and fractional coefficients are allowed on the reactant side. The values for the standard heats of formation (ΔH_f°) may be found in the appendix.
Solution:

a) $C(\text{graphite}) + 2H_2(g) + 1/2O_2(g) \rightarrow CH_3OH(l)$ $\qquad \Delta H_f^\circ = \mathbf{-238.6\text{ kJ/mol}}$

b) $Ca(s) + 1/2O_2(g) \rightarrow CaO(s)$ $\qquad \Delta H_f^\circ = \mathbf{-635.1\text{ kJ/mol}}$

c) $C(\text{graphite}) + 1/4S_8(\text{rhombic}) \rightarrow CS_2(l)$ $\qquad \Delta H_f^\circ = \mathbf{87.9\text{ kJ/mol}}$

6.10B Plan: Write the elements as reactants (each in its standard state), and place one mole of the substance formed on the product side. Balance the equation with the following differences from "normal" balancing — only one mole of the desired product can be on the right hand side of the arrow (and nothing else), and fractional coefficients are allowed on the reactant side. The values for the standard heats of formation (ΔH_f°) may be found in the appendix.
Solution:

a) $C(\text{graphite}) + 1/2H_2(g) + 3/2Cl_2(g) \rightarrow CHCl_3(l)$ $\qquad \Delta H_f^\circ = \mathbf{-132\text{ kJ/mol}}$

b) $1/2N_2(g) + 2H_2(g) + 1/2Cl_2(g) \rightarrow NH_4Cl(s)$ $\qquad \Delta H_f^\circ = \mathbf{-314.4\text{ kJ/mol}}$

c) $Pb(s) + 1/8S_8(\text{rhombic}) + 2O_2(g) \rightarrow PbSO_4(s)$ $\qquad \Delta H_f^\circ = \mathbf{-918.39\text{ kJ/mol}}$

6.11A Plan: Look up ΔH_f° values from the appendix and use the equation $\Delta H_{rxn}^\circ = \Sigma m \Delta H_{f(products)}^\circ - \Sigma n \Delta H_{f(reactants)}^\circ$ to solve for ΔH_{rxn}°.
Solution:

$$\Delta H_{rxn}^\circ = \Sigma m \Delta H_{f(products)}^\circ - \Sigma n \Delta H_{f(reactants)}^\circ$$
$$= \{4 \Delta H_f^\circ [H_3PO_4(l)]\} - \{1 \Delta H_f^\circ [P_4O_{10}(s)] + 6 \Delta H_f^\circ [H_2O(l)]\}$$
$$= (4\text{ mol})(-1271.7\text{ kJ/mol}) - [(1\text{ mol})(-2984\text{ kJ/mol}) + (6\text{ mol})(-285.840\text{ kJ/mol})]$$
$$= -5086.8\text{ kJ} - [-2984\text{ kJ} + -1714.8\text{ kJ}] = \mathbf{-388\text{ kJ}}$$

6.11B Plan: Apply the ΔH_{rxn}° to this reaction, substitute given values, and solve for the ΔH_f° (CH_3OH).
Solution:

$$\Delta H_{rxn}^\circ = \Sigma m \Delta H_{f(products)}^\circ - \Sigma n \Delta H_{f(reactants)}^\circ$$

$$\Delta H_{rxn}^\circ = \{1 \Delta H_f^\circ [CO_2(g)] + 2 \Delta H_f^\circ [H_2O(g)]\} - \{1 \Delta H_f^\circ [CH_3OH(l)] + 3/2 \Delta H_f^\circ [O_2(g)]\}$$

$$-638.6 \text{ kJ} = [(1 \text{ mol})(-393.5 \text{ kJ/mol}) + (2 \text{ mol})(-241.826 \text{ kJ/mol})] - [\Delta H_f^\circ[CH_3OH(l)] + (3/2 \text{ mol})(0 \text{ kJ/mol})]$$

$$-638.6 \text{ kJ} = (-877.152 \text{ kJ}) - \Delta H_f^\circ[CH_3OH(l)]$$

$$\Delta H_f^\circ[CH_3OH(l)] = -238.552 = \mathbf{-238.6 \text{ kJ}}$$

CHEMICAL CONNECTIONS BOXED READING PROBLEMS

B6.1 Plan: Convert the given mass in kg to g, divide by the molar mass to obtain moles, and convert moles to kJ of energy. Sodium sulfate decahydrate will transfer 354 kJ/mol.
Solution:

$$\text{Heat (kJ)} = (500.0 \text{ kg } Na_2SO_4{\bullet}10H_2O)\left(\frac{10^3 \text{ g}}{1 \text{ kg}}\right)\left(\frac{1 \text{ mol } Na_2SO_4{\bullet}10H_2O}{322.20 \text{ g } Na_2SO_4{\bullet}10H_2O}\right)\left(\frac{-354 \text{ kJ}}{1 \text{ mol } Na_2SO_4{\bullet}10H_2O}\right)$$

$$= -5.4935\text{x}10^5 = \mathbf{-5.49x10^5 \text{ kJ}}$$

B6.2 Plan: Three reactions are given. Equation 1) must be multiplied by 2, and then the reactions can be added, canceling substances that appear on both sides of the arrow. Add the ΔH°_{rxn} values for the three reactions to get the ΔH°_{rxn} for the overall gasification reaction of 2 moles of coal. Use the relationship $\Delta H^\circ_{rxn} = \Sigma m \Delta H^\circ_{f(products)} - \Sigma n \Delta H^\circ_{f(reactants)}$ to find the heat of combustion of 1 mole of methane. Then find the ΔH°_{rxn} for the gasification of 1.00 kg of coal and ΔH°_{rxn} for the combustion of the methane produced from 1.00 kg of coal and sum these values.
Solution:

a) 1) $2C(coal) + 2H_2O(g) \rightarrow \cancel{2CO(g)} + \cancel{2H_2(g)}$ $\qquad \Delta H^\circ_{rxn} = 2(129.7 \text{ kJ})$

2) $\cancel{CO(g)} + \cancel{H_2O(g)} \rightarrow CO_2(g) + \cancel{H_2(g)}$ $\qquad \Delta H^\circ_{rxn} = -41 \text{ kJ}$

3) $\cancel{CO(g)} + \cancel{3H_2(g)} \rightarrow CH_4(g) + \cancel{H_2O(g)}$ $\qquad \Delta H^\circ_{rxn} = -206 \text{ kJ}$

$$2C(coal) + 2H_2O(g) \rightarrow CH_4(g) + CO_2(g)$$

b) The total may be determined by doubling the value for equation 1) and adding to the other two values.

$$\Delta H^\circ_{rxn} = 2(129.7 \text{ kJ}) + (-41 \text{ kJ}) + (-206 \text{ kJ}) = 12.4 = \mathbf{12 \text{ kJ}}$$

c) Calculating the heat of combustion of CH_4:

$$CH_4(g) + 2O_2(g) \rightarrow CO_2(g) + 2H_2O(g)$$

$$\Delta H^\circ_{rxn} = \Sigma m \Delta H^\circ_{f(products)} - \Sigma n \Delta H^\circ_{f(reactants)}$$

$$\Delta H^\circ_{rxn} = [(1 \text{ mol } CO_2)(\Delta H^\circ_f \text{ of } CO_2) + (2 \text{ mol } H_2O)(\Delta H^\circ_f \text{ of } H_2O)] - [(1 \text{ mol } CH_4)(\Delta H^\circ_f \text{ of } CH_4) + (2 \text{ mol } O_2)(\Delta H^\circ_f \text{ of } O_2)]$$

$$\Delta H^\circ_{rxn} = [(1 \text{ mol})(-395.5 \text{ kJ/mol}) + (2 \text{ mol})(-241.826 \text{ kJ/mol})] - [(1 \text{ mol})(-74.87 \text{kJ/mol}) + (2 \text{ mol })(0.0 \text{ kJ/mol})]$$

$$\Delta H^\circ_{rxn} = -804.282 \text{ kJ/mol } CH_4$$

Total heat for gasification of 1.00 kg coal:

$$\Delta H^\circ = (1.00 \text{ kg coal})\left(\frac{10^3 \text{ g}}{1 \text{ kg}}\right)\left(\frac{1 \text{ mol coal}}{12.00 \text{ g coal}}\right)\left(\frac{12.4 \text{ kJ}}{2 \text{ mol coal}}\right) = 516.667 \text{ kJ}$$

Total heat from burning the methane formed from 1.00 kg of coal:

$$\Delta H^\circ = (1.00 \text{ kg coal})\left(\frac{10^3 \text{ g}}{1 \text{ kg}}\right)\left(\frac{1 \text{ mol coal}}{12.00 \text{ g coal}}\right)\left(\frac{1 \text{ mol } CH_4}{2 \text{ mol coal}}\right)\left(\frac{-804.282 \text{ kJ}}{1 \text{ mol } CH_4}\right) = -33511.75 \text{ kJ}$$

Total heat = 516.667 kJ + (–33511.75 kJ) = –32995.083 = **–3.30x10⁴ kJ**

END–OF–CHAPTER PROBLEMS

6.4 Plan: Remember that an increase in internal energy is a result of the system (body) gaining heat or having work done on it and a decrease in internal energy is a result of the system (body) losing heat or doing work.
Solution:
The internal energy of the body is the sum of the cellular and molecular activities occurring from skin level inward. The body's internal energy can be increased by adding food, which adds energy to the body through the breaking of bonds in the food. The body's internal energy can also be increased through addition of work and heat, like the rubbing of another person's warm hands on the body's cold hands. The body can lose energy if it performs work, like pushing a lawnmower, and can lose energy by losing heat to a cold room.

6.6 Plan: Use the law of conservation of energy.
Solution:
The amount of the change in internal energy in the two cases is the same. By the law of energy conservation, the change in energy of the universe is zero. This requires that the change in energy of the system (heater or air conditioner) equals an opposite change in energy of the surroundings (room air). Since both systems consume the same amount of electrical energy, the change in energy of the heater equals that of the air conditioner.

6.8 Plan: The change in a system's energy is $\Delta E = q + w$. If the system receives heat, then its q_{final} is greater than q_{initial} so q is positive. Since the system performs work, its $w_{\text{final}} < w_{\text{initial}}$ so w is negative.
Solution:
$\Delta E = q + w$
$\Delta E = (+425\text{ J}) + (-425\text{ J}) = \mathbf{0\text{ J}}$

6.10 Plan: The change in a system's energy is $\Delta E = q + w$. A system that releases thermal energy has a negative value for q and a system that has work done on it has a positive value for work. Convert work in calories to work in joules.
Solution:

$$\text{Work (J)} = (530\text{ cal})\left(\frac{4.184\text{ J}}{1\text{ cal}}\right) = 2217.52\text{ J}$$

$$\Delta E = q + w = -675\text{ J} + 2217.52\text{ J} = 1542.52 = \mathbf{1.54x10^3\text{ J}}$$

6.12 Plan: Convert $6.6\text{x}10^{10}$ J to the other units using conversion factors.
Solution:
$C(s) + O_2(g) \rightarrow CO_2(g) + 6.6\text{x}10^{10}\text{ J}$
(2.0 tons)

$$\text{a) } \Delta E\text{ (kJ)} = (6.6\text{ x }10^{10}\text{ J})\left(\frac{1\text{ kJ}}{10^3\text{ J}}\right) = \mathbf{6.6x10^7\text{ kJ}}$$

$$\text{b) } \Delta E\text{ (kcal)} = (6.6\text{ x }10^{10}\text{ J})\left(\frac{1\text{ cal}}{4.184\text{ J}}\right)\left(\frac{1\text{ kcal}}{10^3\text{ cal}}\right) = 1.577\text{x}10^7 = \mathbf{1.6x10^7\text{ kcal}}$$

$$\text{c) } \Delta E\text{ (Btu)} = (6.6\text{ x }10^{10}\text{ J})\left(\frac{1\text{ Btu}}{1055\text{ J}}\right) = 6.256\text{x}10^7 = \mathbf{6.3x10^7\text{ Btu}}$$

6.15 Plan: 1.0 lb of body fat is equivalent to about $4.1\text{x}10^3$ Calories. Convert Calories to kJ with the appropriate conversion factors.
Solution:

$$\text{Time} = (1.0\text{lb})\left(\frac{4.1\text{x}10^3\text{ Cal}}{1.0\text{ lb}}\right)\left(\frac{10^3\text{ cal}}{1\text{ Cal}}\right)\left(\frac{4.184\text{ J}}{1\text{ cal}}\right)\left(\frac{1\text{ kJ}}{10^3\text{ J}}\right)\left(\frac{\text{h}}{1950\text{ kJ}}\right) = 8.79713 = \mathbf{8.8\text{ h}}$$

6.17 Since many reactions are performed in an open flask, the reaction proceeds at constant pressure. The determination of ΔH (constant pressure conditions) requires a measurement of heat only, whereas ΔE requires measurement of heat and PV work.

6.19 Plan: An exothermic process releases heat and an endothermic process absorbs heat.
Solution:
a) **Exothermic**, the system (water) is releasing heat in changing from liquid to solid.
b) **Endothermic**, the system (water) is absorbing heat in changing from liquid to gas.
c) **Exothermic**, the process of digestion breaks down food and releases energy.
d) **Exothermic**, heat is released as a person runs and muscles perform work.
e) **Endothermic**, heat is absorbed as food calories are converted to body tissue.
f) **Endothermic**, the wood being chopped absorbs heat (and work).
g) **Exothermic**, the furnace releases heat from fuel combustion. Alternatively, if the system is defined as the air in the house, the change is endothermic since the air's temperature is increasing by the input of heat energy from the furnace.

6.22 Plan: Convert the initial volume from mL to L. Subtract the initial V from the final V to find ΔV. Calculate w in atm•L. Convert the answer from atm•L to J.
Solution:
$V_{initial} = 922$ mL
$V_{final} = 1.14$ L
$P = 2.33$ atm

Converting $V_{initial}$ from mL to L: $(922 \text{ mL})\left(\frac{1 \text{ L}}{10^3 \text{ mL}}\right) = 0.922 \text{ L}$

w (atm•L) = $-P\Delta V$ = -(2.33 atm)(1.14 L – 0.922 L) = -0.51 atm•L

$w \text{ (J)} = (-0.51 \text{ atm•L})\left(\frac{1 \text{ J}}{9.87 \times 10^{-3} \text{ atm•L}}\right) = $ **-52 J**

6.24 Plan: An exothermic reaction releases heat, so the reactants have greater H ($H_{initial}$) than the products (H_{final}). $\Delta H = H_{final} - H_{initial} < 0$.
Solution:

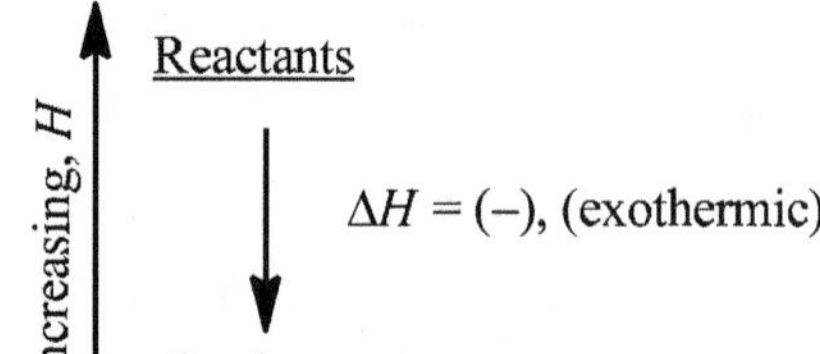

6.26 Plan: Combustion of hydrocarbons and related compounds require oxygen (and a heat catalyst) to yield carbon dioxide gas, water vapor, and heat. Combustion reactions are exothermic. The freezing of liquid water is an exothermic process as heat is removed from the water in the conversion from liquid to solid. An exothermic reaction or process releases heat, so the reactants have greater H ($H_{initial}$) than the products (H_{final}).
Solution:
a) Combustion of ethane: $2C_2H_6(g) + 7O_2(g) \rightarrow 4CO_2(g) + 6H_2O(g)$ + heat

$2C_2H_6 + 7O_2$ (initial)

Increasing, H

$\Delta H = (–)$, (exothermic)

$4CO_2 + 6H_2O$ (final)

b) Freezing of water: $H_2O(l) \rightarrow H_2O(s)$ + heat

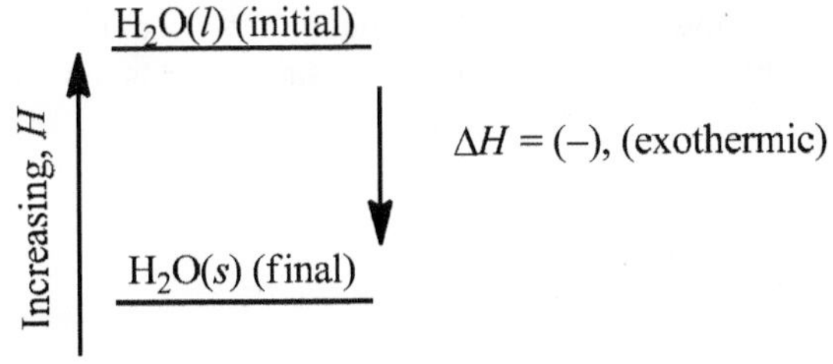

6.28 Plan: Combustion of hydrocarbons and related compounds require oxygen (and a heat catalyst) to yield carbon dioxide gas, water vapor, and heat. Combustion reactions are exothermic. An exothermic reaction releases heat, so the reactants have greater H ($H_{initial}$) than the products (H_{final}). If heat is absorbed, the reaction is endothermic and the products have greater H (H_{final}) than the reactants ($H_{initial}$).

Solution:

a) $2CH_3OH(l) + 3O_2(g) \rightarrow 2CO_2(g) + 4H_2O(g) + \text{heat}$

$2CH_3OH + 3O_2$ (initial)

Increasing, H

$\Delta H = (-)$, (exothermic)

$2CO_2 + 4H_2O$ (final)

b) Nitrogen dioxide, NO_2, forms from N_2 and O_2.

$1/2N_2(g) + O_2(g) + \text{heat} \rightarrow NO_2(g)$

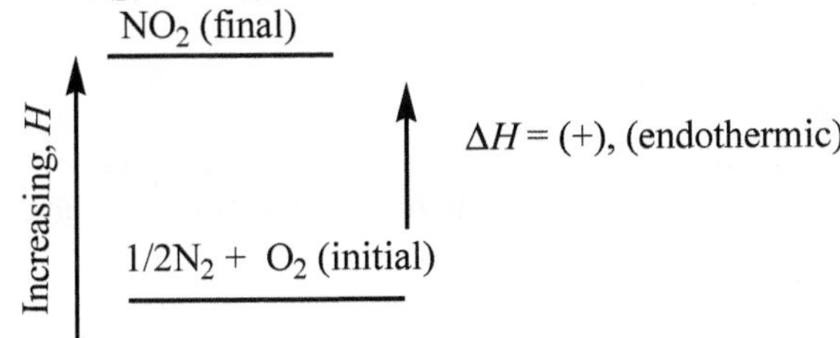

6.30 Plan: Recall that q_{sys} is positive if heat is absorbed by the system (endothermic) and negative if heat is released by the system (exothermic). Since $\Delta E = q + w$, the work must be considered in addition to q_{sys} to find ΔE_{sys}.

Solution:

a) This is a phase change from the solid phase to the gas phase. Heat is absorbed by the system so q_{sys} is **positive (+)**.

b) The system is expanding in volume as more moles of gas exist after the phase change than were present before the phase change. So the system has done work of expansion and w is negative. $\Delta E_{sys} = q + w$. Since q is positive and w is negative, the sign of ΔE_{sys} **cannot be predicted**. It will be positive if $q > w$ and negative if $q < w$.

c) $\Delta E_{univ} = \mathbf{0}$. If the system loses energy, the surroundings gain an equal amount of energy. The sum of the energy of the system and the energy of the surroundings remains constant.

6.33 To determine the specific heat capacity of a substance, you need its mass, the heat added (or lost), and the change in temperature.

6.35 Specific heat capacity is the quantity of heat required to raise 1g of a substance by 1 K. Molar heat capacity is the quantity of heat required to raise 1 mole of substance by 1 K. Heat capacity is also the quantity of heat required for a 1 K temperature change, but it applies to an object instead of a specified amount of a substance. Thus, specific heat capacity and molar heat capacity are used when talking about an element or compound while heat capacity is used for a calorimeter or other object.

6.37 Plan: The heat required to raise the temperature of water is found by using the equation $q = c \times \text{mass} \times \Delta T$. The specific heat capacity, c_{water}, is found in Table 6.2. Because the Celsius degree is the same size as the Kelvin degree, $\Delta T = 100°C - 25°C = 75°C = 75$ K.

Solution:

$$q\ (\text{J}) = c \times \text{mass} \times \Delta T = \left(4.184 \frac{\text{J}}{\text{g•K}}\right)(22.0\ \text{g})(75\ \text{K}) = 6903.6 = \mathbf{6.9x10^3\ J}$$

6.39 Plan: Use the relationship $q = c \times \text{mass} \times \Delta T$. We know the heat (change kJ to J), the specific heat capacity, and the mass, so ΔT can be calculated. Once ΔT is known, that value is added to the initial temperature to find the final temperature.

Solution:

$q\ (\text{J}) = c \times \text{mass} \times \Delta T$ $T_{initial} = 13.00°C$ $T_{final} = ?$ mass = 295 g $c = 0.900$ J/g•K

$$q = (75.0\ \text{kJ})\left(\frac{10^3\ \text{J}}{1\ \text{kJ}}\right) = 7.50\text{x}10^4\ \text{J}$$

$7.50\text{x}10^4\ \text{J} = (0.900\ \text{J/g•K})(295\ \text{g})(\Delta T)$

$$\Delta T = \frac{(7.50\text{x}10^4\ \text{J})}{(295\ \text{g})\left(\frac{0.900\ \text{J}}{\text{g•K}}\right)}$$

$\Delta T = 282.4859\ \text{K} = 282.4859°C$ (Because the Celsius degree is the same size as the Kelvin degree, ΔT is the same in either temperature unit.)

$\Delta T = T_{final} - T_{initial}$

$T_{final} = \Delta T + T_{initial}$

$T_{final} = 282.4859°C + 13.00°C = 295.49 = \mathbf{295°C}$

6.41 Plan: Since the bolts have the same mass and same specific heat capacity, and one must cool as the other heats (the heat lost by the "hot" bolt equals the heat gained by the "cold" bolt), the final temperature is an average of the two initial temperatures.

Solution:

$$\left[\frac{(T_1 + T_2)}{2}\right] = \left[\frac{(100.°C + 55°C)}{2}\right] = \mathbf{77.5°C}$$

6.43 Plan: The heat lost by the water originally at 85°C is gained by the water that is originally at 26°C. Therefore $-q_{lost} = q_{gained}$. Both volumes are converted to mass using the density.

Solution:

$$\text{Mass (g) of 75 mL} = (75\ \text{mL})\left(\frac{1.00\ \text{g}}{1\ \text{mL}}\right) = 75\ \text{g} \qquad \text{Mass (g) of 155 mL} = (155\ \text{mL})\left(\frac{1.00\ \text{g}}{1\ \text{mL}}\right) = 155\ \text{g}$$

$-q_{lost} = q_{gained}$

$c \times \text{mass} \times \Delta T\ (85°C\ \text{water}) = c \times \text{mass} \times \Delta T\ (26°C\ \text{water})$

$-(4.184\ \text{J/g°C})(75\ \text{g})(T_{final} - 85)°C = (4.184\ \text{J/g°C})(155\ \text{g})(T_{final} - 26)°C$

$-(75\ \text{g})(T_{final} - 85)°C = (155\ \text{g})(T_{final} - 26)°C$

$6375 - 75T_{final} = 155T_{final} - 4030$

$6375 + 4030 = 155T_{final} + 75T_{final}$

$10405 = 230.T_{final}$

$T_{final} = (10405/230.) = 45.24 = \mathbf{45°C}$

6.45 Plan: Heat gained by water and the container equals the heat lost by the copper tubing so $q_{water} + q_{calorimeter} = -q_{copper}$.

Solution:

$\Delta T = T_{final} - T_{initial}$

Specific heat capacity in units of J/g•K has the same value in units of J/g°C since the Celsius and Kelvin unit are the same size.

$-q_{\text{lost}} = q_{\text{gained}} = q_{\text{water}} + q_{\text{calorimeter}}$

$-(455 \text{ g Cu})(0.387 \text{ J/g°C})(T_{\text{final}} - 89.5)\text{°C}$

$= (159 \text{ g } H_2O)(4.184 \text{ J/g°C})(T_{\text{final}} - 22.8)\text{°C} + (10.0 \text{ J/°C})(T_{\text{final}} - 22.8)\text{°C}$

$-(176.085)(T_{\text{final}} - 89.5) = (665.256)(T_{\text{final}} - 22.8) + (10.0)(T_{\text{final}} - 22.8)$

$15759.6075 - 176.085T_{\text{final}} = 665.256T_{\text{final}} - 15167.8368 + 10.0T_{\text{final}} - 228$

$15759.6075 + 15167.8368 + 228 = 176.085T_{\text{final}} + 665.256T_{\text{final}} + 10.0T_{\text{final}}$

$31155.4443 = 851.341T_{\text{final}}$

$T_{\text{final}} = 31155.4443/(851.341) = 36.59573 =$ **36.6°C**

6.52 Plan: Recall that ΔH is positive for an endothermic reaction in which heat is absorbed, while ΔH is negative for an exothermic reaction in which heat is released.

Solution:

The reaction has a **positive ΔH_{rxn}**, because this reaction requires the input of energy to break the oxygen-oxygen bond in O_2:

$$O_2(g) + \text{energy} \rightarrow 2O(g)$$

6.53 Plan: Recall that ΔH is positive for an endothermic reaction in which heat is absorbed, while ΔH is negative for an exothermic reaction in which heat is released.

Solution:

As a substance changes from the gaseous state to the liquid state, energy is released so ΔH would be negative for the condensation of 1 mol of water. The value of ΔH for the vaporization of 2 mol of water would be twice the value of ΔH for the condensation of 1 mol of water vapor but would have an opposite sign ($+\Delta H$).

$H_2O(g) \rightarrow H_2O(l) + \text{Energy}$ $\qquad$ $2H_2O(l) + \text{Energy} \rightarrow 2H_2O(g)$

$\Delta H_{\text{condensation}} = (-)$ $\qquad$ $\Delta H_{\text{vaporization}} = (+)2[\Delta H_{\text{condensation}}]$

The enthalpy for 1 mole of water condensing would be opposite in sign to and one-half the value for the conversion of 2 moles of liquid H_2O to H_2O vapor.

6.54 Plan: Recall that ΔH is positive for an endothermic reaction in which heat is absorbed, while ΔH is negative for an exothermic reaction in which heat is released. The ΔH_{rxn} is specific for the reaction as written, meaning that 20.2 kJ is released when one-eighth of a mole of sulfur reacts. Use the ratio between moles of sulfur and ΔH to convert between amount of sulfur and heat released.

Solution:

a) This reaction is **exothermic** because ΔH is negative.

b) Because ΔH is a state function, the total energy required for the reverse reaction, regardless of how the change occurs, is the same magnitude but different sign of the forward reaction. Therefore, $\Delta H =$ **+20.2 kJ**.

c) $\Delta H_{\text{rxn}} = (2.6 \text{ mol } S_8)\left(\frac{-20.2 \text{ kJ}}{(1/8) \text{ mol } S_8}\right) = -420.16 =$ **$-4.2\text{x}10^2$ kJ**

d) The mass of S_8 requires conversion to moles and then a calculation identical to part c) can be performed.

$\Delta H_{\text{rxn}} = (25.0 \text{ g } S_8)\left(\frac{1 \text{ mol } S_8}{256.48 \text{ g } S_8}\right)\left(\frac{-20.2 \text{ kJ}}{(1/8) \text{ mol } S_8}\right) = -15.7517 =$ **-15.8 kJ**

6.56 Plan: A thermochemical equation is a balanced equation that includes the heat of reaction. Since heat is absorbed in this reaction, ΔH will be positive. Convert the mass of NO to moles and use the ratio between NO and ΔH to find the heat involved for this amount of NO.

Solution:

a) $1/2N_2(g) + 1/2O_2(g) \rightarrow NO(g)$ $\qquad$ $\Delta H = 90.29$ kJ

b) $\Delta H_{\text{rxn}} = (3.50 \text{ g NO})\left(\frac{1 \text{ mol NO}}{30.01 \text{ g NO}}\right)\left(\frac{-90.29 \text{ kJ}}{1 \text{ mol NO}}\right) = -10.5303 =$ **-10.5 kJ**

6.58 Plan: For the reaction written, 2 moles of H_2O_2 release 196.1 kJ of energy upon decomposition. Use this ratio to convert between the given amount of reactant and the amount of heat released. The amount of H_2O_2 must be converted from kg to g to moles.

Solution:

$$2H_2O_2(l) \rightarrow 2H_2O(l) + O_2(g) \qquad \Delta H_{rxn} = -196.1 \text{ kJ}$$

$$\text{Heat (kJ)} = q = (652 \text{ kg } H_2O_2)\left(\frac{10^3 \text{ g}}{1 \text{ kg}}\right)\left(\frac{1 \text{ mol } H_2O_2}{34.02 \text{ g } H_2O_2}\right)\left(\frac{-196.1 \text{ kJ}}{2 \text{ mol } H_2O_2}\right) = -1.87915\text{x}10^6 = \mathbf{-1.88x10^6 \text{ kJ}}$$

6.62 Plan: A thermochemical equation is a balanced equation that includes the heat of reaction. Heat is released in this reaction so ΔH is negative. Use the ratio between ΔH and moles of C_2H_4 to find the amount of C_2H_4 that must react to produce the given quantity of heat.

Solution:

a) $C_2H_4(g) + 3O_2(g) \rightarrow 2CO_2(g) + 2H_2O(l) \qquad \Delta H_{rxn} = -1411 \text{ kJ}$

b) $\text{Mass (g) of } C_2H_4 = (-70.0 \text{ kJ})\left(\frac{1 \text{ mol } C_2H_4}{-1411 \text{ kJ}}\right)\left(\frac{28.05 \text{ g } C_2H_4}{1 \text{ mol } C_2H_4}\right) = 1.39157 = \mathbf{1.39 \text{ g } C_2H_4}$

6.66 Plan: Two chemical equations can be written based on the description given:

$C(s) + O_2(g) \rightarrow CO_2(g) \qquad \Delta H_1 \qquad (1)$

$CO(g) + 1/2O_2(g) \rightarrow CO_2(g) \qquad \Delta H_2 \qquad (2)$

The second reaction can be reversed and its ΔH sign changed. In this case, no change in the coefficients is necessary since the CO_2 cancels. Add the two ΔH values together to obtain the ΔH of the desired reaction.

Solution:

$C(s) + O_2(g) \rightarrow$ ~~$CO_2(g)$~~ $\qquad \Delta H_1$

~~$CO_2(g)$~~ $\rightarrow CO(g) + 1/2O_2(g) \qquad -\Delta H_2$ (reaction is reversed)

Total $\quad C(s) + 1/2O_2(g) \rightarrow CO(g) \qquad \Delta H_{rxn} = \Delta H_1 + -(\Delta H_2)$

How are the ΔH values for each reaction determined? The ΔH_1 can be found by using the heats of formation in Appendix B:

$\Delta H_1 = [\Delta H_f(CO_2)] - [\Delta H_f(C) + \Delta H_f(O_2)] = [-393.5 \text{ kJ/mol}] - [0 + 0] = -393.5 \text{ kJ/mol}.$

The ΔH_2 can be found by using the heats of formation in Appendix B:

$\Delta H_2 = [\Delta H_f(CO_2)] - [\Delta H_f(CO) + 1/2\Delta H_f(O_2)] = [-393.5] - [-110.5 \text{ kJ/mol} + 0)] = -283 \text{ kJ/mol}.$

$\Delta H_{rxn} = \Delta H_1 + -(\Delta H_2) = -393.5 \text{ kJ} + -(-283.0 \text{ kJ}) = \mathbf{-110.5 \text{ kJ}}$

6.67 Plan: To obtain the overall reaction, add the first reaction to the reverse of the second. When the second reaction is reversed, the sign of its enthalpy change is reversed from positive to negative.

Solution:

$Ca(s) + 1/2O_2(g) \rightarrow$ ~~$CaO(s)$~~ $\qquad \Delta H = -635.1 \text{ kJ}$

~~$CaO(s)$~~ $+ CO_2(g) \rightarrow CaCO_3(s) \qquad \Delta H = -178.3$ kJ (reaction is reversed)

$Ca(s) + 1/2O_2(g) + CO_2(g) \rightarrow CaCO_3(s) \qquad \Delta H = \mathbf{-813.4 \text{ kJ}}$

6.69 Plan: Add the two equations, canceling substances that appear on both sides of the arrow. When matching the equations with the arrows in the Figure, remember that a positive ΔH corresponds to an arrow pointing up while a negative ΔH corresponds to an arrow pointing down.

Solution:

1) $N_2(g) + O_2(g) \rightarrow$ ~~$2NO(g)$~~ $\qquad \Delta H = 180.6 \text{ kJ}$

2) ~~$2NO(g)$~~ $+ O_2(g) \rightarrow 2NO_2(g) \qquad \Delta H = -114.2 \text{ kJ}$

3) $\mathbf{N_2(g) + 2O_2(g) \rightarrow 2NO_2(g)} \qquad \mathbf{\Delta H_{rxn} = +66.4 \text{ kJ}}$

In Figure P6.67, **A represents reaction 1** with a larger amount of energy absorbed, **B represents reaction 2** with a smaller amount of energy released, and **C represents reaction 3** as the sum of A and B.

6.71 Plan: Vaporization is the change in state from a liquid to a gas: $H_2O(l) \rightarrow H_2O(g)$. The two equations describing the chemical reactions for the formation of gaseous and liquid water can be combined to yield the equation for vaporization.

Solution:

1) Formation of $H_2O(g)$: $H_2(g) + 1/2O_2(g) \rightarrow H_2O(g)$ $\Delta H = -241.8$ kJ

2) Formation of $H_2O(l)$: $H_2(g) + 1/2O_2(g) \rightarrow H_2O(l)$ $\Delta H = -285.8$ kJ

Reverse reaction 2 (change the sign of ΔH) and add the two reactions:

$\cancel{H_2(g)} + \cancel{1/2O_2(g)} \rightarrow H_2O(g)$ $\Delta H = -241.8$ kJ

$H_2O(l) \rightarrow \cancel{H_2(g)} + \cancel{1/2O_2(g)}$ $\Delta H = +285.8$ kJ

$H_2O(l) \rightarrow H_2O(g)$ $\Delta H_{vap} =$ **44.0 kJ**

6.74 The standard heat of reaction, ΔH°_{rxn}, is the enthalpy change for any reaction where all substances are in their standard states. The standard heat of formation, ΔH°_f, is the enthalpy change that accompanies the formation of one mole of a compound in its standard state from elements in their standard states. Standard state is 1 atm for gases, 1 *M* for solutes, and the most stable form for liquids and solids. Standard state does not include a specific temperature, but a temperature must be specified in a table of standard values.

6.76 Plan: ΔH°_f is for the reaction that shows the formation of one mole of compound from its elements in their standard states.

Solution:

a) $1/2Cl_2(g) + Na(s) \rightarrow NaCl(s)$ The element chlorine occurs as Cl_2, not Cl.

b) $H_2(g) + 1/2O_2(g) \rightarrow H_2O(g)$ The element hydrogen exists as H_2, not H, and the formation of water is written with water as the product.

c) No changes

6.77 Plan: Formation equations show the formation of one mole of compound from its elements. The elements must be in their most stable states ($\Delta H^\circ_f = 0$).

Solution:

a) $Ca(s) + Cl_2(g) \rightarrow CaCl_2(s)$

b) $Na(s) + 1/2H_2(g) + C(\text{graphite}) + 3/2O_2(g) \rightarrow NaHCO_3(s)$

c) $C(\text{graphite}) + 2Cl_2(g) \rightarrow CCl_4(l)$

d) $1/2H_2(g) + 1/2N_2(g) + 3/2O_2(g) \rightarrow HNO_3(l)$

6.79 Plan: The enthalpy change of a reaction is the sum of the heats of formation of the products minus the sum of the heats of formation of the reactants. Since the ΔH°_f values (Appendix B) are reported as energy per one mole, use the appropriate stoichiometric coefficient to reflect the higher number of moles.

Solution:

$$\Delta H^\circ_{rxn} = \Sigma m\, \Delta H^\circ_{f\,(\text{products})} - \Sigma n\, \Delta H^\circ_{f\,(\text{reactants})}$$

a) $\Delta H^\circ_{rxn} = \{2\,\Delta H^\circ_f\,[SO_2(g)] + 2\,\Delta H^\circ_f\,[H_2O(g)]\} - \{2\,\Delta H^\circ_f\,[H_2S(g)] + 3\,\Delta H^\circ_f\,[O_2(g)]\}$

$= [(2 \text{ mol})(-296.8 \text{ kJ/mol}) + (2 \text{ mol})(-241.826 \text{ kJ/mol})] - [(2 \text{ mol})(-20.2 \text{ kJ/mol}) + (3 \text{ mol})(0.0 \text{ kJ/mol})]$ $=$ **−1036.9 kJ**

b) The balanced equation is $CH_4(g) + 4Cl_2(g) \rightarrow CCl_4(l) + 4HCl(g)$

$\Delta H^\circ_{rxn} = \{1\,\Delta H^\circ_f\,[CCl_4(l)] + 4\,\Delta H^\circ_f\,[HCl(g)]\} - \{1\,\Delta H^\circ_f\,[CH_4(g)] + 4\,\Delta H^\circ_f\,[Cl_2(g)]\}$

$\Delta H^\circ_{rxn} = [(1 \text{ mol})(-139 \text{ kJ/mol}) + (4 \text{ mol})(-92.31 \text{ kJ/mol})] - [(1 \text{ mol})(-74.87 \text{ kJ/mol}) + (4 \text{ mol})(0 \text{ kJ/mol})]$

$=$ **−433 kJ**

6.81 Plan: The enthalpy change of a reaction is the sum of the heats of formation of the products minus the sum of the heats of formation of the reactants. Since the ΔH_f° values (Appendix B) are reported as energy per one mole, use the appropriate stoichiometric coefficient to reflect the higher number of moles. In this case, ΔH_{rxn}° is known and ΔH_f° of CuO must be calculated.

Solution:

$\Delta H_{rxn}^\circ = \Sigma m \Delta H_{f\,(products)}^\circ - \Sigma n \Delta H_{f\,(reactants)}^\circ$

$Cu_2O(s) + 1/2O_2(g) \rightarrow 2CuO(s)$ $\Delta H_{rxn}^\circ = -146.0$ kJ

$\Delta H_{rxn}^\circ = \{2\,\Delta H_f^\circ [CuO(s)]\} - \{1\,\Delta H_f^\circ [Cu_2O(s)] + 1/2\,\Delta H_f^\circ [O_2(g)]\}$

$-146.0 \text{ kJ} = \{(2 \text{ mol})\,\Delta H_f^\circ [CuO(s)]\} - \{(1 \text{ mol})(-168.6 \text{ kJ/mol}) + (1/2 \text{ mol})(0 \text{ kJ/mol})\}$

$-146.0 \text{ kJ} = 2 \text{ mol}\,\Delta H_f^\circ [CuO(s)] + 168.6 \text{ kJ}$

$\Delta H_f^\circ [CuO(s)] = -\frac{314.6 \text{ kJ}}{2 \text{ mol}} = \mathbf{-157.3\ kJ/mol}$

6.83 Plan: The enthalpy change of a reaction is the sum of the heats of formation of the products minus the sum of the heats of formation of the reactants. Since the ΔH_f° values (Appendix B) are reported as energy per one mole, use the appropriate stoichiometric coefficient to reflect the higher number of moles. Hess's law can also be used to calculate the enthalpy of reaction. In part b), rearrange equations 1) and 2) to give the equation wanted. Reverse the first equation (changing the sign of ΔH_{rxn}°) and multiply the coefficients (and ΔH_{rxn}°) of the second reaction by 2.

Solution:

$2PbSO_4(s) + 2H_2O(l) \rightarrow Pb(s) + PbO_2(s) + 2H_2SO_4(l)$

$\Delta H_{rxn}^\circ = \Sigma m \Delta H_{f\,(products)}^\circ - \Sigma n \Delta H_{f\,(reactants)}^\circ$

a) $\Delta H_{rxn}^\circ = \{1\,\Delta H_f^\circ [Pb(s)] + 1\,\Delta H_f^\circ [PbO_2(s)] + 2\,\Delta H_f^\circ [H_2SO_4(l)]\}$

$- \{2\,\Delta H_f^\circ [PbSO_4(s)] + 2\,\Delta H_f^\circ [H_2O(l)]\}$

$= [(1 \text{ mol})(0 \text{ kJ/mol}) + (1 \text{ mol})(-276.6 \text{ kJmol}) + (2 \text{ mol})(-813.989 \text{ kJ/mol})]$

$- [(2 \text{ mol})(-918.39 \text{ kJ/mol}) + (2 \text{ mol})(-285.840 \text{ kJ/mol})]$

$= \mathbf{503.9\ kJ}$

b) Use Hess's law:

$PbSO_4(s) \rightarrow Pb(s) + PbO_2(s) + \cancel{2SO_3(g)}$ $\Delta H_{rxn}^\circ = -(-768 \text{ kJ})$ Equation has been reversed.

$\cancel{2SO_3(g)} + 2H_2O\,(l) \rightarrow 2H_2SO_4(l)$ $\Delta H_{rxn}^\circ = 2(-132 \text{ kJ})$

$2PbSO_4(s) + 2H_2O(l) \rightarrow Pb(s) + PbO_2(s) + 2H_2SO_4(l)$ $\Delta H_{rxn}^\circ = \mathbf{504\ kJ}$

6.84 Plan: The enthalpy change of a reaction is the sum of the heats of formation of the products minus the sum of the heats of formation of the reactants. Since the ΔH_f° values (Appendix B) are reported as energy per one mole, use the appropriate stoichiometric coefficient to reflect the higher number of moles. Convert the mass of stearic acid to moles and use the ratio between stearic acid and ΔH_{rxn}° to find the heat involved for this amount of acid. For part d), use the kcal/g of fat relationship calculated in part c) to convert 11.0 g of fat to total kcal and compare to the 100. Cal amount.

Solution:

a) $C_{18}H_{36}O_2(s) + 26O_2(g) \rightarrow 18CO_2(g) + 18H_2O(g)$

b) $\Delta H_{rxn}^\circ = \Sigma m \Delta H_{f\,(products)}^\circ - \Sigma n \Delta H_{f\,(reactants)}^\circ$

$\Delta H_{rxn}^\circ = \{18\,\Delta H_f^\circ [CO_2(g)] + 18\,\Delta H_f^\circ [H_2O(g)]\} - \{1\,\Delta H_f^\circ [C_{18}H_{36}O_2(s)] + 26\,\Delta H_f^\circ [O_2(g)]\}$

$= [(18 \text{ mol})(-393.5 \text{ kJ/mol}) + (18 \text{ mol})(-241.826 \text{ kJ/mol})] - [(1 \text{ mol})(-948 \text{ kJ/mol}) + (26 \text{ mol})(0 \text{ kJ/mol})]$

$= -10{,}487.868 = \mathbf{-10{,}488\ kJ}$

c) $q\ (\text{kJ}) = (1.00\ \text{g}\ C_{18}H_{36}O_2)\left(\frac{1\ \text{mol}\ C_{18}H_{36}O_2}{284.47\ C_{18}H_{36}O_2}\right)\left(\frac{-10{,}487.868\ \text{kJ}}{1\ \text{mol}\ C_{18}H_{36}O_2}\right) = -36.8681 = \mathbf{-36.9\ kJ}$

$q\ (\text{kcal}) = (-36.8681\ \text{kJ})\left(\frac{1\ \text{kcal}}{4.184\ \text{kJ}}\right) = -8.811688 = \mathbf{-8.81\ kcal}$

d) $q\ (\text{kcal}) = (11.0\ \text{g fat})\left[\frac{-8.811688\ \text{kcal}}{1.0\ \text{g fat}}\right] = 96.9286 = \mathbf{96.9\ kcal}$

Since 1 kcal = 1 Cal, 96.9 kcal = 96.9 Cal. The calculated calorie content is consistent with the package information.

6.86 Plan: Use the ideal gas law, $PV = nRT$, to calculate the volume of one mole of helium at each temperature. Then use the given equation for ΔE to find the change in internal energy. The equation for work, $w = -P\Delta V$, is needed for part c), and $q_P = \Delta E + P\Delta V$ is used for part d). For part e), recall that $\Delta H = q_P$.

Solution:

a) $PV = nRT$ or $V = \frac{nRT}{P}$

$T = 273 + 15 = 288$ K and $T = 273 + 30 = 303$ K

Initial volume (L) = $V = \frac{nRT}{P} = \frac{\left(0.0821\frac{\text{L•atm}}{\text{mol•K}}\right)(288\ \text{K})}{(1.00\ \text{atm})} = 23.6448 = \mathbf{23.6\ L/mol}$

Final volume (L) = $V = \frac{nRT}{P} = \frac{\left(0.0821\frac{\text{L•atm}}{\text{mol • K}}\right)(303\ \text{K})}{(1.00\ \text{atm})} = 24.8763 = \mathbf{24.9\ L/mol}$

b) Internal energy is the sum of the potential and kinetic energies of each He atom in the system (the balloon). The energy of one mole of helium atoms can be described as a function of temperature, $E = 3/2nRT$, where n = 1 mole. Therefore, the internal energy at 15°C and 30°C can be calculated. The inside back cover lists values of R with different units.

$E = 3/2nRT = (3/2)(1.00\ \text{mol})\ (8.314\ \text{J/mol•K})(303 - 288)\text{K} = 187.065 = \mathbf{187\ J}$

c) When the balloon expands as temperature rises, the balloon performs PV work. However, the problem specifies that pressure remains constant, so work done <u>on</u> the surroundings by the balloon is defined by the equation: $w = -P\Delta V$. When pressure and volume are multiplied together, the unit is L•atm, so a conversion factor is needed to convert work in units of L•atm to joules.

$w = -P\Delta V = -(1.00\ \text{atm})((24.8763 - 23.6448)\ \text{L})\left(\frac{101.3\ \text{J}}{1\ \text{L•atm}}\right) = -124.75 = \mathbf{-1.2x10^2\ J}$

d) $q_P = \Delta E + P\Delta V = (187.065\ \text{J}) + (124.75\ \text{J}) = 311.815 = \mathbf{3.1x10^2\ J}$

e) $\Delta H = q_P = \mathbf{310\ J.}$

f) When a process occurs at constant pressure, the change in heat energy of the system can be described by a state function called enthalpy. The change in enthalpy equals the heat (q) lost at constant pressure: $\Delta H = \Delta E + P\Delta V = \Delta E - w = (q + w) - w = q_P$

6.95 Plan: Use conversion factors to solve parts a) and b). For part c), first find the heat of reaction for the combustion of methane by using the heats of formation of the reactants and products. The enthalpy change of a reaction is the sum of the heats of formation of the products minus the sum of the heats of formation of the reactants. Since the ΔH_f^o values (Appendix B) are reported as energy per one mole, use the appropriate stoichiometric coefficient to reflect the higher number of moles. For part e), convert the amount of water in gal to mass in g and use the relationship $q = c$ x mass x ΔT to find the heat needed; then use the conversion factors between joules and therms and the cost per therm to determine the total cost of heating the water.

Solution:

a) $\left(\frac{1\text{ cal}}{\text{g°C}}\right)\left(\frac{4.184\text{ J}}{1\text{ cal}}\right)\left(\frac{453.6\text{ g}}{1\text{ lb}}\right)\left(\frac{1.0\text{°C}}{1.8\text{°F}}\right)\left(\frac{1.00\text{ lb°F}}{1\text{ Btu}}\right)$ = 1054.368 = **1.1x10³ J/Btu**

b) $E = (1.00\text{ therm})\left(\frac{100{,}000\text{ Btu}}{1\text{ therm}}\right)\left(\frac{1054.368\text{ J}}{\text{Btu}}\right)$ = 1.054368x10⁸ = **1.1x10⁸ J**

c) $CH_4(g) + 2O_2(g) \rightarrow CO_2(g) + 2H_2O(g)$

$\Delta H^\circ_{rxn} = \{1\,\Delta H^\circ_f[CO_2(g)] + 2\,\Delta H^\circ_f[H_2O(g)]\} - \{1\,\Delta H^\circ_f[CH_4(g)] + 2\,\Delta H^\circ_f[O_2(g)]\}$

= [(1 mol)(–393.5 kJ/mol) + (2 mol)(–241.826 kJ/mol)] – [(1 mol)(–74.87 kJ/mol) + (2 mol)(0.0 kJ/mol)]

= –802.282 = –802.3 kJ/mol CH_4

Moles of CH_4 = $(1.00\text{ therm})\left(\frac{1.054368\text{x}10^8\text{ J}}{1\text{ therm}}\right)\left(\frac{1\text{ kJ}}{10^3\text{ J}}\right)\left(\frac{1\text{ mol CH}_4}{802.282\text{ kJ}}\right)$

= 131.4211 = **1.3x10² mol CH₄**

d) Cost = $\left(\frac{\$0.66}{\text{therm}}\right)\left(\frac{1\text{ therm}}{131.4211\text{ mol}}\right)$ = 0.005022 = **$0.0050/mol**

e) Mass (g) of = $(318\text{ gal})\left(\frac{4\text{ qt}}{1\text{ gal}}\right)\left(\frac{1\text{ L}}{1.057\text{ qt}}\right)\left(\frac{1\text{ mL}}{10^{-3}\text{ L}}\right)\left(\frac{1.0\text{ g}}{\text{mL}}\right)$ = 1.203406x10⁶ g

$q = c \text{ x mass x } \Delta T = \left(\frac{4.184\text{ J}}{\text{g°C}}\right)(1.203406\text{x}10^6\text{ g})((42.0 - 15.0)\text{°C}) = 1.359464\text{x}10^8\text{ J}$

Cost = $(1.359494\text{x}10^8\text{ J})\left(\frac{1\text{ therm}}{1.054368\text{x}10^8\text{ J}}\right)\left(\frac{\$0.66}{1\text{ therm}}\right)$ = 0.850999 = **$0.85**

6.100 Plan: Heat of reaction is calculated using the relationship $\Delta H^\circ_{rxn} = \Sigma m\,\Delta H^\circ_{f\,(products)} - \Sigma n\,\Delta H^\circ_{f\,(reactants)}$. The heats of formation for all of the species, except $SiCl_4$, are found in Appendix B. Use reaction 3, with its given ΔH°_{rxn}, to find the heat of formation of $SiCl_4(g)$. Once the heat of formation of $SiCl_4$ is known, the heat of reaction of the other two reactions can be calculated. When reactions 2 and 3 are added to obtain a fourth reaction, the heats of reaction of reactions 2 and 3 are also added to obtain the heat of reaction for the fourth reaction.

Solution:

a) (3) $SiCl_4(g) + 2H_2O(g) \rightarrow SiO_2(s) + 4HCl(g)$

$\Delta H^\circ_{rxn} = \{1\,\Delta H^\circ_f[SiO_2(s)] + 4\,\Delta H^\circ_f[HCl(g)]\} - \{1\,\Delta H^\circ_f[SiCl_4(g)] + 2\,\Delta H^\circ_f[H_2O(g)]\}$

–139.5 kJ = [(1 mol)(–910.9 kJ/mol) + (4 mol)(–92.31 kJ/mol)] – [$\Delta H^\circ_f[SiCl_4(g)]$ + (2 mol)(–241.826 kJ/mol)]

–139.5 kJ = –1280.14 – [$\Delta H^\circ_f[SiCl_4(g)]$ + (–483.652 kJ)]

1140.64 kJ = –$\Delta H^\circ_f[SiCl_4(g)]$ + 483.652 kJ

$\Delta H^\circ_f[SiCl_4(g)]$ = –656.988 kJ/mol

The heats of reaction for the first two steps can now be calculated.

1) $Si(s) + 2Cl_2(g) \rightarrow SiCl_4(g)$

$\Delta H^\circ_{rxn} = \{1\,\Delta H^\circ_f[SiCl_4(g)]\} - \{1\,\Delta H^\circ_f[Si(s)] + 2\,\Delta H^\circ_f[Cl_2(g)]\}$

= [(1 mol)(–656.988 kJ/mol)] – [(1 mol)(0 kJ/mol) + (2 mol)(0 kJ/mol)] = –656.988 = **–657.0 kJ**

2) $SiO_2(s) + 2C(\text{graphite}) + 2Cl_2(g) \rightarrow SiCl_4(g) + 2CO(g)$

$\Delta H^\circ_{rxn} = \{1\,\Delta H^\circ_f[SiCl_4(g)] + 2\,\Delta H^\circ_f[CO(g)]\}$

$- \{1\,\Delta H^\circ_f[SiO_2(g)] + 2\,\Delta H^\circ_f[C(\text{graphite})] + 2\,\Delta H^\circ_f[Cl_2(g)]\}$

= [(1 mol)(–656.988 kJ/mol) + (2 mol)(–110.5 kJ/mol)]

– [(1 mol)(–910.9 kJ/mol) + (2 mol)(0 kJ/mol) + (2 mol)(0 kJ/mol)]

= 32.912 = **32.9 kJ**

b) Adding reactions 2 and 3 yields:

(2) ~~$SiO_2(s)$~~ + 2C(graphite) + $2Cl_2(g)$ → ~~$SiCl_4(g)$~~ + 2CO(g) ΔH°_{rxn} = 32.912 kJ

(3) ~~$SiCl_4(g)$~~ + $2H_2O(g)$ → ~~$SiO_2(s)$~~ + 4HCl(g) ΔH°_{rxn} = –139.5 kJ

2C(graphite) + $2Cl_2(g)$ + $2H_2O(g)$ → 2CO(g) + 4HCl(g) ΔH°_{rxn} = –106.588 kJ = **–106.6 kJ**

Confirm this result by calculating ΔH°_{rxn} using Appendix B values.

2C(graphite) + $2Cl_2(g)$ + $2H_2O(g)$ → 2CO(g) + 4HCl(g)

$\Delta H^\circ_{rxn} = \{2\,\Delta H^\circ_f\,[CO(g)] + 4\,\Delta H^\circ_f\,[HCl(g)]\} - \{2\,\Delta H^\circ_f\,[C(graphite)] + 2\,\Delta H^\circ_f\,[Cl_2(g)] + 2\,\Delta H^\circ_f\,[H_2O(g)]\}$

= [(2 mol)(–110.5 kJ/mol) + (4 mol)(–92.31 kJ)]
– [(2 mol)(0 kJ/mol) + (2 mol)(0 kJ/mol) + (2 mol)(–241.826 kJ/mol)]

= –106.588 = **–106.6 kJ**

6.101 Plan: Use $PV = nRT$ to find the initial volume of nitrogen gas at 0°C and then the final volume at 819°C. Then the relationship $w = -P\Delta V$ can be used to calculate the work of expansion.

Solution:

a) $PV = nRT$

Initial volume at 0°C + 273 = 273 K = $V = \frac{nRT}{P} = \frac{(1\text{ mol})\left(0.0821\frac{\text{L•atm}}{\text{mol•K}}\right)(273\text{ K})}{(1.00\text{ atm})} = 22.4133\text{ L}$

Final volume at 819°C + 273 = 1092 K = $V = \frac{nRT}{P} = \frac{(1\text{ mol})\left(0.0821\frac{\text{L•atm}}{\text{mol•K}}\right)(1092\text{ K})}{(1.00\text{ atm})} = 89.6532\text{ L}$

$\Delta V = V_{final} - V_{initial}$ = 89.6532 L – 22.4133 L = 67.2399 L

$w = -P\Delta V$ = –(1 atm) x 67.2399 L = –67.2399 atm•L

$w\text{ (J)} = (-67.2399\text{ atm•L})\left(\frac{1\text{ J}}{9.87\times 10^{-3}\text{ atm•L}}\right) = -6812.553 = \mathbf{-6.81x10^3\ J}$

b) $q = c$ x mass x ΔT

Mass (g) of N_2 = $(1\text{ mol }N_2)\left(\frac{28.02\text{ g}}{1\text{ mol }N_2}\right) = 28.02\text{ g}$

$\Delta T = \frac{q}{(c)(\text{mass})} = \frac{6.812553\times 10^3\text{ J}}{(28.02\text{ g})(1.00\text{ J/g•K})}$ = 243.132 = 243 K = **243°C**

6.102 Plan: Note the numbers of moles of the reactants and products in the target equation and manipulate equations 1-5 and their ΔH°_{rxn} values so that these equations sum to give the target equation. Then the manipulated ΔH°_{rxn} values will add to give the ΔH°_{rxn} value of the target equation.

Solution:

Only reaction 3 contains $N_2O_4(g)$, and only reaction 1 contains $N_2O_3(g)$, so we can use those reactions as a starting point. N_2O_5 appears in both reactions 2 and 5, but note the physical states present: solid and gas. As a rough start, adding reactions 1, 3, and 5 yields the desired reactants and products, with some undesired intermediates:

Reverse (1) $N_2O_3(g) \rightarrow NO(g) + NO_2(g)$ ΔH°_{rxn} = –(–39.8 kJ) = 39.8 kJ

Multiply (3) by 2 $4NO_2(g) \rightarrow 2N_2O_4(g)$ ΔH°_{rxn} = 2(–57.2 kJ) = –114.4 kJ

(5) $N_2O_5(s) \rightarrow N_2O_5(g)$ ΔH°_{rxn} = (54.1 kJ) = 54.1 kJ

$N_2O_3(g) + 4NO_2(g) + N_2O_5(s) \rightarrow NO(g) + NO_2(g) + 2N_2O_4(g) + N_2O_5(g)$

To cancel out the $N_2O_5(g)$ intermediate, reverse equation 2. This also cancels out some of the undesired $NO_2(g)$ but adds $NO(g)$ and $O_2(g)$. Finally, add equation 4 to remove those intermediates:

Reverse (1)	$N_2O_3(g) \rightarrow \cancel{NO(g)} + \cancel{NO_2(g)}$	$\Delta H^\circ_{rxn} = -(-39.8\text{ kJ}) =$	39.8 kJ
Multiply (3) by 2	$\cancel{4NO_2(g)} \rightarrow 2N_2O_4(g)$	$\Delta H^\circ_{rxn} = 2(-57.2\text{ kJ}) =$	-114.4 kJ
(5)	$N_2O_5(s) \rightarrow \cancel{N_2O_5(g)}$	$\Delta H^\circ_{rxn} =$	54.1 kJ
Reverse (2)	$\cancel{N_2O_5(g)} \rightarrow \cancel{NO(g)} + \cancel{NO_2(g)} + \cancel{O_2(g)}$	$\Delta H^\circ_{rxn} = -(-112.5\text{ kJ}) =$	112.5
(4)	$\cancel{2NO(g)} + \cancel{O_2(g)} \rightarrow \cancel{2NO_2(g)}$	$\Delta H^\circ_{rxn} =$	-114.2 kJ
Total:	$N_2O_3(g) + N_2O_5(s) \rightarrow 2N_2O_4(g)$	$\Delta H^\circ_{rxn} =$	**-22.2 kJ**

6.103 Plan: The enthalpy change of a reaction is the sum of the heats of formation of the products minus the sum of the heats of formation of the reactants. Since the ΔH°_f values (Appendix B) are reported as energy per one mole, use the appropriate stoichiometric coefficient to reflect the higher number of moles. In this case, ΔH°_{rxn} of the second reaction is known and ΔH°_f of $N_2H_4(aq)$ must be calculated. For part b), calculate ΔH°_{rxn} for the reaction between $N_2H_4(aq)$ and O_2, using the value of ΔH°_f for $N_2H_4(aq)$ found in part a); then determine the moles of O_2 present by multiplying volume and molarity and multiply by the ΔH°_{rxn} for the reaction.

Solution:

a) $2NH_3(aq) + NaOCl(aq) \rightarrow N_2H_4(aq) + NaCl(aq) + H_2O(l)$

$$\Delta H^\circ_{rxn} = \{1\,\Delta H^\circ_f[N_2H_4(aq)] + 1\,\Delta H^\circ_f[NaCl(aq)] + 1\,\Delta H^\circ_f[H_2O(l)]\} - \{2\,\Delta H^\circ_f[NH_3(aq)] + 1\,\Delta H^\circ_f[NaOCl(aq)]\}$$

Note that the Appendix B value for N_2H_4 is for $N_2H_4(l)$, not for $N_2H_4(aq)$, so this term must be calculated. In addition, Appendix B does not list a value for $NaCl(aq)$, so this term must be broken down into $\Delta H^\circ_f[Na^+(aq)]$ and $\Delta H^\circ_f[Cl^-(aq)]$.

$$-151\text{ kJ} = [\Delta H^\circ_f[N_2H_4(aq)] + (1\text{ mol})(-239.66\text{ kJ/mol}) + (1\text{ mol})(-167.46\text{ kJ/mol}) + (1\text{ mol})(-285.840\text{ kJ/mol})] - [(2\text{ mol})(-80.83\text{ kJ/mol}) + (1\text{ mol})(-346\text{ kJ/mol})]$$

$$-151\text{ kJ} = [\Delta H^\circ_f[N_2H_4(aq)] + (-692.96\text{ kJ})] - [-507.66\text{ kJ}]$$

$$-151\text{ kJ} = [\Delta H^\circ_f[N_2H_4(aq)] + (-185.3\text{ kJ})$$

$\Delta H^\circ_f[N_2H_4(aq)] = 34.3 =$ **34 kJ**

b) Moles of $O_2 = (5.00\text{x}10^3\text{ L})\left(\frac{2.50\text{x}10^{-4}\text{ mol}}{1\text{ L}}\right) = 1.25\text{ mol }O_2$

$N_2H_4(aq) + O_2(g) \rightarrow N_2(g) + 2H_2O(l)$

$$\Delta H^\circ_{rxn} = \{1\,\Delta H^\circ_f[N_2(g)] + 2\,\Delta H^\circ_f[H_2O(l)]\} - \{1\,\Delta H^\circ_f[N_2H_4(aq)] + 1\,\Delta H^\circ_f[O_2(g)]\}$$
$$= [(1\text{ mol})(0\text{ kJ/mol}) + (2\text{ mol})(-285.840\text{ kJ/mol})] - [(1\text{ mol})(34.3\text{ kJ/mol}) + (1\text{ mol})(0\text{ kJ/mol}]$$
$$= -605.98\text{ kJ}$$

Heat (kJ) $= (1.25\text{ mol }O_2)\left(\frac{-605.98\text{ kJ}}{1\text{ mol }O_2}\right) = -757.475 =$ **-757 kJ**

6.105 Plan: First find the heat of reaction for the combustion of methane. The enthalpy change of a reaction is the sum of the heats of formation of the products minus the sum of the heats of formation of the reactants. Since the ΔH_f° values (Appendix B) are reported as energy per one mole, use the appropriate stoichiometric coefficient to reflect the higher number of moles. Convert the mass of methane to moles and multiply that mole number by the heat of combustion.

Solution:

a) The balanced chemical equation for this reaction is:

$CH_4(g) + 2O_2(g) \rightarrow CO_2(g) + 2H_2O(g)$

$$\Delta H_{rxn}^\circ = \{1\,\Delta H_f^\circ[CO_2(g)] + 2\,\Delta H_f^\circ[H_2O(g)]\} - \{1\,\Delta H_f^\circ[CH_4(g)] + 2\,\Delta H_f^\circ[O_2(g)]\}$$
$$= [(1\text{ mol})(-393.5\text{ kJ/mol}) + (2\text{ mol})(-241.826\text{ kJ/mol})] - [(1\text{mol})(-74.87\text{ kJ/mol}) + (2\text{ mol})(0.0\text{ kJ/mol})]$$
$$= -802.282\text{ kJ}$$

$$\text{Moles of } CH_4 = (25.0\text{ g } CH_4)\left(\frac{1\text{ mol}}{16.04\text{ g } CH_4}\right) = 1.5586\text{ mol } CH_4$$

$$\text{Heat (kJ)} = (1.5586\text{ mol } CH_4)\left(\frac{-802.282\text{ kJ}}{1\text{ mol } CH_4}\right) = -1250.4 = \mathbf{-1.25x10^3\ kJ}$$

b) The heat released by the reaction is "stored" in the gaseous molecules by virtue of their specific heat capacities, c, using the equation $q = c$ x mass x ΔT. The problem specifies heat capacities on a molar basis, so we modify the equation to use moles, instead of mass. The gases that remain at the end of the reaction are CO_2 and H_2O. All of the methane and oxygen molecules were consumed. However, the oxygen was added as a component of air, which is 78% N_2 and 21% O_2, and there is leftover N_2.

$$\text{Moles of } CO_2(g) = (1.5586\text{ mol } CH_4)\left(\frac{1\text{ mol } CO_2}{1\text{ mol } CH_4}\right) = 1.5586\text{ mol } CO_2(g)$$

$$\text{Moles of } H_2O(g) = (1.5586\text{ mol } CH_4)\left(\frac{2\text{ mol } H_2O}{1\text{ mol } CH_4}\right) = 3.1172\text{ mol } H_2O(g)$$

$$\text{Moles of } O_2(g)\text{ reacted} = (1.5586\text{ mol } CH_4)\left(\frac{2\text{ mol } O_2}{1\text{ mol } CH_4}\right) = 3.1172\text{ mol } O_2(g)$$

Mole fraction N_2 = (79%/100%) = 0.79

Mole fraction O_2 = (21%/100%) = 0.21

$$\text{Moles of } N_2(g) = (3.1172\text{ mol } O_2\text{ reacted})\left(\frac{0.79\text{ mol } N_2}{0.21\text{ mol } O_2}\right) = 11.72661\text{ mol } N_2$$

$q = c$ x mass x ΔT

$$q = (1250.4\text{ kJ})\left(\frac{10^3\text{ J}}{1\text{ kJ}}\right) = 1.2504x10^6\text{ J}$$

$$1.2504x10^6\text{ J} = (1.5586\text{ mol } CO_2)(57.2\text{ J/mol°C})(T_{final} - 0.0)°C$$
$$+ (3.1172\text{ mol } H_2O)(36.0\text{ J/mol°C})(T_{final} - 0.0)°C$$
$$+ (11.72661\text{ mol } N_2)(30.5\text{ J/mol°C})(T_{final} - 0.0)°C$$

$$1.2504x10^6\text{ J} = 89.15192\text{ J/°C}(T_{final}) + 112.2192\text{ J/°C}(T_{final}) + 357.6616\text{ J/°C}(T_{final})$$

$$1.2504x10^6\text{ J} = (559.03272\text{ J/°C})T_{final}$$

$$T_{final} = (1.2504x10^6\text{ J})/(559.0324\text{ J/°C}) = 2236.72 = \mathbf{2.24x10^3 °C}$$

CHAPTER 7 QUANTUM THEORY AND ATOMIC STRUCTURE

The value for the speed of light will be $3.00\text{x}10^8$ m/s except when more significant figures are necessary, in which cases, $2.9979\text{x}10^8$ m/s will be used.

FOLLOW–UP PROBLEMS

7.1A Plan: Given the frequency of the light, use the equation $c = \lambda\nu$ to solve for wavelength.
Solution:

$$\lambda = \frac{c}{\nu} = \frac{3.00\text{x}10^8\ \text{m/s}}{7.23\text{x}10^{14}\ \text{s}^{-1}}\left(\frac{1\ \text{nm}}{10^{-9}\ \text{m}}\right) = 414.938 = \mathbf{415\ nm}$$

$$\lambda = \frac{c}{\nu} = \frac{3.00\text{x}10^8\ \text{m/s}}{7.23\text{x}10^{14}\ \text{s}^{-1}}\left(\frac{1\ \text{Å}}{10^{-10}\ \text{m}}\right) = 4149.38 = \mathbf{4150\ Å}$$

7.1B Plan: Given the wavelength of the light, use the equation $c = \lambda\nu$ to solve for frequency. Remember that wavelength must be in units of m in this equation.
Solution:

$$\nu = \frac{c}{\lambda} = \left(\frac{3.00\text{x}10^8\ \text{m/s}}{940\ \text{nm}}\right)\left(\frac{10^9\ \text{nm}}{1\ \text{m}}\right) = 3.1915\text{x}10^{14} = \mathbf{3.2x10^{14}\ s^{-1}}$$

This is **infrared** radiation.

7.2A Plan: Use the formula $E = h\nu$ to solve for the frequency. Then use the equation $c = \lambda\nu$ to solve for the wavelength.
Solution:

$$\nu = \frac{E}{h} = \left(\frac{8.2\text{x}10^{-19}\ \text{J}}{6.626\text{x}10^{-34}\ \text{J•s}}\right) = 1.2375\text{x}10^{15} = \mathbf{1.2x10^{15}\ s^{-1}}$$

(using the unrounded number in the next calculation to avoid rounding errors)

$$\lambda = \frac{c}{\nu} = \left(\frac{3.00\text{x}10^8\ \text{m/s}}{1.2375\text{x}10^{15}\ \text{s}^{-1}}\right)\left(\frac{10^9\ \text{nm}}{1\ \text{m}}\right) = \mathbf{240\ nm}$$

7.2B Plan: To calculate the energy for each wavelength we use the formula $E = hc/\lambda$.
Solution:

$$E = \frac{hc}{\lambda} = \frac{(6.626\text{x}10^{-34}\ \text{J}\cdot\text{s})(3.00\text{x}10^8\ \text{m/s})}{1\text{x}10^{-8}\ \text{m}} = 1.9878\text{x}10^{-17} = \mathbf{2x10^{-17}\ J}$$

$$E = \frac{hc}{\lambda} = \frac{(6.626\text{x}10^{-34}\ \text{J}\cdot\text{s})(3.00\text{x}10^8\ \text{m/s})}{5\text{x}10^{-7}\ \text{m}} = 3.9756\text{x}10^{-19} = \mathbf{4x10^{-19}\ J}$$

$$E = \frac{hc}{\lambda} = \frac{(6.626\text{x}10^{-34}\ \text{J}\cdot\text{s})(3.00\text{x}10^8\ \text{m/s})}{1\text{x}10^{-4}\ \text{m}} = 1.9878\text{x}10^{-21} = \mathbf{2x10^{-21}\ J}$$

As the wavelength of light increases from ultraviolet to visible to infrared, the energy of the light decreases.

7.3A Plan: Use the equation relating $\Delta E = -2.18\text{x}10^{-18}\text{ J}\left(\dfrac{1}{n^2_{\text{final}}} - \dfrac{1}{n^2_{\text{initial}}}\right)$ to find the energy change; a photon in the IR (infrared) region is emitted when has n has a final value of 3. Then use $E = hc/\lambda$ to find the wavelength of the photon.

Solution:

a) $$\Delta E = -2.18\text{x}10^{-18}\text{ J}\left(\frac{1}{n^2_{\text{final}}} - \frac{1}{n^2_{\text{initial}}}\right)$$

$$\Delta E = -2.18\text{x}10^{-18}\text{ J}\left(\frac{1}{3^2} - \frac{1}{6^2}\right)$$

$$\Delta E = -1.8166667\text{x}10^{-19} = \mathbf{-1.82x10^{-19}\ J}$$

b) $$E = \frac{hc}{\lambda}$$

$$\lambda = \frac{hc}{E} = \frac{\left(6.626\text{x}10^{-34}\text{ J}\bullet\text{s}\right)\left(3.00\text{x}10^{8}\text{ m/s}\right)}{1.8166667\text{x}10^{-19}\text{ J}}\left(\frac{1\text{ Å}}{10^{-10}\text{ m}}\right) = 1.094202\text{x}10^{4} = \mathbf{1.09x10^{4}\ Å}$$

7.3B Plan: Use the equation $E = hc/\lambda$ to find the energy change for this reaction. Then use the equation $\Delta E = -2.18\text{x}10^{-18}\text{ J}\left(\dfrac{1}{n^2_{\text{final}}} - \dfrac{1}{n^2_{\text{initial}}}\right)$ to find the final energy level to which the electron moved.

Solution:

a) $$\Delta E = hc/\lambda = \left(\frac{(6.626\text{x}10^{-34}\text{ J•s})\ (3.00\text{x}10^{8}\text{ m/s})}{410.\text{ nm}}\right)\left(\frac{10^{9}\text{ nm}}{1\text{ m}}\right) = \Delta E = 4.8483\text{x}10^{-19} = 4.85\text{x}10^{-19}\text{ J}$$

Because the photon is emitted, energy is being given off, so the sign of ΔE should be negative. Therefore, $\Delta E = -4.85\text{x}10^{-19}\text{ J}$

$$\Delta E\ (\text{kJ/mol}) = \left(\frac{-4.85\text{x}10^{-19}\text{ J}}{1\text{ H atom}}\right)\left(\frac{6.022\text{x}10^{23}\text{ H atoms}}{1\text{ mol H}}\right)\left(\frac{1\text{ kJ}}{1000\text{ J}}\right) = \mathbf{-292\ kJ/mol}$$ (number of atoms is a positive number)

b) $$\Delta E = -2.18\text{x}10^{-18}\text{ J}\left(\frac{1}{n^2_{\text{final}}} - \frac{1}{n^2_{\text{initial}}}\right)$$

$$\frac{1}{n^2_{\text{final}}} = \frac{\Delta E}{-2.18\text{x}10^{-18}\text{ J}} + \frac{1}{n^2_{\text{initial}}}$$

$$\frac{1}{n^2_{\text{final}}} = \frac{-4.85\text{x}10^{-19}\text{ J}}{-2.18\text{x}10^{-18}\text{ J}} + \frac{1}{6^2}$$

$$\frac{1}{n^2_{\text{final}}} = 0.25025$$

$n^2_{\text{final}} = 3.9960 = 4$ (The final energy level is an integer, so its square is also an integer.)

$\mathbf{n_{final} = 2}$

7.4A Plan: With the equation for the de Broglie wavelength, $\lambda = h/mu$ and the given de Broglie wavelength, calculate the electron speed. The wavelength must be expressed in meters. Use the same formulas to calculate the speed of the golf ball. The mass of both the electron and the golf ball must be expressed in kg in their respective calculations.

Solution:

a) $\lambda = h/mu$

$$u = \frac{h}{m\lambda} = \frac{6.626\text{x}10^{-34}\ \text{J} \bullet \text{s}}{\left(9.11\text{x}10^{-31}\ \text{kg}\right)\left[(100.\text{nm})\left(\frac{10^{-9}\ \text{m}}{1\ \text{nm}}\right)\right]}\left(\frac{\text{kg} \bullet \text{m}^2/\text{s}^2}{\text{J}}\right) = 7273.3 = \mathbf{7.27x10^3\ m/s}$$

b) Mass (kg) of the golf ball = (45.9 g) $\left(\frac{1\ \text{kg}}{1000\ \text{g}}\right)$ = 0.0459 kg

$$u = \frac{h}{m\lambda} = \frac{6.626\text{x}10^{-34}\ \text{J}\bullet\text{s}}{(0.0459\ \text{kg})\left[(100.\ \text{nm})\left(\frac{10^{-9}}{1\ \text{nm}}\right)\right]}\left(\frac{\text{kg}\bullet\text{m}^2/\text{s}^2}{\text{J}}\right) = 1.4436\text{x}10^{-25} = \mathbf{1.44x10^{-25}\ m/s}$$

7.4B Plan: Use the equation for the de Broglie wavelength, $\lambda = h/mu$ with the given mass and speed to calculate the de Broglie wavelength of the racquetball. The mass of the racquetball must be expressed in kg, and the speed must be expressed in m/s in the equation for the de Broglie wavelength.

Solution:

Mass (kg) of the racquetball = (39.7 g) $\left(\frac{1\ \text{kg}}{1000\ \text{g}}\right)$ = 0.0397 kg

Speed (m/s) of the racquetball = $\left(\frac{55\ \text{mi}}{\text{hr}}\right)\left(\frac{1\ \text{hr}}{3600\ \text{s}}\right)\left(\frac{1.609\ \text{km}}{\text{mi}}\right)\left(\frac{1000\ \text{m}}{1\ \text{km}}\right)$ = 24.5819 = 25 m/s

$\lambda = h/mu$

$$\lambda = \frac{h}{mu} = \frac{6.626\text{x}10^{-34}\ \text{J}\bullet\text{s}}{(0.0397\ \text{kg})(25\ \text{m/s})} = 6.67607\text{x}10^{-34} = \mathbf{6.7x10^{-34}\ m}$$

7.5A Plan: Use the equation $\Delta x \bullet m\Delta u \geq \frac{h}{4\pi}$ to solve for the uncertainty (Δx) in position of the baseball.

Solution:

$$\Delta x \bullet m\Delta u \geq \frac{h}{4\pi}$$

Δu = 1% of u = 0.0100(44.7 m/s) = 0.447 m/s

$$\Delta x \geq \frac{h}{4\pi m\Delta u} = \frac{6.626\text{x}10^{-34}\ \text{J} \bullet \text{s}}{4\pi(0.142\ \text{kg})(0.447\ \text{m/s})} = 8.3070285\text{x}10^{-34}$$

$\Delta x \geq \mathbf{8.31x10^{-34}\ m}$

7.5B Plan: Use the equation $\Delta x \bullet m\Delta u \geq \frac{h}{4\pi}$ to solve for the uncertainty (Δx) in position of the neutron.

Solution:

$$\Delta x \bullet m\Delta u \geq \frac{h}{4\pi}$$

Δu = 1% of u = 0.0100(8x10^7 m/s) = 8x10^5 m/s

$$\Delta x \geq \frac{h}{4\pi m\Delta u} = \frac{6.626\text{x}10^{-34}\ \text{J}\bullet\text{s}}{4\pi\left(1.67\text{x}10^{-27}\ \text{kg}\right)(8\text{x}10^5\text{m/s})} = 3.9467\text{x}10^{-14}\ \text{m}$$

$\Delta x \geq \mathbf{4x10^{-14}\ m}$

7.6A Plan: Following the rules for l (integer from 0 to n – 1) and m_l (integer from $-l$ to $+l$), write quantum numbers for n = 4.

Solution:

For n = 4 $\quad l$ = **0, 1, 2, 3**

For l = 0, m_l = **0**

For $l = 1$, $m_l =$ **–1, 0, 1**
For $l = 2$, $m_l =$ **–2, –1, 0, 1, 2**
For $l = 3$, $m_l =$ **–3, –2, –1, 0, 1, 2, 3**

7.6B Plan: Following the rules for l (integer from 0 to $n - 1$) and m_l (integer from $-l$ to $+l$), determine which value of the principal quantum number has five allowed levels of l.
Solution:
The number of possible l values is equal to n, so the $\boldsymbol{n = 5}$ principal quantum number has five allowed values of l.
For $n = 5$ $l =$ **0, 1, 2, 3, 4**
For $l = 0$, $m_l =$ **0**
For $l = 1$, $m_l =$ **–1, 0, 1**
For $l = 2$, $m_l =$ **–2, –1, 0, 1, 2**
For $l = 3$, $m_l =$ **–3, –2, –1, 0, 1, 2, 3**
For $l = 4$, $m_l =$ **–4, –3, –2, –1, 0, 1, 2, 3, 4**

7.7A Plan: Identify n and l from the sublevel designation. n is the integer in front of the sublevel letter. The sublevels are given a letter designation, in which s represents $l = 0$, p represents $l = 1$, d represents $l = 2$, f represents $l = 3$. Knowing the value for l, find the m_l values (integer from $-l$ to $+l$).
Solution:

Sublevel name	n value	l value	m_l values
$2p$	2	1	–1, 0, 1
$5f$	5	3	–3, –2, –1, 0, 1, 2, 3

7.7B Plan: Identify n and l from the sublevel designation. n is the integer in front of the sublevel letter. The sublevels are given a letter designation, in which s represents $l = 0$, p represents $l = 1$, d represents $l = 2$, f represents $l = 3$. Knowing the value for l, find the m_l values (integer from $-l$ to $+l$).
Solution:

Sublevel name	n value	l value	m_l values
$4d$	4	2	–2, –1, 0, 1, 2
$6s$	6	0	0

The number of orbitals for each sublevel equals $2l + 1$. Sublevel $4d$ should have **5 orbitals** and sublevel $6s$ should have **1 orbital**. Both of these agree with the number of m_l values for the sublevel.

7.8A Plan: Use the rules for designating quantum numbers to fill in the blanks.
For a given n, l can be any integer from 0 to n–1.
For a given l, m_l can be any integer from $-l$ to $+l$.
The sublevels are given a letter designation, in which s represents $l = 0$, p represents $l = 1$, d represents $l = 2$, f represents $l = 3$.
Solution:
The completed table is:

	n	l	m_l	Name
a)	4	1	0	$4p$
b)	2	1	0	$2p$
c)	3	2	–2	$3d$
d)	2	0	0	$2s$

7.8B Plan: Use the rules for designating quantum numbers to determine what is wrong with the quantum number designations provided in the problem.
For a given n, l can be any integer from 0 to n–1.
For a given l, m_l can be any integer from $-l$ to $+l$.
The sublevels are given a letter designation, in which s represents $l = 0$, p represents $l = 1$, d represents $l = 2$, f represents $l = 3$.

Solution:
The provided table is:

	n	l	m_l	Name
a)	5	3	4	5*f*
b)	2	2	1	2*d*
c)	6	1	–1	6*s*

a) For $l = 3$, the allowed values for m_l are –3, –2, –1, 0, 1, 2, 3, not 4
b) For n = 2, $l = 0$ or 1 only, not 2; the sublevel is 2*p*, since $m_l = 1$.
c) The value $l = 1$ indicates the *p* sublevel, not the *s*; the sublevel name is 6*p*.

TOOLS OF THE LABORATORY BOXED READING PROBLEMS

B7.1 Plan: Plot absorbance on the *y*-axis and concentration on the *x*-axis. Since this is a linear plot, the graph is of the type $y = mx + b$, with m = slope and b = intercept. Any two points may be used to find the slope, and the slope is used to find the intercept. Once the equation for the line is known, the absorbance of the solution in part b) is used to find the concentration of the diluted solution, after which the dilution equation is used to find the molarity of the original solution.
Solution:
a) Absorbance vs. Concentration:

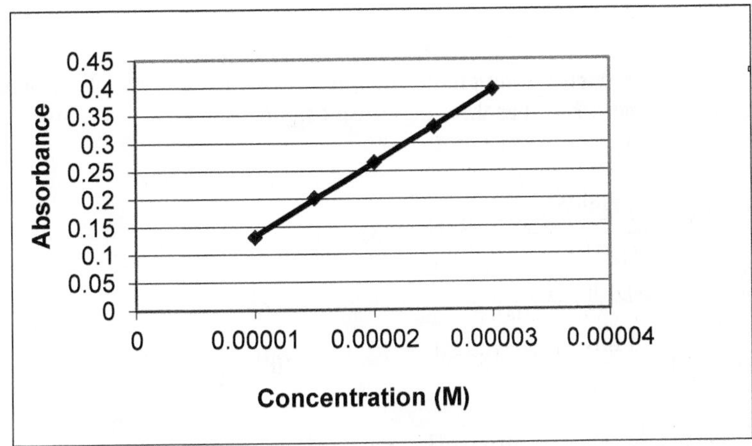

This is a linear plot, thus, using the first and last points given:

$$m = \frac{y_2 - y_1}{x_2 - x_1} = \frac{(0.396 - 0.131)}{\left(3.0\text{x}10^{-5} - 1.0\text{x}10^{-5}\right)M} = 13{,}250 = \mathbf{1.3x10^4/}\boldsymbol{M}$$

Using the slope just calculated and any of the data points, the value of the intercept may be found.
$b = y - mx = 0.396 - (13{,}250/M)(3.0\text{x}10^{-5}\ M) = -0.0015 = \mathbf{0.00}$ (absorbance has no units)
b) Use the equation just determined: $y = (1.3\text{x}10^4/M)\,x + 0.00$.
$x = (y - 0.00)/(1.3\text{x}10^4/M) = (0.236/1.3\text{x}10^4)\ M = 1.81538\text{x}10^{-5}\ M = \mathbf{1.8x10^{-5}}\ \boldsymbol{M}$
This value is M_f in a dilution problem (M_iV_i)= (M_fV_f) with V_i = 20.0 mL and V_f = 150. mL.

$$M_i = \frac{(M_f)(V_f)}{(V_i)} = \frac{\left(1.81538\text{x}10^{-5}\ M\right)(150.\ \text{mL})}{(20.0\ \text{mL})} = 1.361538\text{x}10^{-4} = \mathbf{1.4x10^{-4}}\ \boldsymbol{M}$$

B7.2 Plan: The color of light associated with each wavelength can be found from Figure 7.3. The frequency of each wavelength can be determined from the relationship $c = \lambda\nu$ or $\nu = \dfrac{c}{\lambda}$. The wavelength in nm must be converted to meters.

Solution:

a) red $\nu = \frac{3.00\text{x}10^8 \text{ m/s}}{671 \text{ nm}}\left(\frac{1 \text{ nm}}{10^{-9} \text{ m}}\right) = 4.4709\text{x}10^{14} = \mathbf{4.47x10^{14}\ s^{-1}}$

b) blue $\nu = \frac{3.00\text{x}10^8 \text{ m/s}}{453 \text{ nm}}\left(\frac{1 \text{ nm}}{10^{-9} \text{ m}}\right) = 6.6225\text{x}10^{14} = \mathbf{6.62x10^{14}\ s^{-1}}$

c) yellow-orange $\nu = \frac{3.00\text{x}10^8 \text{ m/s}}{589 \text{ nm}}\left(\frac{1 \text{ nm}}{10^{-9} \text{ m}}\right) = 5.0933786\text{x}10^{14} = \mathbf{5.09x10^{14}\ s^{-1}}$

END–OF–CHAPTER PROBLEMS

7.2 Plan: Recall that the shorter the wavelength, the higher the frequency and the greater the energy. Figure 7.3 describes the electromagnetic spectrum by wavelength and frequency.
Solution:
a) Wavelength increases from left (10^{-2} nm) to right (10^{12} nm) in Figure 7.3. The trend in increasing wavelength is: **x-ray < ultraviolet < visible < infrared < microwave < radio wave.**
b) Frequency is inversely proportional to wavelength according to the equation $c = \lambda\nu$, so frequency has the opposite trend: **radio wave < microwave < infrared < visible < ultraviolet < x-ray.**
c) Energy is directly proportional to frequency according to the equation $E = h\nu$. Therefore, the trend in increasing energy matches the trend in increasing frequency: **radio wave < microwave < infrared < visible < ultraviolet < x-ray.**

7.7 Plan: Wavelength is related to frequency through the equation $c = \lambda\nu$. Recall that a Hz is a reciprocal second, or $1/\text{s} = \text{s}^{-1}$. Assume that the number "950" has three significant figures.
Solution:
$c = \lambda\nu$

$$\lambda\ (\text{m}) = \frac{c}{\nu} = \frac{3.00\text{x}10^8 \text{ m/s}}{(950.\ \text{kHz})\left(\frac{10^3 \text{ Hz}}{1 \text{ kHz}}\right)\left(\frac{\text{s}^{-1}}{\text{Hz}}\right)} = 315.789 = \mathbf{316\ m}$$

$$\lambda\ (\text{nm}) = \frac{c}{\nu} = (315.789 \text{ m})\left(\frac{1 \text{ nm}}{10^{-9} \text{ m}}\right) = 3.15789\text{x}10^{11} = \mathbf{3.16x10^{11}\ nm}$$

$$\lambda\ (\text{Å}) = \frac{c}{\nu} = (315.789 \text{ m})\left(\frac{1 \text{ Å}}{10^{-10} \text{ m}}\right) = 3.158\text{x}10^{12} = \mathbf{3.16x10^{12}\ Å}$$

7.9 Plan: Frequency is related to energy through the equation $E = h\nu$. Note that 1 Hz = 1 s^{-1}.
Solution:
$E = h\nu$
$E = (6.626\text{x}10^{-34} \text{ J•s})(3.8\text{x}10^{10} \text{ s}^{-1}) = 2.51788\text{x}10^{-23} = \mathbf{2.5x10^{-23}\ J}$

7.11 Plan: Energy is inversely proportional to wavelength ($E = \frac{hc}{\lambda}$). As wavelength decreases, energy increases.
Solution:
In terms of increasing energy the order is **red < yellow < blue.**

7.13 Plan: Wavelength is related to frequency through the equation $c = \lambda\nu$. Recall that a Hz is a reciprocal second, or $1/\text{s} = \text{s}^{-1}$.
Solution:

$$\nu = (\text{s}^{-1}) = (22.235 \text{ GHz})\left(\frac{10^9 \text{ Hz}}{1 \text{ GHz}}\right)\left(\frac{\text{s}^{-1}}{\text{Hz}}\right) = 2.2235\text{x}10^{10} \text{ s}^{-1}$$

$$\lambda\,(\text{nm}) = \frac{c}{\nu} = \frac{2.9979\text{x}10^{8}\ \text{m/s}}{2.2235\text{x}10^{10}\ \text{s}^{-1}}\left(\frac{1\ \text{nm}}{10^{-9}\ \text{m}}\right) = 1.3482797\text{x}10^{7} = \mathbf{1.3483x10^{7}\ nm}$$

$$\lambda\,(\text{Å}) = \frac{c}{\nu} = \frac{2.9979\text{x}10^{8}\ \text{m/s}}{2.2235\text{x}10^{10}\ \text{s}^{-1}}\left(\frac{1\ \text{Å}}{10^{-10}\ \text{m}}\right) = 1.3482797\text{x}10^{8} = \mathbf{1.3483x10^{8}}\ \text{Å}$$

7.16 Plan: The least energetic photon in part a) has the longest wavelength (242 nm). The most energetic photon in part b) has the shortest wavelength (2200 Å). Use the relationship $c = \lambda\nu$ to find the frequency of the photons and relationship $E = \frac{hc}{\lambda}$ to find the energy.

Solution:
a) $c = \lambda\nu$

$$\nu = \frac{c}{\lambda} = \frac{3.00\text{x}10^{8}\ \text{m/s}}{242\ \text{nm}}\left(\frac{1\ \text{nm}}{10^{-9}\ \text{m}}\right) = 1.239669\text{x}10^{15} = \mathbf{1.24x10^{15}\ s^{-1}}$$

$$E = \frac{hc}{\lambda} = \frac{\left(6.626\text{x}10^{-34}\ \text{J•s}\right)\left(3.00\text{x}10^{8}\ \text{m/s}\right)}{242\ \text{nm}}\left(\frac{1\ \text{nm}}{10^{-9}\ \text{m}}\right) = 8.2140\text{x}10^{-19} = \mathbf{8.21x10^{-19}\ J}$$

b) $$\nu = \frac{c}{\lambda} = \frac{3.00\text{x}10^{8}\ \text{m/s}}{2200\ \text{Å}}\left(\frac{1\ \text{Å}}{10^{-10}\ \text{m}}\right) = 1.3636\text{x}10^{15} = \mathbf{1.4x10^{15}\ s^{-1}}$$

$$E = \frac{hc}{\lambda} = \frac{\left(6.626\text{x}10^{-34}\ \text{J•s}\right)\left(3.00\text{x}10^{8}\ \text{m/s}\right)}{2200\ \text{Å}}\left(\frac{1\ \text{Å}}{10^{-10}\ \text{m}}\right) = 9.03545\text{x}10^{-19} = \mathbf{9.0x10^{-19}\ J}$$

7.18 Bohr's key assumption was that the electron in an atom does not radiate energy while in a stationary state, and the electron can move to a different orbit by absorbing or emitting a photon whose energy is equal to the difference in energy between two states. These differences in energy correspond to the wavelengths in the known spectra for the hydrogen atoms. A Solar System model does not allow for the movement of electrons between levels.

7.20 Plan: The quantum number n is related to the energy level of the electron. An electron *absorbs* energy to change from lower energy (lower n) to higher energy (higher n), giving an absorption spectrum. An electron *emits* energy as it drops from a higher energy level (higher n) to a lower one (lower n), giving an emission spectrum.
Solution:
a) The electron is moving from a lower value of n (2) to a higher value of n (4): **absorption**
b) The electron is moving from a higher value of n (3) to a lower value of n (1): **emission**
c) The electron is moving from a higher value of n (5) to a lower value of n (2):**emission**
d) The electron is moving from a lower value of n (3) to a higher value of n (4): **absorption**

7.22 The Bohr model has successfully predicted the line spectra for the H atom and Be^{3+} ion since both are one-electron species. The energies could be predicted from $E_n = \frac{-\left(Z^2\right)\left(2.18\text{x}10^{-18}\ \text{J}\right)}{n^2}$ where Z is the atomic number for the atom or ion. The line spectra for H would not match the line spectra for Be^{3+} since the H nucleus contains one proton while the Be^{3+} nucleus contains 4 protons (the Z values in the equation do not match); the force of attraction of the nucleus for the electron would be greater in the beryllium ion than in the hydrogen atom. This means that the pattern of lines would be similar, but at different wavelengths.

7.23 Plan: Calculate wavelength by substituting the given values into Equation 7.3, where $n_1 = 2$ and $n_2 = 5$ because $n_2 > n_1$. Although more significant figures could be used, five significant figures are adequate for this calculation.
Solution:

$$\frac{1}{\lambda} = R\left(\frac{1}{n_1^2} - \frac{1}{n_2^2}\right) \qquad R = 1.096776\text{x}10^{7}\ \text{m}^{-1}$$

$n_1 = 2 \quad n_2 = 5$

$$\frac{1}{\lambda} = R\left(\frac{1}{n_1^2} - \frac{1}{n_2^2}\right) = \left(1.096776\text{x}10^7 \text{ m}^{-1}\right)\left(\frac{1}{2^2} - \frac{1}{5^2}\right) = 2{,}303{,}229.6 \text{ m}^{-1}$$

$$\lambda\text{ (nm)} = \left(\frac{1}{2{,}303{,}229.6 \text{ m}^{-1}}\right)\left(\frac{1 \text{ nm}}{10^{-9} \text{ m}}\right) = 434.1729544 = \mathbf{434.17 \text{ nm}}$$

7.25 Plan: The Rydberg equation is needed. For the infrared series of the H atom, n_1 equals 3. The least energetic spectral line in this series would represent an electron moving from the next highest energy level, $n_2 = 4$. Although more significant figures could be used, five significant figures are adequate for this calculation.
Solution:

$$\frac{1}{\lambda} = R\left(\frac{1}{n_1^2} - \frac{1}{n_2^2}\right) = \left(1.096776\text{x}10^7 \text{ m}^{-1}\right)\left(\frac{1}{3^2} - \frac{1}{4^2}\right) = 533{,}155 \text{ m}^{-1}$$

$$\lambda\text{ (nm)} = \left(\frac{1}{533{,}155 \text{ m}^{-1}}\right)\left(\frac{1 \text{ nm}}{10^{-9} \text{ m}}\right) = 1875.627 = \mathbf{1875.6 \text{ nm}}$$

7.27 Plan: To find the transition energy, use the equation for the energy of an electron transition and multiply by Avogadro's number to convert to energy per mole.
Solution:

$$\Delta E = \left(-2.18\text{x}10^{-18} \text{ J}\right)\left(\frac{1}{n_{\text{final}}^2} - \frac{1}{n_{\text{initial}}^2}\right)$$

$$\Delta E = \left(-2.18\text{x}10^{-18} \text{ J}\right)\left(\frac{1}{2^2} - \frac{1}{5^2}\right) = -4.578\text{x}10^{-19} \text{ J/photon}$$

$$\Delta E = \left(\frac{-4.578\text{x}10^{-19} \text{ J}}{\text{photon}}\right)\left(\frac{6.022\text{x}10^{23} \text{ photons}}{1 \text{ mol}}\right) = -2.75687\text{x}10^5 = \mathbf{-2.76x10^5 \text{ J/mol}}$$

The energy has a negative value since this electron transition to a lower n value is an emission of energy.

7.29 Plan: Determine the relative energy of the electron transitions. Remember that energy is directly proportional to frequency ($E = h\nu$).
Solution:
Looking at an energy chart will help answer this question.

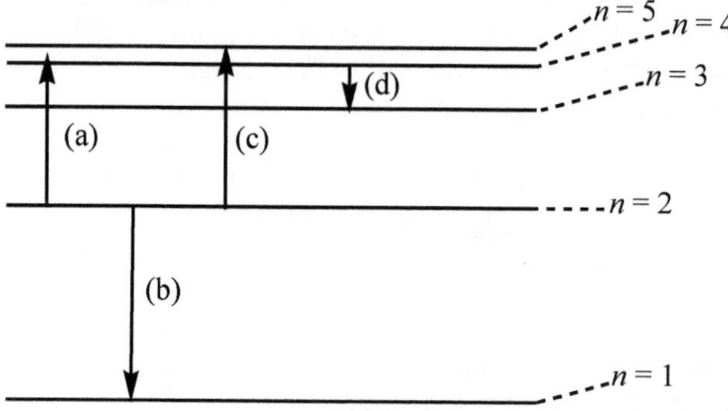

Frequency is proportional to energy so the smallest frequency will be d) $n = 4$ to $n = 3$; levels 3 and 4 have a smaller ΔE than the levels in the other transitions. The largest frequency is b) $n = 2$ to $n = 1$ since levels 1 and 2 have a larger ΔE than the levels in the other transitions. Transition a) $n = 2$ to $n = 4$ will be smaller than transition c) $n = 2$ to $n = 5$ since level 5 is a higher energy than level 4. In order of increasing frequency the transitions are **d < a < c < b**.

7.31 Plan: Use the Rydberg equation. Since the electron is in the ground state (lowest energy level), $n_1 = 1$. Convert the wavelength from nm to units of meters.
Solution:

$$\lambda = (97.20 \text{ nm})\left(\frac{10^{-9} \text{ m}}{1 \text{ nm}}\right) = 9.720\text{x}10^{-8} \text{ m}$$

ground state: $n_1 = 1$; $n_2 = ?$

$$\frac{1}{\lambda} = \left(1.096776\text{x}10^{7} \text{ m}^{-1}\right)\left(\frac{1}{n_1^2} - \frac{1}{n_2^2}\right)$$

$$\frac{1}{9.72\text{x}10^{-8} \text{ m}} = \left(1.096776\text{x}10^{7} \text{ m}^{-1}\right)\left(\frac{1}{1^2} - \frac{1}{n_2^2}\right)$$

$$0.93803 = \left(\frac{1}{1^2} - \frac{1}{n_2^2}\right)$$

$$\frac{1}{n_2^2} = 1 - 0.93803 = 0.06197$$

$$n_2^2 = 16.14$$

$n_2 = \mathbf{4}$

7.37 Macroscopic objects have significant mass. A large m in the denominator of $\lambda = h/mu$ will result in a very small wavelength. Macroscopic objects do exhibit a wavelike motion, but the wavelength is too small for humans to see it.

7.39 Plan: Use the de Broglie equation. Mass in lb must be converted to kg and velocity in mi/h must be converted to m/s because a joule is equivalent to kg•m^2/s^2.
Solution:

a) $$\text{Mass (kg)} = (232 \text{ lb})\left(\frac{1 \text{ kg}}{2.205 \text{ lb}}\right) = 105.2154 \text{ kg}$$

$$\text{Velocity (m/s)} = \left(\frac{19.8 \text{ mi}}{\text{h}}\right)\left(\frac{1 \text{ km}}{0.62 \text{ mi}}\right)\left(\frac{10^3 \text{ m}}{1 \text{ km}}\right)\left(\frac{1 \text{ h}}{3600 \text{ s}}\right) = 8.87097 \text{ m/s}$$

$$\lambda = \frac{h}{mu} = \frac{\left(6.626\text{x}10^{-34} \text{ J•s}\right)}{(105.2154 \text{ kg})\left(8.87097\frac{\text{m}}{\text{s}}\right)}\left(\frac{\text{kg•m}^2/\text{s}^2}{\text{J}}\right) = 7.099063\text{x}10^{-37} = \mathbf{7.10x10^{-37}\ m}$$

b) $$\text{Uncertainty in velocity (m/s)} = \left(\frac{0.1 \text{ mi}}{\text{h}}\right)\left(\frac{1 \text{ km}}{0.62 \text{ mi}}\right)\left(\frac{10^3 \text{ m}}{1 \text{ km}}\right)\left(\frac{1 \text{ h}}{3600 \text{ s}}\right) = 0.0448029 \text{ m/s}$$

$$\Delta x \bullet m\Delta v \geq \frac{h}{4\pi}$$

$$\Delta x \geq \frac{h}{4\pi m\Delta v} \geq \frac{\left(6.626\text{x}10^{-34} \text{ J•s}\right)}{4\pi(105.2154 \text{ kg})\left(\frac{0.0448029 \text{ m}}{\text{s}}\right)}\left(\frac{\text{kg•m}^2/\text{s}^2}{\text{J}}\right) \geq 1.11855\text{x}10^{-35} \geq \mathbf{1x10^{-35}\ m}$$

7.41 Plan: Use the de Broglie equation. Mass in g must be converted to kg and wavelength in Å must be converted to m because a joule is equivalent to kg•m^2/s^2.
Solution:

$$\text{Mass (kg)} = (56.5 \text{ g})\left(\frac{1 \text{ kg}}{10^3 \text{ g}}\right) = 0.0565 \text{ kg}$$

$$\text{Wavelength (m)} = (5400\ \text{Å})\left(\frac{10^{-10}\ \text{m}}{1\ \text{Å}}\right) = 5.4\text{x}10^{-7}\ \text{m}$$

$$\lambda = \frac{h}{mu}$$

$$u = \frac{h}{m\lambda} = \frac{(6.626\text{x}10^{-34}\ \text{J•s})}{(0.0565\ \text{kg})(5.4\text{x}10^{-7}\ \text{m})}\left(\frac{\text{kg•m}^2/\text{s}^2}{\text{J}}\right) = 2.1717\text{x}10^{-26} = \mathbf{2.2x10^{-26}\ m/s}$$

7.43 Plan: The de Broglie wavelength equation will give the mass equivalent of a photon with known wavelength and velocity. The term "mass equivalent" is used instead of "mass of photon" because photons are quanta of electromagnetic energy that have no mass. A light photon's velocity is the speed of light, $3.00\text{x}10^8$ m/s. Wavelength in nm must be converted to m.
Solution:

$$\text{Wavelength (m)} = (589\,\text{nm})\left(\frac{10^{-9}\ \text{m}}{1\ \text{nm}}\right) = 5.89\text{x}10^{-7}\ \text{m}$$

$$\lambda = \frac{h}{mu}$$

$$m = \frac{h}{\lambda u} = \frac{(6.626\text{x}10^{-34}\,\text{J•s})}{(5.89\text{x}10^{-7}\ \text{m})(3.00\text{x}10^{8}\ \text{m/s})}\left(\frac{\text{kg•m}^2/\text{s}^2}{\text{J}}\right) = 3.7499\text{x}10^{-36} = \mathbf{3.75x10^{-36}\ kg/photon}$$

7.47 A peak in the radial probability distribution at a certain distance means that the total probability of finding the electron is greatest within a thin spherical volume having a radius very close to that distance. Since principal quantum number (n) correlates with distance from the nucleus, the peak for $n = 2$ would occur at a greater distance from the nucleus than 0.529 Å. Thus, the probability of finding an electron at 0.529 Å is much greater for the 1*s* orbital than for the 2*s*.

7.48 a) Principal quantum number, n, relates to the size of the orbital. More specifically, it relates to the distance from the nucleus at which the probability of finding an electron is greatest. This distance is determined by the energy of the electron.
b) Angular momentum quantum number, l, relates to the shape of the orbital. It is also called the azimuthal quantum number.
c) Magnetic quantum number, m_l, relates to the orientation of the orbital in space in three-dimensional space.

7.49 Plan: The following letter designations correlate with the following l quantum numbers:
$l = 0 = s$ orbital; $l = 1 = p$ orbital; $l = 2 = d$ orbital; $l = 3 = f$ orbital. Remember that allowed m_l values are $-l$ to $+l$. The number of orbitals of a particular type is given by the number of possible m_l values.
Solution:
a) There is only a single *s* orbital in any shell. $l = 1$ and $m_l = 0$: one value of m_l = **one** *s* orbital.
b) There are five *d* orbitals in any shell. $l = 2$ and $m_l = -2, -1, 0, +1, +2$. Five values of m_l = **five** *d* orbitals.
c) There are three *p* orbitals in any shell. $l = 1$ and $m_l = -1, 0, +1$. Three values of m_l = **three** *p* orbitals.
d) If $n = 3$, $l = 0(s)$, $1(p)$, and $2(d)$. There is a 3*s* (1 orbital), a 3*p* set (3 orbitals), and a 3*d* set (5 orbitals) for a total of **nine** orbitals (1 + 3 + 5 = 9).

7.51 Plan: Magnetic quantum numbers (m_l) can have integer values from $-l$ to $+l$. The l quantum number can have integer values from 0 to $n - 1$.
Solution:
a) $l = 2$ so m_l = **–2, –1, 0, +1, +2**
b) $n = 1$ so $l = 1 - 1 = 0$ and m_l = **0**
c) $l = 3$ so m_l = **–3, –2, –1, 0, +1, +2, +3**

7.53 Plan: The s orbital is spherical; p orbitals have two lobes; the subscript x indicates that this orbital lies along the x-axis.

Solution:

a) s: spherical

b) p_x: 2 lobes along the x-axis

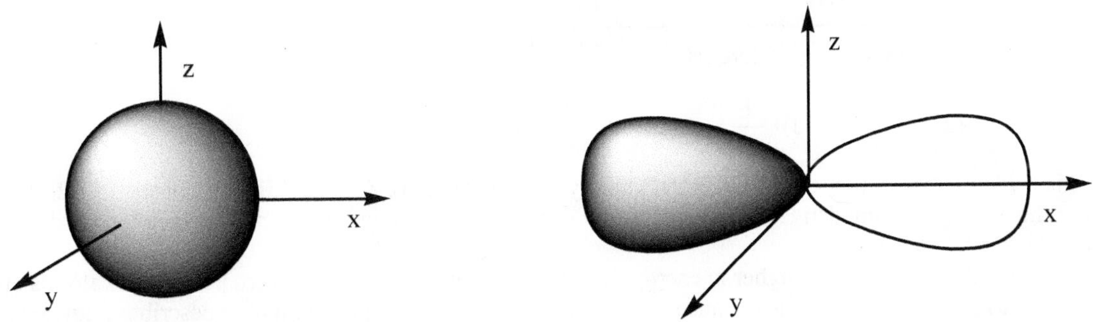

The variations in coloring of the p orbital are a consequence of the quantum mechanical derivation of atomic orbitals that are beyond the scope of this course.

7.55 Plan: The following letter designations for the various sublevels (orbitals) correlate with the following l quantum numbers: $l = 0 = s$ orbital; $l = 1 = p$ orbital; $l = 2 = d$ orbital; $l = 3 = f$ orbital. Remember that allowed m_l values are $-l$ to $+l$. The number of orbitals of a particular type is given by the number of possible m_l values.

Solution:

sublevel	allowable m_l	# of possible orbitals
a) d ($l = 2$)	$-2, -1, 0, +1, +2$	5
b) p ($l = 1$)	$-1, 0, +1$	3
c) f ($l = 3$)	$-3, -2, -1, 0, +1, +2, +3$	7

7.57 Plan: The integer in front of the letter represents the n value. The letter designates the l value: $l = 0 = s$ orbital; $l = 1 = p$ orbital; $l = 2 = d$ orbital; $l = 3 = f$ orbital. Remember that allowed m_l values are $-l$ to $+l$.

Solution:

a) For the 5s subshell, $\boldsymbol{n = 5}$ and $\boldsymbol{l = 0}$. Since $m_l = 0$, there is **one** orbital.

b) For the 3p subshell, $\boldsymbol{n = 3}$ and $\boldsymbol{l = 1}$. Since $m_l = -1, 0, +1$, there are **three** orbitals.

c) For the 4f subshell, $\boldsymbol{n = 4}$ and $\boldsymbol{l = 3}$. Since $m_l = -3, -2, -1, 0, +1, +2, +3$, there are **seven** orbitals.

7.59 Plan: Allowed values of quantum numbers: n = positive integers; l = integers from 0 to $n - 1$; m_l = integers from $-l$ through 0 to $+l$.

Solution:

a) $n = 2$; $l = 0$; $m_l = -1$: With $n = 2$, l can be 0 or 1; with $l = 0$, the only allowable m_l value is 0. This combination is not allowed. To correct, either change the l or m_l value.
Correct: $n = 2$; $l = 1$; $m_l = -1$ or $n = 2$; $l = 0$; $m_l = 0$.

b) $n = 4$; $l = 3$; $m_l = -1$: With $n = 4$, l can be 0, 1, 2, or 3; with $l = 3$, the allowable m_l values are $-3, -2, -1, 0, +1, +2, +3$. Combination is allowed.

c) $n = 3$; $l = 1$; $m_l = 0$: With $n = 3$, l can be 0, 1, or 2; with $l = 1$, the allowable m_l values are $-1, 0, +1$. Combination is allowed.

d) $n = 5$; $l = 2$; $m_l = +3$: With $n = 5$, l can be 0, 1, 2, 3, or 4; with $l = 2$, the allowable m_l values are $-2, -1, 0, +1, +2$. $+3$ is not an allowable m_l value. To correct, either change l or m_l value.
Correct: $n = 5$; $l = 3$; $m_l = +3$ or $n = 5$; $l = 2$; $m_l = 0$.

7.62 Plan: For part a, use the values of the constants h, π, m_e, and a_0 to find the overall constant in the equation. Use the resulting equation to calculate ΔE in part b). Use the relationship $E = \frac{hc}{\lambda}$ to calculate the wavelength in part c). Remember that a joule is equivalent to kg•m^2/s^2.

Solution:

a) $h = 6.626\text{x}10^{-34}$ J•s; $m_e = 9.1094\text{x}10^{-31}$ kg; $a_0 = 52.92\text{x}10^{-12}$ m

$$E = -\frac{h^2}{8\pi^2 m_e a_0^2 n^2} = -\frac{h^2}{8\pi^2 m_e a_0^2}\left(\frac{1}{n^2}\right)$$

$$E = -\frac{\left(6.626\text{x}10^{-34}\ \text{J•s}\right)^2}{8\pi^2\left(9.1094\text{x}10^{-31}\ \text{kg}\right)\left(52.92\text{x}10^{-12}\ \text{m}\right)^2}\left(\frac{\text{kg•m}^2/\text{s}^2}{\text{J}}\right)\left(\frac{1}{n^2}\right)$$

$$= -(2.17963\text{x}10^{-18}\ \text{J})\left(\frac{1}{n^2}\right) = -(2.180\text{x}10^{-18}\ \text{J})\left(\frac{1}{n^2}\right)$$

This is identical with the result from Bohr's theory. For the H atom, $Z = 1$ and Bohr's constant $= -2.18\text{x}10^{-18}$ J. For the hydrogen atom, derivation using classical principles or quantum-mechanical principles yields the same constant.

b) The $n = 3$ energy level is higher in energy than the $n = 2$ level. Because the zero point of the atom's energy is defined as an electron's infinite distance from the nucleus, a larger negative number describes a lower energy level. Although this may be confusing, it makes sense that an energy *change* would be a positive number.

$$\Delta E = -(2.180\text{x}10^{-18}\ \text{J})\left(\frac{1}{2^2} - \frac{1}{3^2}\right) = -3.027778\text{x}10^{-19} = \mathbf{3.028x10^{-19}\ J}$$

c) $E = \dfrac{hc}{\lambda}$

$$\lambda\ (\text{m}) = \frac{hc}{E} = \frac{\left(6.626\text{x}10^{-34}\,\text{J•s}\right)\left(2.9979\text{x}10^{8}\,\text{m/s}\right)}{\left(3.027778\text{x}10^{-19}\,\text{J}\right)} = 6.56061\text{x}10^{-7} = \mathbf{6.561x10^{-7}\ m}$$

$$\lambda\ (\text{nm}) = \left(6.56061\text{x}10^{-7}\ \text{m}\right)\left(\frac{1\ \text{nm}}{10^{-9}\ \text{m}}\right) = 656.061 = \mathbf{656.1\ nm}$$

This is the wavelength for the observed red line in the hydrogen spectrum.

7.63 Plan: When light of sufficient frequency (energy) shines on metal, electrons in the metal break free and a current flows.

Solution:

a) The lines do not begin at the origin because an electron must absorb a minimum amount of energy before it has enough energy to overcome the attraction of the nucleus and leave the atom. This minimum energy is the energy of photons of light at the threshold frequency.

b) The lines for K and Ag do not begin at the same point. The amount of energy that an electron must absorb to leave the K atom is less than the amount of energy that an electron must absorb to leave the Ag atom, where the attraction between the nucleus and outer electron is stronger than in a K atom.

c) Wavelength is inversely proportional to energy. Thus, the metal that requires a larger amount of energy to be absorbed before electrons are emitted will require a shorter wavelength of light. Electrons in Ag atoms require more energy to leave, so Ag requires a shorter wavelength of light than K to eject an electron.

d) The slopes of the line show an increase in kinetic energy as the frequency (or energy) of light is increased. Since the slopes are the same, this means that for an increase of one unit of frequency (or energy) of light, the increase in kinetic energy of an electron ejected from K is the same as the increase in the kinetic energy of an electron ejected from Ag. After an electron is ejected, the energy that it absorbs above the threshold energy becomes the kinetic energy of the electron. For the same increase in energy above the threshold energy, for either K or Ag, the kinetic energy of the ejected electron will be the same.

7.66 Plan: The Bohr model has been successfully applied to predict the spectral lines for one-electron species other than H. Common one-electron species are small cations with all but one electron removed. Since the problem specifies a metal ion, assume that the possible choices are Li^{2+} or Be^{3+}. Use the relationship $E = h\nu$ to convert the frequency to energy and then solve Bohr's equation $E = \left(2.18\text{x}10^{-18}\text{ J}\right)\left(\frac{Z^2}{n^2}\right)$ to verify if a whole number for Z can be calculated. Recall that the negative sign is a convention based on the zero point of the atom's energy; it is deleted in this calculation to avoid taking the square root of a negative number.

Solution:

The highest energy line corresponds to the transition from $n = 1$ to $n = \infty$.

$E = h\nu = (6.626\text{x}10^{-34}\text{ J•s})(2.961\text{x}10^{16}\text{ Hz})(\text{s}^{-1}/\text{Hz}) = 1.9619586\text{x}10^{-17}\text{ J}$

$$E = \left(2.18\text{x}10^{-18}\text{ J}\right)\left(\frac{Z^2}{n^2}\right) \qquad Z = \text{charge of the nucleus}$$

$$Z^2 = \frac{En^2}{2.18\text{x}10^{-18}\text{J}} = \frac{1.9619586\text{x}10^{-17}(1^2)}{2.18\text{x}10^{-18}\text{ J}} = 8.99998$$

Then $Z^2 = 9$ and $Z = 3$.

Therefore, the ion is $\mathbf{Li^{2+}}$ with an atomic number of 3.

7.68 Plan: The electromagnetic spectrum shows that the visible region goes from 400 to 750 nm (4000 Å to 7500 Å). Thus, wavelengths b, c, and d are for the three transitions in the visible series with $n_{\text{final}} = 2$. Wavelength a is in the ultraviolet region of the spectrum and the ultraviolet series has $n_{\text{final}} = 1$. Wavelength e is in the infrared region of the spectrum and the infrared series has $n_{\text{final}} = 3$. Use the Rydberg equation to find the n_{initial} for each line. Convert the wavelengths from Å to units of m.

Solution:

$n = ? \rightarrow n = 1$; $\lambda = 1212.7$ Å (shortest λ corresponds to the largest ΔE)

$$\lambda\text{ (m)} = \left(1212.7\text{ Å}\right)\left(\frac{10^{-10}\text{ m}}{1\text{ Å}}\right) = 1.2127\text{x}10^{-7}\text{ m}$$

$$\frac{1}{\lambda} = \left(1.096776\text{x}10^{7}\text{ m}^{-1}\right)\left(\frac{1}{n_1^2} - \frac{1}{n_2^2}\right)$$

$$\left(\frac{1}{1.2127\text{x}10^{-7}\text{m}}\right) = \left(1.096776\text{x}10^{7}\text{m}^{-1}\right)\left(\frac{1}{1^2} - \frac{1}{n_2^2}\right)$$

$$0.7518456 = \left(\frac{1}{1^2} - \frac{1}{n_2^2}\right)$$

$$\left(\frac{1}{n_2^2}\right) = 1 - 0.7518456$$

$$\left(\frac{1}{n_2^2}\right) = 0.2481544$$

$\boldsymbol{n_2 = 2}$ for line (a) ($n = 2 \rightarrow n = 1$)

$n = ? \rightarrow n = 3$; $\lambda = 10{,}938$ Å (longest λ corresponds to the smallest ΔE)

$$\lambda\text{ (m)} = \left(10{,}938\text{ Å}\right)\left(\frac{10^{-10}\text{ m}}{1\text{ Å}}\right) = 1.0938\text{x}10^{-6}\text{ m}$$

$$\frac{1}{\lambda} = \left(1.096776\text{x}10^{7}\text{ m}^{-1}\right)\left(\frac{1}{n_1^2} - \frac{1}{n_2^2}\right)$$

$$\left(\frac{1}{1.0938\text{x}10^{-6}\text{m}}\right) = \left(1.096776\text{x}10^{7}\text{m}^{-1}\right)\left(\frac{1}{3^2} - \frac{1}{n_2^2}\right)$$

$$0.083357397 = \left(\frac{1}{3^2} - \frac{1}{n_2^2}\right)$$

$$0.083357397 = 0.111111111 - \frac{1}{n_2^2}$$

$$\left(\frac{1}{n_2^2}\right) = 0.11111111 - 0.083357396$$

$$\left(\frac{1}{n_2^2}\right) = 0.0277537151$$

n_2^2 =36.03121

$\boldsymbol{n_2 = 6}$ for line (e) ($n = 6 \rightarrow n = 3$)
For the other three lines, $n_1 = 2$.
For line (d), $\boldsymbol{n_2 = 3}$ (largest $\lambda \rightarrow$ smallest ΔE).
For line (b), $\boldsymbol{n_2 = 5}$ (smallest $\lambda \rightarrow$ largest ΔE).
For line (c), $\boldsymbol{n_2 = 4}$.

7.72 Plan: Allowed values of quantum numbers: n = positive integers; l = integers from 0 to $n - 1$; m_l = integers from $- l$ through 0 to $+ l$.

Solution:

a) The l value must be at least 1 for m_l to be $- 1$, but cannot be greater than $n - 1 = 3 - 1 = 2$. Increase the l value to 1 or 2 to create an allowable combination.

b) The l value must be at least 1 for m_l to be $+1$, but cannot be greater than $n - 1 = 3 - 1 = 2$. Decrease the l value to 1 or 2 to create an allowable combination.

c) The l value must be at least 3 for m_l to be $+3$, but cannot be greater than $n - 1 = 7 - 1 = 6$. Increase the l value to 3, 4, 5, or 6 to create an allowable combination.

d) The l value must be at least 2 for m_l to be -2, but cannot be greater than $n - 1 = 4 - 1 = 3$. Increase the l value to 2 or 3 to create an allowable combination.

7.74 Plan: Ionization occurs when the electron is completely removed from the atom, or when $n_{\text{final}} = \infty$. We can use the equation for the energy of an electron transition to find the quantity of energy needed to remove completely the electron, called the ionization energy (IE). To obtain the ionization energy per mole of species, multiply by Avogadro's number. The charge on the nucleus must affect the IE because a larger nucleus would exert a greater pull on the escaping electron. The Bohr equation applies to H and other one-electron species. Use the expression to determine the ionization energy of B^{4+}. Then use the expression to find the energies of the transitions listed and use $E = \frac{hc}{\lambda}$ to convert energy to wavelength.

Solution:

a) $E = \left(-2.18\text{x}10^{-18}\ \text{J}\right)\left(\frac{Z^2}{n^2}\right)$ Z = atomic number

$$\Delta E = \left(-2.18\text{x}10^{-18}\ \text{J}\right)\left(\frac{1}{n_{\text{final}}^2} - \frac{1}{n_{\text{initial}}^2}\right)Z^2$$

$$\Delta E = \left(-2.18\text{x}10^{-18}\ \text{J}\right)\left(\frac{1}{\infty^2} - \frac{1}{n_{\text{initial}}^2}\right)Z^2\left(\frac{6.022\text{x}10^{23}}{1\ \text{mol}}\right)$$

$= (1.312796\text{x}10^6)\ Z^2$ for $n = 1$

b) In the ground state $n = 1$, the initial energy level for the single electron in B^{4+}. Once ionized, $n = \infty$ is the final energy level.
$Z = 5$ for B^{4+}.
ΔE = IE = $(1.312796\text{x}10^6)\ Z^2 = (1.312796\text{x}10^6\ \text{J/mol})(5^2) = 3.28199\text{x}10^7 = \mathbf{3.28x10^7\ J/mol}$

c) $n_{\text{final}} = \infty$, $n_{\text{initial}} = 3$, and $Z = 2$ for He^+.

$$\Delta E = \left(-2.18\text{x}10^{-18}\text{ J}\right)\left(\frac{1}{n_{\text{final}}^2} - \frac{1}{n_{\text{initial}}^2}\right)Z^2 = \left(-2.18\text{x}10^{-18}\text{ J}\right)\left(\frac{1}{\infty^2} - \frac{1}{3^2}\right)2^2 = 9.68889\text{x}10^{-19}\text{ J}$$

$$E = \frac{hc}{\lambda}$$

$$\lambda\text{ (m)} = \frac{hc}{E} = \frac{\left(6.626\text{x}10^{-34}\text{ J}\bullet\text{s}\right)\left(3.00\text{x}10^{8}\text{ m/s}\right)}{9.68889\text{x}10^{-19}\text{ J}} = 2.051628\text{x}10^{-7}\text{ m}$$

$$\lambda\text{ (nm)} = \left(2.051628\text{x}10^{-7}\text{ m}\right)\left(\frac{1\text{ nm}}{10^{-9}\text{ m}}\right) = 205.1628 = \mathbf{205\text{ nm}}$$

d) $n_{\text{final}} = \infty$, $n_{\text{initial}} = 2$, and $Z = 4$ for Be^{3+}.

$$\Delta E = \left(-2.18\text{x}10^{-18}\text{ J}\right)\left(\frac{1}{\infty^2} - \frac{1}{n_{\text{initial}}^2}\right)Z^2 = \left(-2.18\text{x}10^{-18}\text{ J}\right)\left(\frac{1}{\infty^2} - \frac{1}{2^2}\right)4^2 = 8.72\text{x}10^{-18}\text{ J}$$

$$\lambda\text{ (m)} = \frac{hc}{E} = \frac{\left(6.626\text{x}10^{-34}\text{ J}\bullet\text{s}\right)\left(3.00\text{x}10^{8}\text{ m/s}\right)}{8.72\text{x}10^{-18}\text{ J}} = 2.279587\text{x}10^{-8}\text{ m}$$

$$\lambda\text{ (nm)} = \left(2.279587\text{x}10^{-8}\text{ m}\right)\left(\frac{1\text{ nm}}{10^{-9}\text{ m}}\right) = 22.79587 = \mathbf{22.8\text{ nm}}$$

7.76 Plan: Use the values and the equation given in the problem to calculate the appropriate values.

Solution:

a) $r_n = \dfrac{n^2 h^2 \varepsilon_0}{\pi m_e e^2}$

$$r_1 = \frac{1^2\left(6.626\text{x}10^{-34}\text{ J}\bullet\text{s}\right)^2\left(8.854\text{x}10^{-12}\ \frac{\text{C}^2}{\text{J}\bullet\text{m}}\right)}{\pi\left(9.109\text{x}10^{-31}\text{ kg}\right)\left(1.602\text{x}10^{-19}\text{ C}\right)^2}\left(\frac{\text{kg}\bullet\text{m}^2/\text{s}^2}{\text{J}}\right) = 5.2929377\text{x}10^{-11} = \mathbf{5.293\text{x}10^{-11}\text{ m}}$$

$$\text{b) } r_{10} = \frac{10^2\left(6.626\text{x}10^{-34}\text{ J}\bullet\text{s}\right)^2\left(8.854\text{x}10^{-12}\ \frac{\text{C}^2}{\text{J}\bullet\text{m}}\right)}{\pi\left(9.109\text{x}10^{-31}\text{ kg}\right)\left(1.602\text{x}10^{-19}\text{ C}\right)^2}\left(\frac{\text{kg}\bullet\text{m}^2/\text{s}^2}{\text{J}}\right) = 5.2929377\text{x}10^{-9} = \mathbf{5.293\text{x}10^{-9}\text{ m}}$$

7.78 Plan: Refer to Chapter 6 for the calculation of the amount of heat energy absorbed by a substance from its specific heat capacity and temperature change ($q = c$ x mass x ΔT). Using this equation, calculate the energy absorbed by the water. This energy equals the energy from the microwave photons. The energy of each photon can be calculated from its wavelength: $E = hc/\lambda$. Dividing the total energy by the energy of each photon gives the number of photons absorbed by the water.

Solution:

$q = c$ x mass x ΔT

$q = (4.184\text{ J/g°C})(252\text{ g})(98 - 20.)\text{°C} = 8.22407\text{x}10^4\text{ J}$

$$E = \frac{hc}{\lambda} = \frac{\left(6.626\text{x}10^{-34}\text{ J}\bullet\text{s}\right)\left(3.00\text{x}10^{8}\text{ m/s}\right)}{1.55\text{x}10^{-2}\text{ m}} = 1.28245\text{x}10^{-23}\text{ J/photon}$$

$$\text{Number of photons} = \left(8.22407\text{x}10^{4}\text{ J}\right)\left(\frac{1\text{ photon}}{1.28245\text{x}10^{-23}\text{ J}}\right) = 6.41278\text{x}10^{27} = \mathbf{6.4\text{x}10^{27}\text{ photons}}$$

7.80 Plan: In general, to test for overlap of the two series, compare the longest wavelength in the "n" series with the shortest wavelength in the "n+1" series. The longest wavelength in any series corresponds to the transition between the n_1 level and the next level above it; the shortest wavelength corresponds to the transition between the n_1 level and the $n = \infty$ level. Use the relationship $\frac{1}{\lambda} = R\left(\frac{1}{n_1^2} - \frac{1}{n_2^2}\right)$ to calculate the wavelengths.

Solution:

$$\frac{1}{\lambda} = R\left(\frac{1}{n_1^2} - \frac{1}{n_2^2}\right) = \left(1.096776\text{x}10^7\ \text{m}^{-1}\right)\left(\frac{1}{n_1^2} - \frac{1}{n_2^2}\right)$$

a) The overlap between the $n_1 = 1$ series and the $n_1 = 2$ series would occur between the longest wavelengths for $n_1 = 1$ and the shortest wavelengths for $n_1 = 2$.

Longest wavelength in $n_1 = 1$ series has n_2 equal to 2.

$$\frac{1}{\lambda} = \left(1.096776\text{x}10^7\ \text{m}^{-1}\right)\left(\frac{1}{1^2} - \frac{1}{2^2}\right) = 8{,}225{,}820\ \text{m}^{-1}$$

$$\lambda = \frac{1}{8{,}225{,}820\ \text{m}^{-1}} = 1.215684272\text{x}10^{-7} = \mathbf{1.215684x10^{-7}\ m}$$

Shortest wavelength in the $n_1 = 2$ series:

$$\frac{1}{\lambda} = \left(1.096776\text{x}10^7\text{m}^{-1}\right)\left(\frac{1}{2^2} - \frac{1}{\infty^2}\right) = 2{,}741{,}940\ \text{m}^{-1}$$

$$\lambda = \frac{1}{2{,}741{,}940\ \text{m}^{-1}} = 3.647052817\text{x}10^{-7} = \mathbf{3.647053x10^{-7}\ m}$$

Since the longest wavelength for $n_1 = 1$ series is shorter than shortest wavelength for $n_1 = 2$ series, there is **no overlap** between the two series.

b) The overlap between the $n_1 = 3$ series and the $n_1 = 4$ series would occur between the longest wavelengths for $n_1 = 3$ and the shortest wavelengths for $n_1 = 4$.

Longest wavelength in $n_1 = 3$ series has n_2 equal to 4.

$$\frac{1}{\lambda} = \left(1.096776\text{x}10^7\ \text{m}^{-1}\right)\left(\frac{1}{3^2} - \frac{1}{4^2}\right) = 533{,}155\ \text{m}^{-1}$$

$$\lambda = \frac{1}{533{,}155\ \text{m}^{-1}} = 1.875627163\text{x}10^{-6} = \mathbf{1.875627x10^{-6}\ m}$$

Shortest wavelength in $n_1 = 4$ series has $n_2 = \infty$.

$$\frac{1}{\lambda} = \left(1.096776\text{x}10^7\ \text{m}^{-1}\right)\left(\frac{1}{4^2} - \frac{1}{\infty^2}\right) = 685{,}485\ \text{m}^{-1}$$

$$\lambda = \frac{1}{685{,}485\ \text{m}^{-1}} = 1.458821127\text{x}10^{-6} = \mathbf{1.458821x10^{-6}\ m}$$

Since the $n_1 = 4$ series shortest wavelength is shorter than the $n_1 = 3$ series longest wavelength, the **series do overlap**.

c) Shortest wavelength in $n_1 = 5$ series has $n_2 = \infty$.

$$\frac{1}{\lambda} = \left(1.096776\text{x}10^7\ \text{m}^{-1}\right)\left(\frac{1}{5^2} - \frac{1}{\infty^2}\right) = 438{,}710.4\ \text{m}^{-1}$$

$$\lambda = \frac{1}{438{,}710.4\ \text{m}^{-1}} = 2.27940801\text{x}10^{-6} = \mathbf{2.279408x10^{-6}\ m}$$

Calculate the first few longest lines in the $n_1 = 4$ series to determine if any overlap with the shortest wavelength in the $n_1 = 5$ series:

For $n_1 = 4$, $n_2 = 5$:

$$\frac{1}{\lambda} = \left(1.096776\text{x}10^7\ \text{m}^{-1}\right)\left(\frac{1}{4^2} - \frac{1}{5^2}\right) = 246{,}774.6\ \text{m}^{-1}$$

$$\lambda = \frac{1}{246{,}774.6\ \text{m}^{-1}} = \mathbf{4.052281x10^{-6}\ m}$$

For $n_1 = 4$, $n_2 = 6$:

$$\frac{1}{\lambda} = \left(1.096776\text{x}10^{7}\ \text{m}^{-1}\right)\left(\frac{1}{4^2} - \frac{1}{6^2}\right) = 380{,}825\ \text{m}^{-1}$$

$$\lambda = \frac{1}{380{,}825\ \text{m}^{-1}} = = \mathbf{2.625878x10^{-6}\ m}$$

For $n_1 = 4$, $n_2 = 7$:

$$\frac{1}{\lambda} = \left(1.096776\text{x}10^{7}\ \text{m}^{-1}\right)\left(\frac{1}{4^2} - \frac{1}{7^2}\right) = 461{,}653.2\ \text{m}^{-1}$$

$$\lambda = \frac{1}{461{,}653.2\ \text{m}^{-1}} = \mathbf{2.166128x10^{-6}\ m}$$

The wavelengths of the first **two lines** of the $n_1 = 4$ series are longer than the shortest wavelength in the $n_1 = 5$ series. Therefore, only the first **two lines** of the $n_1 = 4$ series overlap the $n_1 = 5$ series.

d) At longer wavelengths (i.e., lower energies), there is increasing overlap between the lines from different series (i.e., with different n_1 values). The hydrogen spectrum becomes more complex, since the lines begin to merge into a more-or-less continuous band, and much more care is needed to interpret the information.

7.82 Plan: The energy differences sought may be determined by looking at the energy changes in steps. The wavelength is calculated from the relationship $\lambda = \frac{hc}{E}$.

Solution:

a) The difference between levels 3 and 2 (E_{32}) may be found by taking the difference in the energies for the 3 → 1 transition (E_{31}) and the 2 → 1 transition (E_{21}).

$E_{32} = E_{31} - E_{21} = (4.854\text{x}10^{-17}\ \text{J}) - (4.098\text{x}10^{-17}\ \text{J}) = \mathbf{7.56x10^{-18}\ J}$

$$\lambda = \frac{hc}{E} = \frac{\left(6.626\text{x}10^{-34}\ \text{J•s}\right)\left(3.00\text{x}10^{8}\ \text{m/s}\right)}{\left(7.56\text{x}10^{-18}\ \text{J}\right)} = 2.629365\text{x}10^{-8} = \mathbf{2.63x10^{-8}\ m}$$

b) The difference between levels 4 and 1 (E_{41}) may be found by adding the energies for the 4 → 2 transition (E_{42}) and the 2 → 1 transition (E_{21}).

$E_{41} = E_{42} + E_{21} = (1.024\text{x}10^{-17}\ \text{J}) + (4.098\text{x}10^{-17}\ \text{J}) = \mathbf{5.122x10^{-17}\ J}$

$$\lambda = \frac{hc}{E} = \frac{\left(6.626\text{x}10^{-34}\ \text{J•s}\right)\left(3.00\text{x}10^{8}\ \text{m/s}\right)}{\left(5.122\text{x}10^{-17}\ \text{J}\right)} = 3.88091\text{x}10^{-9} = \mathbf{3.881x10^{-9}\ m}$$

c) The difference between levels 5 and 4 (E_{54}) may be found by taking the difference in the energies for the 5 → 1 transition (E_{51}) and the 4 → 1 transition (see part b)).

$E_{54} = E_{51} - E_{41} = (5.242\text{x}10^{-17}\ \text{J}) - (5.122\text{x}10^{-17}\ \text{J}) = \mathbf{1.2x10^{-18}\ J}$

$$\lambda = \frac{hc}{E} = \frac{\left(6.626\text{x}10^{-34}\ \text{J•s}\right)\left(3.00\text{x}10^{8}\ \text{m/s}\right)}{\left(1.2\text{x}10^{-18}\ \text{J}\right)} = 1.6565\text{x}10^{-7} = \mathbf{1.66x10^{-7}\ m}$$

7.84 Plan: For part a), use the equation for kinetic energy, $E_k = ½mu^2$. For part b), use the relationship $E = hc/\lambda$ to find the energy of the photon absorbed. From that energy subtract the kinetic energy of the dislodged electron to obtain the work function.

Solution:

a) The energy of the electron is a function of its speed leaving the surface of the metal. The mass of the electron is $9.109\text{x}10^{-31}$ kg.

$$E_k = \frac{1}{2}mu^2 = \frac{1}{2}\left(9.109\text{x}10^{-31}\ \text{kg}\right)\left(6.40\text{x}10^{5}\ \text{m/s}\right)^2\left(\frac{\text{J}}{\text{kg•m}^2/\text{s}^2}\right) = 1.86552\text{x}10^{-19} = \mathbf{1.87x10^{-19}\ J}$$

b) The minimum energy required to dislodge the electron (ϕ) is a function of the incident light. In this example, the incident light is higher than the threshold frequency, so the kinetic energy of the electron, E_k, must be subtracted from the total energy of the incident light, $h\nu$, to yield the work function, ϕ. (The number of significant figures given in the wavelength requires more significant figures in the speed of light.)

$$\lambda\,(\text{m}) = (358.1\text{ nm})\left(\frac{10^{-9}\text{ m}}{1\text{nm}}\right) = 3.581\text{x}10^{-7}\text{ m}$$

$$E = hc/\lambda = \frac{(6.626\text{x}10^{-34}\text{ J•s})(2.9979\text{x}10^{8}\text{ m/s})}{(3.581\text{x}10^{-7}\text{ m})} = 5.447078\text{x}10^{-19}\text{ J}$$

$$\Phi = h\nu - E_k = (5.447078\text{x}10^{-19}\text{ J}) - (1.86552\text{x}10^{-19}\text{ J}) = 3.581558\text{x}10^{-19} = \mathbf{3.58x10^{-19}\ J}$$

7.86 Plan: Examine Figure 7.3 and match the given wavelengths to their colors. For each salt, convert the mass of salt to moles and multiply by Avogadro's number to find the number of photons emitted by that amount of salt (assuming that each atom undergoes one-electron transition). Use the relationship $E = \frac{hc}{\lambda}$ to find the energy of one photon and multiply by the total number of photons for the total energy of emission.

Solution:
a) Figure 7.3 indicates that the 641 nm wavelength of Sr falls in the **red** region and the 493 nm wavelength of Ba falls in the **green** region.
b) $SrCl_2$

$$\text{Number of photons} = (5.00\text{ g }SrCl_2)\left(\frac{1\text{ mol }SrCl_2}{158.52\text{ g }SrCl_2}\right)\left(\frac{6.022\text{x}10^{23}\text{ photons}}{1\text{ mol }SrCl_2}\right) = 1.8994449\text{x}10^{22}\text{ photons}$$

$$\lambda\,(\text{m}) = (641\text{ nm})\left(\frac{10^{-9}\text{ m}}{1\text{nm}}\right) = 6.41\text{x}10^{-7}\text{ m}$$

$$E_{\text{photon}} = \frac{hc}{\lambda} = \frac{(6.626\text{x}10^{-34}\text{ J•s})(3.00\text{x}10^{8}\text{ m/s})}{6.41\text{x}10^{-7}\text{ m}}\left(\frac{1\text{ kJ}}{10^3\text{ J}}\right) = 3.10109\text{x}10^{-22}\text{ kJ/photon}$$

$$E_{\text{total}} = (1.8994449\text{x}10^{22}\text{ photons})\left(\frac{3.10109\text{x}10^{-22}\text{ kJ}}{1\text{ photon}}\right) = 5.89035 = \mathbf{5.89\ kJ}$$

$BaCl_2$

$$\text{Number of photons} = (5.00\text{ g }BaCl_2)\left(\frac{1\text{ mol }BaCl_2}{208.2\text{ g }BaCl_2}\right)\left(\frac{6.022\text{x}10^{23}\text{ photons}}{1\text{ mol }BaCl_2}\right) = 1.44620557\text{x}10^{22}\text{ photons}$$

$$\lambda\,(\text{m}) = (493\text{ nm})\left(\frac{10^{-9}\text{ m}}{1\text{nm}}\right) = 4.93\text{x}10^{-7}\text{ m}$$

$$E_{\text{photon}} = \frac{hc}{\lambda} = \frac{(6.626\text{x}10^{-34}\text{ J•s})(3.00\text{x}10^{8}\text{m/s})}{4.93\text{x}10^{-7}\text{ m}}\left(\frac{1\text{ kJ}}{10^3\text{ J}}\right) = 4.0320487\text{x}10^{-22}\text{ kJ/photon}$$

$$E_{\text{total}} = (1.44620557\text{x}10^{22}\text{ photons})\left(\frac{4.0320487\text{x}10^{-22}\text{ kJ}}{1\text{ photon}}\right) = 5.83117 = \mathbf{5.83\ kJ}$$

7.88 Plan: Examine Figure 7.3 to find the region of the electromagnetic spectrum in which the wavelength lies. Compare the absorbance of the given concentration of Vitamin A to the absorbance of the given amount of fish-liver oil to find the concentration of Vitamin A in the oil.
Solution:
a) At this wavelength the sensitivity to absorbance of light by Vitamin A is maximized while minimizing interference due to the absorbance of light by other substances in the fish-liver oil.

b) The wavelength 329 nm lies in the **ultraviolet region** of the electromagnetic spectrum.
c) A known quantity of vitamin A ($1.67\text{x}10^{-3}$ g) is dissolved in a known volume of solvent (250. mL) to give a *standard* concentration with a known response (1.018 units). This can be used to find the unknown quantity of Vitamin A that gives a response of 0.724 units. An equality can be made between the two concentration-to-absorbance ratios.

Concentration (C_1, g/mL) of Vitamin A = $\left(\frac{1.67\text{x}10^{-3}\text{ g}}{250.\text{ mL}}\right)$ = $6.68\text{x}10^{-6}$ g/mL Vitamin A

Absorbance (A_1) of Vitamin A = 1.018 units.
Absorbance (A_2) of fish-liver oil = 0.724 units
Concentration (g/mL) of Vitamin A in fish-liver oil sample = C_2

$$\frac{A_1}{C_1} = \frac{A_2}{C_2}$$

$$C_2 = \frac{A_2C_1}{A_1} = \frac{(0.724)(6.68\text{x}10^{-6}\text{ g/mL})}{(1.018)} = 4.7508\text{x}10^{-6}\text{ g/mL Vitamin A}$$

Mass (g) of Vitamin A in oil sample = $(500.\text{ mL oil})\left(\frac{4.7508\text{x}10^{-6}\text{ g Vitamin A}}{1\text{ mL oil}}\right)$ = $2.3754\text{x}10^{-3}$ g Vitamin A

Concentration of Vitamin A in oil sample = $\frac{(2.3754\text{x}10^{-3}\text{ g})}{(0.1232\text{ g Oil})}$ = $1.92808\text{x}10^{-2}$ = $\mathbf{1.93x10^{-2}}$ **g Vitamin A/g oil**

7.92 Plan: First find the energy in joules from the light that shines on the text. Each watt is one joule/s for a total of 75 J; take 5% of that amount of joules and then 10% of that amount. Use $E = \frac{hc}{\lambda}$ to find the energy of one photon of light with a wavelength of 550 nm. Divide the energy that shines on the text by the energy of one photon to obtain the number of photons.
Solution:
The amount of energy is calculated from the wavelength of light:

$$\lambda\text{ (m)} = (550\text{ nm})\left(\frac{10^{-9}\text{ m}}{1\text{ nm}}\right) = 5.50\text{x}10^{-7}\text{ m}$$

$$E = \frac{hc}{\lambda} = \frac{(6.626\text{x}10^{-34}\text{ J•s})(3.00\text{x}10^{8}\text{ m/s})}{5.50\text{x}10^{-7}\text{ m}} = 3.614182\text{x}10^{-19}\text{ J/photon}$$

Amount of power from the bulb = $(75\text{ W})\left(\frac{1\text{ J/s}}{1\text{ W}}\right)$ = 75 J/s

Amount of power converted to light = $(75\text{ J/s})\left(\frac{5\%}{100\%}\right)$ = 3.75 Js

Amount of light shining on book = $(3.75\text{ J/s})\left(\frac{10\%}{100\%}\right)$ = 0.375 J/s

Number of photons: $\left(\frac{0.375\text{ J}}{\text{s}}\right)\left(\frac{1\text{ photon}}{3.614182\text{x}10^{-19}\text{ J}}\right)$ = $1.0376\text{x}10^{18}$ = $\mathbf{1.0x10^{18}}$ **photons/s**

7.95 Plan: In the visible series with $n_{final} = 2$, the transitions will end in either the $2s$ or $2p$ orbitals since those are the only two types of orbitals in the second main energy level. With the restriction that the angular momentum quantum number can change by only ±1, the allowable transitions are from a p orbital to $2s$ ($l = 1$ to $l = 0$), from an s orbital to $2p$ ($l = 0$ to $l = 1$), and from a d orbital to $2p$ ($l = 2$ to $l = 1$). The problem specifies a change in *energy level*, so n_{init} must be 3, 4, 5, etc. (Although a change from $2p$ to $2s$ would result in a +1 change in l, this is not a change in energy level.)

Solution:

The first four transitions are as follows:

$3s \rightarrow 2p$

$3d \rightarrow 2p$

$4s \rightarrow 2p$

$3p \rightarrow 2s$

CHAPTER 8 ELECTRON CONFIGURATION AND CHEMICAL PERIODICITY

FOLLOW–UP PROBLEMS

8.1A Plan: The superscripts can be added to indicate the number of electrons in the element, and hence its identity. A horizontal orbital diagram is written for simplicity, although it does not indicate the sublevels have different energies. Based on the orbital diagram, we identify the electron of interest and determine its four quantum numbers.
Solution:
The number of electrons = 2 + 2 + 4 = 8; element = **oxygen**, atomic number 8.
Orbital diagram:

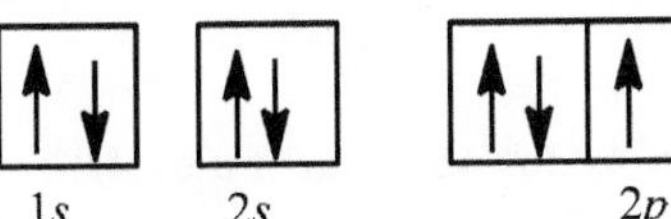

The electron in the middle $2p$ orbital is the sixth electron (this electron would have entered in this position due to Hund's rule). This electron has the following quantum numbers: $\boldsymbol{n = 2, l = 1}$ **(for** $\boldsymbol{p}$ **orbital),** $\boldsymbol{m_l = 0, m_s = +1/2}$. By convention, +1/2 is assigned to the first electron in an orbital. Also, the first p orbital is assigned an m_l value of −1, the middle p orbital a m_l value of 0, and the last p orbital a m_l value of +1.

8.1B Plan: Use the quantum numbers to determine the orbital into which the last electron is added and whether the electron is the first or second electron added to that orbital. Draw the orbital diagram that matches the quantum numbers. Then use the orbital diagram and the periodic table to identify the element. Finally, write the electron configuration for the element.
Solution:
The last electron added to the atom has the quantum numbers $n = 2$, $l = 1$, $m_l = 0$ and $m_s = +1/2$. This electron is in the second 2p orbital ($n = 2$, $l = 1$ tells us that the orbital is 2p; $m_l = 0$ tells us that the orbital is the 2nd of the three 2p orbitals). Additionally, because $m_s = +1/2$, we know the electron is the first electron in that orbital. The orbital diagram that matches this description is:
Orbital diagram:

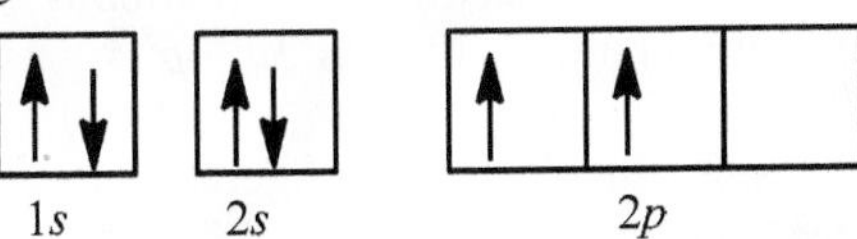

There are a total of 6 electrons in the orbital diagram. **Carbon** is the element with 6 protons and, in its neutral state, 6 electrons. Its electron configuration is: $\mathbf{1s^22s^22p^2}$.

8.2A Plan: The atomic number gives the number of electrons. The order of filling may be inferred by the location of the element on the periodic table. The partial orbital diagrams shows only those electrons after the preceding noble gas except those used to fill inner d and f subshells. The number of inner electrons is simply the total number of electrons minus those electrons in the partial orbital diagram.
Solution:
a) For Ni (Z = 28), the full electron configuration is $\mathbf{1s^22s^22p^63s^23p^64s^23d^8}$.
The condensed configuration is $\mathbf{[Ar]4s^23d^8}$.

The partial orbital diagram for the valence electrons is

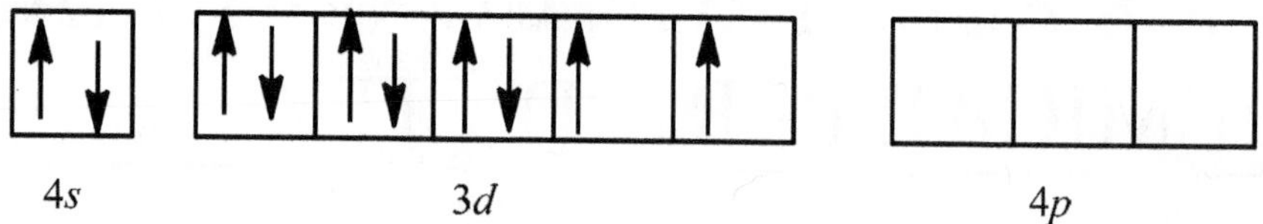

There are 28 – 10(valence) = **18 inner electrons.**
b) For Sr (Z = 38), the full electron configuration is $\mathbf{1s^22s^22p^63s^23p^64s^23d^{10}4p^65s^2}$.
The condensed configuration is $\mathbf{[Kr]5s^2}$. The partial orbital diagram is

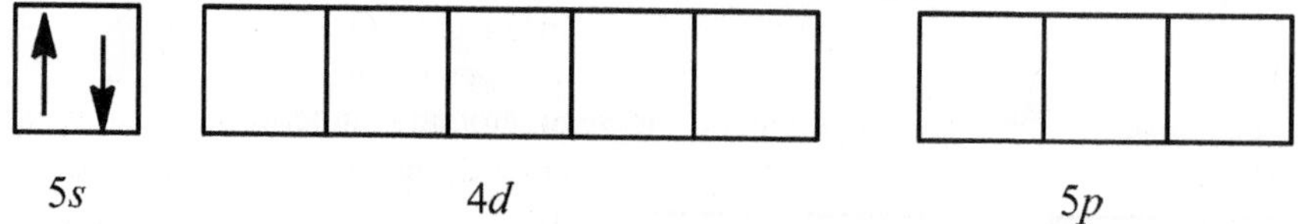

There are 38 – 2(valence) = **36 inner electrons.**
c) For Po (84 electrons), the full configuration $\mathbf{1s^22s^22p^63s^23p^64s^23d^{10}4p^65s^24d^{10}5p^66s^24f^{14}5d^{10}6p^4}$.
The condensed configuration is $\mathbf{[Xe]6s^24f^{14}5d^{10}6p^4}$.
The partial orbital diagram represents valence electrons only; the inner electrons are those in the previous noble gas (Xe or $1s^22s^22p^63s^23p^64s^23d^{10}4p^65s^24d^{10}5p^6$) and *filled* transition ($5d^{10}$) and inner transition ($4f^{14}$) levels.

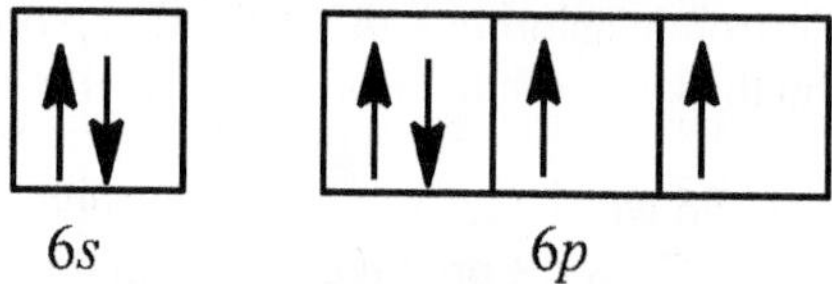

There are 84 – 6(valence) = **78 inner electrons.**

8.2B Plan: The partial orbital diagrams show the electrons that have been added after the preceding noble gas except for those used to fill inner d and f subshells (in most cases). Use the orbital diagrams and the periodic table to identify the elements. Write their full and condensed electron configurations. The number of inner electrons is simply the total number of electrons minus those electrons in the partial orbital diagram.
Solution:
a) **As** (Z = 33) has two $4s$ electrons and three $4p$ electrons. Its full electron configuration is $\mathbf{1s^22s^22p^63s^23p^64s^23d^{10}4p^3}$ and its condensed electron configuration is $\mathbf{[Ar]\ 4s^23d^{10}4p^3}$.
There are 33 – 5(valence) = **28 inner electrons.**
b) **Zr** (Z = 40) has two $5s$ electrons and two $4d$ electrons. Its full electron configuration is $\mathbf{1s^22s^22p^63s^23p^64s^23d^{10}4p^65s^24d^2}$ and its condensed electron configuration is $\mathbf{[Kr]\ 5s^24d^2}$.
There are 40 – 4(valence) = **36 inner electrons.**
c) **I** (Z = 53) has two $5s$ electrons and five $5p$ electrons. Its full electron configuration is $\mathbf{1s^22s^22p^63s^23p^64s^23d^{10}4p^65s^24d^{10}5p^5}$ and its condensed electron configuration is $\mathbf{[Kr]\ 5s^24d^{10}5p^5}$.
There are 53 – 7(valence) = **46 inner electrons.**

8.3A Plan: Locate each of the elements on the periodic table. All of these are main-group elements, so their sizes increase down and to the left in the periodic table.
Solution:
a) **Cl < Br < Se**. Cl has a smaller n than Br and Se. Br experiences a higher Z_{eff} than Se and is smaller.
b) **Xe < I < Ba**. Xe and I have the same n, but Xe experiences a higher Z_{eff} and is smaller. Ba has the highest n and is the largest.

8.3B Plan: Locate each of the elements on the periodic table. All of these are main-group elements, so their sizes increase down and to the left in the periodic table.

Solution:
a) **Cs > As > S**. Cs has the largest n of the group. Additionally, it is further to the left of the table than the other two elements. Therefore, Cs is the largest. As has a larger n than S and is further to the left on the periodic table, so it is the next largest element of this group.
b) **K > P > F**. K has the largest n of the group. Additionally, it is further to the left of the table than the other two elements. Therefore, K is the largest. P has a larger n than F and is further to the left on the periodic table, so it is the next largest element of this group.

8.4A Plan: These main-group elements must be located on the periodic table. The value of IE_1 increases toward the top (same column) and the right of the periodic table (same n).
Solution:
a) **Sn < Sb < I**. These elements have the same n, so the values increase to the right on the periodic table. Iodine has the highest IE, because its outer electron is most tightly held and hardest to remove.
b) **Cs < Na < Mg**. Mg is farther to the right on the periodic table than either of the other two elements, so it has the largest IE. Cs and Na are in the same column, so the values decrease towards the bottom of the column. Because Cs is lower than Na in the column, it has a lower IE.

8.4B Plan: These main-group elements must be located on the periodic table. The value of IE_1 increases toward the top (same column) and the right of the periodic table (same n).
Solution:
a) **O > As > Rb**. Oxygen is the farthest to the right on the periodic table (and closer to the top of the table), so it has the largest IE. Similarly, As is farther to the right and closer to the top of the table than Rb and, thus, has a higher IE.
b) **Cl > Si > Sn**. Cl and Si have the same n value and are closer to the top of the periodic table than Sn. Therefore, Sn has the lowest IE. Because Cl is closer to the right hand side of the periodic table than Si, Cl has the highest IE.

8.5A Plan: We must look for a large "jump" in the IE values. This jump occurs after the valence electrons have been removed. The next step is to determine the element in the designated period with the proper number of valence electrons.
Solution:
The exceptionally large jump from IE_3 to IE_4 means that the fourth electron is an inner electron. Thus, Q has three valence electrons. Since Q is in period 3, it must be **aluminum**, Al: $\mathbf{1s^22s^22p^63s^23p^1}$.

8.5B Plan: A large jump in IE values occurs after the valence electrons have been removed. Thus, the highest IE_3, for example, will be for an element that has 2 valence electrons because it will require much more energy to remove the third electron, an inner electron. Write the condensed electron configurations for the atoms, determine the number of valence electrons for each, and use this information to determine where the jump in IE values will occur.
Solution:
Rb: **[Kr] $5s^1$**
Sr: **[Kr] $5s^2$**
Y: **[Kr] $5s^24d^1$**
Because Rb has one valence electron, a large jump in IE values will occur between IE_1 and IE_2. Therefore, **IE_2 will be largest for Rb**. Because Sr has two valence electrons, a large jump in IE values will occur between IE_2 and IE_3. Therefore, **IE_3 will be largest for Sr.**

8.6A Plan: We need to locate each element on the periodic table. Elements in the first two columns on the left or the two columns to the left of the noble gases tend to adopt ions with a noble gas configuration. Elements in the remaining columns may use either their ns and np electrons, or just their np electrons.
Solution:
a) Barium loses two electrons to be isoelectronic with Xe: Ba ([Xe] $6s^2$) $\rightarrow$ Ba^{2+} ([Xe]) + $2e^-$
b) Oxygen gains two e^- to be isoelectronic with Ne: O ([He] $2s^22p^4$ + $2e^-$ $\rightarrow$ O^{2-} ([Ne])
c) Lead can lose two electrons to form an "inert pair" configuration:
Pb ([Xe]$6s^24f^{14}5d^{10}6p^2$) $\rightarrow$ Pb^{2+} ([Xe]$6s^24f^{14}5d^{10}$) + $2e^-$
or lead can lose four electrons to form a "pseudo–noble gas" configuration:
Pb ([Xe]$6s^24f^{14}5d^{10}6p^2$) $\rightarrow$ Pb^{4+} ([Xe]$4f^{14}5d^{10}$) + $4e^-$

8.6B Plan: We need to locate each element on the periodic table. Elements in the first two columns on the left or the two columns to the left of the noble gases tend to adopt ions with a noble gas configuration. Elements in the remaining columns may use either their *ns* and *np* electrons, or just their *np* electrons.
Solution:
a) Fluorine gains one electron to be isoelectronic with Ne: F ([He] $2s^22p^5$) + e^- → F^- ([He] $2s^22p^6$)
b) Thallium loses 1 e^- to form an "inert pair" configuration: Tl ([Xe] $6s^24f^{14}5d^{10}6p^1$ → Tl^+ ([Xe] $6s^24f^{14}5d^{10}$) + e^-
or thallium can lose 3 e^- to form a "pseudo-noble gas" configuration:
Tl ([Xe] $6s^24f^{14}5d^{10}6p^1$ → Tl^{3+} ([Xe] $4f^{14}5d^{10}$) + $3e^-$
c) Magnesium loses two electrons to be isoelectronic with Ne: Mg ([Ne] $3s^2$) → Mg^{2+} ([Ne]) + $2e^-$

8.7A Plan: Write the condensed electron configuration for each atom, being careful to note those elements which are irregular. The charge on the cation tells how many electrons are to be removed. The electrons are removed beginning with the *ns* electrons. If any electrons in the final ion are unpaired, the ion is paramagnetic. If it is not obvious that there are unpaired electrons, a partial orbital diagram might help.
Solution:
a) The V atom ([Ar]$4s^23d^3$) loses the two 4*s* electrons and one 3*d* electron to form V^{3+} (**[Ar]$3d^2$**). There are two unpaired *d* electrons, so V^{3+} is **paramagnetic.**
b) The Ni atom ([Ar]$4s^23d^8$) loses the two 4*s* electrons to form Ni^{2+} (**[Ar]$3d^8$**). There are two unpaired *d* electrons, so Ni^{2+} is **paramagnetic.**

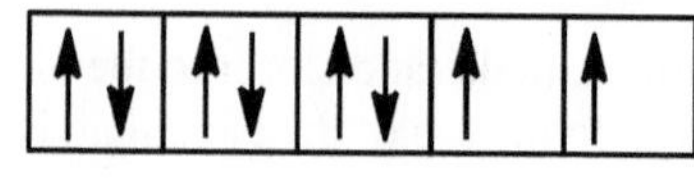

3*d*

c) The La atom ([Xe]$6s^25d^1$) loses all three valence electrons to form La^{3+} (**[Xe]**). There are no unpaired electrons, so La^{3+} is **diamagnetic.**

8.7B Plan: Write the condensed electron configuration for each atom, being careful to note those elements which are irregular. The charge on the cation tells how many electrons are to be removed. The electrons are removed beginning with the *ns* electrons. If it is not obvious that there are unpaired electrons, a partial orbital diagram might help.
Solution:
a) The Zr atom ([Kr]$5s^24d^2$) loses the two 5*s* electrons to form Zr^{2+} (**[Kr]$4d^2$**). There are **two unpaired *d* electrons.**
b) The Os atom ([Xe] $6s^24f^{14}5d^6$) loses the two 6*s* electrons and one 5*d* electron to form Os^{3+} (**[Xe] $4f^{14}5d^5$**). There are **five unpaired *d* electrons.**
c) The Co atom ([Ar] $4s^23d^7$) loses the two 4*s* electrons to form Co^{2+} (**[Ar] $3d^7$**). There are **three unpaired *d* electrons.**

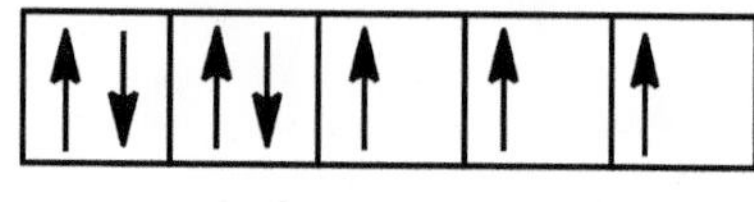

3*d*

8.8A Plan: Locate each of the elements on the periodic table. Cations are smaller than the parent atoms, and anions are larger than the parent atoms. If the electrons are equal, anions are larger than cations. The more electrons added or removed; the greater the change in size.
Solution:
a) Ionic size increases down a group, so **F^- < Cl^- < Br^-**.
b) These species are isoelectronic (all have 10 electrons), so size increases with increasing negative charge: **Mg^{2+} < Na^+ < F^-**
c) Ionic size increases as charge decreases for different cations of the same element, so **Cr^{3+} < Cr^{2+}**.

8.8B Plan: Locate each of the elements on the periodic table. Cations are smaller than the parent atoms, and anions are larger than the parent atoms. If the electrons are equal, anions are larger than cations. The more electrons added or removed; the greater the change in size.

Solution:
a) Ionic size decreases as charge increases for different cations of the same element, so V^{2+} **>** V^{3+}.
b) Ionic size decreases up (toward the top of) a group, so Cs^+ **>** Rb^+ **>** K^+.
c) These species are isoelectronic (all have 54 electrons), so size decreases with increasing positive charge:
I^- **>** Cs^+ **>** Ba^{2+}.

END–OF–CHAPTER PROBLEMS

8.1 Elements are listed in the periodic table in an ordered, systematic way that correlates with a periodicity of their chemical and physical properties. The theoretical basis for the table in terms of atomic number and electron configuration does not allow for an "unknown element" between Sn and Sb.

8.3 Plan: The value should be the average of the elements above and below the one of interest.
Solution:
a) Predicted atomic mass (K) =

$$\frac{\text{Na} + \text{Rb}}{2} = \frac{22.99 + 85.47}{2} = \mathbf{54.23\ amu} \qquad \text{(actual value = 39.10 amu)}$$

b) Predicted melting point (Br_2) =

$$\frac{Cl_2 + I_2}{2} = \frac{-101.0 + 113.6}{2} = \mathbf{6.3°C} \qquad \text{(actual value = −7.2°C)}$$

8.6 The quantum number m_s relates to just the electron; all the others describe the orbital.

8.9 Shielding occurs when inner electrons protect or shield outer electrons from the full nuclear attractive force. The effective nuclear charge is the nuclear charge an electron actually experiences. As the number of inner electrons increases, shielding increases, and the effective nuclear charge decreases.

8.11 Plan: The integer in front of the letter represents the n value. The l value designates the orbital type: $l = 0 = s$ orbital; $l = 1 = p$ orbital; $l = 2 = d$ orbital; $l = 3 = f$ orbital. Remember that a p orbital set contains 3 orbitals, a d orbital set has 5 orbitals, and an f orbital set has 7 orbitals. Any one orbital can hold a maximum of 2 electrons.
Solution:
a) The $l = 1$ quantum number can only refer to a p orbital. These quantum numbers designate the $2p$ orbital set ($n = 2$), which hold a maximum of **6** electrons, 2 electrons in each of the three $2p$ orbitals.
b) There are five $3d$ orbitals, therefore a maximum of **10** electrons can have the $3d$ designation, 2 electrons in each of the five $3d$ orbitals.
c) There is one $4s$ orbital which holds a maximum of **2** electrons.

8.13 Plan: The integer in front of the letter represents the n value. The l value designates the orbital type: $l = 0 = s$ orbital; $l = 1 = p$ orbital; $l = 2 = d$ orbital; $l = 3 = f$ orbital. Remember that a p orbital set contains 3 orbitals, a d orbital set has 5 orbitals, and an f orbital set has 7 orbitals. Any one orbital can hold a maximum of 2 electrons.
Solution:
a) **6** electrons can be found in the three $4p$ orbitals, 2 in each orbital.
b) The $l = 1$ quantum number can only refer to a p orbital, and the m_l value of +1 specifies one particular p orbital, which holds a maximum of **2** electrons with the difference between the two electrons being in the m_s quantum number.
c) **14** electrons can be found in the $5f$ orbitals ($l = 3$ designates f orbitals; there are $7f$ orbitals in a set).

8.16 Hund's rule states that electrons will fill empty orbitals in the same sublevel before filling half-filled orbitals. This lowest-energy arrangement has the maximum number of unpaired electrons with parallel spins. In the correct electron configuration for nitrogen shown in (a), the $2p$ orbitals each have one unpaired electron; in the incorrect configuration shown in (b), electrons were paired in one of the $2p$ orbitals while leaving one $2p$ orbital empty. The arrows in the $2p$ orbitals of configuration (a) could alternatively all point down.

(a) – correct

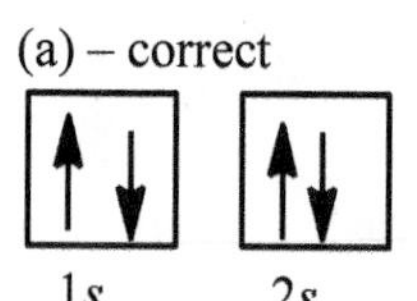
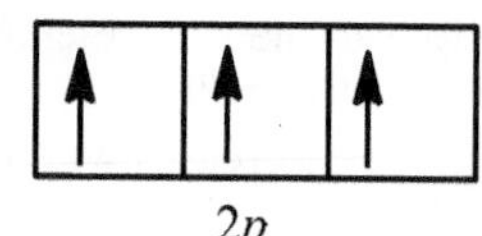

1*s* 2*s* 2*p*

(b) – incorrect

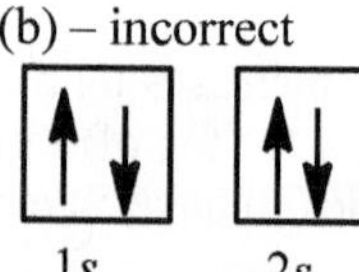
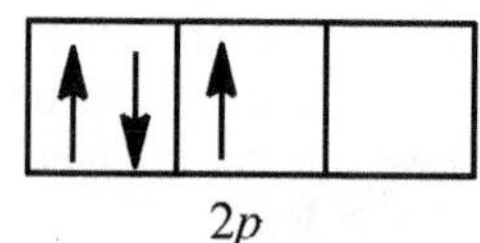

1*s* 2*s* 2*p*

8.18 For elements in the same group (vertical column in periodic table), the electron configuration of the outer electrons are identical except for the n value. For elements in the same period (horizontal row in periodic table), their configurations vary because each succeeding element has one additional electron. The electron configurations are similar only in the fact that the same level (principal quantum number) is the outer level.

8.20 The total electron capacity for an energy level is $\mathbf{2n^2}$, so the $n = 4$ energy level holds a maximum of $2(4^2) = \mathbf{32}$ **electrons**. A filled $n = 4$ energy level would have the following configuration: $4s^24p^64d^{10}4f^{14}$.

8.21 Plan: Write the electron configuration for the atom or ion and find the electron for which you are writing the quantum numbers. Assume that the electron is in the ground-state configuration and that electrons fill in a p_x–p_y–p_z order. By convention, we assign the first electron to fill an orbital with an m_s value of +1/2. Also by convention, $m_l = -1$ for the p_x orbital, $m_l = 0$ for the p_y orbital, and $m_l = +1$ for the p_z orbital. Also, keep in mind the following letter orbital designation for each l value: $l = 0 = s$ orbital, $l = 1 = p$ orbital, $l = 2 = d$ orbital, and $l = 3 = f$ orbital.

Solution:

a) Rb: [Kr]$5s^1$. The outermost electron in a rubidium atom would be in a 5*s* orbital (rubidium is in Row 5, Group 1). The quantum numbers for this electron are $\mathbf{n = 5, l = 0, m_l = 0}$, and $\mathbf{m_s = +1/2}$.

b) The S^- ion would have the configuration [Ne]$3s^23p^5$. The electron added would go into the $3p_z$ orbital and is the second electron in that orbital. Quantum numbers are $\mathbf{n = 3, l = 1, m_l = +1}$, and $\mathbf{m_s = -1/2}$.

c) Ag atoms have the configuration [Kr]$5s^14d^{10}$. The electron lost would be from the 5*s* orbital with quantum numbers $\mathbf{n = 5, l = 0, m_l = 0}$, and $\mathbf{m_s = +1/2}$.

d) The F atom has the configuration [He]$2s^22p^5$. The electron gained would go into the $2p_z$ orbital and is the second electron in that orbital. Quantum numbers are $\mathbf{n = 2, l = 1, m_l = +1}$, and $\mathbf{m_s = -1/2}$.

8.23 Plan: The atomic number gives the number of electrons and the periodic table shows the order for filling sublevels. Recall that *s* orbitals hold a maximum of 2 electrons, a *p* orbital set holds 6 electrons, a *d* orbital set holds 10 electrons, and an *f* orbital set holds 14 electrons.

Solution:

a) Rb: $\mathbf{1s^22s^22p^63s^23p^64s^23d^{10}4p^65s^1}$

b) Ge: $\mathbf{1s^22s^22p^63s^23p^64s^23d^{10}4p^2}$

c) Ar: $\mathbf{1s^22s^22p^63s^23p^6}$

8.25 Plan: The atomic number gives the number of electrons and the periodic table shows the order for filling sublevels. Recall that *s* orbitals hold a maximum of 2 electrons, a *p* orbital set holds 6 electrons, a *d* orbital set holds 10 electrons, and an *f* orbital set holds 14 electrons.

Solution:

a) Cl: $\mathbf{1s^22s^22p^63s^23p^5}$

b) Si: $\mathbf{1s^22s^22p^63s^23p^2}$

c) Sr: $\mathbf{1s^22s^22p^63s^23p^64s^23d^{10}4p^65s^2}$

8.27 Plan: The atomic number gives the number of electrons and the periodic table shows the order for filling sublevels. Recall that *s* orbitals hold a maximum of 2 electrons, a *p* orbital set holds 6 electrons, a *d* orbital set holds 10 electrons, and an *f* orbital set holds 14 electrons. Valence electrons are those in the highest energy level; in transition metals, the $(n - 1)d$ electrons are also counted as valence electrons. For a condensed ground-state electron configuration, the electron configuration of the previous noble gas is shown by its element symbol in brackets, followed by the electron configuration of the energy level being filled.

Solution:

a) Ti (Z = 22); [Ar]$4s^23d^2$

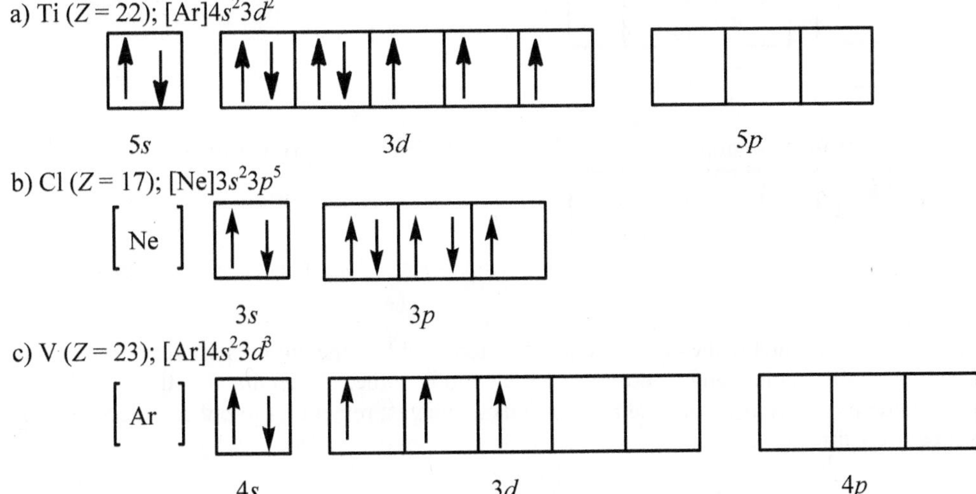

b) Cl (Z = 17); [Ne]$3s^23p^5$

c) V (Z = 23); [Ar]$4s^23d^3$

8.29 Plan: The atomic number gives the number of electrons and the periodic table shows the order for filling sublevels. Recall that *s* orbitals hold a maximum of 2 electrons, a *p* orbital set holds 6 electrons, a *d* orbital set holds 10 electrons, and an *f* orbital set holds 14 electrons. Valence electrons are those in the highest energy level; in transition metals, the $(n-1)d$ electrons are also counted as valence electrons. For a condensed ground-state electron configuration, the electron configuration of the previous noble gas is shown by its element symbol in brackets, followed by the electron configuration of the energy level being filled.

Solution:

a) Mn (Z = 25); [Ar]$4s^23d^5$

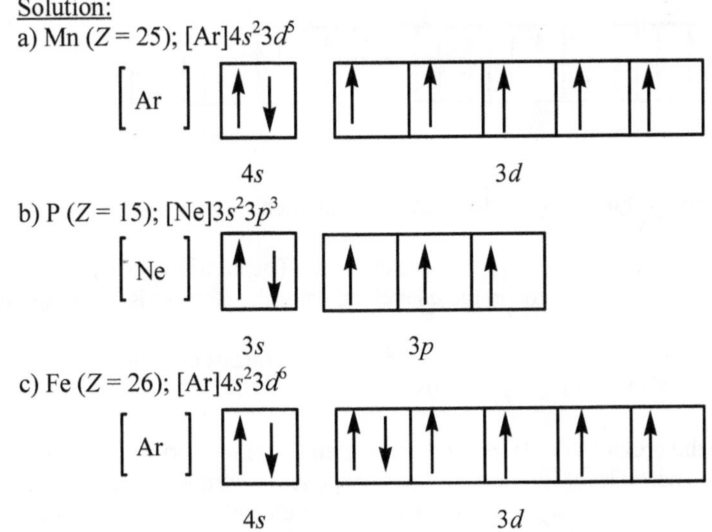

b) P (Z = 15); [Ne]$3s^23p^3$

c) Fe (Z = 26); [Ar]$4s^23d^6$

8.31 Plan: Add up all of the electrons in the electron configuration to obtain the atomic number of the element which is then used to identify the element and its position in the periodic table. When drawing the partial orbital diagram, only include electrons after those of the previous noble gas; remember to put one electron in each orbital in a set before pairing electrons.

Solution:

a) There are 8 electrons in the configuration; the element is O, Group 6A(16), Period 2.

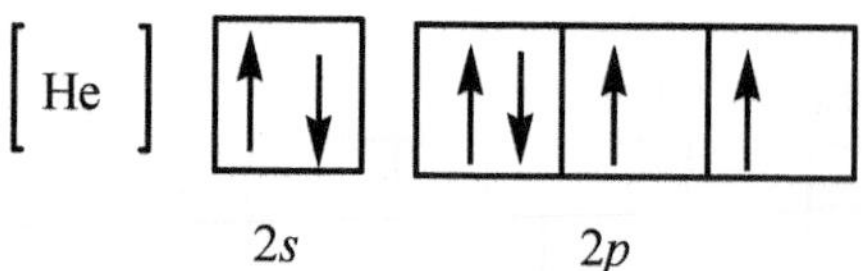

b) There are 15 electrons in the configuration; the element is P, Group 5A(15), Period 3.

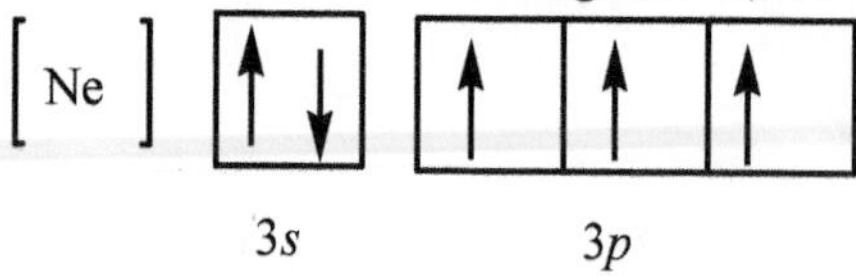

8.33 Plan: Add up all of the electrons in the electron configuration to obtain the atomic number of the element which is then used to identify the element and its position in the periodic table. When drawing the partial orbital diagram, only include electrons after those of the previous noble gas; remember to put one electron in each orbital in a set before pairing electrons.

Solution:

a) There are 17 electrons in the configuration; the element is Cl; Group 7A(17); Period 3.

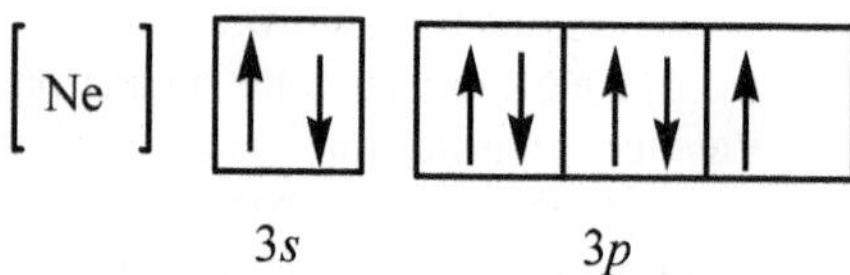

b) There are 33 electrons in the configuration; the element is As; Group 5A(15); Period 4.

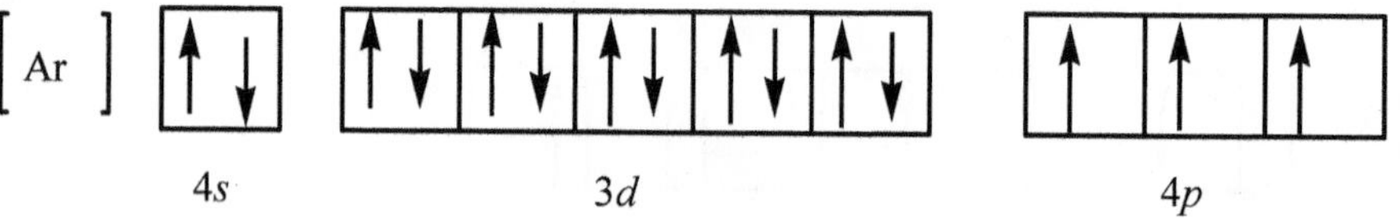

8.35 Plan: Use the periodic table and the partial orbital diagram to identify the element.

Solution:

a) The orbital diagram shows the element is in Period 4 ($n = 4$ as outer level). The configuration is $\mathbf{1s^22s^22p^63s^23p^64s^23d^{10}4p^1}$ or [Ar]$4s^23d^{10}4p^1$. One electron in the *p* level indicates the element is in Group **3A(13)**. The element is Ga.

b) The orbital diagram shows the $2s$ and $2p$ orbitals filled which would represent the last element in Period 2, Ne. The configuration is $\mathbf{1s^22s^22p^6}$ or [He]$2s^22p^6$. Filled *s* and *p* orbitals indicate Group **8A(18)**.

8.37 Plan: Inner electrons are those seen in the previous noble gas and completed transition series (*d* orbitals). Outer electrons are those in the highest energy level (highest *n* value). Valence electrons are the outer electrons for main-group elements; for transition metals, valence electrons also include electrons in the outermost *d* set of orbitals. It is easiest to determine the types of electrons by writing a condensed electron configuration.

Solution:

a) O ($Z = 8$); [He]$2s^22p^4$. There are **2** inner electrons (represented by [He]) and **6** outer electrons. The number of valence electrons (**6**) equals the outer electrons in this case.

b) Sn ($Z = 50$); [Kr]$5s^24d^{10}5p^2$. There are 36 (from [Kr]) + 10 (from the filled $4d$ set) = **46** inner electrons. There are **4** outer electrons (highest energy level is $n = 5$) and **4** valence electrons.

c) Ca ($Z = 20$); [Ar]$4s^2$. There are **2** outer electrons (the $4s$ electrons), **2** valence electrons, and **18** inner electrons (from [Ar]).

d) Fe ($Z = 26$); [Ar]$4s^23d^6$. There are **2** outer electrons (from $n = 4$ level), **8** valence electrons (the *d* orbital electrons count in this case because the sublevel is not full), and **18** inner electrons (from [Ar]).

e) Se ($Z = 34$); [Ar]$4s^23d^{10}4p^4$. There are **6** outer electrons (2 + 4 in the $n = 4$ level), **6** valence electrons (filled *d* sublevels count as inner electrons), and **28** inner electrons (18 from [Ar] and 10 from the filled $3d$ set).

8.39 Plan: Add up all of the electrons in the electron configuration to obtain the atomic number of the element which is then used to identify the element and its position in the periodic table.
Solution:
a) The electron configuration $[He]2s^22p^1$ has a total of 5 electrons (3 + 2 from He configuration) which is element boron with symbol **B**. Boron is in Group 3A(13). Other elements in this group are **Al, Ga, In,** and **Tl**.
b) The electrons in this element total 16, 10 from the neon configuration plus 6 from the rest of the configuration. Element 16 is sulfur, **S**, in Group 6A(16). Other elements in Group 6A(16) are **O, Se, Te,** and **Po**.
c) Electrons total 3 + 54 (from xenon) = 57. Element 57 is lanthanum, **La**, in Group 3B(3). Other elements in this group are **Sc, Y,** and **Ac**.

8.41 Plan: Add up all of the electrons in the electron configuration to obtain the atomic number of the element which is then used to identify the element and its position in the periodic table.
Solution:
a) The electron configuration $[He]2s^22p^2$ has a total of 6 electrons (4 + 2 from He configuration) which is element carbon with symbol **C**; other Group 4A(14) elements include **Si, Ge, Sn,** and **Pb**.
b) Electrons total 5 + 18 (from argon) = 23 which is **vanadium**; other Group 5B(5) elements include **Nb, Ta,** and **Db**.
c) The electrons in this element total 15, 10 from the neon configuration plus 5 from the rest of the configuration. Element 15 is **phosphorus**; other Group 5A(15) elements include **N, As, Sb,** and **Bi**.

8.43 Plan: Write the ground-state electron configuration of sodium; for the excited state, move the outermost electron to the next orbital.
Solution:
The ground-state configuration of Na is $1s^22s^22p^63s^1$. Upon excitation, the $3s^1$ electron is promoted to the $3p$ level, with configuration $1s^22s^22p^63p^1$.

1*s*	2*s*	2*p*			3*s*	3*p*		
↑↓	↑↓	↑↓	↑↓	↑↓		↑		

8.50 A high, endothermic IE_1 means it is very difficult to remove the first outer electron. This value would exclude any metal, because metals lose an outer electron easily. A very negative, exothermic EA_1 suggests that this element easily gains one electron. These values indicate that the element belongs to the halogens, Group **7A(17)**, which form **–1** ions.

8.53 Plan: Atomic size decreases up a main group and left to right across a period.
Solution:
a) Increasing atomic size: **K < Rb < Cs**; these three elements are all part of the same group, the alkali metals. Atomic size decreases up a main group (larger outer electron orbital), so potassium is the smallest and cesium is the largest.
b) Increasing atomic size: **O < C < Be**; these three elements are in the same period and atomic size decreases across a period (increasing effective nuclear charge), so beryllium is the largest and oxygen the smallest.
c) Increasing atomic size: **Cl < S < K**; chlorine and sulfur are in the same period so chlorine is smaller since it is further to the right in the period. Potassium is the first element in the next period so it is larger than either Cl or S.
d) Increasing atomic size: **Mg < Ca < K**; calcium is larger than magnesium because Ca is further down the alkaline earth metal group on the periodic table than Mg. Potassium is larger than calcium because K is further to the left than Ca in Period 4 of the periodic table.

8.55 Plan: Ionization energy increases up a group and left to right across a period.
Solution:
a) **Ba < Sr < Ca** The "group" rule applies in this case. Ionization energy increases up a main group. Barium's outer electron receives the most shielding; therefore, it is easiest to remove and has the lowest IE.
b) **B < N < Ne** These elements have the same *n*, so the "period" rule applies. Ionization energy increases from left to right across a period. B experiences the lowest Z_{eff} and has the lowest IE. Ne has the highest IE, because it's very difficult to remove an electron from the stable noble gas configuration.

c) **Rb < Se < Br** IE decreases with increasing atomic size, so Rb (largest atom) has the smallest IE. Se has a lower IE than Br because IE increases across a period.
d) **Sn < Sb < As** IE increases up a group, so Sn and Sb will have smaller IEs than As. The "period" rule applies for ranking Sn and Sb.

8.57 Plan: When a large jump between successive ionization energies is observed, the subsequent electron must come from a full lower energy level. Thus, by looking at a series of successive ionization energies, we can determine the number of valence electrons. The number of valence electrons identifies which group the element is in.
Solution:
The successive ionization energies show a very significant jump between the third and fourth IEs. This indicates that the element has three valence electrons. The fourth electron must come from the core electrons and thus has a very large ionization energy. The electron configuration of the Period 2 element with three valence electrons is $\mathbf{1s^22s^22p^1}$ which represents boron, **B**.

8.59 Plan: For a given element, successive ionization energies always increase. As each successive electron is removed, the positive charge on the ion increases, which results in a stronger attraction between the leaving electron and the ion. A very large jump between successive ionization energies will occur when the electron to be removed comes from a full lower energy level. Examine the electron configurations of the atoms. If the IE_2 represents removing an electron from a full orbital, then the IE_2 will be very large. In addition, for atoms with the same outer electron configuration, IE_2 is larger for the smaller atom.
Solution:
a) **Na** would have the highest IE_2 because ionization of a second electron would require breaking the stable [Ne] configuration:
First ionization: Na ([Ne]$3s^1$) $\rightarrow$ Na^+ ([Ne]) + e^- (low IE)
Second ionization: Na^+ ([Ne]) $\rightarrow$ Na^{+2} ([He]$2s^22p^5$) + e^- (high IE)
b) **Na** would have the highest IE_2 because it has one valence electron and is smaller than K.
c) You might think that Sc would have the highest IE_2, because removing a second electron would require breaking the stable, filled 4*s* shell. However, **Be** has the highest IE_2 because Be's small size makes it difficult to remove a second electron.

8.61 Three of the ways that metals and nonmetals differ are: 1) metals conduct electricity, nonmetals do not; 2) when they form stable ions, metal ions tend to have a positive charge, nonmetal ions tend to have a negative charge; and 3) metal oxides are ionic and act as bases, nonmetal oxides are covalent and act as acids.

8.62 Metallic character decreases up a group and decreases toward the right across a period. These trends are the same as those for atomic size and opposite those for ionization energy.

8.65 Plan: Write the electron configurations for the two elements. Remember that these elements lose electrons to achieve pseudo-noble gas configurations.
Solution:
The two largest elements in Group 4A, Sn and Pb, have atomic electron configurations that look like $ns^2(n-1)d^{10}np^2$. Both of these elements are metals so they will form positive ions. To reach the noble gas configuration of xenon the atoms would have to lose 14 electrons, which is not likely. Instead the atoms lose either 2 or 4 electrons to attain a stable configuration with either the *ns* and $(n-1)d$ filled for the 2+ ion or the $(n-1)d$ orbital filled for the 4+ ion. The Sn^{2+} and Pb^{2+} ions form by losing the two *p* electrons:
Sn ([Kr]$5s^24d^{10}5p^2$) $\rightarrow$ Sn^{2+} ([Kr]$5s^24d^{10}$) + 2 e^-
Pb ([Xe]$6s^25d^{10}6p^2$) $\rightarrow$ Pb^{2+} ([Xe]$6s^25d^{10}$) + 2 e^-
The Sn^{4+} and Pb^{4+} ions form by losing the two *p* and two *s* electrons:
Sn ([Kr]$5s^24d^{10}5p^2$) $\rightarrow$ Sn^{4+} ([Kr]$4d^{10}$) + 4 e^-
Pb ([Xe]$6s^25d^{10}6p^2$) $\rightarrow$ Pb^{4+} ([Xe]$5d^{10}$) + 4 e^-
Possible ions for tin and lead have **+2** and **+4** charges. The +2 ions form by loss of the outermost two *p* electrons, while the +4 ions form by loss of these and the outermost two *s* electrons.

8.69 Plan: Metallic behavior decreases up a group and decreases left to right across a period.

Solution:
a) **Rb** is more metallic because it is to the left and below Ca.
b) **Ra** is more metallic because it lies below Mg in Group 2A(2).
c) **I** is more metallic because it lies below Br in Group 7A(17).

8.71 Plan: Metallic behavior decreases up a group and decreases left to right across a period.
Solution:
a) **As** should be less metallic than antimony because it lies above Sb in the same group of the periodic table.
b) **P** should be less metallic because it lies to the right of silicon in the same period of the periodic table.
c) **Be** should be less metallic since it lies above and to the right of sodium on the periodic table.

8.73 Plan: Generally, oxides of metals are basic while oxides of nonmetals are acidic.
Solution:
The reaction of a nonmetal oxide in water produces an **acidic** solution. An example of a Group 6A(16) nonmetal oxide is $SO_2(g)$: $SO_2(g) + H_2O(g) \rightarrow H_2SO_3(aq)$.

8.75 Plan: For main-group elements, the most stable ions have electron configurations identical to noble gas atoms. Write the electron configuration of the atom and then remove or add electrons until a noble gas configuration is achieved. Metals lose electrons and nonmetals gain electrons.
Solution:
a) Cl: $1s^22s^22p^63s^23p^5$; chlorine atoms are one electron short of a noble gas configuration, so a **–1** ion will form by adding an electron to have the same electron configuration as an argon atom: Cl^-, $\mathbf{1s^22s^22p^63s^23p^6}$.
b) Na: $1s^22s^22p^63s^1$; sodium atoms contain one more electron than the noble gas configuration of neon. Thus, a sodium atom loses one electron to form a **+1** ion: Na^+, $\mathbf{1s^22s^22p^6}$.
c) Ca: $1s^22s^22p^63s^23p^64s^2$; calcium atoms contain two more electrons than the noble gas configuration of argon. Thus, a calcium atom loses two electrons to form a **+2** ion: Ca^{2+}, $\mathbf{1s^22s^22p^63s^23p^6}$.

8.77 Plan: For main-group elements, the most stable ions have electron configurations identical to noble gas atoms. Write the electron configuration of the atom and then remove or add electrons until a noble gas configuration is achieved. Metals lose electrons and nonmetals gain electrons.
Solution:
a) Al: $1s^22s^22p^63s^23p^1$; aluminum atoms contain three more electrons than the noble gas configuration of Ne. Thus, an aluminum atom loses its 3 outer shell electrons to form a **+3** ion: Al^{3+}, $\mathbf{1s^22s^22p^6}$.
b) S: $1s^22s^22p^63s^23p^4$; sulfur atoms are two electrons short of the noble gas configuration of argon. Thus, a sulfur atom gains two electrons to form a **–2** ion: S^{2-}, $\mathbf{1s^22s^22p^63s^23p^6}$.
c) Sr: $1s^22s^22p^63s^23p^64s^23d^{10}4p^65s^2$; strontium atoms contain two more electrons than the noble gas configuration of krypton. Thus, a strontium atom loses two electrons to form a **+2** ion: Sr^{2+}, $\mathbf{1s^22s^22p^63s^23p^64s^23d^{10}4p^6}$.

8.79 Plan: To find the number of unpaired electrons look at the electron configuration expanded to include the different orientations of the orbitals, such as p_x and p_y and p_z. Remember that one electron will occupy every orbital in a set (*p*, *d*, or *f*) before electrons will pair in an orbital in that set. In the noble gas configurations, all electrons are paired because all orbitals are filled.
Solution:
a) Configuration of 2A(2) group elements: [noble gas]ns^2, **no unpaired electrons**. The electrons in the *ns* orbital are paired.
b) Configuration of 5A(15) group elements: [noble gas]$ns^2np_x^1np_y^1np_z^1$. **Three** unpaired electrons, one each in p_x, p_y, and p_z.
c) Configuration of 8A(18) group elements: noble gas configuration ns^2np^6 with no half-filled orbitals, **no unpaired electrons**.
d) Configuration of 3A(13) group elements: [noble gas]ns^2np^1. There is **one** unpaired electron in one of the *p* orbitals.

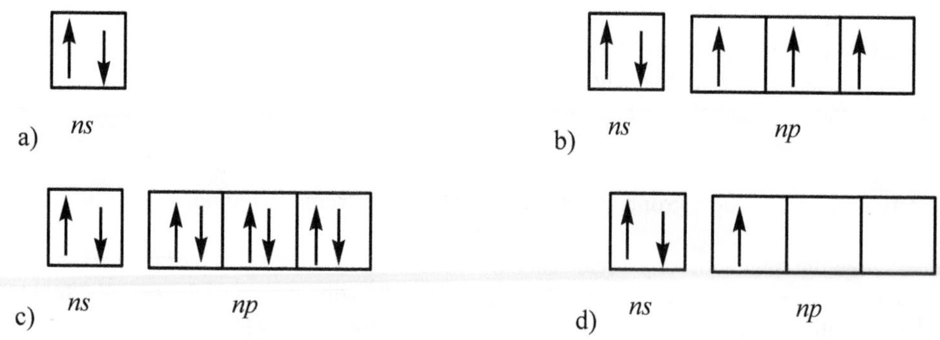

8.81 Plan: Substances are paramagnetic if they have unpaired electrons. To find the number of unpaired electrons look at the electron configuration expanded to include the different orientations of the orbitals, such as p_x and p_y and p_z. Remember that all orbitals in a *p*, *d*, or *f* set will each have one electron before electrons pair in an orbital. In the noble gas configurations, all electrons are paired because all orbitals are filled.

Solution:

a) Ga ($Z = 31$) = [Ar]$4s^2 3d^{10} 4p^1$. The *s* and *d* sublevels are filled, so all electrons are paired. The lone *p* electron is unpaired, so this element is **paramagnetic**.

b) Si ($Z = 14$) = [Ne]$3s^2 3p_x^1 3p_y^1 3p_z^0$. This element is **paramagnetic** with two unpaired electrons.

c) Be ($Z = 4$) = [He]$2s^2$. The two *s* electrons are paired so Be is **not paramagnetic**.

d) Te ($Z = 52$) = [Kr]$5s^2 4d^{10} 5p_x^2 5p_y^1 5p_z^1$ is **paramagnetic** with two unpaired electrons in the *5p* set.

8.83 Plan: Substances are paramagnetic if they have unpaired electrons. Write the electron configuration of the atom and then remove the specified number of electrons. Remember that all orbitals in a *p*, *d*, or *f* set will each have one electron before electrons pair in an orbital. In the noble gas configurations, all electrons are paired because all orbitals are filled.

Solution:

a) V: [Ar]$4s^2 3d^3$; **V^{3+}: [Ar]$3d^2$** Transition metals first lose the *s* electrons in forming ions, so to form the +3 ion a vanadium atom loses two 4*s* electrons and one 3*d* electron. **Paramagnetic**

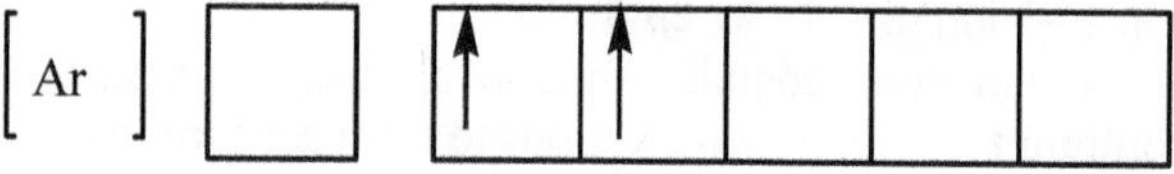

b) Cd: [Kr]$5s^2 4d^{10}$; **Cd^{2+}: [Kr]$4d^{10}$** Cadmium atoms lose two electrons from the 4*s* orbital to form the +2 ion. **Diamagnetic**

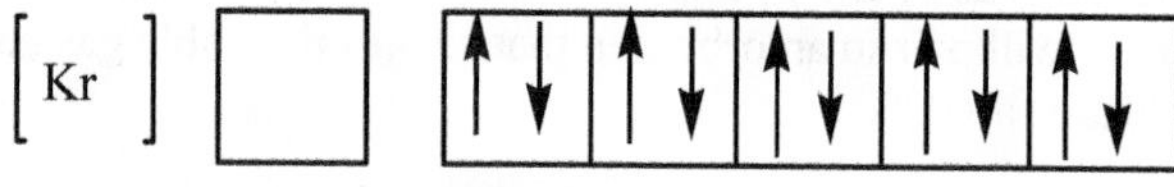

c) Co: [Ar]$4s^2 3d^7$; **Co^{3+}: [Ar]$3d^6$** Cobalt atoms lose two 4*s* electrons and one 3*d* electron to form the +3 ion. **Paramagnetic**

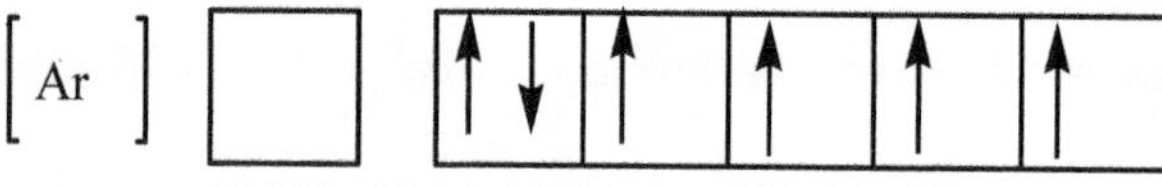

d) Ag: [Kr]$5s^1 4d^{10}$; **Ag^+: [Kr]$4d^{10}$** Silver atoms lose the one electron in the 5*s* orbital to form the +1 ion. **Diamagnetic**

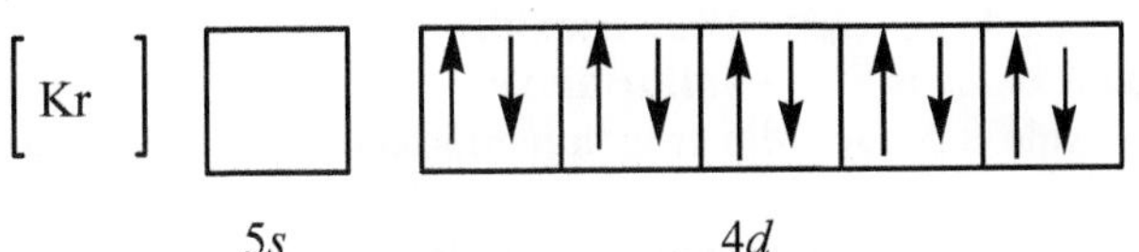

8.85 Plan: Substances are diamagnetic if they have no unpaired electrons. Draw the partial orbital diagrams, remembering that all orbitals in *d* set will each have one electron before electrons pair in an orbital.
Solution:
You might first write the condensed electron configuration for Pd as $[Kr]5s^24d^8$. However, the partial orbital diagram is not consistent with diamagnetism.

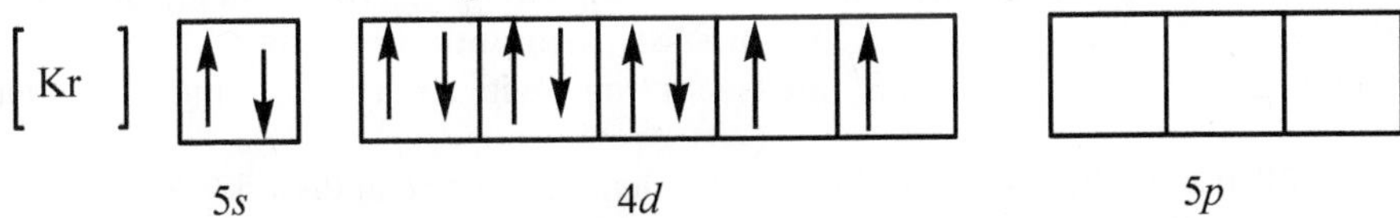

Promoting an *s* electron into the *d* sublevel (as in (c) $[Kr]5s^14d^9$) still leaves two electrons unpaired.

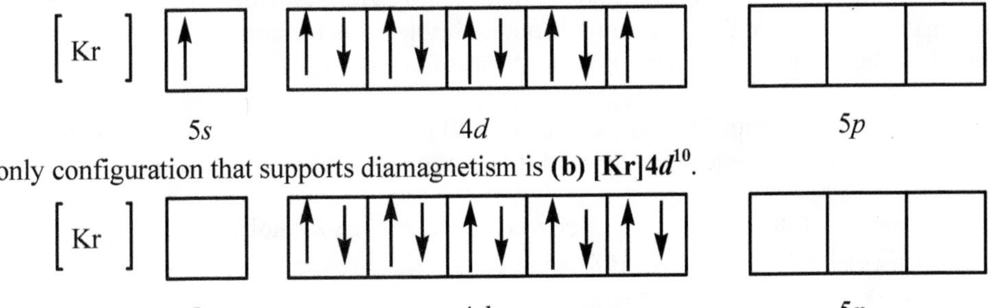

The only configuration that supports diamagnetism is **(b)** $\mathbf{[Kr]4d^{10}}$.

8.87 Plan: The size of ions increases down a group. For ions that are isoelectronic (have the same electron configuration) size decreases with increasing atomic number.
Solution:
a) Increasing size: $\mathbf{Li^+ < Na^+ < K^+}$, size increases down Group 1A(1).
b) Increasing size: $\mathbf{Rb^+ < Br^- < Se^{2-}}$, these three ions are isoelectronic with the same electron configuration as krypton. Size decreases with increasing atomic number in an isoelectronic series.
c) Increasing size: $\mathbf{F^- < O^{2-} < N^{3-}}$, the three ions are isoelectronic with an electron configuration identical to neon. Size decreases with increasing atomic number in an isoelectronic series.

8.90 Plan: Write the electron configuration for each atom. Remove the specified number of electrons, given by the positive ionic charge, to write the configuration for the ions. Remember that electrons with the highest *n* value are removed first.
Solution:

Ce:	$[Xe]6s^24f^15d^1$	Eu:	$[Xe]6s^24f^7$
Ce^{4+}:	[Xe]	Eu^{2+}:	$[Xe]4f^7$

Ce^{4+} has a noble gas configuration and Eu^{2+} has a half-filled *f* subshell.

8.91 Plan: Write the formula of the oxoacid. Remember that in naming oxoacids (H + polyatomic ion), the suffix of the polyatomic changes: -ate becomes -ic acid and -ite becomes -ous acid. Determine the oxidation state of the nonmetal in the oxoacid; hydrogen has an O.N. of +1 and oxygen has an O.N. of –2. Based on the oxidation state of the nonmetal, and the oxidation state of the oxide ion (–2), the formula of the nonmetal oxide may be determined. The name of the nonmetal oxide comes from the formula; remember that nonmetal compounds use prefixes to indicate the number of each type of atom in the formula.
Solution:
a) hypochlorous acid = HClO has Cl^+ so the oxide is $\mathbf{Cl_2O}$ = **dichlorine oxide** or **dichlorine monoxide**
b) chlorous acid = $HClO_2$ has Cl^{3+} so the oxide is $\mathbf{Cl_2O_3}$ = **dichlorine trioxide**
c) chloric acid = $HClO_3$ has Cl^{5+} so the oxide is $\mathbf{Cl_2O_5}$ = **dichlorine pentaoxide**
d) perchloric acid = $HClO_4$ has Cl^{7+} so the oxide is $\mathbf{Cl_2O_7}$ = **dichlorine heptaoxide**

e) sulfuric acid = H_2SO_4 has S^{6+} so the oxide is $\mathbf{SO_3}$ = **sulfur trioxide**
f) sulfurous acid = H_2SO_3 has S^{4+} so the oxide is $\mathbf{SO_2}$ = **sulfur dioxide**
g) nitric acid = HNO_3 has N^{5+} so the oxide is $\mathbf{N_2O_5}$ = **dinitrogen pentaoxide**
h) nitrous acid = HNO_2 has N^{3+} so the oxide is $\mathbf{N_2O_3}$ = **dinitrogen trioxide**
i) carbonic acid = H_2CO_3 has C^{4+} so the oxide is $\mathbf{CO_2}$ = **carbon dioxide**
j) phosphoric acid = H_3PO_4 has P^{5+} so the oxide is $\mathbf{P_2O_5}$ = **diphosphorus pentaoxide**

8.94 Plan: Remember that isoelectronic species have the same electron configuration. Atomic radius decreases up a group and left to right across a period.
Solution:
a) A chemically unreactive Period 4 element would be Kr in Group 8A(18). Both the Sr^{2+} ion and Br^- ion are isoelectronic with Kr. Their combination results in $\mathbf{SrBr_2}$, **strontium bromide.**
b) Ar is the Period 3 noble gas. Ca^{2+} and S^{2-} are isoelectronic with Ar. The resulting compound is **CaS, calcium sulfide.**
c) The smallest filled *d* subshell is the 3*d* shell, so the element must be in Period 4. Zn forms the Zn^{2+} ion by losing its two *s* subshell electrons to achieve a *pseudo–noble gas* configuration ($[Ar]3d^{10}$). The smallest halogen is fluorine, whose anion is F^-. The resulting compound is $\mathbf{ZnF_2}$, **zinc fluoride.**
d) Ne is the smallest element in Period 2, but it is not ionizable. Li is the largest atom whereas F is the smallest atom in Period 2. The resulting compound is **LiF, lithium fluoride.**

8.95 Plan: Recall Hess's law: the enthalpy change of an overall process is the sum of the enthalpy changes of its individual steps. Both the ionization energies and the electron affinities of the elements are needed.
Solution:
a) F: ionization energy = 1681 kJ/mol   electron affinity = –328 kJ/mol

$F(g) \rightarrow F^+(g) + e^-$ $\Delta H = 1681$ kJ/mol
$F(g) + e^- \rightarrow F^-(g)$ $\Delta H = -328$ kJ/mol

Reverse the electron affinity reaction to give: $F^-(g) \rightarrow F(g) + e^-$ $\Delta H = +328$ kJ/mol
Summing the ionization energy reaction with the reversed electron affinity reaction (Hess's law):

$\cancel{F(g)} \rightarrow F^+(g) + e^-$ $\Delta H = 1681$ kJ/mol
$F^-(g) \rightarrow \cancel{F(g)} + e^-$ $\Delta H = +328$ kJ/mol
$F^-(g) \rightarrow F^+(g) + 2e^-$ $\Delta H =$ **2009 kJ/mol**

b) Na: ionization energy = 496 kJ/mol   electron affinity = –52.9 kJ/mol

$Na(g) \rightarrow Na^+(g) + e^-$ $\Delta H = 496$ kJ/mol
$Na(g) + e^- \rightarrow Na^-(g)$ $\Delta H = -52.9$ kJ/mol

Reverse the ionization reaction to give: $Na^+(g) + e^- \rightarrow Na(g)$ $\Delta H = -496$ kJ/mol
Summing the electron affinity reaction with the reversed ionization reaction (Hess's law):

$\cancel{Na(g)} + e^- \rightarrow Na^-(g)$ $\Delta H = -52.9$ kJ/mol
$Na^+(g) + e^- \rightarrow \cancel{Na(g)}$ $\Delta H = -496$ kJ/mol
$Na^+(g) + 2e^- \rightarrow Na^-(g)$ $\Delta H = -548.9 =$ **–549 kJ/mol**

8.97 Plan: Determine the electron configuration for iron, and then begin removing one electron at a time. Remember that all orbitals in a *d* set will each have one electron before electrons pair in an orbital, and electrons with the highest *n* value are removed first. Ions with all electrons paired are diamagnetic. Ions with at least one unpaired electron are paramagnetic. The more unpaired electrons, the greater the attraction to a magnetic field.
Solution:

Fe	$[Ar]4s^23d^6$	partially filled 3*d* = **paramagnetic**	number of unpaired electrons = 4
Fe^+	$[Ar]4s^13d^6$	partially filled 3*d* = **paramagnetic**	number of unpaired electrons = 5
Fe^{2+}	$[Ar]3d^6$	partially filled 3*d* = **paramagnetic**	number of unpaired electrons = 4
Fe^{3+}	$[Ar]3d^5$	partially filled 3*d* = **paramagnetic**	number of unpaired electrons = 5
Fe^{4+}	$[Ar]3d^4$	partially filled 3*d* = **paramagnetic**	number of unpaired electrons = 4
Fe^{5+}	$[Ar]3d^3$	partially filled 3*d* = **paramagnetic**	number of unpaired electrons = 3
Fe^{6+}	$[Ar]3d^2$	partially filled 3*d* = **paramagnetic**	number of unpaired electrons = 2
Fe^{7+}	$[Ar]3d^1$	partially filled 3*d* = **paramagnetic**	number of unpaired electrons = 1
Fe^{8+}	[Ar]	filled orbitals = **diamagnetic**	number of unpaired electrons = 0
Fe^{9+}	$[Ne]3s^23p^5$	partially filled 3*p* = **paramagnetic**	number of unpaired electrons = 1
Fe^{10+}	$[Ne]3s^23p^4$	partially filled 3*p* = **paramagnetic**	number of unpaired electrons = 2

Fe^{11+}	$[Ne]3s^2 3p^3$	partially filled $3p$ = **paramagnetic**	number of unpaired electrons = 3
Fe^{12+}	$[Ne]3s^2 3p^2$	partially filled $3p$ = **paramagnetic**	number of unpaired electrons = 2
Fe^{13+}	$[Ne]3s^2 3p^1$	partially filled $3p$ = **paramagnetic**	number of unpaired electrons = 1
Fe^{14+}	$[Ne]3s^2$	filled orbitals = **diamagnetic**	number of unpaired electrons = 0

Fe^+ and **Fe^{3+}** would both be most attracted to a magnetic field. They each have 5 unpaired electrons.

CHAPTER 9 MODELS OF CHEMICAL BONDING

FOLLOW–UP PROBLEMS

9.1A Plan: First, write out the condensed electron configuration, partial orbital diagram, and electron-dot structure for magnesium atoms and chlorine atoms. In the formation of the ions, each magnesium atom will lose two electrons to form the +2 ion and each chlorine atom will gain one electron to form the –1 ion. Write the condensed electron configuration, partial orbital diagram, and electron-dot structure for each of the ions. The formula of the compound is found by combining the ions in a ratio that gives a neutral compound.

Solution:

Condensed electron configurations:

Mg ([Ne]$3s^2$) + Cl ([Ne]$3s^23p^5$) → Mg^{2+} ([Ne]) + Cl^- ([Ne]$3s^23p^6$)

In order to balance the charge (or the number of electrons lost and gained) two chlorine atoms are needed:

Mg ([Ne]$3s^2$) + 2Cl ([Ne]$3s^23p^5$) → Mg^{2+} ([Ne]) + $2Cl^-$ ([Ne]$3s^23p^6$)

Partial orbital diagrams:

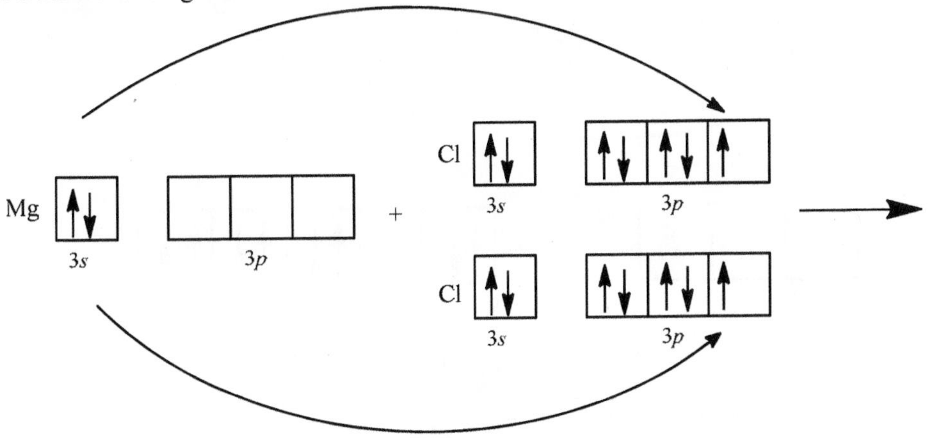

Lewis electron–dot symbols:

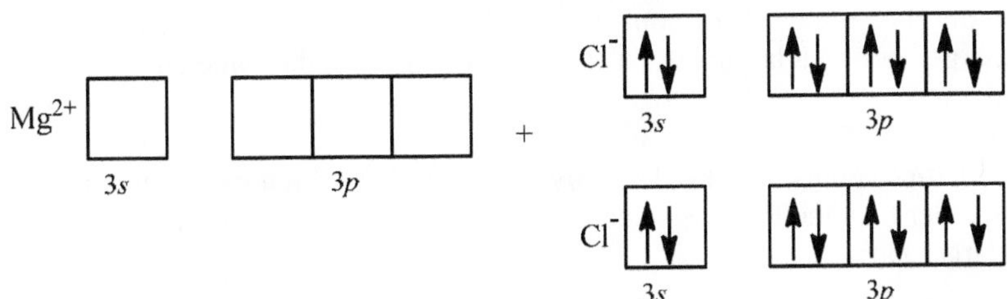

The formula of the compound would contain two chloride ions for each magnesium ion, **$MgCl_2$**.

9.1B Plan: First, write out the condensed electron configuration, partial orbital diagram, and electron-dot structure for calcium atoms and oxygen atoms. In the formation of the ions, each calcium atom will lose two electrons to form the +2 ion and each oxygen atom will gain two electrons to form the –2 ion. Write the condensed electron configuration, partial orbital diagram, and electron-dot structure for each of the ions. The formula of the compound is found by combining the ions in a ratio that gives a neutral compound.
Solution:
Condensed electron configurations:
Ca ([Ar]4s^2) + O ([He]2$s^2$2p^4) → Ca^{2+} ([Ar]) + O^{2-} ([He]2$s^2$2p^6)
The charge is balanced (the number of electrons lost equals the number of electrons gained).
Partial orbital diagrams:

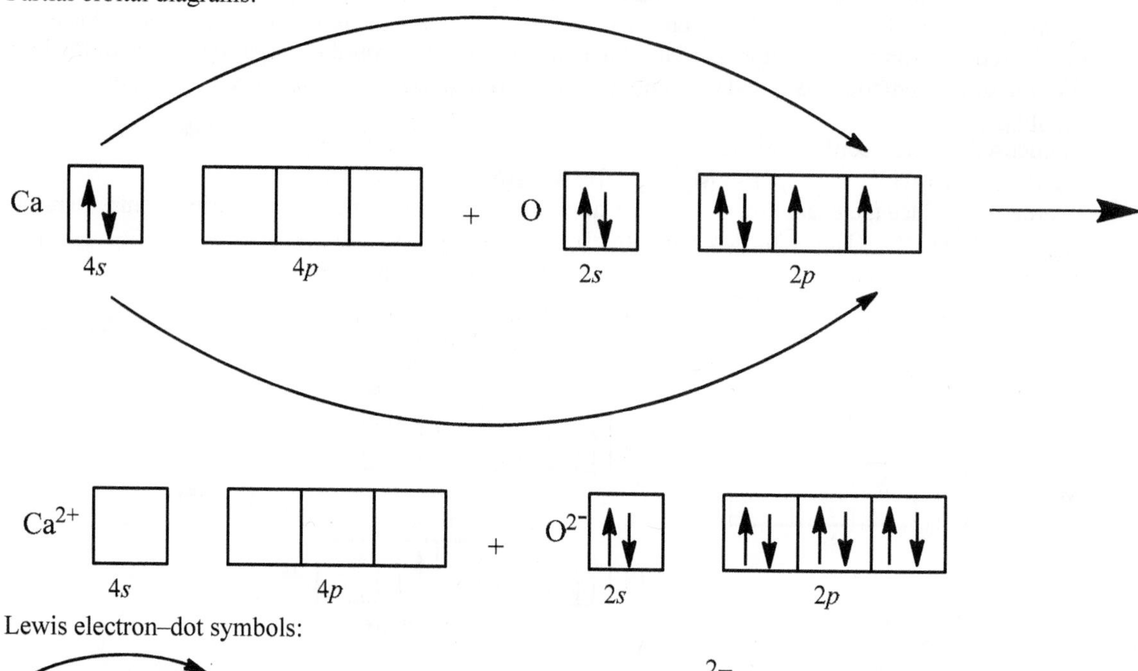

Lewis electron–dot symbols:

$\cdot Ca \cdot + \cdot\ddot{O}: \longrightarrow Ca^{2+} + :\ddot{O}:^{2-}$

The formula of the compound would contain one oxide ion for each calcium ion, **CaO**.

9.2A Plan: Examine the charge of the ions involved in the compounds. Use periodic trends in ionic radii to determine the relative size of the ions in the compounds. Then apply Coulomb's law. According to Coulomb's law, for ions of similar size, higher charge leads to a larger lattice energy. For ions with the same charge, smaller size leads to larger lattice energy.
Solution:
The compound with the larger lattice energy is **SrF_2**. The only difference between these compounds is the size of the cation: the Sr^{2+} ion is smaller than the Ba^{2+} ion. According to Coulomb's law, for ions with the same charge, smaller size leads to larger lattice energy.

9.2B Plan: Examine the charge of the ions involved in the compounds. Use periodic trends in ionic radii to determine the relative size of the ions in the compounds. Then apply Coulomb's law. According to Coulomb's law, for ions of similar size, higher charge leads to a larger lattice energy. For ions with the same charge, smaller size leads to larger lattice energy.
Solution:
The compound with the smaller lattice energy is **RbCl**. The sizes of the cations and of the anions are nearly the same, but the charges of Rb^+ and Cl^- are half as much as the charges of Sr^{2+} and S^{2-}. According to Coulomb's law, for ions of similar size, higher charge leads to a *larger* lattice energy.

9.3A Plan: a) All bonds are triple bonds from carbon to a second row element. The trend in bond length can be predicted from the fact that atomic radii decrease across a row, so oxygen will be smaller than nitrogen, which is smaller than carbon. Bond length will therefore decrease across the row while bond energy increases.
b) All the bonds are single bonds from phosphorus to a group 7A element. The trend in bond length can be predicted from the fact that atomic radii increase down a column, so fluorine will be smaller than bromine, which is smaller than iodine. Bond length will therefore *increase* down the column while bond energy increases.
Solution:
a) Bond length: C≡C > C≡N > C≡O — Bond strength: C≡O > C≡N > C≡C
b) Bond length: P–I > P–Br > P–F — Bond energy: P–F > P–Br > P–I
Check: (Use the tables in the chapter.)
Bond lengths from Table: C≡C, 121 pm > C≡N, 115 pm > C≡O, 113 pm
Bond energies from Table: C≡O, 1070 kJ/mol > C≡N, 891 kJ/mol > C≡C, 839 kJ/mol
Bond lengths from Table: P–I, 246 pm > P–Br, 222 pm > P–F, 156 pm
Bond energies from Table: P–F, 490 kJ/mol > P–Br, 272 kJ/mol > P–I, 184 kJ/mol
The values from the tables agree with the order predicted.

9.3B Plan: a) All bonds are single bonds from silicon to a second row element. The trend in bond length can be predicted from the fact that atomic radii decrease across a row, so fluorine will be smaller than oxygen, which is smaller than carbon. Bond length will therefore decrease across the row while bond energy increases.
b) All the bonds are between two nitrogen atoms, but differ in the number of electrons shared between the atoms. The more electrons shared the shorter the bond length and the greater the bond energy.
Solution:
a) Bond length: Si–F < Si–O < Si–C — Bond strength: Si–C < Si–O < Si–F
b) Bond length: N≡N < N=N < N–N — Bond energy: N–N < N=N < N≡N
Check: (Use the tables in the chapter.)
Bond lengths from Table: Si–F, 156 pm < Si–O, 161 pm < Si–C, 186 pm
Bond energies from Table: Si–C, 301 kJ < Si–O, 368 kJ < Si–F, 565 kJ
Bond lengths from Table: N≡N, 110 pm < N=N, 122 pm < N–N, 146 pm
Bond energies from Table: N–N, 160 kJ < N=N, 418 kJ < N≡N, 945 kJ
The values from the tables agree with the order predicted.

9.4A Plan: Assume that all reactant bonds break and all product bonds form. Use the bond energy table to find the values for the different bonds. Sum the values for the reactants, and sum the values for the products (these are all negative values). Add the sum of product to the values from the sum of the reactant values.
Solution:

Calculating ΔH° for the bonds broken:

$$1 \text{ x N≡N} = (1 \text{ mol})(945 \text{ kJ/mol}) = 945 \text{ kJ}$$
$$3 \text{ x H–H} = (3 \text{ mol})(432 \text{ kJ/mol}) = \underline{1296 \text{ kJ}}$$
$$\Sigma \Delta H^\circ_{\text{bonds broken}} = 2241 \text{ kJ}$$

Calculating ΔH° for the bonds formed:

$$1 \text{ x } NH_3 = (3 \text{ mol})(-391 \text{ kJ/mol}) = -1173 \text{ kJ}$$
$$1 \text{ x } NH_3 = (3 \text{ mol})(-391 \text{ kJ/mol}) = \underline{-1173 \text{ kJ}}$$
$$\Sigma \Delta H^\circ_{\text{bonds formed}} = -2346 \text{ kJ}$$

$$\Delta H^\circ_{\text{rxn}} = \Sigma \Delta H^\circ_{\text{bonds broken}} + \Sigma \Delta H^\circ_{\text{bonds formed}}$$

$$\Delta H^\circ_{\text{rxn}} = 2241 \text{ kJ} + (-2346 \text{ kJ}) = \mathbf{-105 \text{ kJ}}$$

9.4B Plan: Assume that all reactant bonds break and all product bonds form. Use the bond energy table to find the values for the different bonds. Sum the values for the reactants, and sum the values for the products (these are all negative values). Add the sum of product to the values from the sum of the reactant values.

Solution:

Calculating ΔH° for the bonds broken:

$$2 \text{ x N}{\equiv}\text{O} = (2 \text{ mol})(631 \text{ kJ/mol}) = 1262 \text{ kJ}$$
$$1 \text{ x Cl–Cl} = (1 \text{ mol})(243 \text{ kJ/mol}) = \underline{243 \text{ kJ}}$$

$$\Sigma \Delta H^\circ_{\text{bonds broken}} = 1505 \text{ kJ}$$

Calculating ΔH° for the bonds formed:

$$2 \text{ x N–O} = (2 \text{ mol})(-201 \text{ kJ/mol}) = -402 \text{ kJ}$$
$$2 \text{ x N–Cl} = (2 \text{ mol})(-200 \text{ kJ/mol}) = \underline{-400 \text{ kJ}}$$

$$\Sigma \Delta H^\circ_{\text{bonds formed}} = -802 \text{ kJ}$$

$$\Delta H^\circ_{\text{rxn}} = \Sigma \Delta H^\circ_{\text{bonds broken}} + \Sigma \Delta H^\circ_{\text{bonds formed}}$$

$$\Delta H^\circ_{\text{rxn}} = 1505 \text{ kJ} + (-802 \text{ kJ}) = \mathbf{703 \text{ kJ}}$$

9.5A Plan: Bond polarity can be determined from the difference in electronegativity of the two atoms. The more electronegative atom holds the δ– charge and the other atom holds the δ+ charge.

Solution:

a) From the electronegativity figure, EN of Cl = 3.0, EN of F = 4.0, EN of Br = 2.8. Cl–Cl will be the least polar since there is no difference between the electronegativity of the two chlorine atoms. Cl–F will be more polar than Cl–Br since the electronegativity difference between Cl and F (4.0 – 3.0 = 1.0) is greater than the electronegativity difference between Cl and Br (3.0 – 2.8 = 0.2).

δ+ δ– δ+ δ–
Cl–Cl < Br–Cl < Cl-F

b) EN of F = 4.0, EN of Si = 1.8, EN of P = 2.1, EN of S = 2.5. The most polar is Si–F with an EN difference of 2.2, next is P–F with an EN difference of 1.9, and next is S–F with an EN of 1.5.

δ+ δ– δ+ δ– δ+ δ–
S–F < P–F < Si–F

9.5B Plan: Bond polarity can be determined from the difference in electronegativity of the two atoms. The more electronegative atom holds the δ– charge and the other atom holds the δ+ charge.

Solution:

a) From the electronegativity figure, EN of Cl = 3.0, EN of F = 4.0, EN of Br = 2.8, and EN of Se = 2.4. Se–F will be more polar than Se–Cl, which will be more polar than Se–Br since the electronegativity difference between Se and F (4.0 – 2.4 = 1.6) is greater than the electronegativity difference between Se and Cl (3.0 – 2.4 = 0.6), which is greater than the electronegativity difference between Se and Br (2.8 – 2.4 = 0.4).

⟼ ⟼ ⟼
Se–F > Se–Cl > Se-Br

b) EN of Cl = 3.0, EN of B = 2.0, EN of F = 4.0, EN of S = 2.5. The most polar is F–B with an EN difference of 2.0, next is Cl–B with an EN difference of 1.0, and next is S–B with an EN of 0.5.

⟻ ⟻ ⟻
F–B > Cl–B > S–B

TOOLS OF THE LABORATORY BOXED READING PROBLEMS

B9.1 Plan: Bond strength increases as the number of electrons in the bond increases.
Solution:
The C=C bond would show absorption of IR at shorter wavelength (higher energy) due to it being a stronger bond than C–C. The C≡C bond would show absorption at a shorter wavelength (higher energy) than the C=C bond since the triple bond has a larger bond energy than the double bond.

B9.2 Plan: The frequencies of the vibrations are given and are converted to wavelength with the relationship $c = \lambda\nu$. The energy of each vibration is calculated by using $E = h\nu$.
Solution:

a) $c = \lambda\nu$ or $\lambda = \dfrac{c}{\nu}$

$$\lambda\ (\text{nm}) = \frac{c}{\nu} = \frac{3.00\text{x}10^8\ \text{m/s}}{4.02\text{x}10^{13}/\text{s}}\left(\frac{10^9\ \text{nm}}{1\ \text{m}}\right) = 7462.687 = \mathbf{7460\ nm}\ \text{(symmetric stretch)}$$

$$\lambda\ (\text{nm}) = \frac{c}{\nu} = \frac{3.00\text{x}10^8\ \text{m/s}}{2.00\text{x}10^{13}/\text{s}}\left(\frac{10^9\ \text{nm}}{1\ \text{m}}\right) = \mathbf{1.50x10^4\ nm}\ \text{(bending)}$$

$$\lambda\ (\text{nm}) = \frac{c}{\nu} = \frac{3.00\text{x}10^8\ \text{m/s}}{7.05\text{x}10^{13}/\text{s}}\left(\frac{10^9\ \text{nm}}{1\ \text{m}}\right) = 4255.32 = \mathbf{4260\ nm}\ \text{(asymmetrical stretch)}$$

b) $E = h\nu$
$E = (6.626\text{x}10^{-34}\ \text{J•s})(4.02\text{x}10^{13}\ \text{s}^{-1}) = 2.66365\text{x}10^{-20} = \mathbf{2.66x10^{-20}\ J}$ (symmetric stretch)
$E = (6.626\text{x}10^{-34}\ \text{J•s})(2.00\text{x}10^{13}\ \text{s}^{-1}) = 1.3252\text{x}10^{-20} = \mathbf{1.33x10^{-20}\ J}$ (bending)
$E = (6.626\text{x}10^{-34}\ \text{J•s})(7.05\text{x}10^{13}\ \text{s}^{-1}) = 4.6713\text{x}10^{-20} = \mathbf{4.67x10^{-20}\ J}$ (asymmetrical stretch)
Bending requires the least amount of energy.

END–OF–CHAPTER PROBLEMS

9.1 a) Larger ionization energy decreases metallic character.
b) Larger atomic radius increases metallic character.
c) Larger number of outer electrons decreases metallic character.
d) Larger effective nuclear charge decreases metallic character.

9.4 Plan: Metallic behavior increases to the left and down a group in the periodic table.
Solution:
a) **Cs** is more metallic since it is further down the alkali metal group than Na.
b) **Rb** is more metallic since it is both to the left and down from Mg.
c) **As** is more metallic since it is further down Group 5A(15) than N.

9.6 Plan: Ionic bonding occurs between metals and nonmetals, covalent bonding between nonmetals, and metallic bonds between metals.
Solution:
a) Bond in CsF is **ionic** because Cs is a metal and F is a nonmetal.
b) Bonding in N_2 is **covalent** because N is a nonmetal.
c) Bonding in Na(*s*) is **metallic** because this is a monatomic, metal solid.

9.8 Plan: Ionic bonding occurs between metals and nonmetals, covalent bonding between nonmetals, and metallic bonds between metals.
Solution:
a) Bonding in O_3 would be **covalent** since O is a nonmetal.
b) Bonding in $MgCl_2$ would be **ionic** since Mg is a metal and Cl is a nonmetal.
c) Bonding in BrO_2 would be **covalent** since both Br and O are nonmetals.

9.10 Plan: Lewis electron-dot symbols show valence electrons as dots. Place one dot at a time on the four sides (this method explains the structure in b) and then pair up dots until all valence electrons are used. The group number of the main-group elements (Groups **1**A(1)-**8**A(18)) gives the number of valence electrons. Rb is Group **1**A(1), Si is Group **4**A(14), and I is Group **7**A(17).
Solution:

a) Rb·   b) ·Si· (with one dot above and one below)   c) :I· (with two dots above and two below)

9.12 Plan: Lewis electron-dot symbols show valence electrons as dots. Place one dot at a time on the four sides (this method explains the structure in b) and then pair up dots until all valence electrons are used. The group number of the main main-group elements (Groups **1**A(1)-**8**A(18)) gives the number of valence electrons. Sr is Group 2A(2), P is Group **5**A(15), and S is Group **6**A(16).
Solution:

a) ·Sr·   b) ·P· (with two dots above and one below)   c) :S· (with two dots above and one below)

9.14 Plan: Assuming X is an A-group element, the number of dots (valence electrons) equals the group number. Once the group number is known, the general electron configuration of the element can be written.
Solution:
a) Since there are 6 dots in the Lewis electron-dot symbol, element X has 6 valence electrons and is a Group **6A(16)** element. Its general electron configuration is **[noble gas]**ns^2np^4, where n is the energy level.
b) Since there are 3 dots in the Lewis electron-dot symbol, element X has 3 valence electrons and is a Group **3A(13)** element with general electron configuration **[noble gas]**ns^2np^1.

9.17 a) Because the lattice energy is the result of electrostatic attractions among the oppositely charged ions, its magnitude depends on several factors, including ionic size, ionic charge, and the arrangement of ions in the solid. For a particular arrangement of ions, the lattice energy increases as the charges on the ions increase and as their radii decrease.
b) Increasing lattice energy: **A < B < C**

9.20 Plan: Write condensed electron configurations and draw the Lewis electron-dot symbols for the atoms. The group number of the main-group elements (Groups **1**A(1)-**8**A(18)) gives the number of valence electrons. Remove electrons from the metal and add electrons to the nonmetal to attain filled outer levels. The number of electrons lost by the metal must equal the number of electrons gained by the nonmetal.
Solution:
a) Barium is a metal and loses 2 electrons to achieve a noble gas configuration:

$$\text{Ba }([\text{Xe}]6s^2) \rightarrow \text{Ba}^{2+}\ ([\text{Xe}]) + 2e^-$$

$$\cdot\text{Ba}\cdot \longrightarrow [\text{Ba}]^{2+} + 2\ e-$$

Chlorine is a nonmetal and gains 1 electron to achieve a noble gas configuration:

$$\text{Cl }([\text{Ne}]3s^23p^5) + 1e^- \rightarrow \text{Cl}^-\ ([\text{Ne}]3s^23p^6)$$

$$:\ddot{\underset{\cdot\cdot}{\text{Cl}}}\cdot + 1\ e^- \longrightarrow [:\ddot{\underset{\cdot\cdot}{\text{Cl}}}:]^-$$

Two Cl atoms gain the 2 electrons lost by Ba. The ionic compound formed is $\mathbf{BaCl_2}$.

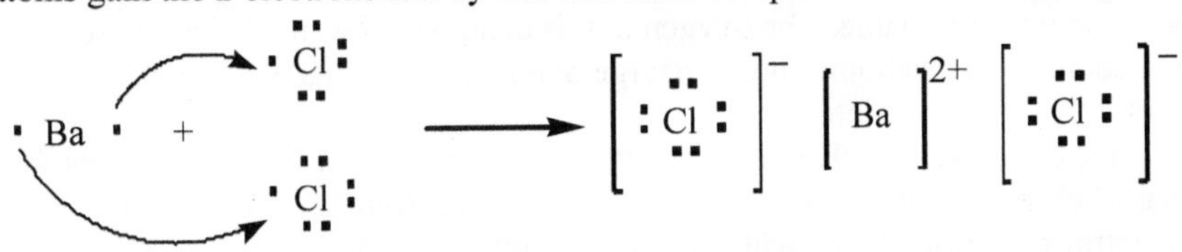

b) Strontium is a metal and loses 2 electrons to achieve a noble gas configuration:

$Sr\ ([Kr]5s^2) \rightarrow Sr^{2+}\ ([Kr]) + 2e^-$

Oxygen is a nonmetal and gains 2 electrons to achieve a noble gas configuration:

$O\ ([He]2s^22p^4) + 2e^- \rightarrow O^{2-}\ ([He]2s^22p^6)$

One O atom gains the two electrons lost by one Sr atom. The ionic compound formed is **SrO**.

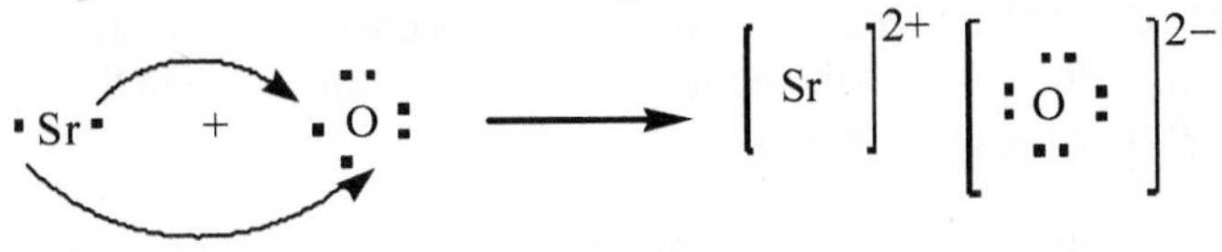

c) Aluminum is a metal and loses 3 electrons to achieve a noble gas configuration:

$Al\ ([Ne]3s^23p^1) \rightarrow Al^{3+}\ ([Ne]) + 3e^-$

Fluorine is a nonmetal and gains 1 electron to achieve a noble gas configuration:

$F\ ([He]2s^22p^5) + 1e^- \rightarrow F^-\ ([He]2s^22p^6)$

Three F atoms gains the three electrons lost by one Al atom. The ionic compound formed is $\mathbf{AlF_3}$.

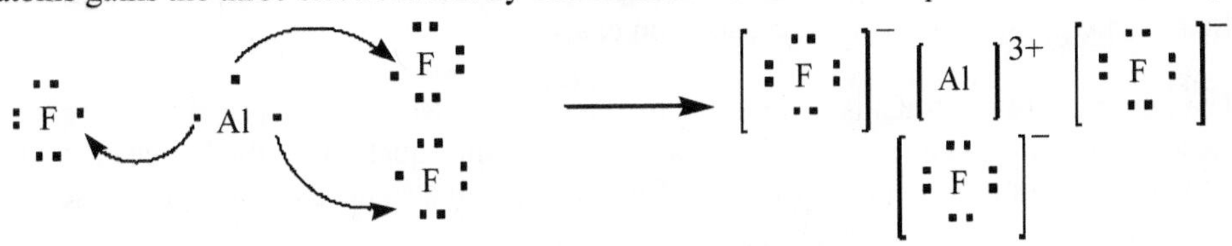

d) Rubidium is a metal and loses 1 electron to achieve a noble gas configuration:

$Rb\ ([Kr]5s^1) \rightarrow Rb^+\ ([Kr]) + 1e^-$

Oxygen is a nonmetal and gains 2 electrons to achieve a noble gas configuration:

$O\ ([He]2s^22p^4) + 2e^- \rightarrow O^{2-}\ ([He]2s^22p^6)$

One O atom gains the two electrons lost by two Rb atoms. The ionic compound formed is $\mathbf{Rb_2O}$.

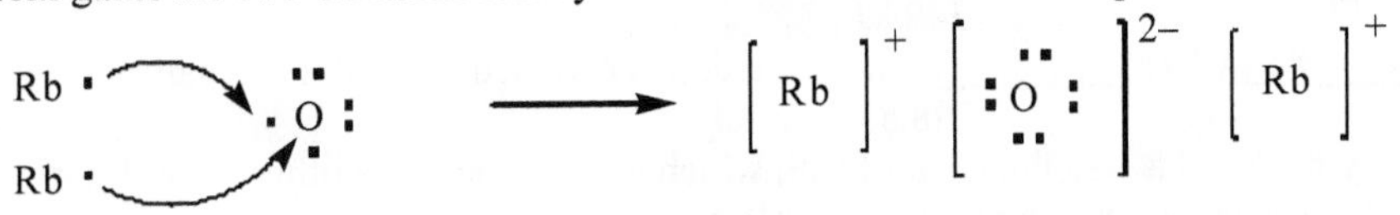

9.22 Plan: Find the charge of the known atom and use that charge to find the ionic charge of element X. For A-group cations, ion charge = the group number; for anions, ion charge = the group number – 8. Once the ion charge of X is known, the group number can be determined.

Solution:

a) X in XF_2 is a cation with +2 charge since the anion is F^- and there are two fluoride ions in the compound. **Group 2A(2)** metals form +2 ions.

b) X in MgX is an anion with – 2 charge since Mg^{2+} is the cation. Elements in **Group 6A(16)** form –2 ions (6 – 8 = –2).

c) X in X_2SO_4 must be a cation with +1 charge since the polyatomic sulfate ion has a charge of –2. X comes from **Group 1A(1)**.

9.24 Plan: Find the charge of the known atom and use that charge to find the ionic charge of element X. For A-group cations, ion charge = the group number; for anions, ion charge = the group number – 8. Once the ion charge of X is known, the group number can be determined.

Solution:
a) X in X_2O_3 is a cation with +3 charge. The oxygen in this compound has a –2 charge. To produce an electrically neutral compound, 2 cations with +3 charge bond with 3 anions with –2 charge: 2(+3) + 3(–2) = 0. Elements in **Group 3A(13)** form +3 ions.
b) The carbonate ion, CO_3^{2-}, has a –2 charge, so X has a +2 charge. **Group 2A(2)** elements form +2 ions.
c) X in Na_2X has a –2 charge, balanced with the +2 overall charge from the two Na^+ ions. Group **6A(16)** elements gain 2 electrons to form –2 ions with a noble gas configuration.

9.26 Plan: The magnitude of the lattice energy depends on ionic size and ionic charge. For a particular arrangement of ions, the lattice energy increases as the charges on the ions increase and as their radii decrease.
Solution:
a) **BaS** would have the higher lattice energy since the charge on each ion (+2 for Ba and –2 for S) is twice the charge on the ions in CsCl (+1 for Cs and –1 for Cl) and lattice energy is greater when ionic charges are larger.
b) **LiCl** would have the higher lattice energy since the ionic radius of Li^+ is smaller than that of Cs^+ and lattice energy is greater when the distance between ions is smaller.

9.28 Plan: The magnitude of the lattice energy depends on ionic size and ionic charge. For a particular arrangement of ions, the lattice energy increases as the charges on the ions increase and as their radii decrease.
Solution:
a) **BaS** has the lower lattice energy because the ionic radius of Ba^{2+} is larger than Ca^{2+}. A larger ionic radius results in a greater distance between ions. The lattice energy decreases with increasing distance between ions.
b) **NaF** has the lower lattice energy since the charge on each ion (+1, –1) is half the charge on the Mg^{2+} and O^{2-} ions. Lattice energy increases with increasing ion charge.

9.30 Plan: The lattice energy of NaCl is represented by the equation $NaCl(s) \rightarrow Na^+(g) + Cl^-(g)$. Use Hess's law and arrange the given equations so that they sum up to give the equation for the lattice energy. You will need to reverse the last equation (and change the sign of $\Delta H°$); you will also need to multiply the second equation ($\Delta H°$) by ½.
Solution:

	$\Delta H°$
~~Na(s)~~ → ~~Na(g)~~	109 kJ
~~1/2Cl₂(g)~~ → ~~Cl(g)~~	243/2 = 121.5 kJ
~~Na(g)~~ → $Na^+(g)$ + ~~e⁻~~	496 kJ
~~Cl(g)~~ + ~~e⁻~~ → $Cl^-(g)$	–349 kJ
NaCl(s) → ~~Na(s)~~ + ~~1/2Cl₂(g)~~	411 kJ (Reaction is reversed; sign of $\Delta H°$ changed.)
$NaCl(s) \rightarrow Na^+(g) + Cl^-(g)$	788.5 = **788 kJ**

The lattice energy for NaCl is less than that of LiF, which is expected since lithium and fluoride ions are smaller than sodium and chloride ions, resulting in a larger lattice energy for LiF.

9.33 Plan: The electron affinity of fluorine is represented by the equation $F(g) + e^- \rightarrow F^-(g)$. Use Hess's law and arrange the given equations so that they sum up to give the equation for the lattice energy, $KF(s) \rightarrow K^+(g) + F^-(g)$. You will need to reverse the last two given equations (and change the sign of $\Delta H°$); you will also need to multiply the third equation ($\Delta H°$) by ½. Solve for EA.

Solution:
An analogous Born-Haber cycle has been described in Figure 9.7 for LiF. Use Hess's law and solve for the EA of fluorine:

	ΔH°
~~K(*s*)~~ → ~~K(*g*)~~	90 kJ
~~K(*g*)~~ → $K^+(g) + e^-$	419 kJ
~~$1/2F_2(g)$~~ → ~~F(*g*)~~	1/2(159) = 79.5 kJ
~~F(*g*)~~ + e^- → $F^-(g)$	? = EA
KF(*s*) → ~~K(*s*)~~ + ~~$1/2F_2(g)$~~	569 kJ (Reverse the reaction and change the sign of ΔH°.)
$KF(s) \rightarrow K^+(g) + F^-(g)$	821 kJ (Reverse the reaction and change the sign of ΔH°.)

821 kJ = 90 kJ + 419 kJ + 79.5 kJ + EA + 569 kJ
EA = 821 kJ – (90 + 419 + 79.5 + 569)kJ
EA = –336.5 = **–336 kJ**

9.34 When two chlorine atoms are far apart, there is no interaction between them. Once the two atoms move closer together, the nucleus of each atom attracts the electrons on the other atom. As the atoms move closer this attraction increases, but the repulsion of the two nuclei also increases. When the atoms are very close together the repulsion between nuclei is much stronger than the attraction between nuclei and electrons. The final internuclear distance for the chlorine molecule is the distance at which maximum attraction is achieved in spite of the repulsion. At this distance, the energy of the molecule is at its lowest value.

9.35 The bond energy is the energy required to overcome the attraction between H atoms and Cl atoms in one mole of HCl molecules in the gaseous state. Energy input is needed to break bonds, so bond energy is always absorbed (endothermic) and $\Delta H^{\circ}_{\text{bond breaking}}$ is positive. The same amount of energy needed to break the bond is released upon its formation, so $\Delta H^{\circ}_{\text{bond forming}}$ has the same magnitude as $\Delta H^{\circ}_{\text{bond breaking}}$, but opposite in sign (always exothermic and negative).

9.39 Plan: Bond strength increases as the atomic radii of atoms in the bond decrease; bond strength also increases as bond order increases.
Solution:
a) **I–I < Br–Br < Cl–Cl**. Atomic radii decrease up a group in the periodic table, so I is the largest and Cl is the smallest of the three.
b) **S–Br < S–Cl < S–H**. H has the smallest radius and Br has the largest, so the bond strength for S–H is the greatest and that for S–Br is the weakest.
c) **C–N < C=N < C≡N**. Bond strength increases as the number of electrons in the bond increases. The triple bond is the strongest and the single bond is the weakest.

9.41 Plan: Bond strength increases as the atomic radii of atoms in the bond decrease; bond strength also increases as bond order increases.
Solution:
a) The C=O bond (bond order = 2) is stronger than the C–O bond (bond order = 1).
b) O is smaller than C so the O–H bond is shorter and stronger than the C–H bond.

9.43 Reaction between molecules requires the breaking of existing bonds and the formation of new bonds. Substances with weak bonds are more reactive than are those with strong bonds because less energy is required to break weak bonds.

9.45 Plan: Write the combustion reactions of methane and of formaldehyde. The reactants requiring the smaller amount of energy to break bonds will have the greater heat of reaction. Examine the bonds in the reactant molecules that will be broken. In general, more energy is required to break double bonds than to break single bonds.

Solution:
For methane: $CH_4(g) + 2O_2(g) \rightarrow CO_2(g) + 2H_2O(l)$ which requires that 4 C–H bonds and 2 O=O bonds be broken and 2 C=O bonds and 4 O–H bonds be formed.
For formaldehyde: $CH_2O(g) + O_2(g) \rightarrow CO_2(g) + H_2O(l)$ which requires that 2 C–H bonds, 1 C=O bond, and 1 O=O bond be broken and 2 C=O bonds and 2 O–H bonds be formed.
Methane contains more C–H bonds and fewer C=O bonds than formaldehyde. Since C–H bonds take less energy to break than C=O bonds, more energy is released in the combustion of methane than of formaldehyde.

9.47 Plan: To find the heat of reaction, add the energy required to break all the bonds in the reactants to the energy released to form all bonds in the product. Remember to use a negative sign for the energy of the bonds formed since bond formation is exothermic. The bond energy values are found in Table 9.2.
Solution:
Reactant bonds broken:
1 x C=C = (1 mol)(614 kJ/mol) = 614 kJ
4 x C–H = (4 mol)(413 kJ/mol) = 1652 kJ
1 x Cl–Cl = (1 mol)(243 kJ/mol) = 243 kJ

$$\Sigma\Delta H^\circ_{\text{bonds broken}} = 2509 \text{ kJ}$$

Product bonds formed:
1 x C–C = (1 mol)(–347 kJ/mol) = –347 kJ
4 x C–H = (4 mol)(–413 kJ/mol) = –1652 kJ
2 x C–Cl = (2 mol)(–339 kJ/mol) = –678 kJ

$$\Sigma\Delta H^\circ_{\text{bonds formed}} = -2677 \text{ kJ}$$

$$\Delta H^\circ_{\text{rxn}} = \Sigma\Delta H^\circ_{\text{bonds broken}} + \Sigma\Delta H^\circ_{\text{bonds formed}} = 2509 \text{ kJ} + (-2677 \text{ kJ}) = \mathbf{-168\ kJ}$$

9.49 Plan: To find the heat of reaction, add the energy required to break all the bonds in the reactants to the energy released to form all bonds in the product. Remember to use a negative sign for the energy of the bonds formed since bond formation is exothermic. The bond energy values are found in Table 9.2.
Solution:
The reaction:

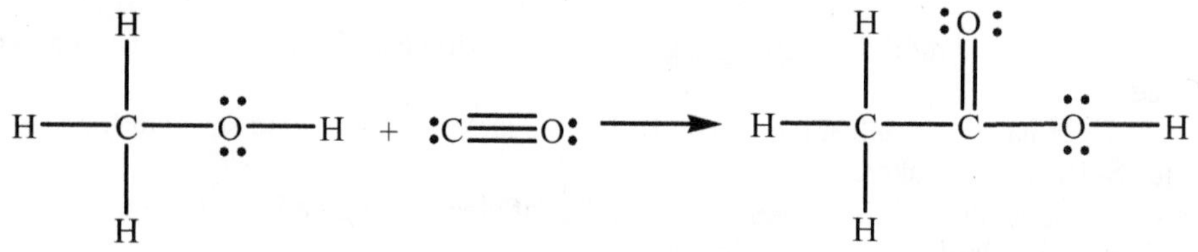

$$\text{H}_3\text{C–}\ddot{\text{O}}\text{–H} + :\text{C}{\equiv}\text{O}: \longrightarrow \text{H}_3\text{C–C}(=\ddot{\text{O}})\text{–}\ddot{\text{O}}\text{–H}$$

Reactant bonds broken:
1 x C–O = (1 mol)(358 kJ/mol) = 358 kJ
3 x C–H = (3 mol)(413 kJ/mol) = 1239 kJ
1 x O–H = (1 mol)(467 kJ/mol) = 467 kJ
1 x C≡O = (1 mol)(1070 kJ/mol) = 1070 kJ

$$\Sigma\Delta H^\circ_{\text{bonds broken}} = 3134 \text{ kJ}$$

Product bonds formed:

3 x C–H = (3 mol)(–413 kJ/mol) = –1239 kJ
1 x C–C = (1 mol)(–347 kJ/mol) = –347 kJ
1 x C=O = (1 mol)(–745 kJ/mol) = –745 kJ
1 x C–O = (1 mol)(–358 kJ/mol) = –358 kJ
1 x O–H = (1 mol)(–467 kJ/mol) = –467 kJ

$$\Sigma\Delta H^\circ_{\text{bonds formed}} = -3156 \text{ kJ}$$

$$\Delta H^\circ_{\text{rxn}} = \Sigma\Delta H^\circ_{\text{bonds broken}} + \Sigma\Delta H^\circ_{\text{bonds formed}} = 3134 \text{ kJ} + (-3156 \text{ kJ}) = \mathbf{-22\ kJ}$$

9.50 Plan: To find the heat of reaction, add the energy required to break all the bonds in the reactants to the energy released to form all bonds in the product. Remember to use a negative sign for the energy of the bonds formed since bond formation is exothermic. The bond energy values are found in Table 9.2.

Solution:

$H_2C{=}CH_2 + H{-}\ddot{\underset{..}{Br}}{:} \longrightarrow H{-}CH_2{-}CH_2{-}\ddot{\underset{..}{Br}}{:}$

Reactant bonds broken:

1 x C=C = (1 mol)(614 kJ/mol) = 614 kJ
4 x C–H = (4 mol)(413 kJ/mol) = 1652 kJ
1 x H–Br = (1 mol)(363 kJ/mol) = 363 kJ

$$\Sigma\Delta H^\circ_{\text{bonds broken}} = 2629 \text{ kJ}$$

Product bonds formed:

5 x C–H = (5 mol)(–413 kJ/mol) = –2065 kJ
1 x C–C = (1 mol)(–347 kJ/mol) = –347 kJ
1 x C–Br = (1 mol)(–276 kJ/mol) = –276 kJ

$$\Sigma\Delta H^\circ_{\text{bonds formed}} = -2688 \text{ kJ}$$

$$\Delta H^\circ_{\text{rxn}} = \Sigma\Delta H^\circ_{\text{bonds broken}} + \Sigma\Delta H^\circ_{\text{bonds formed}} = 2629 \text{ kJ} + (-2688 \text{ kJ}) = \mathbf{-59\ kJ}$$

9.51 Electronegativity increases from left to right across a period (except for the noble gases) and increases from bottom to top within a group. Fluorine (F) and oxygen (O) are the two most electronegative elements. Cesium (Cs) and francium (Fr) are the two least electronegative elements.

9.53 Ionic bonds occur between two elements of very different electronegativity, generally a metal with low electronegativity and a nonmetal with high electronegativity. Although electron sharing occurs to a very small extent in some ionic bonds, the primary force in ionic bonds is attraction of opposite charges resulting from electron transfer between the atoms. A nonpolar covalent bond occurs between two atoms with identical electronegativity values where the sharing of bonding electrons is equal. A polar covalent bond is between two atoms (generally nonmetals) of different electronegativities so that the bonding electrons are unequally shared. The H–O bond in water is **polar covalent**. The bond is between two nonmetals so it is covalent and not ionic, but atoms with different electronegativity values are involved.

9.56 Plan: Electronegativity increases from left to right across a period (except for the noble gases) and increases from bottom to top within a group.

Solution:

a) **Si < S < O**, sulfur is more electronegative than silicon since it is located further to the right in the table. Oxygen is more electronegative than sulfur since it is located nearer the top of the table.

b) **Mg < As < P**, magnesium is the least electronegative because it lies on the left side of the periodic table and phosphorus and arsenic on the right side. Phosphorus is more electronegative than arsenic because it is higher in the table.

9.58 Plan: Electronegativity increases from left to right across a period (except for the noble gases) and increases from bottom to top within a group.
Solution:
a) **N > P > Si**, nitrogen is above P in Group 5(A)15 and P is to the right of Si in Period 3.
b) **As > Ga > Ca**, all three elements are in Period 4, with As the rightmost element.

9.60 Plan: The polar arrow points toward the more electronegative atom. Electronegativity increases from left to right across a period (except for the noble gases) and increases from bottom to top within a group.
Solution:

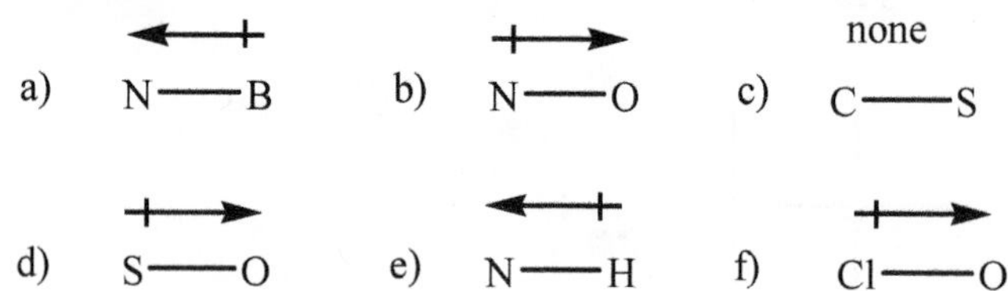

9.62 Plan: The more polar bond will have a greater difference in electronegativity, ΔEN.
Solution:
a) N: EN = 3.0; B: EN = 2.0; $\Delta EN_a = 3.0 - 2.0 = 1.0$
b) N: EN = 3.0; O: EN = 3.5; $\Delta EN_b = 3.5 - 3.0 = 0.5$
c) C: EN = 2.5; S: EN = 2.5; $\Delta EN_c = 2.5 - 2.5 = 0$
d) S: EN = 2.5; O: EN = 3.5; $\Delta EN_d = 3.5 - 2.5 = 1.0$
e) N: EN = 3.0; H: EN = 2.1; $\Delta EN_e = 3.0 - 2.1 = 0.9$
f) Cl: EN = 3.0; O: EN = 3.5; $\Delta EN_f = 3.5 - 3.0 = 0.5$
(a), (d), and (e) have greater bond polarity.

9.64 Plan: Ionic bonds occur between two elements of very different electronegativity, generally a metal with low electronegativity and a nonmetal with high electronegativity. Although electron sharing occurs to a very small extent in some ionic bonds, the primary force in ionic bonds is attraction of opposite charges resulting from electron transfer between the atoms. A nonpolar covalent bond occurs between two atoms with identical electronegativity values where the sharing of bonding electrons is equal. A polar covalent bond is between two atoms (generally nonmetals) of different electronegativities so that the bonding electrons are unequally shared. For polar covalent bonds, the larger the ΔEN, the more polar the bond.
Solution:
a) Bonds in S_8 are **nonpolar covalent.** All the atoms are nonmetals so the substance is covalent and bonds are nonpolar because all the atoms are of the same element and thus have the same electronegativity value. ΔEN = 0.
b) Bonds in RbCl are **ionic** because Rb is a metal and Cl is a nonmetal. ΔEN is large.
c) Bonds in PF_3 are **polar covalent.** All the atoms are nonmetals so the substance is covalent. The bonds between P and F are polar because their electronegativity differs (by 1.9 units for P–F).
d) Bonds in SCl_2 are **polar covalent.** S and Cl are nonmetals and differ in electronegativity (by 0.5 unit for S–Cl).
e) Bonds in F_2 are **nonpolar covalent.** F is a nonmetal. Bonds between two atoms of the same element are nonpolar since ΔEN = 0.
f) Bonds in SF_2 are **polar covalent.** S and F are nonmetals that differ in electronegativity (by 1.5 units for S–F).
Increasing bond polarity: $SCl_2 < SF_2 < PF_3$

9.66 Plan: Increasing ionic character occurs with increasing ΔEN. Electronegativity increases from left to right across a period (except for the noble gases) and increases from bottom to top within a group. The polar arrow points toward the more electronegative atom.

Solution:

a) H: EN = 2.1; Cl: EN = 3.0; Br: EN = 2.8; I: EN = 2.5

$\Delta EN_{HBr} = 2.8 - 2.1 = 0.7$; $\Delta EN_{HCl} = 3.0 - 2.1 = 0.9$; $\Delta EN_{HI} = 2.5 - 2.1 = 0.4$

b) H: EN = 2.1; O: EN = 3.5; C: EN = 2.5; F: EN = 4.0

$\Delta EN_{HO} = 3.5 - 2.1 = 1.4$; $\Delta EN_{CH} = 2.5 - 2.1 = 0.4$; $\Delta EN_{HF} = 4.0 - 2.1 = 1.9$

c) Cl: EN = 3.0; S: EN = 2.5; P: EN = 2.1; Si: EN = 1.8

$\Delta EN_{SCl} = 3.0 - 2.5 = 0.5$; $\Delta EN_{PCl} = 3.0 - 2.1 = 0.9$; $\Delta EN_{SiCl} = 3.0 - 1.8 = 1.2$

a) $\overset{+\!\!\longrightarrow}{\text{H—I}}$ < $\overset{+\!\!\longrightarrow}{\text{H—Br}}$ < $\overset{+\!\!\longrightarrow}{\text{H—Cl}}$

b) $\overset{+\!\!\longrightarrow}{\text{H—C}}$ < $\overset{+\!\!\longrightarrow}{\text{H—O}}$ < $\overset{+\!\!\longrightarrow}{\text{H—F}}$

c) $\overset{+\!\!\longrightarrow}{\text{S—Cl}}$ < $\overset{+\!\!\longrightarrow}{\text{P—Cl}}$ < $\overset{+\!\!\longrightarrow}{\text{Si—Cl}}$

9.69 a) A solid metal is a shiny solid that conducts heat, is malleable, and melts at high temperatures. (Other answers include relatively high boiling point and good conductor of electricity.)

b) Metals lose electrons to form positive ions and metals form basic oxides.

9.73 Plan: Write a balanced chemical reaction. The given heat of reaction is the sum of the energy required to break all the bonds in the reactants and the energy released to form all bonds in the product. Remember to use a negative sign for the energy of the bonds formed since bond formation is exothermic. The bond energy values are found in Table 9.2. Use the ratios from the balanced reaction between the heat of reaction and acetylene and between acetylene and CO_2 and O_2 to find the amounts needed. The ideal gas law is used to convert from moles of oxygen to volume of oxygen.

Solution:

a) $C_2H_2 + 5/2O_2 \rightarrow 2CO_2 + H_2O$ $\qquad \Delta H^\circ_{rxn} = -1259$ kJ/mol

H–C≡C–H + 5/2O=O → 2O=C=O + H–O–H

$\Delta H^\circ_{rxn} = \Sigma\Delta H^\circ_{\text{bonds broken}} + \Sigma\Delta H^\circ_{\text{bonds formed}}$

$\Delta H^\circ_{rxn} = [2\ BE_{C-H} + BE_{C\equiv C} + 5/2\ BE_{O=O}] + [4\ (-BE_{C=O}) + 2\ (-BE_{O-H})]$

$-1259\text{ kJ} = [2(413) + BE_{C\equiv C} + 5/2(498)] + [4(-799) + 2(-467)]$

$-1259\text{ kJ} = [826 + BE_{C\equiv C} + 1245] + [-4130)]\text{ kJ}$

$-1259\text{ kJ} = -2059 + BE_{C\equiv C}\text{ kJ}$

$BE_{C\equiv C} =$ **800. kJ/mol** Table 9.2 lists the value as 839 kJ/mol.

b) $\text{Heat (kJ)} = (500.0\text{ g }C_2H_2)\left(\frac{1\text{ mol }C_2H_2}{26.04\text{ g }C_2H_2}\right)\left(\frac{-1259\text{ kJ}}{1\text{ mol }C_2H_2}\right)$

$= -2.4174347\text{x}10^4 = \mathbf{-2.417x10^4\ kJ}$

c) $\text{Mass (g) of }CO_2 = (500.0\text{ g }C_2H_2)\left(\frac{1\text{ mol }C_2H_2}{26.04\text{ g }C_2H_2}\right)\left(\frac{2\text{ mol }CO_2}{1\text{ mol }C_2H_2}\right)\left(\frac{44.01\text{ g }CO_2}{1\text{ mol }CO_2}\right)$

$= 1690.092 = \mathbf{1690.\ g\ CO_2}$

d) $\text{Amount (mol) of }O_2 = (500.0\text{ g }C_2H_2)\left(\frac{1\text{ mol }C_2H_2}{26.04\text{ g }C_2H_2}\right)\left(\frac{(5/2)\text{ mol }O_2}{1\text{ mol }C_2H_2}\right)$

$= 48.0030722\text{ mol }O_2$

$PV = nRT$

$$\text{Volume (L) of } O_2 = \frac{nRT}{P} = \frac{(48.0030722 \text{ mol } O_2)\left(0.08206 \frac{\text{L} \bullet \text{atm}}{\text{mol} \bullet \text{K}}\right)(298 \text{ K})}{18.0 \text{ atm}}$$

$= 65.2145 =$ **65.2 L O_2**

9.75 Plan: The heat of formation of MgCl is represented by the equation $Mg(s) + 1/2Cl_2(g) \rightarrow MgCl(s)$. Use Hess's law and arrange the given equations so that they sum up to give the equation for the heat of formation of MgCl. You will need to multiply the second equation by ½; you will need to reverse the equation for the lattice energy $[MgCl(s) \rightarrow Mg^+(g) + Cl^-(g)]$ and change the sign of the given lattice energy value. Negative heats of formation are energetically favored.

Solution:

a)

1) $Mg(s) \rightarrow \cancel{Mg(g)}$	$\Delta H_1^\circ = 148$ kJ
2) $1/2Cl_2(g) \rightarrow \cancel{Cl(g)}$	$\Delta H_2^\circ = 1/2(243 \text{ kJ}) = 121.5$ kJ
3) $\cancel{Mg(g)} \rightarrow \cancel{Mg^+(g)} + e^-$	$\Delta H_3^\circ = 738$ kJ
4) $\cancel{Cl(g)} + e^- \rightarrow \cancel{Cl^-(g)}$	$\Delta H_4^\circ = -349$ kJ
5) $\cancel{Mg^+(g)} + \cancel{Cl^-(g)} \rightarrow MgCl(s)$	$\Delta H_5^\circ = -783.5 \text{ kJ } (= -\Delta H^\circ_{\text{lattice}} (MgCl))$
$Mg(s) + 1/2Cl_2(g) \rightarrow MgCl(s)$	ΔH_f° (MgCl) = ?

$$\Delta H_f^\circ(\text{MgCl}) = \Delta H_1^\circ + \Delta H_2^\circ + \Delta H_3^\circ + \Delta H_4^\circ + \Delta H_5^\circ$$

$= 148 \text{ kJ} + 121.5 \text{ kJ} + 738 \text{ kJ} + (-349 \text{ kJ}) + (-783.5 \text{ kJ}) =$ **–125 kJ**

b) **Yes**, since ΔH_f° for MgCl is negative, $MgCl(s)$ is stable relative to its elements.

c) $2MgCl(s) \rightarrow MgCl_2(s) + Mg(s)$

$$\Delta H^\circ_{\text{rxn}} = \Delta H^\circ_{\text{rxn}} = \Sigma m \Delta H^\circ_{f(\text{products})} - \Sigma n \Delta H^\circ_{f(\text{reactants})}$$

$$\Delta H^\circ_{\text{rxn}} = \{1 \Delta H_f^\circ [MgCl_2(s)] + 1 \Delta H_f^\circ [Mg(s)]\} - \{2 \Delta H_f^\circ [MgCl(s)]\}$$

$$\Delta H^\circ_{\text{rxn}} = [1 \text{ mol}(-641.6 \text{ kJ/mol}) + 1 \text{ mol}(0)] - [2 \text{ mol}(-125 \text{ kJ/mol})]$$

$\Delta H^\circ_{\text{rxn}} = -391.6 =$ **–392 kJ**

d) **No**, ΔH_f° for $MgCl_2$ is much more negative than that for MgCl. This makes the $\Delta H^\circ_{\text{rxn}}$ value for the above reaction very negative, and the formation of $MgCl_2$ would be favored.

9.77 Plan: Find the bond energy for an H–I bond from Table 9.2. For part a), calculate the wavelength with this energy using the relationship from Chapter 7: $E = hc/\lambda$. For part b), calculate the energy for a wavelength of 254 nm and then subtract the energy from part a) to get the excess energy.
For part c), speed can be calculated from the excess energy since $E_k = 1/2mu^2$.

Solution:

a) Bond energy for H–I is 295 kJ/mol (Table 9.2).

$$\text{Bond energy (J/photon)} = \left(\frac{295 \text{ kJ}}{\text{mol}}\right)\left(\frac{10^3 \text{ J}}{1 \text{ kJ}}\right)\left(\frac{1 \text{ mol}}{6.022\text{x}10^{23} \text{ photons}}\right) = 4.898705\text{x}10^{-19} \text{ J/photon}$$

$E = hc/\lambda$

$$\lambda \text{ (m)} = hc/E = \frac{(6.626\text{x}10^{-34} \text{ J}\bullet\text{s})(3.00\text{x}10^8 \text{ m/s})}{(4.898705\text{x}10^{-19} \text{ J})} = 4.057807\text{x}10^{-7} \text{ m}$$

$$\lambda \text{ (nm)} = (4.057807\text{x}10^{-7} \text{ m})\left(\frac{1 \text{ nm}}{10^{-9} \text{ m}}\right) = 405.7807 = \mathbf{406 \text{ nm}}$$

b) E (HI) $= 4.898705\text{x}10^{-19}$ J

$$E\ (254\ \text{nm}) = hc/\lambda = \frac{(6.626\text{x}10^{-34}\ \text{J•s})(3.00\text{x}10^{8}\ \text{m/s})}{254\ \text{nm}}\left(\frac{1\ \text{nm}}{10^{-9}\ \text{m}}\right) = 7.82598\text{x}10^{-19}\ \text{J}$$

Excess energy $= 7.82598\text{x}10^{-19}$ J – $4.898705\text{x}10^{-19}$ J $= 2.92728\text{x}10^{-19} =$ **$2.93\text{x}10^{-19}$ J**

$$\text{c) Mass (kg) of H} = \left(\frac{1.008\ \text{g H}}{\text{mol}}\right)\left(\frac{\text{mol}}{6.022\text{x}10^{23}}\right)\left(\frac{1\ \text{kg}}{10^{3}\ \text{g}}\right) = 1.67386\text{x}10^{-27}\ \text{kg}$$

$$E_k = 1/2mu^2 \text{ thus, } u = \sqrt{\frac{2E}{m}}$$

$$u = \sqrt{\frac{2(2.92728\text{x}10^{-19}\ \text{J})}{1.67386\text{x}10^{-27}\ \text{kg}}\left(\frac{\text{kg•m}^2/\text{s}^2}{\text{J}}\right)} = 1.8701965\text{x}10^{4} = \mathbf{1.87x10^{4}\ m/s}$$

9.80 Plan: Find the appropriate bond energies in Table 9.2. Calculate the wavelengths using $E = hc/\lambda$.
Solution:
C–Cl bond energy = 339 kJ/mol

$$\text{Bond energy (J/photon)} = \left(\frac{339\ \text{kJ}}{\text{mol}}\right)\left(\frac{10^3\ \text{J}}{1\ \text{kJ}}\right)\left(\frac{1\ \text{mol}}{6.022\text{x}10^{23}\ \text{photons}}\right) = 5.62936\text{x}10^{-19}\ \text{J/photon}$$

$E = hc/\lambda$

$$\lambda\ (\text{m}) = hc/E = \frac{(6.626\text{x}10^{-34}\ \text{J•s})(3.00\text{x}10^{8}\ \text{m/s})}{(5.62936\text{x}10^{-19}\ \text{J})} = 3.5311296\text{x}10^{-7} = \mathbf{3.53x10^{-7}\ m}$$

O_2 bond energy = 498 kJ/mol

$$\text{Bond energy (J/photon)} = \left(\frac{498\ \text{kJ}}{\text{mol}}\right)\left(\frac{10^3\ \text{J}}{1\ \text{kJ}}\right)\left(\frac{1\ \text{mol}}{6.022\text{x}10^{23}\ \text{photons}}\right) = 8.269678\text{x}10^{-19}\ \text{J/photon}$$

$E = hc/\lambda$

$$\lambda\ (\text{m}) = hc/E = \frac{(6.626\text{x}10^{-34}\ \text{J•s})(3.00\text{x}10^{8}\ \text{m/s})}{(8.269678\text{x}10^{-19}\ \text{J})} = 2.40372\text{x}10^{-7} = \mathbf{2.40x10^{-7}\ m}$$

9.81 Plan: Write balanced chemical equations for the formation of each of the compounds. Obtain the bond energy of fluorine from Table 9.2 (159 kJ/mol). Determine the average bond energy from ΔH = bonds broken + bonds formed. Remember that the bonds formed (Xe–F) have negative values since bond formation is exothermic.
Solution:

$\Delta H^\circ_{rxn} = \Sigma\Delta H^\circ_{\text{bonds broken}} + \Sigma\Delta H^\circ_{\text{bonds formed}}$

XeF_2 $Xe(g) + F_2(g) \rightarrow XeF_2(g)$

ΔH°_{rxn} = –105 kJ/mol = [1 mol F_2 (159 kJ/mol)] + [2 (–Xe–F)]
–264 kJ/mol = 2 (–Xe–F)
Xe–F = **132 kJ/mol**

XeF_4 $Xe(g) + 2F_2(g) \rightarrow XeF_4(g)$

ΔH°_{rxn} = –284 kJ/mol = [2 mol F_2 (159 kJ/mol)] + [4 (–Xe–F)]
–602 kJ/mol = 4 (–Xe–F)
Xe–F = 150.5 = **150. kJ/mol**

XeF_6 $Xe(g) + 3F_2(g) \rightarrow XeF_6(g)$

ΔH°_{rxn} = –402 kJ/mol = [3 mol F_2 (159 kJ/mol)] + [6 (–Xe–F)]
–879 kJ/mol = 6 (–Xe–F)
Xe–F = 146.5 = **146 kJ/mol**

9.83 a) The presence of the very electronegative fluorine atoms bonded to one of the carbon atoms in $H_3C—CF_3$ makes the C–C bond polar. This polar bond will tend to undergo heterolytic rather than homolytic cleavage. More energy is required to force heterolytic cleavage.
b) Since one atom gets both of the bonding electrons in heterolytic bond breakage, this results in the formation of ions. In heterolytic cleavage a cation is formed, involving ionization energy; an anion is also formed, involving electron affinity. The bond energy of the O_2 bond is 498 kJ/mol.
ΔH = (homolytic cleavage + electron affinity + first ionization energy)
ΔH = (498/2 kJ/mol + (–141 kJ/mol) + 1314 kJ/mol) = 1422 = **1420 kJ/mol**
It would require 1420 kJ to heterolytically cleave 1 mol of O_2.

9.86 Plan: The heat of formation of SiO_2 is represented by the equation $Si(s) + O_2(g) \rightarrow SiO_2(s)$. Use Hess's law and arrange the given equations so that they sum up to give the equation for the heat of formation. The lattice energy of SiO_2 is represented by the equation $SiO_2(s) \rightarrow Si^{4+}(g) + 2O^{2-}(g)$. You will need to reverse the lattice energy equation (and change the sign of ΔH^o); you will also need to multiply the fourth given equation by 2.
Solution:
Use Hess' law. ΔH°_f of SiO_2 is found in Appendix B.

1)	$Si(s) \rightarrow \cancel{Si(g)}$	$\Delta H^\circ_1 = 454$ kJ
2)	$\cancel{Si(g)} \rightarrow \cancel{Si^{4+}(g)} + \cancel{4e^-}$	$\Delta H^\circ_2 = 9949$ kJ
3)	$O_2(g) \rightarrow \cancel{2O(g)}$	$\Delta H^\circ_3 = 498$ kJ
4)	$\cancel{2O(g)} + \cancel{4e^-} \rightarrow \cancel{2O^{2-}(g)}$	$\Delta H^\circ_4 = 2(737)$ kJ
5)	$\cancel{Si^{4+}(g)} + \cancel{2O^{2-}(g)} \rightarrow SiO_2(s)$	$\Delta H^\circ_5 = -\Delta H^\circ_{lattice}\ (SiO_2) = ?$
	$Si(s) + O_2(g) \rightarrow SiO_2(s)$	$\Delta H^\circ_f\ (SiO_2) = -910.9$ kJ

$$\Delta H^\circ_f = [\Delta H^\circ_1 + \Delta H^\circ_2 + \Delta H^\circ_3 + \Delta H^\circ_4 + (-\Delta H^\circ_{lattice})]$$

$$-910.9 \text{ kJ} = [454 \text{ kJ} + 9949 \text{ kJ} + 498 \text{ kJ} + 2(737) \text{ kJ} + (-\Delta H^\circ_{lattice})]$$

$$-\Delta H^\circ_{lattice} = -13{,}285.9 \text{ kJ}$$

$$\Delta H^\circ_{lattice} = \mathbf{13{,}286\ kJ}$$

9.88 Plan: Convert the bond energy in kJ/mol to units of J/photon. Use the equations $E = h\nu$, and $E = hc/\lambda$ to find the frequency and wavelength of light associated with this energy.
Solution:

$$\text{Bond energy (J/photon)} = \left(\frac{347 \text{ kJ}}{\text{mol}}\right)\left(\frac{10^3 \text{ J}}{1 \text{ kJ}}\right)\left(\frac{1 \text{ mol}}{6.022\text{x}10^{23} \text{ photons}}\right) = 5.762205\text{x}10^{-19} \text{ J/photon}$$

$$E = h\nu \text{ or } \nu = \frac{E}{h}$$

$$\nu = \frac{E}{h} = \frac{5.762205\text{x}10^{-19} \text{ J}}{6.626\text{x}10^{-34} \text{ J•s}} = 8.6963553\text{x}10^{14} = \mathbf{8.70x10^{14}\ s^{-1}}$$

$E = hc/\lambda$ or $\lambda = hc/E$

$$\lambda \text{ (m)} = hc/E = \frac{\left(6.626\text{x}10^{-34} \text{ J•s}\right)\left(3.00\text{x}10^{8} \text{ m/s}\right)}{5.762205\text{x}10^{-19} \text{ J}} = 3.44972\text{x}10^{-7} = \mathbf{3.45x10^{-7}\ m}$$

This is in the **ultraviolet** region of the electromagnetic spectrum.

9.90 Plan: Write the balanced equations for the reactions. Determine the heat of reaction from ΔH = bonds broken + bonds formed. Remember that the bonds formed have negative values since bond formation is exothermic.

<u>Solution:</u>

a) $2CH_4(g) + O_2(g) \rightarrow CH_3OCH_3(g) + H_2O(g)$

$\Delta H^\circ_{rxn} = \Sigma\Delta H^\circ_{\text{bonds broken}} + \Sigma\Delta H^\circ_{\text{bonds formed}}$

$\Delta H^\circ_{rxn} = [8 \times (BE_{C-H}) + 1 \times (BE_{O=O})] + [6 \times (BE_{C-H}) + 2 \times (BE_{C-O}) + 2 \times (BE_{O-H})]$

$\Delta H^\circ_{rxn} = [8 \text{ mol}(413 \text{ kJ/mol}) + 1 \text{ mol}(498 \text{ kJ/mol})]$
$+ [6 \text{ mol}(-413 \text{ kJ/mol}) + 2 \text{ mol}(-358 \text{ kJ/mol}) + 2 \text{ mol}(-467 \text{ kJ/mol})]$

$\Delta H^\circ_{rxn} = \mathbf{-326\ kJ}$

$2CH_4(g) + O_2(g) \rightarrow CH_3CH_2OH(g) + H_2O(g)$

$\Delta H^\circ_{rxn} = \Sigma\Delta H^\circ_{\text{bonds broken}} + \Sigma\Delta H^\circ_{\text{bonds formed}}$

$\Delta H^\circ_{rxn} = [8 \times (BE_{C-H}) + 1 \times (BE_{O=O})] + [5 \times (BE_{C-H}) + 1 \times (BE_{C-C}) + 1 \times (BE_{C-O}) + 3 \times (BE_{O-H})]$

$\Delta H^\circ_{rxn} = [8 \text{ mol}(413 \text{ kJ/mol}) + 1 \text{ mol}(498 \text{ kJ/mol})]$
$+ [5 \text{ mol}(-413 \text{ kJ/mol}) + 1 \text{ mol}(-347 \text{ kJ/mol}) + 1 \text{ mol}(-358 \text{ kJ/mol}) + 3 \text{ mol}(-467 \text{ kJ/mol})]$

$\Delta H^\circ_{rxn} = \mathbf{-369\ kJ}$

b) The formation of gaseous **ethanol** is more exothermic.

c) The conversion reaction is $CH_3CH_2OH(g) \rightarrow CH_3OCH_3(g)$.

Use Hess's law:

$CH_3CH_2OH(g) + \cancel{H_2O(g)} \rightarrow \cancel{2CH_4(g)} + \cancel{O_2(g)}$ $\Delta H^\circ_{rxn} = -(-369 \text{ kJ}) = 369 \text{ kJ}$

$\cancel{2CH_4(g)} + \cancel{O_2(g)} \rightarrow CH_3OCH_3(g) + \cancel{H_2O(g)}$ $\Delta H^\circ_{rxn} = -326 \text{ kJ}$

$CH_3CH_2OH(g) \rightarrow CH_3OCH_3(g)$ $\Delta H^\circ_{rxn} = -326 \text{ kJ} + 369 \text{ kJ} = \mathbf{43\ kJ}$

CHAPTER 10 THE SHAPES OF MOLECULES

FOLLOW–UP PROBLEMS

10.1A Plan: Count the valence electrons and follow the steps outlined in the sample problem to draw the Lewis structures.

Solution:

a) The sulfur is the central atom, as the hydrogen is never central. Each of the hydrogen atoms is placed around the sulfur. The actual positions of the hydrogen atoms are not important. The total number of valence electrons available is [2 x H(1e$^-$)] + [1 x S(6e$^-$)] = 8e$^-$. Connect each hydrogen atom to the sulfur with a single bond. These bonds use 4 of the electrons leaving 4 electrons. The last 4e$^-$ go to the sulfur because the hydrogen atoms can take no more electrons.

```
    ••
H—S :
   |
   H
```

Solution:

b) The aluminum has the lower group number so it is the central atom. Each of the chlorine atoms will be attached to the central aluminum. The total number of valence electrons available is [4 x F(7e$^-$)] + [1 x Al(3e$^-$)] + 1e$^-$ (for the negative charge) = 32e$^-$. Connecting the four chlorine atoms to the aluminum with single bonds uses 4 x 2 = 8e$^-$, leaving 32 – 8 = 24e$^-$. The more electronegative chlorine atoms each need 6 electrons to complete their octets. This requires 4 x 6 = 24e$^-$. There are no more remaining electrons at this step; however, the aluminum has 8 electrons around it.

```
 [        ••        ]⁻
 [       :Cl:       ]
 [        |         ]
 [  ••          ••  ]
 [ :Cl — Al — Cl:   ]
 [  ••          ••  ]
 [        |         ]
 [       :Cl:       ]
 [        ••        ]
```

Check: Count the electrons. Each of the five atoms has an octet.

Solution:

c) Both S and O have a lower group number than Cl, thus, one of these two elements must be central. Between S and O, S has the higher period number so it is the central atom. The total number of valence electrons available is [2 x Cl(7e$^-$)] + [1 x S(6e$^-$)] + [1 x O(6e$^-$)] = 26e$^-$. Begin by distributing the two chlorine atoms and the oxygen atom around the central sulfur atom. Connect each of the three outlying atoms to the central sulfur with single bonds. This uses 3 x 2 = 6e$^-$, leaving 26 – 6 = 20e$^-$. Each of the outlying atoms still needs 6 electrons to complete their octets. Completing these octets uses 3 x 6 = 18 electrons. The remaining 2 electrons are all the sulfur needs to complete its octet.

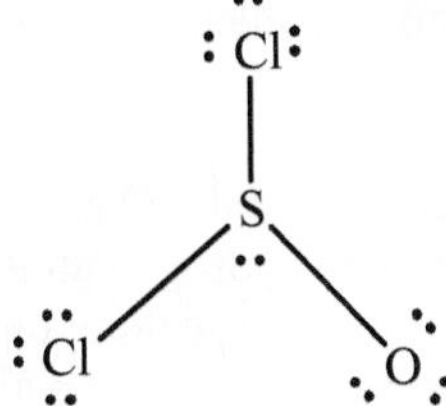

Check: Count the electrons. Each of the four atoms has an octet.

10.1B Plan: Count the valence electrons and follow the steps outlined in the sample problem to draw the Lewis structures.

Solution:
a) The oxygen has the lower group number so it is the central atom. Each of the fluorine atoms will be attached to the central oxygen. The total number of valence electrons available is [2 x F(7e$^-$)] + [1 x O(6e$^-$)] = 20e$^-$. Connecting the two fluorine atoms to the oxygen with single bonds uses 2 x 2 = 4e$^-$, leaving 20 – 4 = 16e$^-$. The more electronegative fluorine atoms each need 6 electrons to complete their octets. This requires 2 x 6 = 12e$^-$. The 4 remaining electrons go to the oxygen.

```
 ..   ..
: F — O :
 ..   |
     :F:
      ..
```

Check: Count the electrons. Each of the three atoms has an octet.
Solution:
b) The carbon has the lower group number so it is the central atom (technically, hydrogen is in group 1A, but it can only form one bond and, thus, cannot be the central atom). Each of the hydrogen and bromine atoms will be attached to the central carbon. The total number of valence electrons available is [1 x C(4e$^-$)] + [2 x H(1e$^-$)] + [2 x Br(7e$^-$)] = 20e$^-$. Connecting the two hydrogen atoms and the two bromine atoms to the carbon with single bonds uses 4 x 2 = 8e$^-$, leaving 20 – 8 = 12e$^-$. The "octets" of the two hydrogen atoms (2 electrons) are filled through their bonds to the carbon. The more electronegative bromine atoms each need 6 electrons to complete their octets. This requires 2 x 6 = 12e$^-$.

```
          H
          |
  ..      |
 :Br ——— C ——— H
  ..      |
          |
        :Br:
         ..
```

Check: Count the electrons. Each of the five atoms has an octet.
Solution:
c) Both I and Br have the same group number. Between the two atoms, I has the higher period number so it is the central atom. The total number of valence electrons available is [1 x I(7e$^-$)] + [2 x Br(7e$^-$)] – 1e$^-$ (for the positive charge) = 20e$^-$. Connecting the two bromine atoms to the iodine with single bonds uses 2 x 2 = 4e$^-$, leaving 20 – 4 = 16e$^-$. Each of the outlying atoms still needs 6 electrons to complete their octets. Completing these octets uses 2 x 6 = 12 electrons. The remaining 4 electrons are all the iodine needs to complete its octet.

```
                      +
 [  ..       . .   ]
 [ :Br ——— I       ]
 [  ..     |       ]
 [        :Br:     ]
 [         ..      ]
```

Check: Count the electrons. Each of the three atoms has an octet.

10.2A Plan: Count the valence electrons and follow the steps outlined in the sample problem to draw the Lewis structures.
Solution:
a) As in CH_4O, the N and O both serve as "central" atoms. The N is placed next to the O and the H atoms are distributed around them. The N needs more electrons so it gets two of the three hydrogen atoms. You can try placing the N in the center with all the other atoms around it, but you will quickly see that you will have trouble with the oxygen. The number of valence electrons is [3 x H(1e$^-$)] + [1 x N(5e$^-$)] + [1 x O(6e$^-$)] = 14e$^-$. Four single bonds are needed (4 x 2 = 8e$^-$). This leaves 6 electrons. The oxygen needs 4 electrons, and the nitrogen needs 2. These last 6 electrons serve as three lone pairs.

correct incorrect

Solution:
b) The hydrogen atoms cannot be the central atoms. The problem states that there are no O–H bonds, so the oxygen must be connected to the carbon atoms. Place the O atom between the two C atoms, and then distribute the H atoms equally around each of the C atoms. The total number of valence electrons is [6 x H(1e$^-$)] + [2 x C(4e$^-$)] + [1 x O(6e$^-$)] = 20e$^-$ Draw single bonds between each of the atoms. This creates six C–H bonds, and two C–O bonds, and uses 8 x 2 = 16 electrons. The four remaining electrons will become two lone pairs on the O atom to complete its octet.

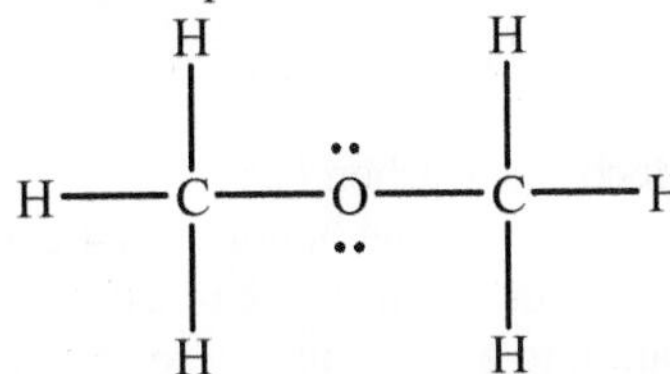

Check: Count the electrons. Both the C's and the O have octets. Each H has its pair.

10.2B Plan: Count the valence electrons and follow the steps outlined in the sample problem to draw the Lewis structures.

Solution:
a) The hydrogen atoms cannot be the central atoms, so the two N atoms both serve as "central" atoms, bonded to each other, and the H atoms are distributed around them (2 hydrogens per N atom). The number of valence electrons is [4 x H(1e$^-$)] + [2 x N(5e$^-$)] = 14e$^-$. Connect the two nitrogen atoms to each other via single bonds. Connect two hydrogens to each of the two nitrogen atoms via single bonds. These five single bonds require 5 x 2 = 10e$^-$. This leaves 4 electrons. Each of the nitrogen atoms needs 2 electrons to complete its octet. These last 4 electrons serve as two lone pairs.

Solution:
b) The hydrogen atoms cannot be the central atoms. The C and the N atoms both serve as "central" atoms, bonded to each other. According to the formula, three hydrogen atoms are bonded to the C and two hydrogen atoms are bonded to the N. The number of valence electrons is [5 x H(1e$^-$)] + [1 x N(5e$^-$)] + [1 x C(4e$^-$)] = 14e$^-$. Connect the C and N atoms via a single bond. Connect the appropriate number of hydrogen atoms to the C and N. These six bonds require 6 x 2 = 12e$^-$. This leaves 2 electrons. The nitrogen atom needs 2 electrons to complete its octet. These last 2 electrons serve as a lone pair on the nitrogen.

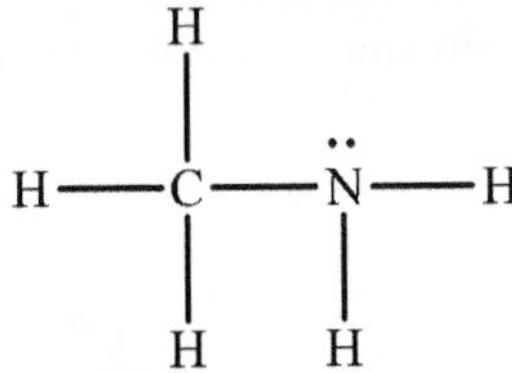

Check: Count the electrons. Both the C and the N have octets. Each H has its pair.

10.3A Plan: Count the valence electrons and follow the steps outlined in the sample problem to draw the Lewis structures.

Solution:
a) In CO there are a total of [1 x C(4e$^-$)] + [1 x O(6e$^-$)] = 10e$^-$. The hint states that carbon has three bonds. Since oxygen is the only other atom present, these bonds must be between the C and the O. This uses 6 of the 10 electrons. The remaining 4 electrons become two lone pairs, one pair for each of the atoms.

: C≡O:

Check: Count the electrons. Both the C and the O have octets.

Solution:
b) In HCN there are a total of [1 x H(1e$^-$)] + [1 x C(4e$^-$)] + [1 x N(5e$^-$)] = 10 electrons. Carbon has a lower group number, so it is the central atom. Place the C between the other two atoms and connect each of the atoms to the central C with a single bond. This uses 4 of the 10 electrons, leaving 6 electrons. Distribute these 6 to nitrogen to complete its octet. However, the carbon atom is 4 electrons short of an octet. Change two lone pairs on the nitrogen atom to bonding pairs to form two more bonds between carbon and nitrogen for a total of three bonds.

H—C≡N:

Check: Count the electrons. Both the C and the N have octets. The H has its pair.

Solution:
c) In CO_2 there are a total of [1 x C(4e$^-$)] + [2 x O(6e$^-$)] = 16 electrons. Carbon has a lower group number, so it is the central atom. Placing the C between the two O atoms and adding single bonds uses 4 electrons, leaving 16 – 4 = 12e$^-$. Distributing these 12 electrons to the oxygen atoms completes those octets, but the carbon atom does not have an octet. Change one lone pair on each oxygen atom to a bonding pair to form two double bonds to the carbon atom, completing its octet.

O=C=O

Check: Count the electrons. Both the C and the O atoms have octets.

10.3B Plan: Count the valence electrons and follow the steps outlined in the sample problem to draw the Lewis structures.

Solution:
a) In NO^+ there are a total of [1 x N(5e$^-$)] + [1 x O(6e$^-$)] – 1e$^-$ (for the positive charge on the ion) = 10e$^-$. Connecting the N and O atoms via a single bond uses 1 x 2 = 2e$^-$, leaving 10 – 2 = 8e$^-$. The more electronegative O atom needs 6 more electrons to complete its octet. The remaining 2 electrons become a lone pair on the N atom. However, this only gives the N atom 4 electrons. Change two lone pairs on the oxygen atom to bonding pairs to form a triple bond between the N and O atoms. In this way, the atoms' octets are complete.

$[:N\equiv O:]^+$

Check: Count the electrons. Both the N and the O have octets.

Solution:
b) In H_2CO there are a total of [1 x C(4e$^-$)] + [1 x O(6e$^-$)] + [2 x H(1e$^-$)] = 12 electrons. Carbon has a lower group number, so it is the central atom (H has a lower group number, but it cannot be a central atom). Place the C between the other three atoms and connect each of the atoms to the central C with a single bond. This uses 6 of the 12 electrons, leaving 6 electrons. Distribute these 6 to oxygen to complete its octet. However, the carbon atom is 2 electrons short of an octet. Change one lone pair on the oxygen atom to a bonding pair between the oxygen and carbon.

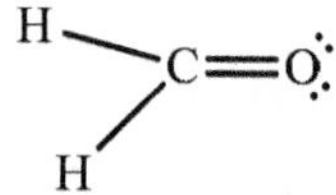

Check: Count the electrons. Both the C and the O have octets. The H atoms have 2 electrons each.

Solution:
c) In N_2H_2 there are a total of [2 x N(5e$^-$)] + [2 x H(1e$^-$)] = 12 electrons. Hydrogen cannot be a central atom, so the nitrogen atoms are the central atoms (there is more than one central atom). Connecting the nitrogen atoms via a single bond and attaching one hydrogen to each nitrogen atom uses 6 electrons, leaving six electrons. Each nitrogen needs four more electrons to complete its octet; however, there are not enough electrons to complete both octets. Four electrons can be added to one of the nitrogen atoms, but this only leaves two electrons to add to the other nitrogen atom. The octet of the first nitrogen atom is complete, but the octet of the second nitrogen atom is not complete. Change one lone pair on the first nitrogen to a bonding pair to complete both atoms' octets.

H—N̈=N̈—H

Check: Count the electrons. Both N atoms have octets, and each H atom has 2 electrons.

10.4A Plan: Count the valence electrons and follow the steps to draw the Lewis structures. Each new resonance structure is obtained by shifting the position of a multiple bond and the electron pairs.

Solution:

H_3CNO_2 has a total of $[1 \times C(4e^-)] + [2 \times O(6e^-)] + [3 \times H(1e^-)] + [1 \times N(5e^-)] = 24$ electrons. According to the problem, the H atoms are bonded to C, and the C atom is bonded to N, which is bonded to both O atoms. Connect all of these atoms via single bonds. This uses $6 \times 2 = 12e^-$. There are 12 electrons remaining. Each of the oxygen atoms needs 6 more electrons to complete its octet. Placing 6 electrons on each of the oxygen atoms leaves the nitrogen two electrons short of an octet. Change one of the lone pairs on one of the oxygen atoms to a bonding pair to complete the octets. The other resonance structure is obtained by taking a lone pair from the *other* oxygen to create the double bond.

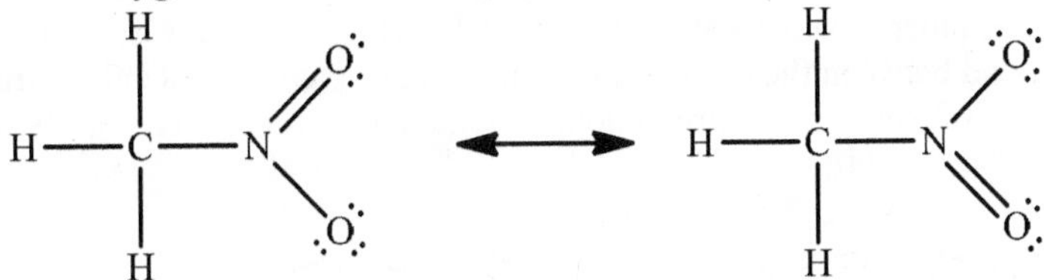

10.4B Plan: Count the valence electrons and follow the steps to draw the Lewis structures. Each new resonance structure is obtained by shifting the position of a multiple bond and the electron pairs.

Solution:

SCN^- has a total of $[1 \times C(4e^-)] + [1 \times S(6e^-)] + [1 \times N(5e^-)] + 1e^-$ (for the negative charge) = 16 electrons. According to the problem, the C is the central atom. Connect it via single bonds to both the S and the N atoms. This uses $2 \times 2 = 4e^-$. There are 12 electrons remaining. The outlying sulfur and nitrogen each require 6 electrons to complete their octets. Placing 6 electrons each on the N and on the S leaves the C atom 4 electrons short of an octet. Convert two lone pairs on the outer atoms to bonding pairs to complete the octet. The lone pairs can come from the N, from the S, or from both the S and the N. Each of the generated structures is a resonance structure.

[:S̈=C=N̈:]⁻ ⟷ [:S̤̈—C≡N:]⁻ ⟷ [:S≡C—N̤̈:]⁻

10.5A Plan: The presence of available *d* orbitals makes checking formal charges more important. Use the equation for formal charge: FC = # of valence e^- – [# unshared valence e^- + ½(# shared valence e^-)]

Solution:

a) In $POCl_3$, the P is the most likely central atom because all the other elements have higher group numbers. The molecule contains: $[1 \times P(5e^-)] + [1 \times O(6e^-)] + [3 \times Cl(7e^-)] = 32$ electrons. Placing the P in the center with single bonds to all the surrounding atoms uses 8 electrons and gives P an octet. The remaining 24 can be split into 12 pairs with each of the surrounding atoms receiving three pairs. At this point, in structure **I** below, all the atoms have an octet. The central atom is P (smallest group number, highest period number) and can have more than an octet. To see how reasonable this structure is, calculate the formal (FC) for each atom. The +1 and –1 formal charges are not too unreasonable, but , 0 charges are better. If one of the lone pairs is moved from the O (the atom with the negative FC) to form a double bond to the P (the atom with the positive FC), structure **II** results. The calculated formal changes in structure II are all 0 so this is a better structure even though P has 10 electrons.

:Ö:
|
:C̤̈l—P—C̤̈l:
|
:C̤l:

:O:
‖
:C̤̈l—P—C̤̈l:
|
:C̤l:

I	II
$FC_P = 5 - [0 + 1/2(8)] = +1$	$FC_P = 5 - [0 + 1/2(10)] = 0$
$FC_O = 6 - [6 + 1/2(2)] = -1$	$FC_O = 6 - [4 + 1/2(4)] = 0$
$FC_{Cl} = 7 - [6 + 1/2(2)] = 0$	$FC_{Cl} = 7 - [6 + 1/2(2)] = 0$

Solution:

b) In ClO_2, the Cl is probably the central atom because the O atoms have a lower period. The molecule contains $[1 \times Cl(7e^-)] + [2 \times O(6e^-)] = 19$ electrons. The presence of an odd number of electrons means that there will be an exception to the octet rule. Placing the O atoms around the Cl and using 4 electrons to form single bonds leaves 15 electrons, 14 of which may be separated into 7 pairs. If 3 of these pairs are given to each O, and the remaining pair plus the lone electron are given to the Cl, we have the following structure:

O—Cl—O

Calculating formal charges: $FC_{Cl} = 7 - [3 + 1/2(4)] = +2$ $\quad FC_O = 6 - [6 + 1/2(2)] = -1$

The +2 charge on the Cl is a little high, so other structures should be tried. Moving a lone pair from one of the O atoms (negative FC) to form a double bond between the Cl and one of the oxygen atoms gives either structure **I** or **II** below. If both O atoms donate a pair of electrons to form a double bond, then structure **III** results. The next step is to calculate the formal charges.

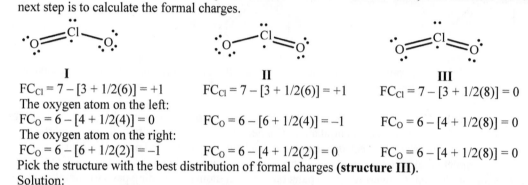

I	II	III
$FC_{Cl} = 7 - [3 + 1/2(6)] = +1$	$FC_{Cl} = 7 - [3 + 1/2(6)] = +1$	$FC_{Cl} = 7 - [3 + 1/2(8)] = 0$
The oxygen atom on the left:		
$FC_O = 6 - [4 + 1/2(4)] = 0$	$FC_O = 6 - [6 + 1/2(4)] = -1$	$FC_O = 6 - [4 + 1/2(8)] = 0$
The oxygen atom on the right:		
$FC_O = 6 - [6 + 1/2(2)] = -1$	$FC_O = 6 - [4 + 1/2(2)] = 0$	$FC_O = 6 - [4 + 1/2(8)] = 0$

Pick the structure with the best distribution of formal charges **(structure III)**.

Solution:

c) In $SClF_5$, S is most likely to be the central atom because it has a lower group number than the other atoms. If single bonds are drawn between the S atom and each of the other atoms in the compound, S will have a total of 12 electrons (an octet rule exception). It is possible for S to have more electrons than an octet because it has *d* orbitals available to it (the 3*d* orbitals). Thus, it can have an *expanded valence shell.* The molecule contains $[1 \times S(6e^-)] + [5 \times F(7e^-)] + [1 \times Cl(7e^-)] = 48$ electrons. Drawing a single bond between S and each of the other atoms uses $6 \times 2 = 12e^-$, leaving 36 electrons. Placing 6 electrons around each of outer atoms to complete their octets uses these remaining atoms. This gives the structure:

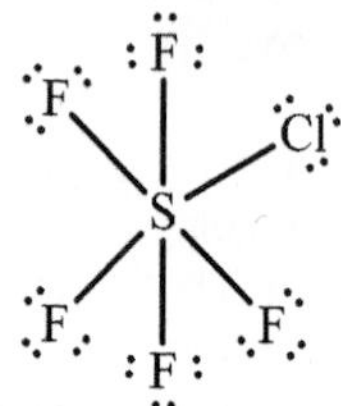

Determine the formal charges for each atom:

$FC_S = 6 - [0 + 1/2(12)] = 0$ $\quad FC_F = 7 - [6 + 1/2(2)] = 0$ $\quad FC_{Cl} = 7 - [6 + 1/2(2)] = 0$

10.5B Plan: The presence of available *d* orbitals makes checking formal charges more important. Use the equation for formal charge: FC = # of valence e^- – [# unshared valence e^- + ½(# shared valence e^-)]

Solution:

a) In BeH_2, the Be is the central atom (H cannot be a central atom). The molecule contains: $[1 \times Be(2e^-)] + [2 \times H(1e^-)] = 4$ electrons. Placing the Be in the center with single bonds to all the surrounding atoms uses all 4 electrons, leaving Be 4 atoms short of an octet. There are not any more electrons to add to Be. Nor are there any lone pairs to change to bonding pairs. Thus, BeH_2 is an exception to the octet rule in that Be does not have a complete octet.

H—Be—H

Determine the formal charges for each atom:
$FC_{Be} = 2 - [0 + 1/2(4)] = 0$ $\qquad$ $FC_H = 1 - [0 + 1/2(2)] = 0$

Solution:
b) In I_3^-, one of the I atoms is central, and the other two I atoms are bonded to it. The molecule contains $[3 \times I(7e^-)] + 1e^-$ (for the negative charge) = 22 electrons. Placing one I atom in the center and connecting each of the other two I atoms to it by single bonds uses $2 \times 2 = 4e^-$. This leaves 18 electrons. Placing 6 electrons on each of the outer I atoms leaves $18 - 12 = 6e^-$. These remaining 6 electrons are placed, as three lone pairs on the central I atom.

Calculating formal charges: $FC_{I\,(central)} = 7 - [6 + 1/2(4)] = -1$ $\qquad$ $FC_{I\,(outer)} = 7 - [6 + 1/2(2)] = 0$
These are low, reasonable formal charges, and we do not need to adjust the structure.

Solution:
c) XeO_3 is a noble gas compound, thus, there will be an exception to the octet rule. The molecule contains $[1 \times Xe(8e^-)] + [3 \times O(6e^-)] = 26$ electrons. The Xe is in a higher period than O so Xe is the central atom. If it is placed in the center with a single bond to each of the three oxygen atoms, 6 electrons are used, and 20 electrons remain. The remaining electrons can be divided into 10 pairs with 3 pairs given to each O and the last pair being given to the Xe. This gives the structure:

Determine the formal charges for each atom:
$FC_{Xe} = 8 - [2 + 1/2(6)] = +3$ $\qquad$ $FC_O = 6 - [6 + 1/2(2)] = -1$
The +3 charge on the Xe is a little high, so other structures should be tried. Moving a lone pair from one of the O atoms (negative FC) to form a double bond between the Xe and one of the oxygen atoms gives structure **I** (or one of its resonance structures). Moving two lone pair from two of the O atoms (negative FC) gives structure **II** below (or one of its resonance structures). If all three O atoms donate a pair of electrons to form a double bond, then structure **III** results. The next step is to calculate the formal charges.

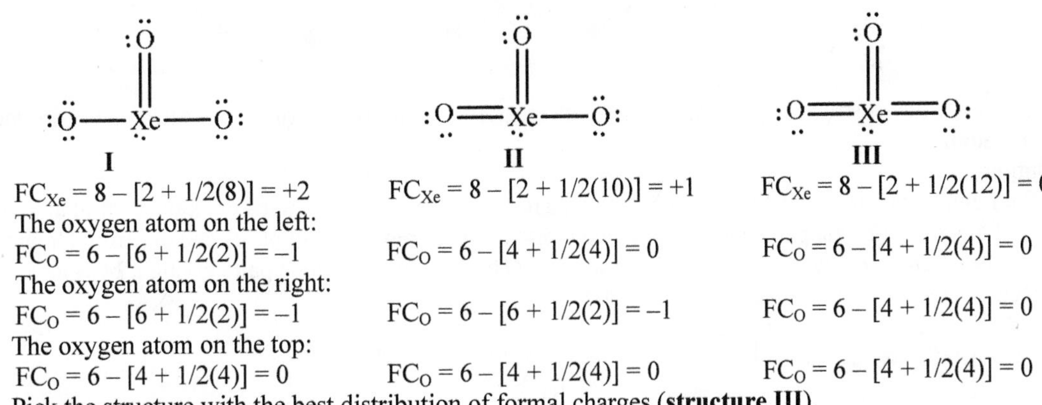

I	II	III
$FC_{Xe} = 8 - [2 + 1/2(8)] = +2$	$FC_{Xe} = 8 - [2 + 1/2(10)] = +1$	$FC_{Xe} = 8 - [2 + 1/2(12)] = 0$
The oxygen atom on the left:		
$FC_O = 6 - [6 + 1/2(2)] = -1$	$FC_O = 6 - [4 + 1/2(4)] = 0$	$FC_O = 6 - [4 + 1/2(4)] = 0$
The oxygen atom on the right:		
$FC_O = 6 - [6 + 1/2(2)] = -1$	$FC_O = 6 - [6 + 1/2(2)] = -1$	$FC_O = 6 - [4 + 1/2(4)] = 0$
The oxygen atom on the top:		
$FC_O = 6 - [4 + 1/2(4)] = 0$	$FC_O = 6 - [4 + 1/2(4)] = 0$	$FC_O = 6 - [4 + 1/2(4)] = 0$

Pick the structure with the best distribution of formal charges (**structure III**).

10.6A Plan: Draw a Lewis structure. Determine the electron arrangement by counting the electron pairs around the central atom.

Solution:
a) The Lewis structure for CS_2 is shown below. The central atom, C, has two pairs (double bonds only count once). The two pair arrangement is **linear** with the designation, AX_2. The absence of lone pairs on the C means there is no deviation in the bond angle **(180°)**.

S=C=S

Solution:
b) Even though this is a combination of a metal with a nonmetal, it may be treated as a molecular species. The Lewis structure for $PbCl_2$ is shown below. The molecule is of the AX_2E type; the central atom has three pairs of electrons (1 lone pair and two bonding pairs). This means the *electron-group arrangement* is trigonal planar **(120°),** with a lone pair giving a **bent or V-shaped** molecule. The lone pair causes the ideal bond angle to decrease to **< 120°**.

Solution:
c) The Lewis structure for the CBr_4 molecule is shown below. It has the AX_4 type formula which is a perfect **tetrahedron** (with **109.5°** bond angles) because all bonds are identical, and there are no lone pairs.

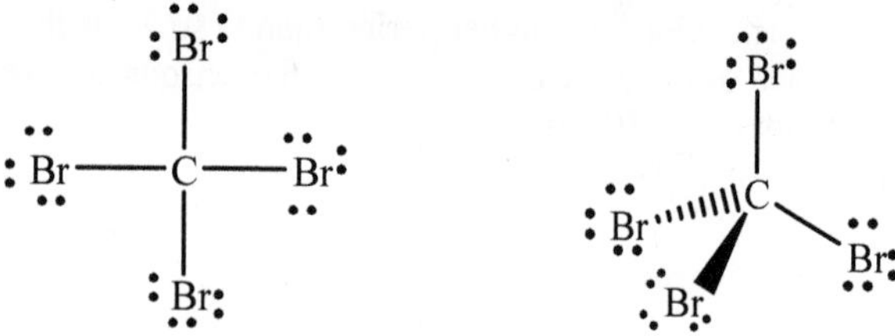

Solution:
d) The SF_2 molecule has the Lewis structure shown below. This is a AX_2E_2 molecule; the central atom is surrounded by four electron pairs, two of which are lone pairs and two of which are bonding pairs. The *electron group arrangement* is tetrahedral. The two lone pairs give a **V-shaped or bent** arrangement. The ideal tetrahedral bond angle is **decreased from the ideal 109.5°** value.

10.6B Plan: Draw a Lewis structure. Determine the electron arrangement by counting the electron pairs around the central atom.

Solution:
a) The Lewis structure for BrO_2^- is shown below. The molecule is of the AX_2E_2 type; the central atom has four pairs of electrons (2 lone pairs and two bonding pairs; each double bond counts as one electron domain). This means the *electron-group arrangement* is tetrahedral **(109.5°),** with two lone pairs giving a **bent or V-shaped** molecule. The lone pairs cause the bond angle to decrease to **<109.5°.**

The molecular shape of BrO_2^-:

Solution:
b) The Lewis structure for AsH_3 is shown below. The molecule is of the AX_3E type; the central atom has four pairs of electrons (1 lone pair and three bonding pairs). This means the *electron-group arrangement* is tetrahedral **(109.5°),** with a lone pair giving a **trigonal pyramidal** molecule. The lone pair causes the bond angle to decrease to **< 109.5°**.

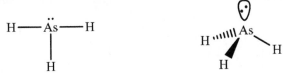

Solution:
c) The Lewis structure for N_3^- is shown below. The two pair electron arrangement is **linear** with the designation, AX_2. The molecular shape is also **linear.** The absence of lone pairs on the central N means there is no deviation in the bond angle **(180°).**

$$[:\ddot{N}=N=\ddot{N}:]^-$$

Solution:
d) The SeO_3 molecule has the Lewis structure shown below. This is an AX_3 molecule; the central atom is surrounded by three electron pairs (each double bond counts as one electron domain). The *electron group arrangement* and molecular shape is **trigonal planar.** The absence of lone pairs on the central atom means there is no deviation in the bond angle (**120°**).

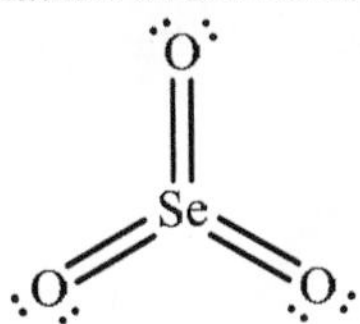

10.7A Plan: Draw a Lewis structure. Determine the electron arrangement by counting the electron pairs around the central atom.
Solution:
a) The Lewis structure for the ICl_2^- is shown below. This is an AX_2E_3 type structure. The five pairs give a trigonal bipyramidal arrangement of electron groups. The presence of 3 lone pairs leads to a **linear** shape **(180°).** The usual distortions caused by lone pairs cancel in this case. In the trigonal bipyramidal geometry, lone pairs always occupy equatorial positions.

Solution:
b) The Lewis structure for the ClF_3 molecule is given below. Like ICl_2^- there are 5 pairs around the central atom; however, there are only 2 lone pairs. This gives a molecule that is **T-shaped.** The presence of the lone pairs decreases the ideal bond angles to **less than 90°**.

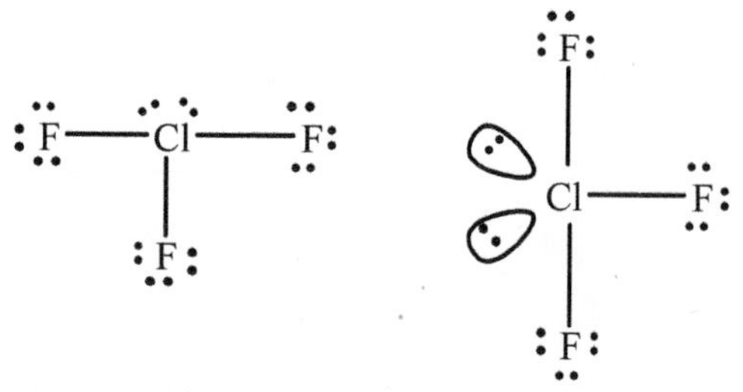

Solution:

c) The SOF_4 molecule has several possible Lewis structures, two of which are shown below. In both cases, the central atom has 5 atoms attached with no lone pairs. The formal charges work out the same in both structures. The structure on the right has an equatorial double bond. Double bonds require more room than single bonds, and equatorial positions have this extra room.

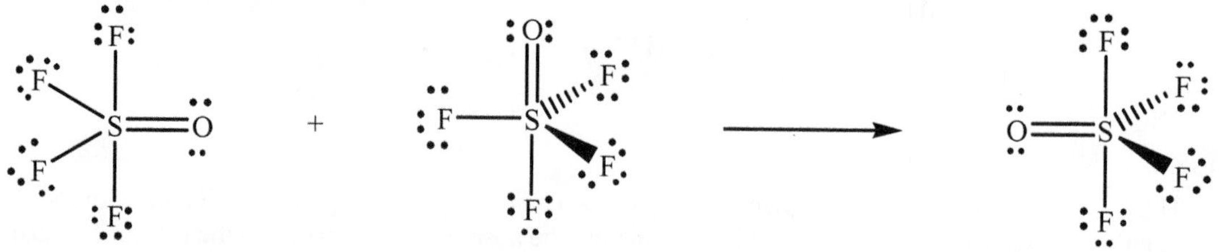

The molecule is **trigonal bipyramidal**, and the double bond causes deviation from ideal bond angles. All of the F atoms move away from the O. Thus, all angles involving the O are increased, and all other angles are decreased.

10.7B Plan: Draw a Lewis structure. Determine the electron arrangement by counting the electron pairs around the central atom.

Solution:

a) The Lewis structure for the BrF_4^- ion is shown below. This is an AX_4E_2 type structure. The six pairs give an octahedral arrangement of electron groups. The presence of 2 lone pairs on the central atom leads to a **square planar** shape **(90°)**. The usual distortions caused by lone pairs cancel in this case. In the square planar, lone pairs always occupy axial positions.

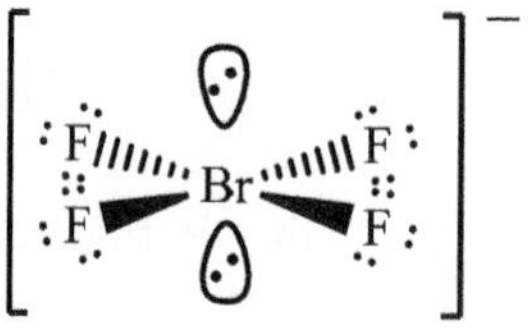

Solution:

b) The Lewis structure for the ClF_4^+ ion is given below. This is an AX_4E type structure. There are 5 pairs around the central atom; however, there is 1 lone pair. This gives a molecule that has a **seesaw** shape. The presence of the lone pair decreases the ideal bond angles to **less than 90°** (F_{ax}–Cl–F_{eq}) and **less than 120°** (F_{eq}–Cl–F_{eq}).

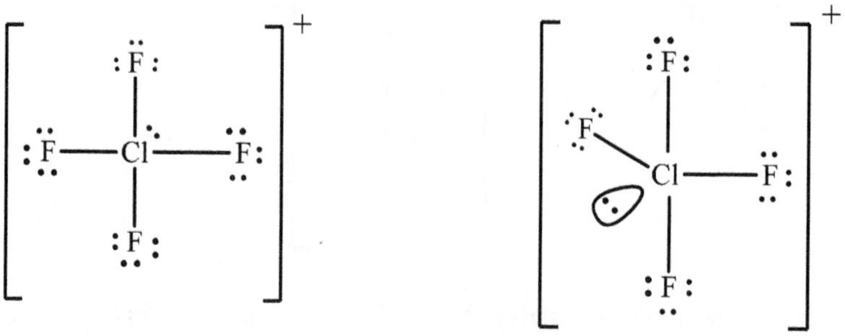

Solution:
c) The Lewis structure for the PCl_6^- is shown below. This is an AX_6 type structure. The six pairs give an octahedral arrangement of electron groups and an **octahedral** shape, with **90°** bond angles. The absence of lone pair electrons on the central atom means there is no deviation from the ideal bond angles.

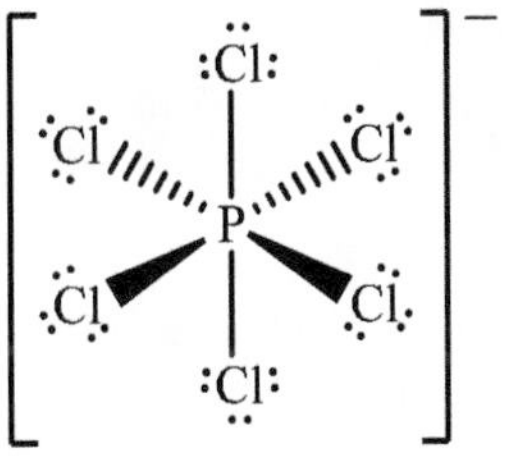

10.8A Plan: Draw the Lewis structure for each of the substances, and determine the molecular geometry of each.
Solution:
a) The Lewis structure for H_2SO_4 is shown below. The double bonds ease the problem of a high formal charge on the sulfur. Sulfur is allowed to exceed an octet. The S has 4 groups around it, making it **tetrahedral**. The ideal angles around the S are **109.5°**. The double bonds move away from each other, and force the single bonds away. This opens the angle between the double bonded oxygen atoms, and results in an angle between the single bonded oxygen atoms that is less than ideal. Each single bonded oxygen atom has 4 groups around it; since two of the 4 groups are lone pairs, the shape around each of these oxygen atoms is **bent.** The lone pairs compress the H–O–S bond angle to < **109.5°.**

Solution:
b) The hydrogen atoms cannot be central so the carbons must be attached to each other. The problem states that there is a carbon-carbon triple bond. This leaves only a single bond to connect the third carbon to a triple-bonded carbon, and give that carbon an octet. The other triple-bonded carbon needs one hydrogen to complete its octet. The remaining three hydrogen atoms are attached to the single-bonded carbon, which allows it to complete its octet. This structure is shown below. The single-bonded carbon has four groups **tetrahedrally** around it leading to bond angles ~**109.5°** (little or no deviation). The triple-bonded carbons each have two groups (the triple bond counts as one electron group) so they should be **linear (180°).**

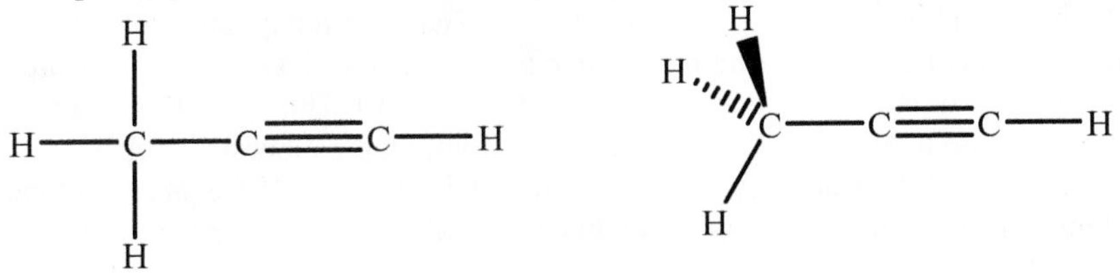

Solution:
c) Fluorine, like hydrogen, is never a central atom. Thus, the sulfur atoms must be bonded to each other. Each F has 3 lone pairs, and the sulfur atoms have 2 lone pairs. All 4 atoms now have an octet. This structure is shown below. Each sulfur has four groups around it, so the electron arrangement is **tetrahedral**. The presence of the lone pairs on the sulfur atoms results in a geometry that is **V-shaped or bent** and in a bond angle that is **< 109.5°**.

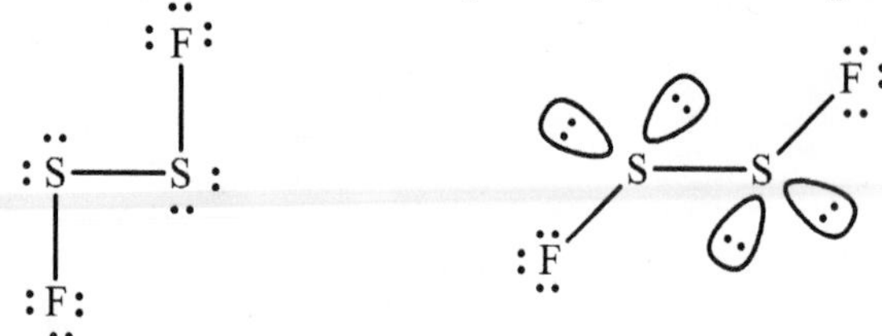

10.8B Plan: Draw the Lewis structure for each of the substances, and determine the molecular geometry of each.
Solution:
a) The Lewis structure for CH_3NH_2 is shown below. The C has 4 groups around it (AX_4), making it **tetrahedral**. The ideal angles around the C are **109.5°**. The nitrogen also has 4 groups around it, but one of those groups is a lone pair. The lone pair makes the N an AX_3E central atom with **trigonal pyramidal** geometry. The presence of the lone pair compresses the H–N–H angle to **<109.5°**.

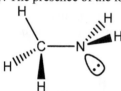

Solution:
b) The Lewis structure for C_2Cl_4 is shown below. The carbons are central and connected to each other. There are a total of 36 valence electrons. In order for all of the atoms to have a full octet, there must be a double bond between the two carbon atoms. Each of the carbon atoms has three electron groups around it, yielding a **trigonal planar** geometry. The presence of the double bond compresses each Cl–C–Cl angle to **<120°**.

Solution:
c) The Lewis structure for Cl_2O_7 is shown below. The problem states that three oxygen atoms are bonded to the first Cl atom, which is then bonded to a fourth oxygen atom. That fourth oxygen atom is bonded, in turn, to a second Cl atom, which is bonded to 3 additional oxygen atoms. Each Cl has 4 electron groups (3 of which are double bonds to oxygen and one of which is a single bond to oxygen). This gives the Cl a **tetrahedral** geometry with bond angles very close to **109.5°**. The central oxygen atom, on the other hand, also has four electron pairs around it. In this case, two of the electron pairs are bonding pairs and two of the pairs are lone pairs. The presence of the lone pairs give the central oxygen a **bent or V-shaped geometry** and compresses the Cl–O–Cl bond angle to **<109.5°**.

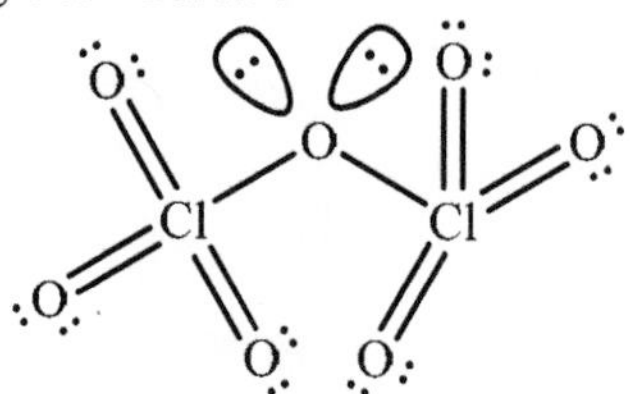

10.9A Plan: Draw the Lewis structures, predict the shapes, and then examine the positions of the bond dipoles.
Solution:
a) Dichloromethane, CH_2Cl_2, has the Lewis structure shown below. It is tetrahedral, and if the outlying atoms were identical, it would be nonpolar. However, the chlorine atoms are more electronegative than hydrogen so there is a general shift in their direction resulting in the arrows shown.

Solution:
b) Iodine oxide pentafluoride, IOF_5, has the Lewis structure shown below. The overall geometry is octahedral. All six bonds are polar, with the more electronegative O and F atoms shifting electron density away from the I. The 4 equatorial fluorines counterbalance each other. The axial F is not equivalent to the axial O. The more electronegative F results in an overall polarity in the direction of the axial F.

The lone electron pairs are left out for simplicity.
Solution:
c) Iodine pentafluoride, IF_5, has the square pyramidal Lewis structure shown below. The fluorine is more electronegative than the I, so the shift in electron density is towards the F, resulting in the dipole indicated below.

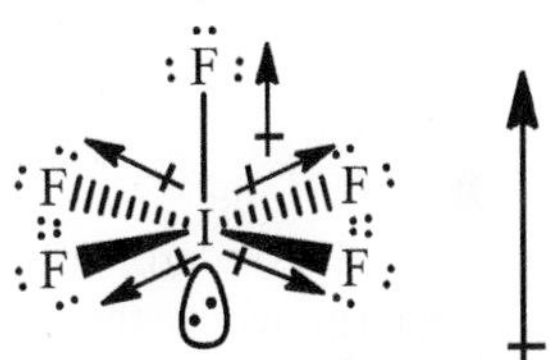

10.9B Plan: Draw the Lewis structures, predict the shapes, and then examine the positions of the bond dipoles.
Solution:
a) Xenon tetrafluoride, XeF_4, has the Lewis structure shown below. It is square planar, and, because the outlying atoms are identical, it is nonpolar. However, the fluorine atoms are more electronegative than xenon, so the individual bonds are polar. Because of the square planar geometry, those polar bonds cancel each other out.

Solution:
b) Chlorine trifluoride, ClF_3, has the Lewis structure shown below. The overall geometry is T-shaped. All three bonds are polar, with the more electronegative F atoms shifting electron density away from the Cl. The more electronegative F results in an overall dipole indicated below.

Solution:
c) Sulfur monoxide tetrafluoride, SOF_4, has the trigonal bipyramidal Lewis structure shown below. Both the F atoms and the O atom are more electronegative than the S, and F is more electronegative than O, so the shift in electron density is towards the F atoms, resulting in the dipole indicated below.

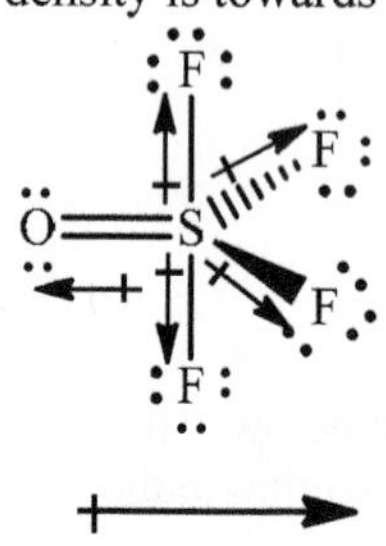

CHEMICAL CONNECTIONS BOXED READING PROBLEMS

B10.1 Plan: Examine the Lewis structure, noting the number of regions of electron density around the carbon and nitrogen atoms in the two resonance structures. The molecular shape is determined by the number of electron regions. An electron region is any type of bond (single, double, or triple) and an unshared pair of electrons.
Solution:
Resonance structure on the left:
Carbon has three electron regions (two single bonds and one double bond); three electron regions are arranged in a trigonal planar arrangement. The molecular shape around the C atom is **trigonal planar**. Nitrogen has four electron regions (three single bonds and an unshared pair of electrons); the four electron regions are arranged tetrahedrally; since one corner of the tetrahedron is occupied by an unshared electron pair, the shape around N is **trigonal pyramidal.**
Resonance structure on the right:
This C atom also has three electrons regions (two single bond and one double bond) so the molecular shape is again **trigonal planar**. The N atom also has three electron regions (two single bonds and one double bond); the molecular shape is **trigonal planar**.

B10.2 The top portion of both molecules is similar so the top portions will interact with biomolecules in a similar manner. The mescaline molecule may fit into the same nerve receptors as dopamine due to the similar molecular shape.

END–OF–CHAPTER PROBLEMS

10.1 Plan: To be the central atom in a compound, an atom must be able to simultaneously bond to at least two other atoms.

Solution:

He, F, and H cannot serve as central atoms in a Lewis structure. Helium ($1s^2$) is a noble gas, and as such, it does not need to bond to any other atoms. Hydrogen ($1s^1$) and fluorine ($1s^2 2s^2 2p^5$) only need one electron to complete their valence shells. Thus, they can only bond to one other atom, and they do not have *d* orbitals available to expand their valence shells.

10.3 Plan: For an element to obey the octet rule it must be surrounded by eight electrons. To determine the number of electrons present, (1) count the individual electrons actually shown adjacent to a particular atom (lone pairs), and (2) add two times the number of bonds to that atom: number of electrons = individual electrons + 2(number of bonds).

Solution:

(a) $0 + 2(4) = 8$; (b) $2 + 2(3) = 8$; (c) $0 + 2(5) = 10$; (d) $2 + 2(3) = 8$; (e) $0 + 2(4) = 8$; (f) $2 + 2(3) = 8$; (g) $0 + 2(3) = 6$; (h) $8 + 2(0) = 8$. **All the structures obey the octet rule except: c and g.**

10.5 Plan: Count the valence electrons and draw Lewis structures.

Solution:

Total valence electrons: SiF_4: [1 x Si($4e^-$] + [4 x F($7e^-$)] = 32; $SeCl_2$: [1 x Se($6e^-$)] + [2 x Cl($7e^-$)] = 20; COF_2: [1 x C($4e^-$)] + [1 x O($6e^-$)] + [2 x F($7e^-$)] = 24. The Si, Se, and the C are the central atoms, because these are the elements in their respective compounds with the lower group number (in addition, we are told C is central). Place the other atoms around the central atoms and connect each to the central atom with a single bond.
SiF_4: At this point, eight electrons ($2e^-$ in four Si–F bonds) have been used with $32 - 8 = 24$ remaining; the remaining electrons are placed around the fluorine atoms (three pairs each). All atoms have an octet.
$SeCl_2$: The two bonds use $4e^-$ ($2e^-$ in two Se–Cl bonds) leaving $20 - 4 = 16e^-$. These $16e^-$ are used to complete the octets on Se and the Cl atoms.
COF_2: The three bonds to the C use $6e^-$ ($2e^-$ in three bonds) leaving $24 - 6 = 18\ e^-$. These $18e^-$ are distributed to the surrounding atoms first to complete their octets. After the $18e^-$ are used, the central C is two electrons short of an octet. Forming a double bond to the O (change a lone pair on O to a bonding pair on C) completes the C octet.

(a) SiF_4 (b) $SeCl_2$

```
      :F:
       |
  :F—Si—F:           :Cl—Se—Cl:
       |
      :F:
```

(c) COF_2

```
 :F—C—F:      ——→      :F—C—F:
    |                     ||
   :O:                   :O:
```

10.7 Plan: Count the valence electrons and draw Lewis structures.

Solution:

a) PF_3: [1 x P($5e^-$)] + [3 x F($7e^-$)] = 26 valence electrons. P is the central atom. Draw single bonds from P to the three F atoms, using $2e^-$ x 3 bonds = $6e^-$. Remaining e^-: $26 - 6 = 20e^-$. Distribute the $20e^-$ around the P and F atoms to complete their octets.

b) H_2CO_3: [2 x H($1e^-$)] + [1 x C($4e^-$)] + 3 x O($6e^-$)] = 24 valence electrons. C is the central atom with the H atoms attached to the O atoms. Place appropriate single bonds between all atoms using $2e^-$ x 5 bonds = $10e^-$ so that $24 - 10 = 14e^-$ remain. Use these $14e^-$ to complete the octets of the O atoms (the H atoms already have their

two electrons). After the $14e^-$ are used, the central C is two electrons short of an octet. Forming a double bond to the O that does not have an H bonded to it (change a lone pair on O to a bonding pair on C) completes the C octet.
c) CS_2: [1 x C($4e^-$)] + [2 x S($6e^-$)] = 16 valence electrons. C is the central atom. Draw single bonds from C to the two S atoms, using $2e^-$ x 2 bonds = $4e^-$. Remaining e^-: 16 – 4 = $12e^-$. Use these $12e^-$ to complete the octets of the surrounding S atoms; this leaves C four electrons short of an octet. Form a double bond from each S to the C by changing a lone pair on each S to a bonding pair on C.

a) PF_3 (26 valence e^-) b) H_2CO_3 (24 valence e^-)

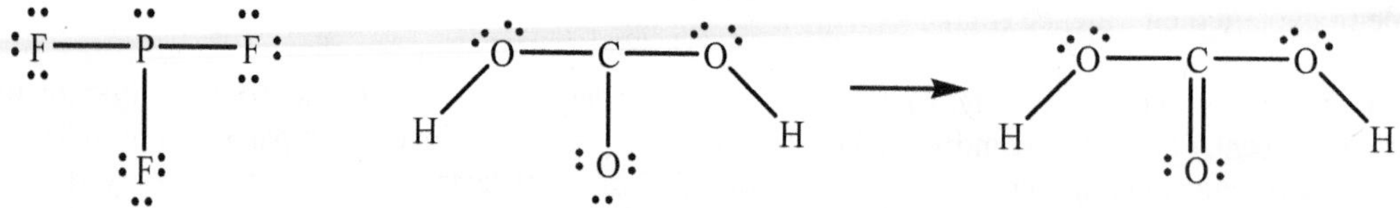

c) CS_2 (16 valence e^-)

10.9 Plan: The problem asks for resonance structures, so there must be more than one answer for each part.
Solution:
a) NO_2^+ has [1 x N($5e^-$)] + [2 x O($6e^-$)] – $1e^-$ (+ charge) = 16 valence electrons. Draw a single bond from N to each O, using $2e^-$ x 2 bonds = $4e^-$; 16 – 4 = $12e^-$ remain. Distribute these $12e^-$ to the O atoms to complete their octets. This leaves N $4e^-$ short of an octet. Form a double bond from each O to the N by changing a lone pair on each O to a bonding pair on N. No resonance is required as all atoms can achieve an octet with double bonds.

b) NO_2F has [1 x N($5e^-$)] + [2 x O($6e^-$)] + [1 x F($7e^-$)] = 24 valence electrons. Draw a single bond from N to each surrounding atom, using $2e^-$ x 3 bonds = $6e^-$; 24 – 6 = $18e^-$ remain. Distribute these $18e^-$ to the O and F atoms to complete their octets. This leaves N $2e^-$ short of an octet. Form a double bond from either O to the N by changing a lone pair on O to a bonding pair on N. There are two resonance structures since a lone pair from either of the two O atoms can be moved to a bonding pair with N:

10.11 Plan: Count the valence electrons and draw Lewis structures. Additional structures are needed to show resonance.
Solution:
a) N_3^- has [3 x N($5e^-$)] + [1 e^-(from charge)] = 16 valence electrons. Place a single bond between the nitrogen atoms. This uses $2e^-$ x 2 bonds = 4 electrons, leaving 16 – 4 = 12 electrons (6 pairs). Giving three pairs on each end nitrogen gives them an octet, but leaves the central N with only four electrons as shown below:

The central N needs four electrons. There are three options to do this: (1) each of the end N atoms could form a double bond to the central N by sharing one of its pairs; (2) one of the end N atoms could form a triple bond by sharing two of its lone pairs; (3) the other end N atom could form the triple bond instead.

$[\ddot{N}=N=\ddot{N}]^- \longleftrightarrow [:N\equiv N-\ddot{N}:]^- \longleftrightarrow [:\ddot{N}-N\equiv N:]^-$

b) NO_2^- has [1 x N(5e$^-$)] + [2 x O(6e$^-$)] + [1 e$^-$ (from charge)] = 18 valence electrons. The nitrogen should be the central atom with each of the oxygen atoms attached to it by a single bond (2e$^-$ x 2 bonds = 4 electrons). This leaves 18 – 4 = 14 electrons (seven pairs). If three pairs are given to each O and one pair is given to the N, then both O atoms have an octet, but the N atom only has six. To complete an octet the N atom needs to gain a pair of electrons from one O atom or the other (form a double bond). The resonance structures are:

$[:\ddot{O}-\ddot{N}-\ddot{O}:]^- \longrightarrow [:\ddot{O}-\ddot{N}=\ddot{O}]^- \longleftrightarrow [\ddot{O}=\ddot{N}-\ddot{O}:]^-$

10.13 Plan: Initially, the method used in the preceding problems may be used to establish a Lewis structure. The total of the formal charges must equal the charge on an ion or be equal to 0 for a compound. The formal charge only needs to be calculated once for a set of identical atoms. Formal charge (FC) = no. of valence electrons – [no. of unshared valence electrons + ½ no. of shared valence electrons].

Solution:

a) IF_5 has [1 x I(7e$^-$)] + [5 x F(7e$^-$)] = 42 valence electrons. The presence of five F atoms around the central I means that the I atom will have a minimum of ten electrons; thus, this is an exception to the octet rule. The five I–F bonds use 2e$^-$ x 5 bonds = 10 electrons leaving 42 – 10 = 32 electrons (16 pairs). Each F needs three pairs to complete an octet. The five F atoms use fifteen of the sixteen pairs, so there is one pair left for the central I. This gives:

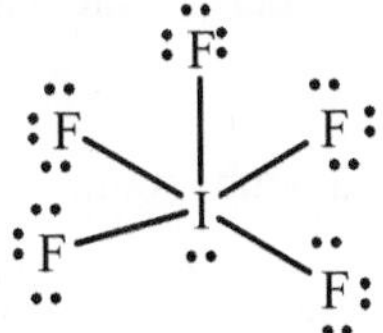

Calculating formal charges:

FC = no. of valence electrons – [no. of unshared valence electrons + ½ no. of shared valence electrons].

For iodine: $FC_I = 7 - [2 + ½(10)] = 0$ For each fluorine: $FC_F = 7 - [6 + ½(2)] = 0$

Total formal charge = 0 = charge on the compound.

b) AlH_4^- has [1 x Al(3e$^-$)] + [4 x H(1e$^-$)] + [1e$^-$ (from charge)] = 8 valence electrons.

The four Al–H bonds use all the electrons and Al has an octet.

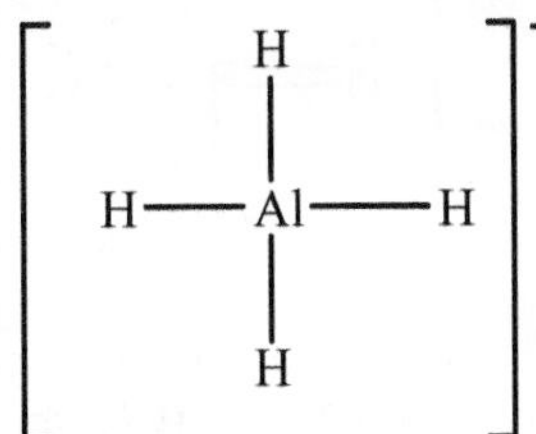

FC = no. of valence electrons – [no. of unshared valence electrons + ½ no. of shared valence electrons].

For aluminum: $FC_{Al} = 3 - [0 + ½(8)] = -1$

For each hydrogen: $FC_H = 1 - [0 + ½(2)] = 0$

10.15 Plan: Initially, the method used in the preceding problems may be used to establish a Lewis structure. The total of the formal charges must equal the charge on an ion or be equal to 0 for a compound. The formal charge only needs to be calculated once for a set of identical atoms. Formal charge (FC) = no. of valence electrons – [no. of unshared valence electrons + ½ no. of shared valence electrons].

Solution:

a) CN^-: [1 x C(4e$^-$)] + [1 x N(5e$^-$)] + [1 e$^-$ from charge] = 10 valence electrons. Place a single bond between the carbon and nitrogen atoms. This uses 2e$^-$ x 1 bond = 2 electrons, leaving 10 – 2 = 8 electrons (four pairs). Giving three pairs of electrons to the nitrogen atom completes its octet but that leaves only one pair of electrons for the carbon atom which will not have an octet. The nitrogen could form a triple bond by sharing two of its lone pairs with the carbon atom. A triple bond between the two atoms plus a lone pair on each atom satisfies the octet rule and uses all ten electrons.

$$\left[:C\equiv N:\right]^-$$

FC = no. of valence electrons – [no. of unshared valence electrons + ½ no. of shared valence electrons].
$FC_C = 4 - [2 + ½(6)] = -1$; $FC_N = 5 - [2 + ½(6)] = 0$
Check: The total formal charge equals the charge on the ion (–1).
b) ClO^-: [1 x Cl(7e⁻)] + [1 x O(6e⁻)] + [1e⁻ from charge] = 14 valence electrons. Place a single bond between the chlorine and oxygen atoms. This uses 2e⁻ x 1 bond = 2 electrons, leaving 14 – 2 = 12 electrons (six pairs). Giving three pairs of electrons each to the carbon and oxygen atoms completes their octets.

$$\left[:\ddot{\underset{\cdot\cdot}{Cl}}-\ddot{\underset{\cdot\cdot}{O}}:\right]^-$$

FC = no. of valence electrons – [no. of unshared valence electrons + ½ no. of shared valence electrons].
$FC_{Cl} = 7 - [6 + ½(2)] = 0$ $FC_O = 6 - [6 + ½(2)] = -1$
Check: The total formal charge equals the charge on the ion (–1).

10.17 Plan: The general procedure is similar to the preceding problems, plus the oxidation number determination.
Solution:
a) BrO_3^- has [1 x Br(7e⁻)] + 3 x O(6e⁻)] + [1e⁻ (from charge)] = 26 valence electrons.
Placing the O atoms around the central Br and forming three Br–O bonds uses 2e⁻ x 3 bonds = 6 electrons and leaves 26 – 6 = 20 electrons (ten pairs). Placing three pairs on each O (3 x 3 = 9 total pairs) leaves one pair for the Br and yields structure I below. In structure I, all the atoms have a complete octet. Calculating formal charges:
$FC_{Br} = 7 - [2 + ½(6)] = +2$ $FC_O = 6 - [6 + ½(2)] = -1$
The FC_O is acceptable, but FC_{Br} is larger than is usually acceptable. Forming a double bond between any one of the O atoms gives structure II. Calculating formal charges:
$FC_{Br} = 7 - [2 + ½(8)] = +1$ $FC_O = 6 - [6 + ½(2)] = -1$ $FC_O = 6 - [4 + ½(4)] = 0$ (Double bonded O)
The FC_{Br} can be improved further by forming a second double bond to one of the other O atoms (structure III).
$FC_{Br} = 7 - [2 + ½(10)] = 0$ $FC_O = 6 - [6 + ½(2)] = -1$ $FC_O = 6 - [4 + ½(4)] = 0$ (Double bonded O atoms)

Structure III has the most reasonable distribution of formal charges.

I → II → III

The oxidation numbers (O.N.) are: $O.N._{Br} = +5$ and $O.N._O = -2$.
Check: The total formal charge equals the charge on the ion (–1).

–6
+5 –2
BrO_3^-

b) SO_3^{2-} has [1 x S(6e⁻)] + [3 x O(6e⁻)] + [2e⁻ (from charge)] = 26 valence electrons.
Placing the O atoms around the central S and forming three S–O bonds uses 2e⁻ x 3 bonds = 6 electrons and leaves 26 – 6 = 20 electrons (ten pairs). Placing three pairs on each O (3 x 3 = 9 total pairs) leaves one pair for the S and yields structure I below. In structure I all the atoms have a complete octet. Calculating formal charges:
$FC_S = 6 - [2 + ½(6)] = +1$; $FC_O = 6 - [6 + ½(2)] = -1$

The FC_O is acceptable, but FC_S is larger than is usually acceptable. Forming a double bond between any one of the O atoms (structure II) gives:

$FC_S = 6 - [2 + ½(8)] = 0$ $FC_O = 6 - [6 + ½(2)] = -1$ $FC_O = 6 - [4 + ½(4)] = 0$ (Double bonded O)

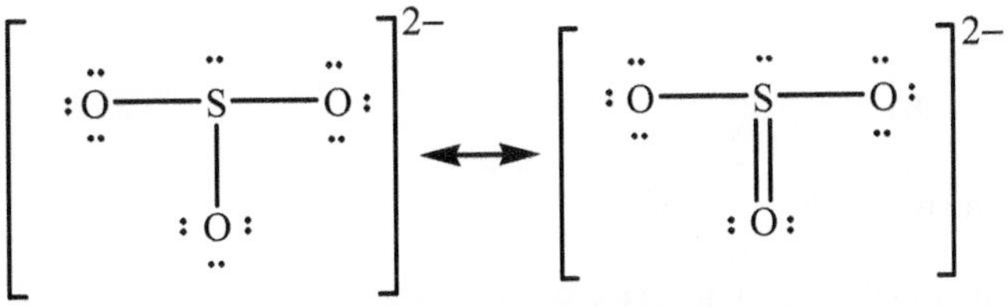

I II

$\overset{-6}{\underset{+4\ -2}{}}$ SO_3^{2-}

Structure II has the more reasonable distribution of formal charges.
The oxidation numbers (O.N.) are: $O.N._S = +4$ and $O.N._O = -2$.
Check: The total formal charge equals the charge on the ion (–2).

10.19 Plan: The octet rule states that when atoms bond, they share electrons to attain a filled outer shell of eight electrons. If an atom has fewer than eight electrons, it is electron deficient; if an atom has more than eight electrons around it, the atom has an expanded octet.

Solution:
a) BH_3 has $[1 \text{ x } B(3e^-)] + [3 \text{ x } H(1e^-)] = 6$ valence electrons. These are used in three B–H bonds. The B has six electrons instead of an octet; this molecule is **electron deficient**.
b) AsF_4^- has $[1 \text{ x } As(5e^-)] + [4 \text{ x } F(7e^-)] + [1e^- \text{ (from charge)}] = 34$ valence electrons. Four As–F bonds use eight electrons leaving 34 – 8 = 26 electrons (13 pairs). Each F needs three pairs to complete its octet and the remaining pair goes to the As. The As has an **expanded octet** with ten electrons. The F cannot expand its octet.
c) $SeCl_4$ has $[1 \text{ x } Se(6e^-)] + 4 \text{ x } Cl(7e^-)] = 34$ valence electrons. The $SeCl_4$ is isoelectronic (has the same electron structure) as AsF_4^-, and so its Lewis structure looks the same. Se has an **expanded octet** of ten electrons.

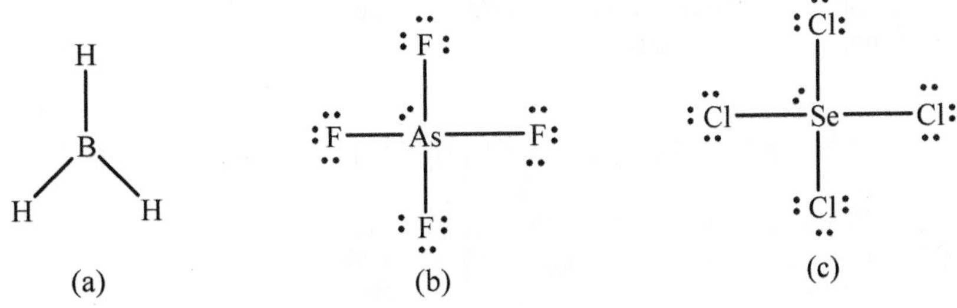

10.21 Plan: The octet rule states that when atoms bond, they share electrons to attain a filled outer shell of eight electrons. If an atom has fewer than eight electrons, it is electron deficient; if an atom has more than eight electrons around it, the atom has an expanded octet.

Solution:
a) BrF_3 has $[1 \text{ x } Br(7e^-)] + [3 \text{ x } F(7e^-)] = 28$ valence electrons. Placing a single bond between Br and each F uses $2e^- \text{ x } 3 \text{ bonds} = 6e^-$, leaving 28 – 6 = 22 electrons (eleven pairs). After the F atoms complete their octets with three pairs each, the Br gets the last two lone pairs. The Br has an **expanded octet** of ten electrons.
b) ICl_2^- has $[1 \text{ x } I(7e^-)] + [2 \text{ x } Cl(7e^-)] + [1e^- \text{ (from charge)}] = 22$ valence electrons. Placing a single bond between I and each Cl uses $2e^- \text{ x } 2 \text{ bond} = 4e^-$, leaving 22 – 4 = 18 electrons (nine pairs). After the Cl atoms complete their octets with three pairs each, the iodine finishes with the last three lone pairs. The iodine has an **expanded octet** of ten electrons.
c) BeF_2 has $[1 \text{ x } Be(2e^-)] + [2 \text{ x } F(7e^-)] = 16$ valence electrons. Placing a single bond between Be and each of the F atoms uses $2e^- \text{ x } 2 \text{ bonds} = 4e^-$, leaving 16 – 4 = 12 electrons (six pairs).The F atoms complete their octets with three pairs each, and there are no electrons left for the Be. Formal charges work against the formation of double bonds. Be, with only four electrons, is **electron deficient**.

a) b) c)

10.23 Plan: Draw Lewis structures for the reactants and products.

Solution:

Beryllium chloride has the formula $BeCl_2$. $BeCl_2$ has [1 x Be($2e^-$)] + [2 x Cl($7e^-$)] = 16 valence electrons. Four of these electrons are used to place a single bond between Be and each of the Cl atoms, leaving 16 – 4 = 12 electrons (six pairs). These six pairs are used to complete the octets of the Cl atoms, but Be does not have an octet – it is electron deficient.

Chloride ion has the formula Cl^- with an octet of electrons.

$BeCl_4^{2-}$ has [1 x Be($2e^-$)] + [4 x Cl($7e^-$)] + [$2e^-$ (from charge)] = 32 valence electrons. Eight of these electrons are used to place a single bond between Be and each Cl atom, leaving 32 – 8 = 24 electrons (twelve pairs). These twelve pairs complete the octet of the Cl atoms (Be already has an octet).

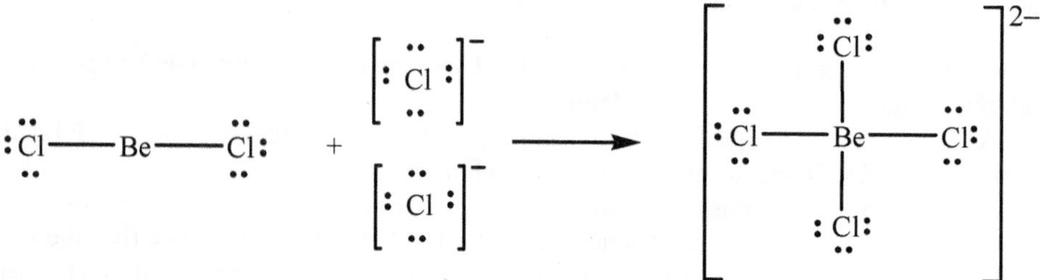

10.26 Plan: Use the structures in the text to determine the formal charges.

Formal charge (FC) = no. of valence electrons – [no. of unshared valence electrons + ½ no. of shared valence electrons].

Solution:

Structure **A**: FC_C = 4 – [0 + ½(8)] = 0; FC_O = 6 – [4 + ½(4)] = 0; FC_{Cl} = 7 – [6 + ½(2)] = 0

Total FC = 0

Structure **B**: FC_C = 4 – [0 + ½(8)] = 0; FC_O = 6 – [6 + ½(2)] = –1;

$FC_{Cl(double\ bonded)}$ = 7 – [4 + ½(4)] = +1; $FC_{Cl(single\ bonded)}$ = 7 – [6 + ½(2)] = 0

Total FC = 0

Structure **C**: FC_C = 4 – [0 + ½(8)] = 0; FC_O = 6 – [6 + ½(2)] = –1;

$FC_{Cl(double\ bonded)}$ = 7 – [4 + ½(4)] = +1; $FC_{Cl(single\ bonded)}$ = 7 – [6 + ½(2)] = 0

Total FC = 0

Structure **A** has the most reasonable set of formal charges.

10.28 The molecular shape and the electron-group arrangement are the same when there are no lone pairs on the central atom.

10.30 Plan: Examine a list of all possible structures, and choose the ones with four electron groups since the tetrahedral electron-group arrangement has four electron groups.

Solution:

Tetrahedral	AX_4
Trigonal pyramidal	AX_3E
Bent or V shaped	AX_2E_2

10.32 Plan: Begin with the basic structures and redraw them.

Solution:

a) A molecule that is V shaped has two bonds and generally has either one (AX_2E) or two (AX_2E_2) lone electron pairs.

b) A trigonal planar molecule follows the formula AX_3 with three bonds and no lone electron pairs.
c) A trigonal bipyramidal molecule contains five bonding pairs (single bonds) and no lone pairs (AX_5).
d) A T-shaped molecule has three bonding groups and two lone pairs (AX_3E_2).
e) A trigonal pyramidal molecule follows the formula AX_3E with three bonding pairs and one lone pair.
f) A square pyramidal molecule shape follows the formula AX_5E with five bonding pairs and one lone pair.

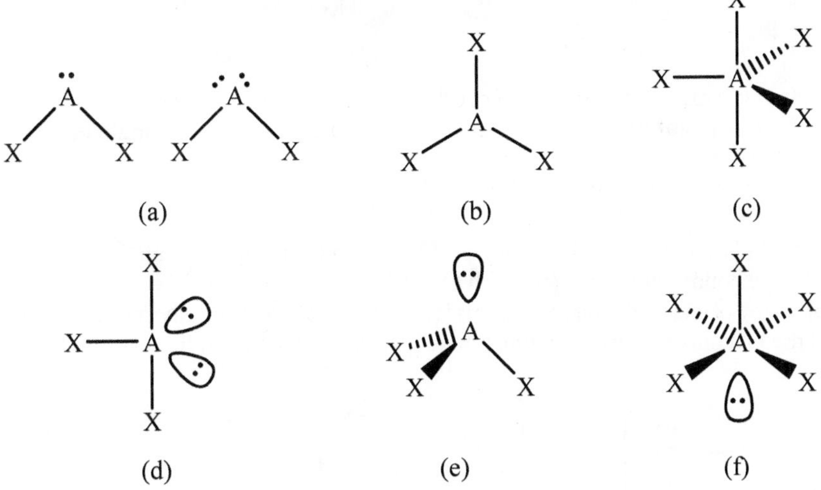

10.34 Plan: First, draw a Lewis structure, and then apply VSEPR.

Solution:

a) O_3: The molecule has [3 x O(6e$^-$)] = 18 valence electrons. Four electrons are used to place single bonds between the oxygen atoms, leaving 18 – 4 = 14e$^-$ (seven pairs). Six pairs are required to give the end oxygen atoms an octet; the last pair is distributed to the central oxygen, leaving this atom two electrons short of an octet. Form a double bond from one of the end O atoms to the central O by changing a lone pair on the end O to a bonding pair on the central O. This gives the following Lewis structure:

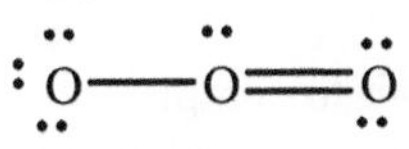

or

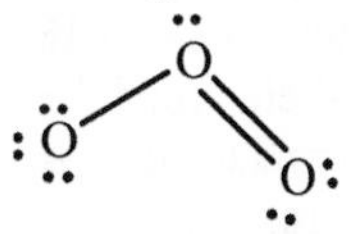

There are three electron groups around the central O, one of which is a lone pair. This gives a **trigonal planar** electron-group arrangement (AX_2E), a **bent** molecular shape, and an ideal bond angle of **120°**.

b) H_3O^+: This ion has [3 x H(1e$^-$)] + [1 x O(6e$^-$)] – [1e$^-$ (due to + charge] = eight valence electrons. Six electrons are used to place a single bond between O and each H, leaving 8 – 6 = 2e$^-$ (one pair). Distribute this pair to the O atom, giving it an octet (the H atoms only get two electrons). This gives the following Lewis structure:

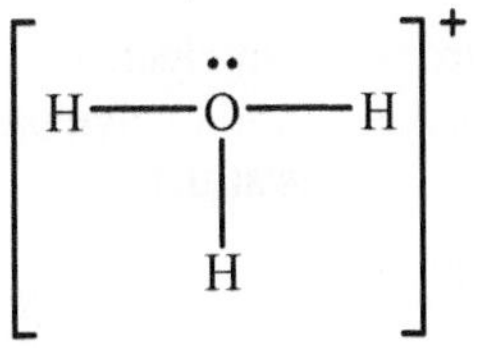

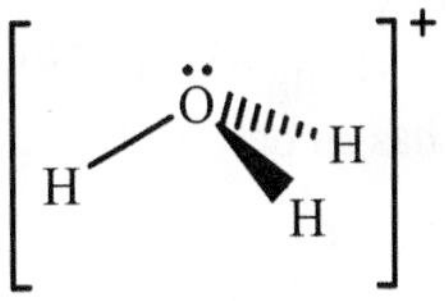

There are four electron groups around the O, one of which is a lone pair. This gives a **tetrahedral** electron-group arrangement (AX_3E), a **trigonal pyramidal** molecular shape, and an ideal bond angle of **109.5°**.

c) NF_3: The molecule has [1 x N(5e^-)] + [3 x F(7e^-)] = 26 valence electrons. Six electrons are used to place a single bond between N and each F, leaving 26 – 6 = 20e^- (ten pairs). These ten pairs are distributed to all of the F atoms and the N atoms to give each atom an octet. This gives the following Lewis structure:

There are four electron groups around the N, one of which is a lone pair. This gives a **tetrahedral** electron-group arrangement (AX_3E), a **trigonal pyramidal** molecular shape, and an ideal bond angle of **109.5°**.

10.36 Plan: First, draw a Lewis structure, and then apply VSEPR.

Solution:

(a) CO_3^{2-}: This ion has [1 x C(4e^-)] + [3 x O(6e^-)] + [2e^- (from charge)] = 24 valence electrons. Six electrons are used to place single bonds between C and each O atom, leaving 24 – 6 = 18 e^- (nine pairs). These nine pairs are used to complete the octets of the three O atoms, leaving C two electrons short of an octet. Form a double bond from one of the O atoms to C by changing a lone pair on an O to a bonding pair on C. This gives the following Lewis structure:

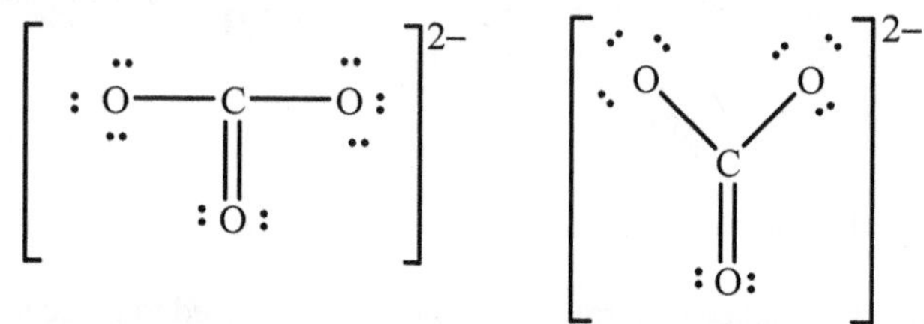

There are two additional resonance forms. There are three groups of electrons around the C, none of which are lone pairs. This gives a **trigonal planar** electron-group arrangement (AX_3), a **trigonal planar** molecular shape, and an ideal bond angle of **120°**.

(b) SO_2: This molecule has [1 x S(6e^-)] + [2 x S(6e^-)] = 18 valence electrons. Four electrons are used to place a single bond between S and each O atom, leaving 18 – 4 = 14e^- (seven pairs). Six pairs are needed to complete the octets of the O atoms, leaving a pair of electrons for S. S needs one more pair to complete its octet. Form a double bond from one of the end O atoms to the S by changing a lone pair on the O to a bonding pair on the S. This gives the following Lewis structure:

There are three groups of electrons around the C, one of which is a lone pair.
This gives a **trigonal planar** electron-group arrangement (AX_2E), a **bent (V-shaped)** molecular shape, and an ideal bond angle of **120°**.

(c) CF_4: This molecule has [1 x C(4e^-)] + [4 x F(7e^-)] = 32 valence electrons. Eight electrons are used to place a single bond between C and each F, leaving 32 – 8 = 24e^- (twelve pairs). Use these twelve pairs to complete the octets of the F atoms (C already has an octet). This gives the following Lewis structure:

There are four groups of electrons around the C, none of which is a lone pair.
This gives a **tetrahedral** electron-group arrangement (AX_4), a **tetrahedral** molecular shape, and an ideal bond angle of **109.5°**.

10.38 Plan: Examine the structure shown, and then apply VSEPR.

Solution:

a) This structure shows three electron groups with three bonds around the central atom.
There appears to be no distortion of the bond angles so the shape is **trigonal planar**, the classification is **AX_3**, with an ideal bond angle of **120°**.

b) This structure shows three electron groups with three bonds around the central atom.
The bonds are distorted down indicating the presence of a lone pair. The shape of the molecule is **trigonal pyramidal** and the classification is **AX_3E**, with an ideal bond angle of **109.5°**.

c) This structure shows five electron groups with five bonds around the central atom.
There appears to be no distortion of the bond angles so the shape is **trigonal bipyramidal** and the classification is **AX_5**, with ideal bond angles of **90°** and **120°**.

10.40 Plan: The Lewis structures must be drawn, and VSEPR applied to the structures. Lone pairs on the central atom generally result in a deviation of the ideal bond angle.

Solution:

a) The ClO_2^- ion has [1 x Cl(7e$^-$)] + [2 x O(6e$^-$)] + [1e$^-$ (from charge)] = 20 valence electrons. Four electrons are used to place a single bond between the Cl and each O, leaving 20 – 4 = 16 electrons (eight pairs). All eight pairs are used to complete the octets of the Cl and O atoms. There are two bonds (to the O atoms) and two lone pairs on the Cl for a total of four electron groups (AX_2E_2). The structure is based on a tetrahedral electron-group arrangement with an ideal bond angle of **109.5°**. The shape is **bent** (or V shaped). The presence of the lone pairs will cause the remaining angles to be **less than 109.5°**.

b) The PF_5 molecule has [1 x P(5e$^-$)] + [5 x F(7e$^-$)] = 40 valence electrons. Ten electrons are used to place single bonds between P and each F atom, leaving 40 – 10 = 30e$^-$ (fifteen pairs). The fifteen pairs are used to complete the octets of the F atoms. There are five bonds to the P and no lone pairs (AX_5). The electron-group arrangement and the shape is **trigonal bipyramidal.** The ideal bond angles are **90° and 120°**. The absence of lone pairs means the **angles are ideal.**

c) The SeF_4 molecule has [1 x Se(6e$^-$)] + [4 x F(7e$^-$)] = 34 valence electrons. Eight electrons are used to place single bonds between Se and each F atom, leaving 34 – 8 = 26e$^-$ (thirteen pairs). Twelve pairs are used to complete the octets of the F atoms which leaves one pair of electrons. This pair is placed on the central Se atom. There are four bonds to the Se which also has a lone pair (AX_4E). The structure is based on a trigonal bipyramidal structure with ideal angles of **90° and 120°**. The shape is **seesaw**. The presence of the lone pairs means the angles are **less than ideal.**

d) The KrF_2 molecule has [1 x Kr(8e$^-$)] + [2 x F(7e$^-$)] = 22 valence electrons. Four electrons are used to place a single bond between the Kr atom and each F atom, leaving 22 – 4 = 18e$^-$ (nine pairs). Six pairs are used to complete the octets of the F atoms. The remaining three pairs of electrons are placed on the Kr atom. The Kr is the central atom. There are two bonds to the Kr and three lone pairs (AX_2E_3). The structure is based on a trigonal bipyramidal structure with ideal angles of 90° and 120°. The shape is **linear**. The placement of the F atoms makes their ideal bond angle to be 2 x 90° = **180°**. The placement of the lone pairs is such that they cancel each other's repulsion, thus the actual **bond angle is ideal.**

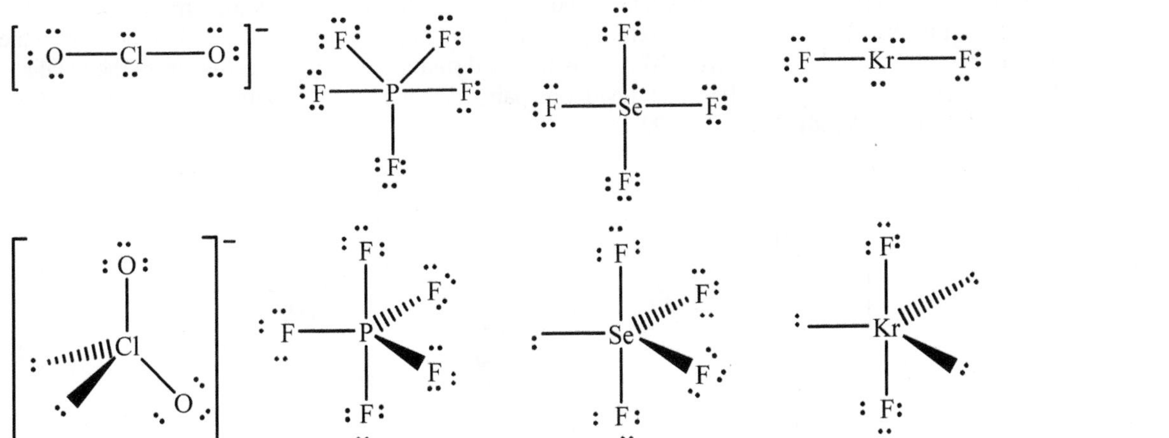

a) b) c) d)

10.42 Plan: The Lewis structures must be drawn, and VSEPR applied to the structures.

Solution:

a) CH_3OH: This molecule has [1 x C(4e$^-$)] + [4 x H(1e$^-$)] + [1 x O(6e$^-$)] = fourteen valence electrons. In the CH_3OH molecule, both carbon and oxygen serve as central atoms. (H can never be central.) Use eight electrons to place a single bond between the C and the O atom and three of the H atoms and another two electrons to place a single bond between the O and the last H atom. This leaves 14 – 10 = 4e$^-$ (two pairs). Use these two pairs to complete the octet of the O atom. C already has an octet and each H only gets two electrons. The carbon has four bonds and no lone pairs (AX_4), so it is **tetrahedral** with **no deviation** (no lone pairs) from the ideal angle of 109.5°. The oxygen has two bonds and two lone pairs (AX_2E_2), so it is **V shaped** or **bent** with the angles **less than the ideal** angle of 109.5°.

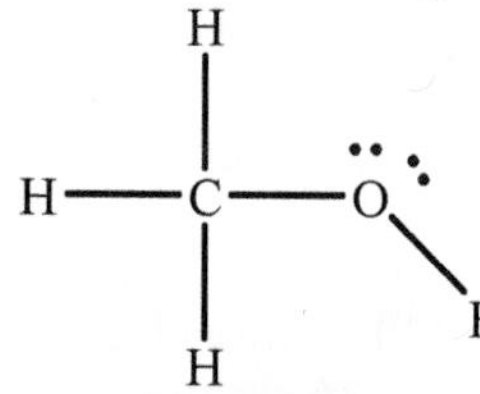

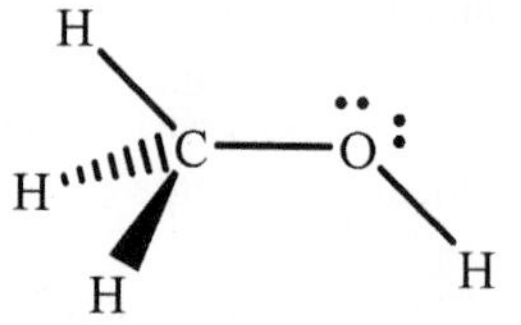

b) N_2O_4: This molecule has [2 x N(5e$^-$)] + [4 x O(6e$^-$)] = 34 valence electrons. Use ten electrons to place a single bond between the two N atoms and between each N and two of the O atoms. This leaves 34 – 10 = 24e$^-$ (twelve pairs). Use the twelve pairs to complete the octets of the oxygen atoms. Neither N atom has an octet, however. Form a double bond from one O atom to one N atom by changing a lone pair on the O to a bonding pair on the N. Do this for the other N atom as well. In the N_2O_4 molecule, both nitrogen atoms serve as central atoms. This is the arrangement given in the problem. Both nitrogen atoms are equivalent with three groups and no lone pairs (AX_3), so the arrangement is **trigonal planar** with **no deviation** (no lone pairs) from the ideal angle of 120°. The same results arise from the other resonance structures.

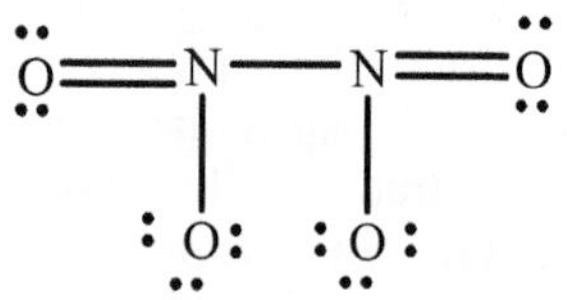

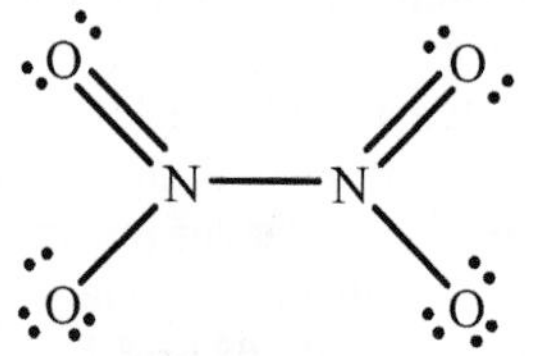

10.44 Plan: The Lewis structures must be drawn, and VSEPR applied to the structures.

Solution:

a) CH_3COOH has [2 x C(4e$^-$)] + [4 x H(1e$^-$)] + [2 x O(6e$^-$)] = twenty-four valence electrons. Use fourteen electrons to place a single bond between all of the atoms. This leaves 24 – 14 = 10e$^-$ (five pairs). Use these five pairs to complete the octets of the O atoms; the C atom bonded to the H atoms has an octet but the other C atom does not have a complete octet. Form a double bond from the O atom (not bonded to H) to the C by changing a lone pair on the O to a bonding pair on the C. In the CH_3COOH molecule, the carbons and the O with H attached serve as central atoms. The carbon bonded to the H atoms has four groups and no lone pairs (AX_4), so it is **tetrahedral** with **no deviation** from the ideal angle of 109.5°. The carbon bonded to the O atoms has three groups and no lone pairs (AX_3), so it is **trigonal planar** with **no deviation** from the ideal angle of 120°. The H bearing O has two bonds and two lone pairs (AX_2E_2), so the arrangement is **V shaped** or **bent** with an angle **less than the ideal** value of 109.5°.

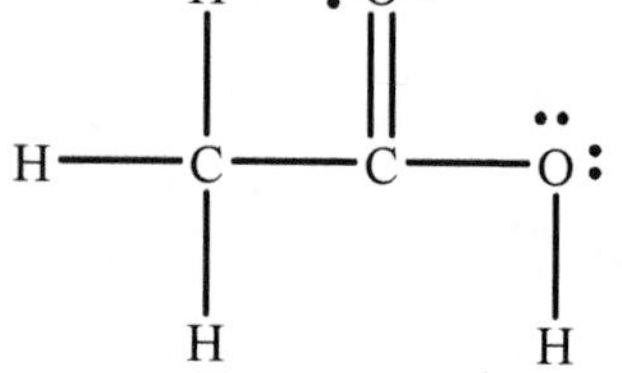

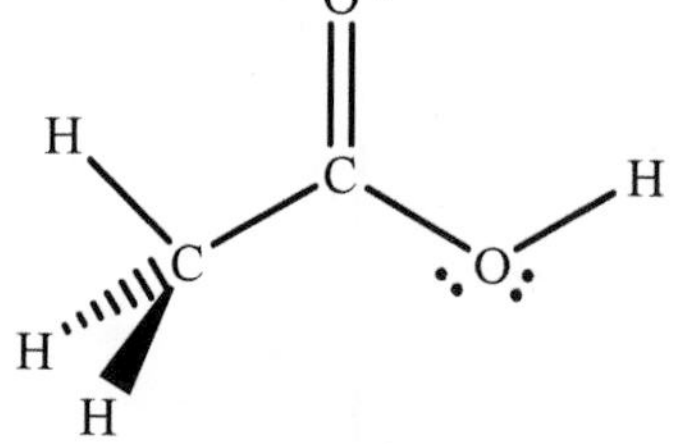

b) H_2O_2 has [2 x H(1e$^-$)] + [2 x O(6e$^-$)] = fourteen valence electrons. Use six electrons to place single bonds between the O atoms and between each O atom and an H atom. This leaves 14 – 6 = 8e$^-$ (four pairs). Use these four pairs to complete the octets of the O atoms. In the H_2O_2 molecule, both oxygen atoms serve as central atoms. Both O atoms have tw bonds and two2 lone pairs (AX_2E_2), so they are **V shaped** or **bent** with angles **less than the ideal** value of 109.5°.

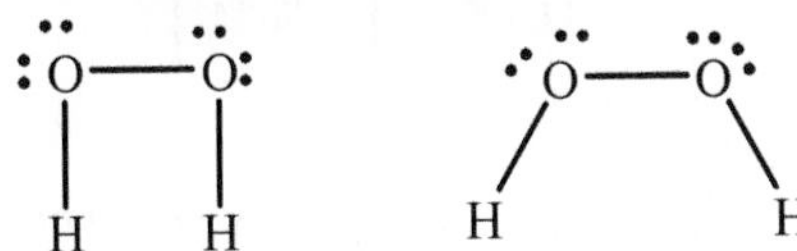

10.46 Plan: First, draw a Lewis structure, and then apply VSEPR. The presence of lone pairs on the central atom generally results in a smaller than ideal bond angle.
Solution:

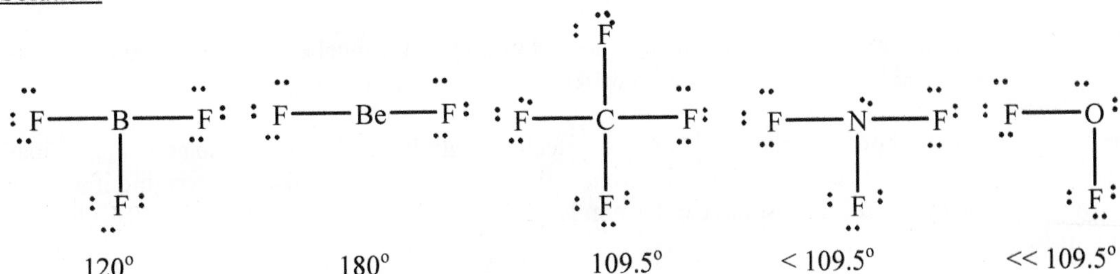

Bond angles: **$OF_2 < NF_3 < CF_4 < BF_3 < BeF_2$**
BeF_2 is an AX_2 type molecule, so the angle is the ideal 180°. BF_3 is an AX_3 molecule, so the angle is the ideal 120°. CF_4, NF_3, and OF_2 all have tetrahedral electron-group arrangements of the following types: AX_4, AX_3E, and AX_2E_2, respectively. The ideal tetrahedral bond angle is 109.5°, which is present in CF_4. The one lone pair in NF_3 decreases the angle a little. The two lone pairs in OF_2 decrease the angle even more.

10.48 Plan: The ideal bond angles depend on the electron-group arrangement. Deviations depend on lone pairs.
Solution:
a) The C and N have three groups, so they are **ideally 120°**, and the O has four groups, so **ideally the angle is 109.5°**. The N and O have lone pairs, so the **angles are less than ideal.**
b) All central atoms have four pairs, so ideally all the angles are **109.5°**. The lone pairs on the O **reduce** this value.
c) The B has three groups (no lone pairs) leading to an **ideal bond angle of 120°**. All the O atoms have four pairs **(ideally 109.5°)**, two of which are lone, and **reduce the angle.**

10.51 Plan: The Lewis structures are needed to predict the ideal bond angles.
Solution:
The P atoms have no lone pairs in any case so the angles are ideal.

PCl_5: PCl_4^+: PCl_6^-:

The original PCl_5 is AX_5, so the shape is trigonal bipyramidal, and the angles are 120° and 90°.
The PCl_4^+ is AX_4, so the shape is tetrahedral, and the angles are 109.5°.
The PCl_6^- is AX_6, so the shape is octahedral, and the angles are 90°.
Half the PCl_5 (trigonal bipyramidal, 120° and 90°) become tetrahedral PCl_4^+ (tetrahedral, 109.5°), and the other half become octahedral PCl_6^- (octahedral, 90°).

10.52 Molecules are polar if they have polar bonds that are not arranged to cancel each other. A polar bond is present any time there is a bond between elements with differing electronegativities.

10.55 Plan: To determine if a bond is polar, determine the electronegativity difference of the atoms participating in the bond. The greater the electronegativity difference, the more polar the bond. To determine if a molecule is polar (has a dipole moment), it must have polar bonds, and a certain shape determined by VSEPR.
Solution:

a) Molecule	Bond	Electronegativities		Electronegativity difference
SCl_2	S–Cl	S = 2.5	Cl = 3.0	3.0 – 2.5 = 0.5
F_2	F–F	F = 4.0	F = 4.0	4.0 – 4.0 = 0.0
CS_2	C–S	C = 2.5	S = 2.5	2.5 – 2.5 = 0.0
CF_4	C–F	C = 2.5	F = 4.0	4.0 – 2.5 = 1.5
BrCl	Br–Cl	Br = 2.8	Cl = 3.0	3.0 – 2.8 = 0.2

The polarities of the bonds increase in the order: F–F = C–S < Br–Cl < S–Cl < C–F. Thus, **CF_4** has the most polar bonds.
b) The F_2 and CS_2 cannot be polar since they do not have polar bonds. CF_4 is an AX_4 molecule, so it is tetrahedral with the four polar C–F bonds arranged to cancel each other giving an overall nonpolar molecule. **BrCl has a dipole moment** since there are no other bonds to cancel the polar Br–Cl bond. **SCl_2 has a dipole moment** (is polar) because it is a bent molecule, AX_2E_2, and the electron density in both S–Cl bonds is pulled towards the more electronegative chlorine atoms.

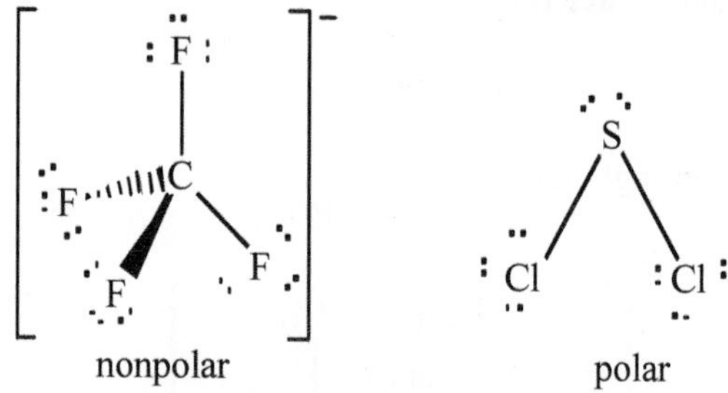

10.57 Plan: If only two atoms are involved, only an electronegativity difference is needed. The greater the difference in electronegativity, the more polar the bond. If there are more than two atoms, the molecular geometry must be determined.
Solution:
a) All the bonds are polar covalent. The SO_3 molecule is trigonal planar, AX_3, so the bond dipoles cancel leading to a nonpolar molecule (no dipole moment). The SO_2 molecule is bent, AX_2E, so the polar bonds result in electron density being pulled towards one side of the molecule. **SO_2 has a greater dipole moment** because it is the only one of the pair that is polar.

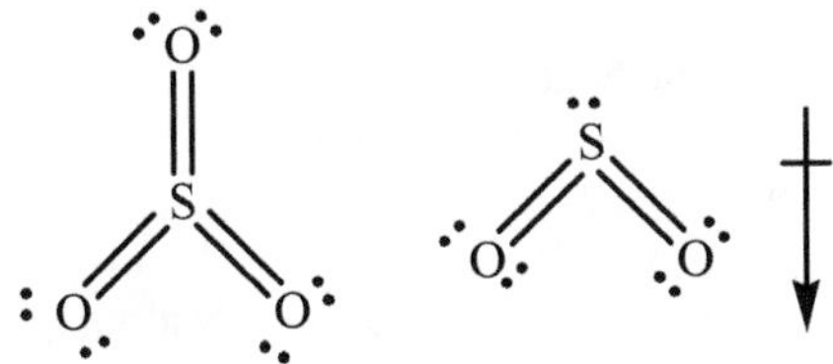

b) ICl and IF are polar, as are all diatomic molecules composed of atoms with differing electronegativities. The electronegativity difference for ICl (3.0 – 2.5 = 0.5) is less than that for IF (4.0 – 2.5 = 1.5). The greater difference means that **IF has a greater dipole moment.**

c) All the bonds are polar covalent. The SiF_4 molecule is nonpolar (has no dipole moment) because the bonds are arranged tetrahedrally, AX_4. SF_4 is AX_4E, so it has a see-saw shape, where the bond dipoles do not cancel. **SF_4 has the greater dipole moment.**

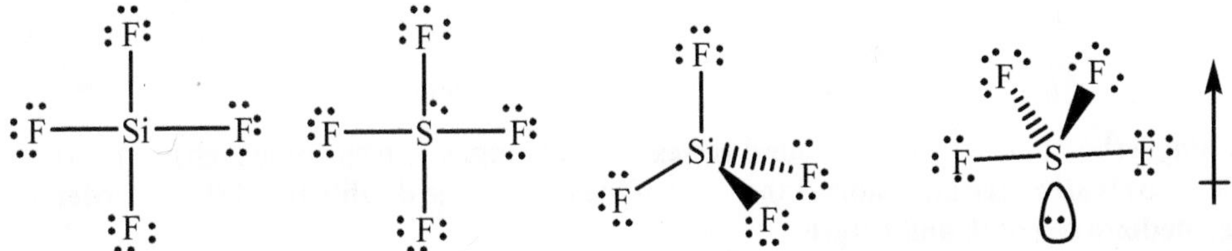

d) H_2O and H_2S have the same basic structure. They are both bent molecules, AX_2E_2, and as such, they are polar. The electronegativity difference in H_2O (3.5 – 2.1 = 1.4) is greater than the electronegativity difference in H_2S (2.5 – 2.1 = 0.4) so **H_2O has a greater dipole moment.**

10.59 Plan: Draw Lewis structures, and then apply VSEPR. A molecule has a dipole moment if polar bonds do not cancel.

Solution:

$C_2H_2Cl_2$ has [2 x C(4e$^-$)] + [2 x H(1e$^-$)] + [2 x Cl(7e$^-$)] = 24 valence electrons. The two carbon atoms are bonded to each other. The H atoms and Cl atoms are bonded to the C atoms. Use ten electrons to place a single bond between all of the atoms. This leaves 24 – 10 = 14e$^-$ (seven pairs). Use these seven pairs to complete the octets of the Cl atoms and one of the C atoms; the other C atom does not have a complete octet. Form a double bond between the carbon atoms by changing the lone pair on one C atom to a bonding pair. There are three possible structures for the compound $C_2H_2Cl_2$:

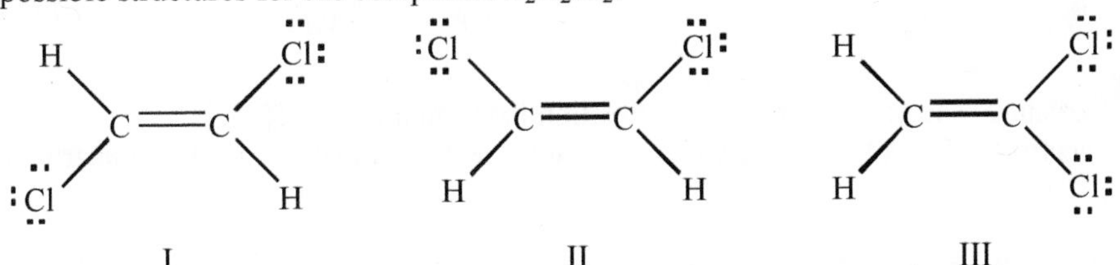

The presence of the double bond prevents rotation about the C=C bond, so the structures are "fixed." The C–Cl bonds are more polar than the C–H bonds, so the key to predicting the polarity is the positioning of the C–Cl bonds. Structure I has the C–Cl bonds arranged so that they cancel leaving I as a nonpolar molecule. Both II and III have C–Cl bonds on the same side so the bonds work together making both molecules polar. Both I and II will react with H_2 to give a compound with a Cl attached to each C (same product). Structure III will react with H_2 to give a compound with two Cl atoms on one C and none on the other (different product). **Structure I must be X** as it is the only one that is nonpolar (has no dipole moment). **Structure II must be Z** because it is polar and gives the same product as compound X. This means that **Structure III must be the remaining compound, Y. Compound Y (III) has a dipole moment.**

10.61 Plan: The Lewis structures are needed to do this problem. A single bond (bond order = 1) is weaker and longer than a double bond (bond order = 2) which is weaker and longer than a triple bond (bond order = 3). To find the heat of reaction, add the energy required to break all the bonds in the reactants to the energy released to form all bonds in the product. Remember to use a negative sign for the energy of the bonds formed since bond formation is exothermic. The bond energy values are found in Table 9.2.

Solution:

a) The H atoms cannot be central, and they are evenly distributed on the N atoms.

N_2H_4 has [2 x N(5e⁻)] + [4 x H(1e⁻)] = fourteen valence electrons, ten of which are used in the bonds between the atoms. The remaining two pairs are used to complete the octets of the N atoms.

N_2H_2 has [2 x N(5e⁻)] + (2 x H(1e⁻)] = twelve valence electrons, six of which are used in the bonds between the atoms. The remaining three pairs of electrons are not enough to complete the octets of both N atoms, so one lone pair is moved to a bonding pair between the N atoms.

N_2 has [2 x N(5e⁻)] = ten valence electrons, two of which are used to place a single bond between the two N atoms. Since only four pairs of electrons remain and six pairs are required to complete the octets, two lone pairs become bonding pairs to form a triple bond.

H—N̈—N̈—H (each N also bonded to H) H—N̈=N̈—H :N≡N:

Hydrazine Diazene Nitrogen

The **single (bond order = 1) N–N bond is weaker and longer** than any of the others are. The **triple bond (bond order = 3) is stronger and shorter** than any of the others. The **double bond (bond order = 2) has an intermediate strength and length**.

b) N_4H_4 has [4 x N(5e⁻)] + [4 x H(1e⁻)] = twenty-four valence electrons, fourteen of which are used for single bonds between the atoms. When the remaining five pairs are distributed to complete the octets, one N atom lacks two electrons. A lone pair is moved to a bonding pair for a double bond.

H—N̈(H)—N̈=N̈—N̈(H)—H ⟶ H—N̈(H)—N̈(H)—H + :N≡N:

Reactant bonds broken:

4 N–H = 4 mol (391 kJ/mol) = 1564 kJ
2 N–N = 2 mol (160 kJ/mol) = 320 kJ
1 N=N = 1 mol (418 kJ/mol) = 418 kJ

$\Sigma\Delta H^\circ_{\text{bonds broken}} = 2302\text{ kJ}$

Product bonds formed:

4 N–H = 4 mol (–391 kJ/mol) = –1564 kJ
1 N–N = 1 mol (–160 kJ/mol) = –160 kJ
1 N≡N = 1 mol (–945 kJ/mol) = –945 kJ

$\Sigma\Delta H^\circ_{\text{bonds formed}} = -2669\text{ kJ}$

$$\Delta H^\circ_{\text{rxn}} = \Sigma\Delta H^\circ_{\text{bonds broken}} + \Sigma\Delta H^\circ_{\text{bonds formed}} = 2302\text{ kJ} + (-2669\text{ kJ}) = \mathbf{-367\text{ kJ}}$$

10.65 Plan: Use the Lewis structures shown in the text. The equation for formal charge (FC) is
FC = no. of valence electrons – [no. of unshared valence electrons + ½ no. of shared valence electrons].

Solution:

a) Formal charges for Al_2Cl_6:

$FC_{Al} = 3 - [0 + ½(8)] = \mathbf{-1}$

$FC_{Cl,\ ends} = 7 - [6 + ½(2)] = \mathbf{0}$

$FC_{Cl,\ bridging} = 7 - [4 + ½(4)] = \mathbf{+1}$

(Check: Formal charges add to zero, the charge on the compound.)

Formal charges for I_2Cl_6:

$FC_I = 7 - [4 + ½(8)] = \mathbf{-1}$

$FC_{Cl,\ ends} = 7 - [6 + ½(2)] = \mathbf{0}$

$FC_{Cl,\ bridging} = 7 - [4 + ½(4)] = \mathbf{+1}$

(Check: Formal charges add to zero, the charge on the compound.)

b) The aluminum atoms have no lone pairs and are AX_4, so they are tetrahedral. The two tetrahedral Al atoms cannot give a planar structure. The iodine atoms in $\mathbf{I_2Cl_6}$ have two lone pairs each and are AX_4E_2 so they are square planar. Placing the square planar I atoms adjacent can give a planar molecule.

10.70 Plan: Draw the Lewis structures, and then use VSEPR to describe propylene oxide.

Solution:

a)

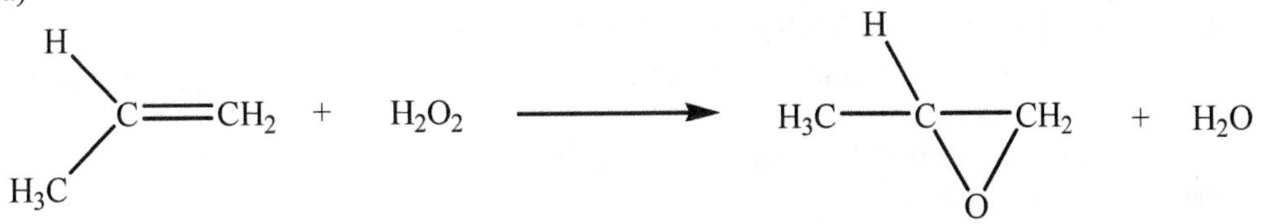

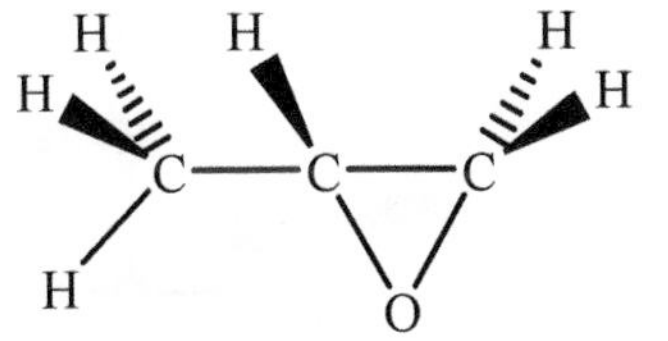

$H(H_3C)C{=}CH_2 \; + \; H_2O_2 \longrightarrow H_3C{-}CH(O){-}CH_2 \; + \; H_2O$

In propylene oxide, the C atoms are all AX_4. The C atoms do not have any unshared (lone) pairs. All of the ideal bond angles for the C atoms in propylene oxide are **109.5°** and the molecular shape around each carbon atom is **tetrahedral**.

b) In propylene oxide, the C that is not part of the three-membered ring should have an ideal angle. The atoms in the ring form an equilateral triangle. The angles in an equilateral triangle are 60°. The angles around the two carbons in the rings are reduced from the ideal 109.5° to 60°.

10.75 Plan: Ethanol burns (combusts) with O_2 to produce CO_2 and H_2O. To find the heat of reaction in part a), add the energy required to break all the bonds in the reactants to the energy released to form all bonds in the product. Remember to use a negative sign for the energy of the bonds formed since bond formation is exothermic. The bond energy values are found in Table 9.2. The heat of vaporization of ethanol must be included for part b). The enthalpy change in part c) is the sum of the heats of formation of the products minus the sum of the heats of formation of the reactants. The calculation for part d) is the same as in part a).

Solution:

a) $CH_3CH_2OH(g) + 3O_2(g) \rightarrow 2CO_2(g) + 3H_2O(g)$

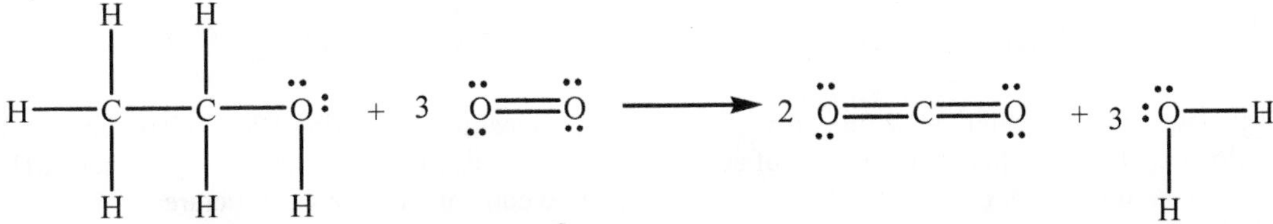

Reactant bonds broken:

1 x C–C = (1 mol)(347 kJ/mol) = 347 kJ
5 x C–H = (5 mol)(413 kJ/mol) = 2065 kJ
1 x C–O = (1 mol)(358 kJ/mol) = 358 kJ
1 x O–H = (1 mol)(467 kJ/mol) = 467 kJ
3 x O=O = (3 mol)(498 kJ/mol) = 1494 kJ

$\Sigma\Delta H^\circ_{\text{bonds broken}} = 4731 \text{ kJ}$

Product bonds formed:

4 x C=O = (4 mol)(–799 kJ/mol) = –3196 kJ
6 x O–H = (6 mol)(–467 kJ/mol) = –2802 kJ

$\Sigma\Delta H^\circ_{\text{bonds formed}} = -5998 \text{ kJ}$

$\Delta H^\circ_{\text{rxn}} = \Sigma\Delta H^\circ_{\text{bonds broken}} + \Sigma\Delta H^\circ_{\text{bonds formed}} = 4731 \text{ kJ} + (-5998 \text{ kJ}) = \mathbf{-1267 \text{ kJ}}$ for each mole of ethanol burned

b) If it takes 40.5 kJ/mol to vaporize the ethanol, part of the heat of combustion must be used to convert liquid ethanol to gaseous ethanol. The new value becomes:

$\Sigma\Delta H^\circ_{\text{combustion (liquid)}} = -1267 \text{ kJ} + (1 \text{ mol})\left[\frac{40.5 \text{ kJ}}{1 \text{ mol}}\right] = -1226.5 = \mathbf{-1226 \text{ kJ per mole}}$ of liquid ethanol burned

c) $\Delta H^\circ_{rxn} = \Sigma m\,\Delta H^\circ_{f\,(products)} - \Sigma n\,\Delta H^\circ_{f\,(reactants)}$

$\Delta H^\circ_{rxn} = \{2\,\Delta H^\circ_f\,[CO_2(g)] + 3\,\Delta H^\circ_f\,[H_2O(g)]\} - \{1\,\Delta H^\circ_f\,[C_2H_5OH(l)] + 3\,\Delta H^\circ_f\,[O_2(g)]\}$
$= [(2\text{ mol})(-393.5\text{ kJ/mol}) + (3\text{ mol})(-241.826\text{ kJ/mol})] - [(1\text{ mol})(-277.63\text{ kJ/mol}) + 3\text{ mol}(0\text{ kJ/mol})]$
$= -1234.848 = \mathbf{-1234.8\ kJ}$

The two answers differ by less than 10 kJ. This is a very good agreement since average bond energies were used to calculate the answers in a) and b).

d) $C_2H_4(g) + H_2O(g) \rightarrow CH_3CH_2OH(g)$

The Lewis structures for the reaction are:

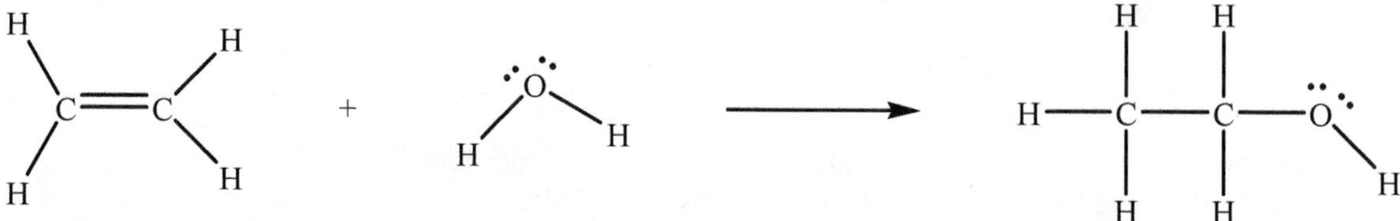

Reactant bonds broken:

1 x C=C = (1 mol)(614 kJ/mol) = 614 kJ
4 x C–H = (4 mol)(413 kJ/mol) = 1652 kJ
2 x O–H = (2 mol)(467 kJ/mol) = 934 kJ

$\Sigma\Delta H^\circ_{bonds\ broken} = 3200\text{ kJ}$

Product bonds formed:

1 x C–C = (1 mol)(–347 kJ/mol) = –347 kJ
5 x C–H = (5 mol)(–413 kJ/mol) = –2065 kJ
1 x C–O = (1 mol)(–358 kJ/mol) = –358 kJ
1 x O–H = (1 mol)(–467 kJ/mol) = –467 kJ

$\Sigma\Delta H^\circ_{bonds\ formed} = -3237\text{ kJ}$

$\Delta H^\circ_{rxn} = \Sigma\Delta H^\circ_{bonds\ broken} + \Sigma\Delta H^\circ_{bonds\ formed} = 3200\text{ kJ} + (-3237\text{ kJ}) = \mathbf{-37\ kJ}$

10.77 Plan: Determine the empirical formula from the percent composition (assuming 100 g of compound). Use the titration data to determine the mole ratio of acid to the NaOH. This ratio gives the number of acidic H atoms in the formula of the acid. Finally, combine this information to construct the Lewis structure.

Solution:

$$\text{Moles of H} = (2.24\text{ g H})\left(\frac{1\text{ mol}}{1.008\text{ g H}}\right) = 2.222\text{ mol H}$$

$$\text{Moles of C} = (26.7\text{ g C})\left(\frac{1\text{ mol}}{12.01\text{ g C}}\right) = 2.223\text{ mol C}$$

$$\text{Moles of O} = (71.1\text{ g O})\left(\frac{1\text{ mol}}{16.00\text{ g O}}\right) = 4.444\text{ mol O}$$

The preliminary formula is $H_{2.222}C_{2.223}O_{4.444}$.

Dividing all subscripts by the smallest subscript to obtain integer subscripts:

$$H_{\frac{2.222}{2.222}}C_{\frac{2.223}{2.222}}O_{\frac{4.444}{2.222}} = HCO_2$$

The empirical formula is HCO_2.

Calculate the amount of NaOH required for the titration:

$$\text{Mmoles of NaOH} = (50.0\text{ mL})\left(\frac{1\text{ L}}{1000\text{ mL}}\right)\left(\frac{0.040\text{ mol NaOH}}{\text{L}}\right)\left(\frac{1\text{ mmol}}{0.001\text{ mol}}\right) = 2.0\text{ mmol NaOH}$$

Thus, the ratio is 2.0 mmole base/1.0 mmole acid, or each acid molecule has two hydrogen atoms to react (diprotic). The empirical formula indicates a monoprotic acid, so the formula must be doubled to: $H_2C_2O_4$.

$H_2C_2O_4$ has [2 x H(1e$^-$)] + [2 x C(4e$^-$)] + [4 x O(6e$^-$)] = 34 valence electrons to be used in the Lewis structure. Fourteen of these electrons are used to bond the atoms with single bonds, leaving 34 – 14 = 20 electrons or ten pairs of electrons. When these ten pairs of electrons are distributed to the atoms to complete octets, neither C atom has an octet; a lone pair from the oxygen without hydrogen is changed to a bonding pair on C.

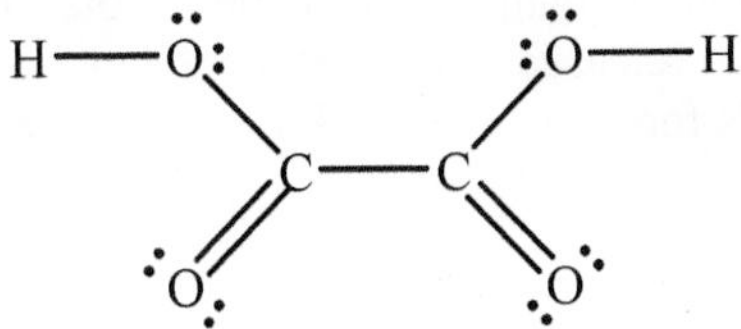

10.80 Plan: Write the balanced chemical equations for the reactions and draw the Lewis structures. To find the heat of reaction, add the energy required to break all the bonds in the reactants to the energy released to form all bonds in the product. Remember to use a negative sign for the energy of the bonds formed since bond formation is exothermic. The bond energy values are found in Table 9.2. Divide the heat of reaction by the number of moles of oxygen gas appearing in each reaction to get the heat of reaction per mole of oxygen.

Solution:

$CH_4(g) + 2O_2(g) \rightarrow CO_2(g) + 2H_2O(g)$

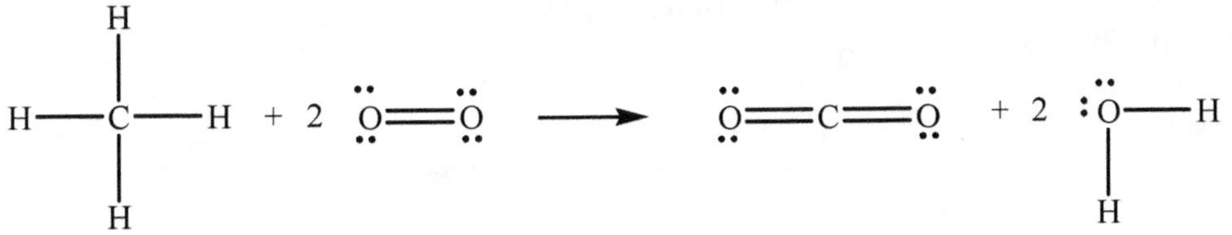

Reactant bonds broken:

4 x C–H = (4 mol)(413 kJ/mol) = 1652 kJ

2 x O=O = (2 mol)(498 kJ/mol) = 996 kJ

$\Sigma\Delta H^\circ_{\text{bonds broken}} = 2648$ kJ

Product bonds formed:

2 x C=O = (2 mol)(–799 kJ/mol) = –1598 kJ

4 x O–H = (4 mol)(–467 kJ/mol) = –1868 kJ

$\Sigma\Delta H^\circ_{\text{bonds formed}} = -3466$ kJ

$\Delta H^\circ_{\text{rxn}} = \Sigma\Delta H^\circ_{\text{bonds broken}} + \Sigma\Delta H^\circ_{\text{bonds formed}} = 2648 \text{ kJ} + (-3466 \text{ kJ}) = -818 \text{ kJ for 2 mol } O_2$

Per mole of O_2 = –818/2 = **–409 kJ/mol O_2**

$2H_2S(g) + 3O_2(g) \rightarrow 2SO_2(g) + 2H_2O(g)$

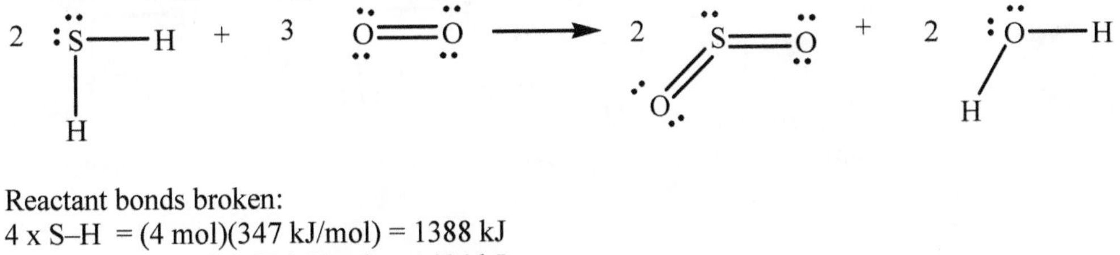

Reactant bonds broken:

4 x S–H = (4 mol)(347 kJ/mol) = 1388 kJ

3 x O=O = (3 mol)(498 kJ/mol) = 1494 kJ

$\Sigma\Delta H^\circ_{\text{bonds broken}} = 2882$ kJ

Product bonds formed:

4 x S=O = (4 mol)(–552 kJ/mol) = –2208 kJ

4 x O–H = (4 mol)(–467 kJ/mol) = –1868 kJ

$\Sigma\Delta H^\circ_{\text{bonds formed}} = -4076$ kJ

$\Delta H^\circ_{rxn} = \Sigma\Delta H^\circ_{\text{bonds broken}} + \Sigma\Delta H^\circ_{\text{bonds formed}} = 2882\text{ kJ} + (-4076\text{ kJ}) = -1194\text{ kJ for 3 mol } O_2$
Per mole of $O_2 = -1194/3 =$ **-398 kJ/mol O_2**

10.82 Plan: Draw the Lewis structure of the OH species. The standard enthalpy of formation is the sum of the energy required to break all the bonds in the reactants and the energy released to form all bonds in the product. Remember to use a negative sign for the energy of the bonds formed since bond formation is exothermic. The bond energy values are found in Table 9.2.
Solution:
a) The OH molecule has $[1 \times O(6e^-)] + [1 \times H(1e^-)] = 7$ valence electrons to be used in the Lewis structure. Two of these electrons are used to bond the atoms with a single bond, leaving $7 - 2 = 5$ electrons. Those five electrons are given to oxygen. But no atom can have an octet, and one electron is left unpaired. The Lewis structure is:

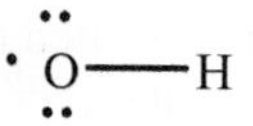

·O—H (with two lone pairs on O)

b) The formation reaction is: $1/2O_2(g) + 1/2H_2(g) \rightarrow OH(g)$. The heat of reaction is:

$\Delta H^\circ_{rxn} = \Sigma\Delta H^\circ_{\text{bonds broken}} + \Sigma\Delta H^\circ_{\text{bonds formed}} = 39.0\text{ kJ}$
$[\frac{1}{2}(BE_{O=O}) + \frac{1}{2}(BE_{H-H})] + [BE_{O-H}] = 39.0\text{ kJ}$
$[(\frac{1}{2}\text{ mol})(498\text{ kJ/mol}) + (\frac{1}{2}\text{ mol})(432\text{ kJ/mol})] + [BE_{O-H}] = 39.0\text{ kJ}$
$465\text{ kJ} + [BE_{O-H}] = 39.0\text{ kJ}$
$BE_{O-H} =$ **-426 kJ or 426 kJ**
c) The average bond energy (from the bond energy table) is 467 kJ/mol. There are two O–H bonds in water for a total of 2 x 467 kJ/mol = 934 kJ. The answer to part b) accounts for 426 kJ of this, leaving:
934 kJ – 426 kJ = **508 kJ**

10.84 Plan: The basic Lewis structure will be the same for all species. The Cl atoms are larger than the F atoms. All of the molecules are of the type AX_5 and have trigonal bipyramidal molecular shape. The equatorial positions are in the plane of the triangle and the axial positions above and below the plane of the triangle. In this molecular shape, there is more room in the equatorial positions.
Solution:
a) The F atoms will occupy the smaller axial positions first so that the larger Cl atoms can occupy the equatorial positions which are less crowded.
b) The molecule containing only F atoms is nonpolar (has no dipole moment), as all the polar bonds would cancel. The molecules with one F or one Cl would be polar since the P–F and P–Cl bonds are not equal in polarity and thus do not cancel each other. The presence of two axial F atoms means that their polarities will cancel (as would the three Cl atoms) giving a nonpolar molecule. The molecule with three F atoms is also polar.

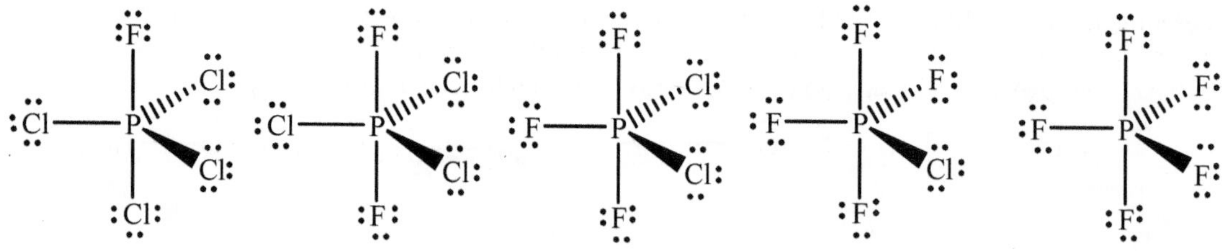

$PFCl_4$	PF_2Cl_3	PF_3Cl_2	PF_4Cl	PF_5
Polar	Nonpolar No dipole moment	Polar	Polar	Nonpolar No dipole moment

10.86 Plan: Count the valence electrons and draw Lewis structures for the resonance forms.
Solution:
The $H_2C_2O_4$ molecule has $[2 \times H(1e^-)] + [2 \times C(4e^-)] + [4 \times O(6e^-)] = 34$ valence electrons to be used in the Lewis structure. Fourteen of these electrons are used to bond the atoms with a single bond, leaving $34 - 14 = 20$ electrons. If these twenty electrons are given to the oxygen atoms to complete their octet, the carbon atoms do not have octets. A lone pair from each of the oxygen atoms without hydrogen is changed to a bonding pair on C.

The $HC_2O_4^-$ ion has [1 x H(1e$^-$)] + [2 x C(4e$^-$)] + [4 x O(6e$^-$)] + [1e$^-$ (from the charge)] = 34 valence electrons to be used in the Lewis structure. Twelve of these electrons are used to bond the atoms with a single bond, leaving 34 – 12 = 22 electrons. If these twenty-two electrons are given to the oxygen atoms to complete their octet, the carbon atoms do not have octets. A lone pair from two of the oxygen atoms without hydrogen is changed to a bonding pair on C. There are two resonance structures.
The $C_2O_4^{2-}$ ion has [2 x C(4e$^-$)] + [4 x O(6e$^-$)] + [2e$^-$ (from the charge)] = 34 valence electrons to be used in the Lewis structure. Ten of these electrons are used to bond the atoms with a single bond, leaving 34 – 10 = 24 electrons. If these twenty-four electrons are given to the oxygen atoms to complete their octets, the carbon atoms do not have octets. A lone pair from two oxygen atoms is changed to a bonding pair on C. There are four resonance structures.

$H_2C_2O_4$:

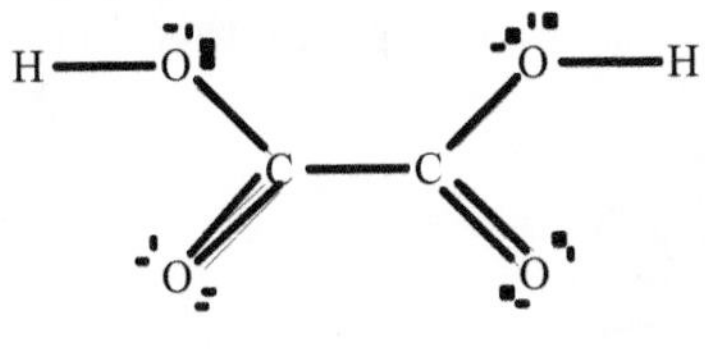

$HC_2O_4^-$:

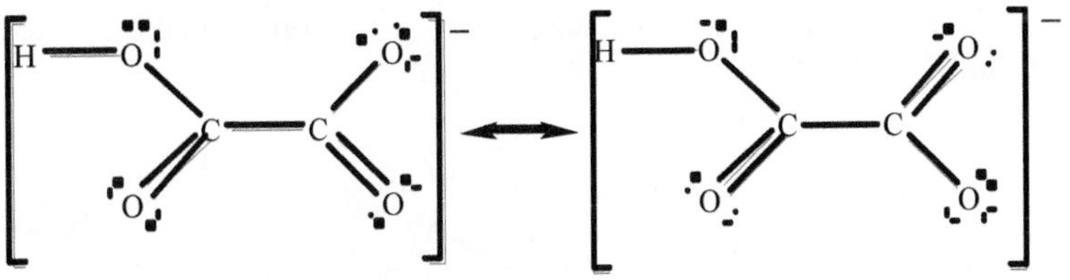

$C_2O_4^{2-}$:

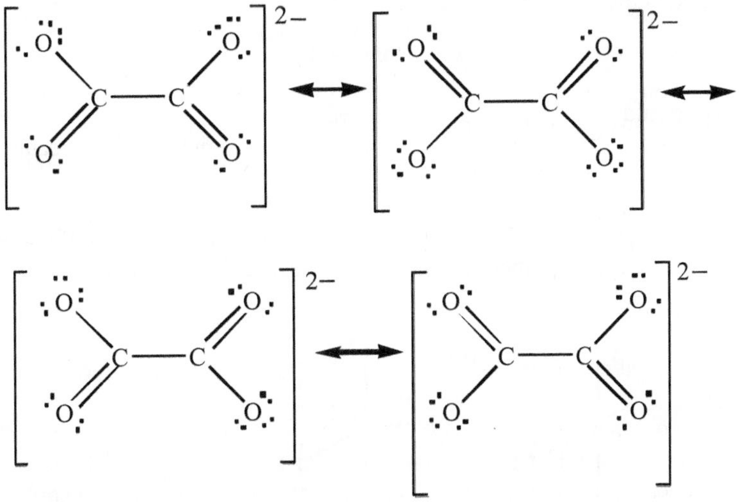

In $H_2C_2O_4$, there are two shorter C=O bonds and two longer, weaker C—O bonds.
In $HC_2O_4^-$, the C—O bonds on the side retaining the H remain as one long C—O bond and one shorter, stronger C=O bond. The C—O bonds on the other side of the molecule have resonance forms with an average bond order of 1.5, so they are intermediate in length and strength.
In $C_2O_4^{2-}$, all the carbon to oxygen bonds are resonating and have an average bond order of 1.5.

10.90 Plan: Draw the Lewis structures. Calculate the heat of reaction using the bond energies in Table 9.2.
Solution:

$SO_3(g) + H_2SO_4(l) \rightarrow H_2S_2O_7(l)$

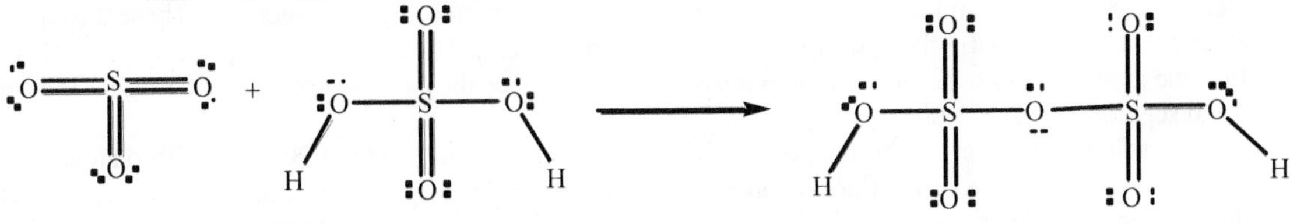

Reactant bonds broken:
5 x S=O = (5 mol)(552 kJ/mol) = 2760 kJ
2 x S–O = (2 mol)(265 kJ/mol) = 530 kJ
2 x O–H = (2 mol)(467 kJ/mol) = 934 kJ

$\Sigma\Delta H^\circ_{\text{bonds broken}}$ = 4224 kJ

Product bonds formed:

$4 \times S{=}O = (4\ mol)(-552\ kJ/mol) = -2208\ kJ$

$4 \times S{-}O = (4\ mol)(-265\ kJ/mol) = -1060\ kJ$

$2 \times O{-}H = (2\ mol)(-467\ kJ/mol) = -934\ kJ$

$$\Sigma\Delta H^\circ_{\text{bonds formed}} = -4202\ kJ$$

$$\Delta H^\circ_{\text{rxn}} = \Sigma\Delta H^\circ_{\text{bonds broken}} + \Sigma\Delta H^\circ_{\text{bonds formed}} = 4224\ kJ + (-4202\ kJ) = \mathbf{22\ kJ}$$

10.91 Plan: Pick the VSEPR structures for AY_3 substances. Then determine which are polar.

Solution:

The molecular shapes that have a central atom bonded to three other atoms are trigonal planar, trigonal pyramidal, and T shaped:

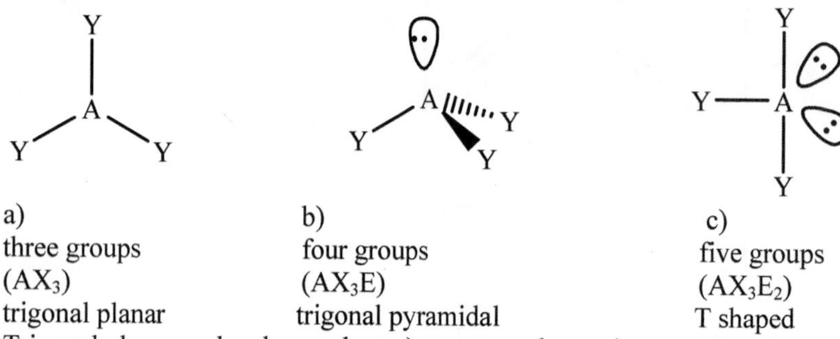

Trigonal planar molecules, such as a), are nonpolar, so it cannot be AY_3. Trigonal pyramidal molecules b) and T-shaped molecules c) are polar, so either could represent AY_3.

10.95 Plan: Draw the Lewis structure of each compound. Atoms 180° apart are separated by the sum of the bond's length. Atoms not at 180° apart must have their distances determined by geometrical relationships.

Solution:

(a) H—C≡C—H (b) SF_6 (c) PF_5

a) C_2H_2 has $[2 \times C(4e^-)] + [2 \times H(1e^-)] = 10$ valence electrons to be used in the Lewis structure. Six of these electrons are used to bond the atoms with a single bond, leaving $10 - 6 = 4$ electrons. Giving one carbon atom the four electrons to complete its octet results in the other carbon atom not having an octet. The two lone pairs from the carbon with an octet are changed to two bonding pairs for a triple bond between the two carbon atoms. The molecular shape is linear. The H atoms are separated by two carbon-hydrogen bonds (109 pm) and a carbon-carbon triple bond (121 pm).

Total separation = 2(109 pm) + 121 pm = **339 pm**

b) SF_6 has $[1 \times S(6e^-)] + [6 \times F(7e^-)] = 48$ valence electrons to be used in the Lewis structure. Twelve of these electrons are used to bond the atoms with a single bond, leaving 48 – 12= 36 electrons. These thirty-six electrons are given to the fluorine atoms to complete their octets. The molecular shape is octahedral. The fluorine atoms on opposite sides of the S are separated by twice the sulfur-fluorine bond length (158 pm).

Total separation = 2(158 pm) = **316 pm**

Adjacent fluorines are at two corners of a right triangle, with the sulfur at the 90° angle. Two sides of the triangle are equal to the sulfur-fluorine bond length (158 pm). The separation of the fluorine atoms is at a distance equal to the hypotenuse of this triangle. This length of the hypotenuse may be found using the Pythagorean Theorem ($a^2 + b^2 = c^2$). In this case a = b = 158 pm. Thus, $c^2 = (158\ pm)^2 + (158\ pm)^2$, and so c = 223.4457 = **223 pm**.

c) PF_5 has [1 x P(5e$^-$)] + [5 x F(7e$^-$)] = 40 valence electrons to be used in the Lewis structure. Ten of these electrons are used to bond the atoms with a single bond, leaving 40 – 10= 30 electrons. These thirty electrons are given to the fluorine atoms to complete their octets. The molecular shape is trigonal bipyramidal. Adjacent equatorial fluorine atoms are at two corners of a triangle with an F-P-F bond angle of 120°. The length of the P-F bond is 156 pm. If the 120° bond angle is A, then the F-F bond distance is a and the P-F bond distances are b and c. The F-F bond distance can be found using the Law of Cosines: $a^2 = b^2 + c^2 - 2bc (\cos A)$.
$a^2 = (156)^2 + (156)^2 - 2(156)(156)\cos 120°$. a = 270.1999 = **270 pm.**

CHAPTER 11 THEORIES OF COVALENT BONDING

FOLLOW–UP PROBLEMS

11.1A Plan: Draw a Lewis structure. Determine the number and arrangement of the electron pairs about the central atom. From this, determine the type of hybrid orbitals involved. Write the partial orbital diagram of the central atoms before and after the orbitals are hybridized.

Solution:

a) Be is surrounded by two electron groups (two single bonds) so hybridization around Be is *sp*.

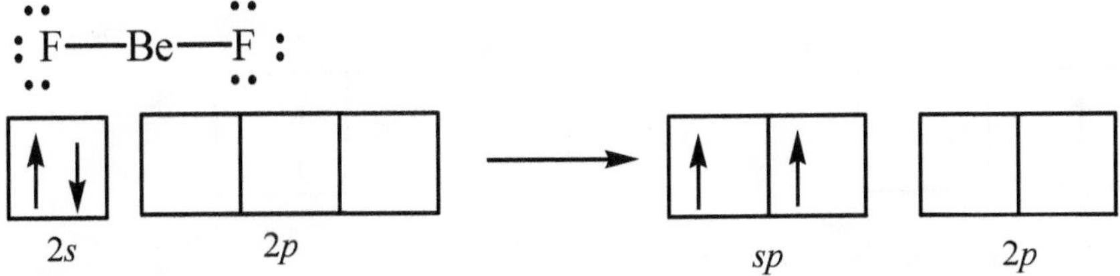

Isolated Be atom   Hybridized Be atom

b) In $SiCl_4$, Si is surrounded by four electron groups (four single bonds) so its hybridization is sp^3.

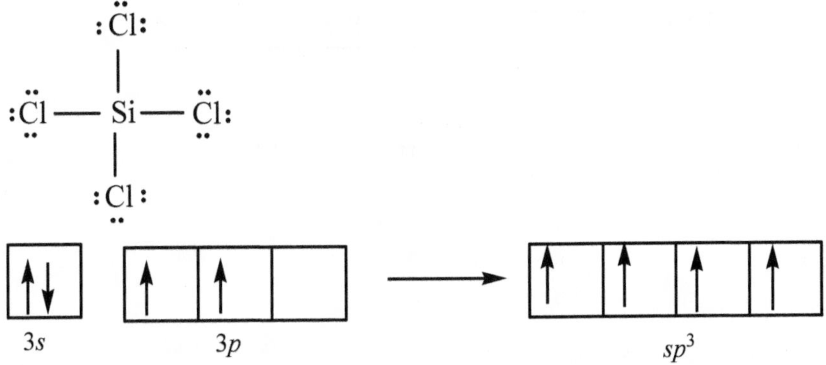

Isolated Si atom   Hybridized Si atom

c) In XeF_4, xenon is surrounded by 6 electron groups (4 bonds and 2 lone pairs) so the hybridization is sp^3d^2.

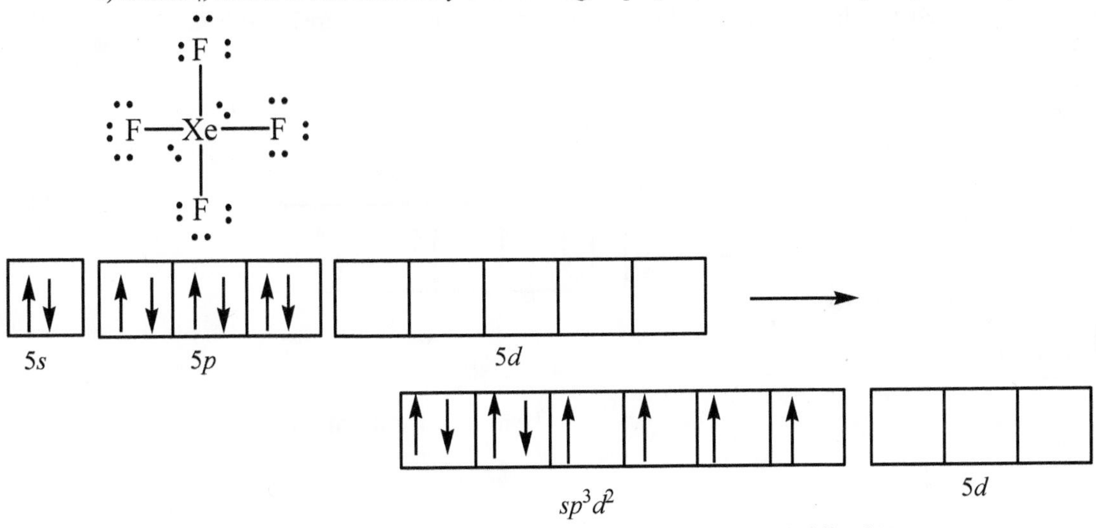

Isolated Xe atom   Hybridized Xe atom

11.1B Plan: Draw a Lewis structure. Determine the number and arrangement of the electron pairs about the central atom. From this, determine the type of hybrid orbitals involved. Write the partial orbital diagram of the central atoms before and after the orbitals are hybridized.

Solution:

a) NO_2 has 17 valence electrons and the resonance structures shown below:

The electron group arrangement is trigonal planar, so the central N atom is sp^2 hybridized, which means one *2s* and two *2p* orbital are mixed. One hybrid orbital is filled with a lone pair, and two are half-filled. One electron remains in the unhybridized p orbital to form the π bond between the central N and one of the neighboring O atoms.

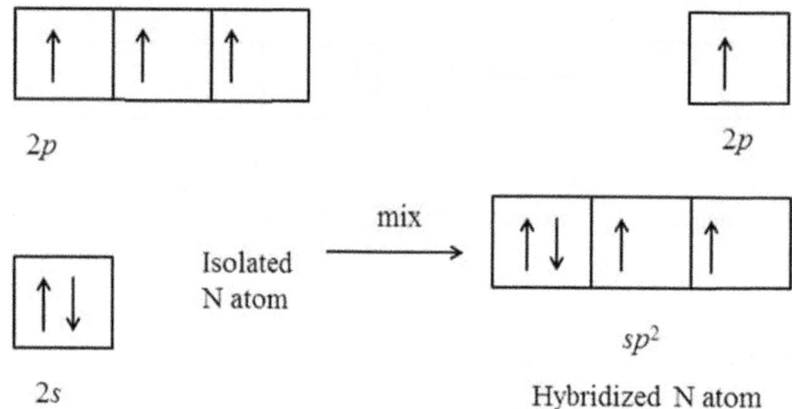

b) PCl_3 has 26 valence electrons and the Lewis structure shown below:

:C̈l:
|
:C̈l—P—C̈l:

The electron-group arrangement is tetrahedral, so the central P atom is sp^3 hybridized, which means one *3s* and three *3p* orbital are mixed. One hybrid orbital is filled with a lone pair, and three are half-filled.

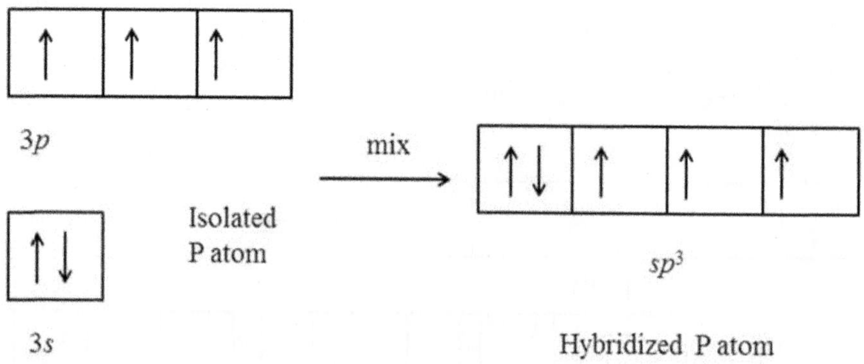

c) BrF_5 has 42 valence electrons and the Lewis structure shown below:

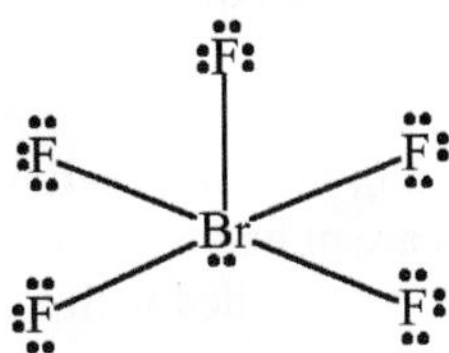

The electron-group arrangement is octahedral, so the central Br atom is sp^3d^2 hybridized, which means one *4s*, three *4p*, and two *4d* orbital are mixed. One hybrid orbital is filled with a lone pair, and five are half-filled. Three unhybridized *4d* orbitals remain empty.

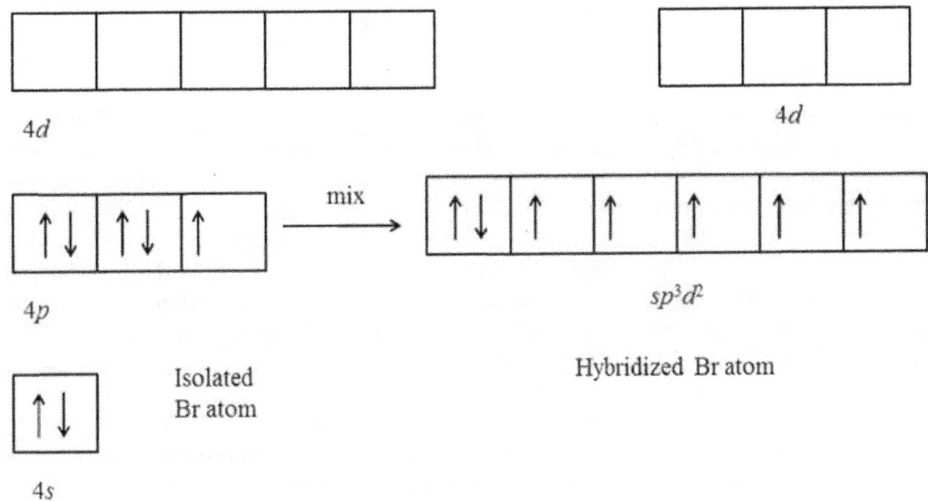

11.2A Plan: First, determine the Lewis structure for the molecule. Then count the number of electron groups around each atom. Hybridization is *sp* if there are two groups, sp^2 if there are three groups, and sp^3 if there are four groups. No hybridization occurs with only one group of electrons. The bonds are then designated as sigma or pi. A single bond is a sigma bond. A double bond consists of one sigma and one pi bond. A triple bond includes one sigma bond and two pi bonds. Hybridized orbitals overlap head on to form sigma bonds whereas pi bonds form through the sideways overlap of *p* or *d* orbitals.

Solution:

a) Hydrogen cyanide has H–C≡N: as its Lewis structure. The single bond between carbon and hydrogen is a sigma bond formed by the overlap of a hybridized *sp* orbital on carbon with the 1*s* orbital from hydrogen. Between carbon and nitrogen are three bonds. One is a sigma bond formed by the overlap of a hybridized *sp* orbital on carbon with a hybridized *sp* orbital on nitrogen. The other two bonds between carbon and nitrogen are pi bonds formed by the overlap of *p* orbitals from carbon and nitrogen. One *sp* orbital on nitrogen is filled with a lone pair of electrons.

b) The Lewis structure of carbon dioxide, CO_2, is

O═C═O

Both oxygen atoms are sp^2 hybridized (the O atoms have three electron groups – one double bond and two lone pairs) and form a sigma bond and a pi bond with carbon. The sigma bonds are formed by the overlap of a hybridized *sp* orbital on carbon with a hybridized sp^2 orbital on oxygen. The pi bonds are formed by the overlap of an oxygen *p* orbital with a carbon *p* orbital. Two sp^2 orbitals on each oxygen are filled with a lone pair of electrons.

11.2B Plan: First, determine the Lewis structure for the molecule. Then count the number of electron groups around each atom. Hybridization is *sp* if there are two groups, sp^2 if there are three groups, and sp^3 if there are four groups. No hybridization occurs with only one group of electrons. The bonds are then designated as sigma or pi. A single bond is a sigma bond. A double bond consists of one sigma and one pi bond. A triple bond includes one sigma bond and two pi bonds. Hybridized orbitals overlap head on to form sigma bonds whereas pi bonds form through the sideways overlap of *p* or *d* orbitals.

Solution:

a) Carbon monoxide has :C≡O: as its Lewis structure. Both C and O are *sp* hybridized. Between carbon and oxygen are three bonds. One is a sigma bond formed by the overlap of a hybridized *sp* orbital on carbon with a hybridized *sp* orbital on oxygen. The other two bonds between carbon and oxygen are pi bonds formed by the overlap of unhybridized *p* orbitals from carbon and oxygen. One *sp* orbital on nitrogen is filled with a lone pair of electrons, as is one *sp* orbital on oxygen.

b) The Lewis structure of urea, H_2NCONH_2, is

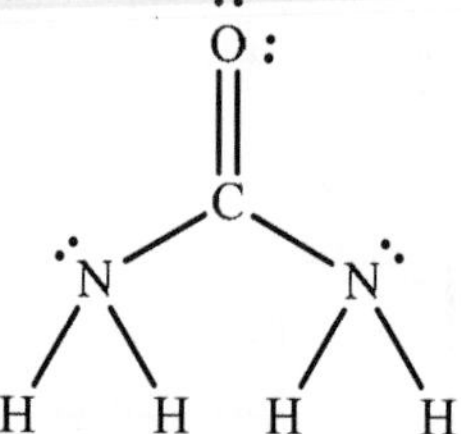

Both nitrogen atoms are sp^3 hybridized (the N atoms have four electron groups – three single bonds and one lone pair). The carbon and the oxygen are sp^2 hybridized (the C atom has three electron groups – two single bonds to nitrogen and one double bond to oxygen; the O atom also has three electron groups – two lone pairs and one double bond to carbon). One sp^3 hybrid orbital of each nitrogen forms a sigma bond with a sp^2 hybrid orbital of carbon. Two sp^3 hybrid orbitals of each nitrogen form two sigma bonds with two *s* orbitals from the hydrogen atoms (one *s* orbital from each hydrogen atom). The fourth sp^3 hybrid orbital on each of the nitrogens is filled with a lone pair of electrons. The remaining sp^2 hybrid orbital on carbon forms a sigma bond with an sp^2 hybrid orbital on the oxygen. The remaining sp^2 hybrid orbitals on oxygen are filled with lone pair electrons. Unhybridized *p* orbitals on the C and O overlap to form a pi bond.

11.3A Plan: Draw the molecular orbital diagram. Determine the bond order from calculation: BO = 1/2(# e^- in bonding orbitals – #e^- in antibonding orbitals). A bond order of zero indicates the molecule will not exist. A bond order greater than zero indicates that the molecule is at least somewhat stable and is likely to exist. H_2^{2-} has 4 electrons (1 from each hydrogen and two from the –2 charge).

Solution:

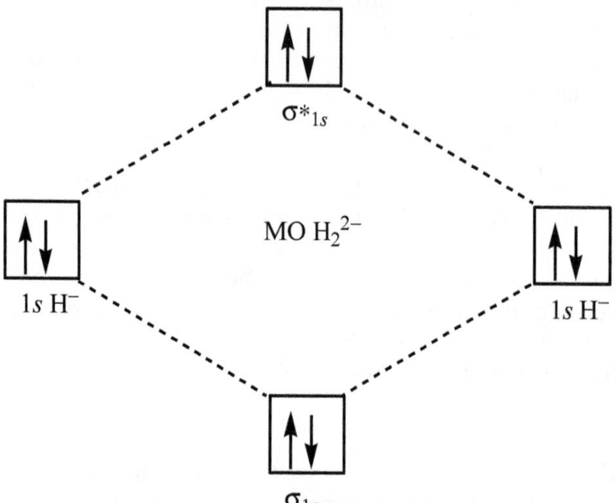

Configuration for H_2^{2-} is $(\sigma_{1s})^2(\sigma^*_{1s})^2$. Bond order of H_2^{2-} is 1/2(2 – 2) = 0. Thus, it is not likely that two H^- ions would combine to form the ion H_2^{2-}.

11.3B Plan: Draw the molecular orbital diagram. Determine the bond order from calculation: BO = 1/2(# e^- in bonding orbitals – #e^- in antibonding orbitals). A bond order of zero indicates the molecule will not exist. A bond order greater than zero indicates that the molecule is at least somewhat stable and is likely to exist. He_2^{2+} has 2 electrons (2 from each helium less two from the +2 charge).
Solution:

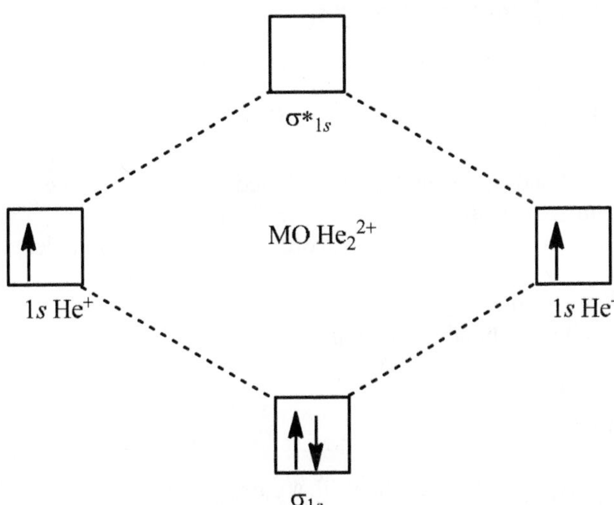

Configuration for He_2^{2+} is $(\sigma_{1s})^2$. Bond order of He_2^{2+} is 1/2(2 – 0) = 1. Thus, we predict that He_2^{2+} does exist.

11.4A Plan: To find bond order it is necessary to determine the molecular orbital electron configuration from the total number of electrons. Bond order is calculated from the configuration as 1/2(# e^- in bonding orbitals – #e^- in antibonding orbitals).
Solution:
N_2^{2+}: total electrons = 7 + 7 – 2 = 12
Configuration: $(\sigma_{1s})^2(\sigma^*_{1s})^2(\sigma_{2s})^2(\sigma^*_{2s})^2(\pi_{2p})^4$
Bond order = 1/2(8 – 4) = 2
N_2^-: total electrons = 7 + 7 + 1 = 15
Configuration: $(\sigma_{1s})^2(\sigma^*_{1s})^2(\sigma_{2s})^2(\sigma^*_{2s})^2(\pi_{2p})^4(\sigma_{2p})^2(\pi^*_{2p})^1$
Bond order = 1/2(10 – 5) = 2.5
N_2^{2-}: total electrons = 7 + 7 + 2 = 16
Configuration: $(\sigma_{1s})^2(\sigma^*_{1s})^2(\sigma_{2s})^2(\sigma^*_{2s})^2(\pi_{2p})^4(\sigma_{2p})^2(\pi^*_{2p})^2$
Bond order = 1/2(10 – 6) = 2
Bond energy decreases as bond order decreases: $N_2^- > N_2^{2+} = N_2^{2-}$
Bond length increases as bond energy decreases, so the order of decreasing bond length will be opposite that of decreasing bond energy.
Decreasing bond length: $N_2^{2+} = N_2^{2-} > N_2^-$

11.4B Plan: To find bond order it is necessary to determine the molecular orbital electron configuration from the total number of electrons. Bond order is calculated from the configuration as 1/2(# e^- in bonding orbitals – #e^- in antibonding orbitals).
Solution:
F_2^{2-}: total electrons = 9 + 9 + 2 = 20
Configuration: $(\sigma_{1s})^2(\sigma^*_{1s})^2(\sigma_{2s})^2(\sigma^*_{2s})^2(\sigma_{2p})^2(\pi_{2p})^4(\pi^*_{2p})^4(\sigma^*_{2p})^2$
Bond order = 1/2(10 – 10) = 0
F_2^-: total electrons = 9 + 9 + 1 = 19
Configuration: $(\sigma_{1s})^2(\sigma^*_{1s})^2(\sigma_{2s})^2(\sigma^*_{2s})^2(\sigma_{2p})^2(\pi_{2p})^4(\pi^*_{2p})^4(\sigma^*_{2p})^1$
Bond order = 1/2(10 – 9) = 0.5

F_2: total electrons = 9 + 9 = 18

Configuration: $(\sigma_{1s})^2(\sigma^*_{1s})^2(\sigma_{2s})^2(\sigma^*_{2s})^2(\sigma_{2p})^2(\pi_{2p})^4(\pi^*_{2p})^4$

Bond order = 1/2(10 – 8) = 1

F_2^+: total electrons = 9 + 9 – 1 = 17

Configuration: $(\sigma_{1s})^2(\sigma^*_{1s})^2(\sigma_{2s})^2(\sigma^*_{2s})^2(\sigma_{2p})^2(\pi_{2p})^4(\pi^*_{2p})^3$

Bond order = 1/2(10 – 7) = 1.5

F_2^{2+}: total electrons = 9 + 9 – 2 = 16

Configuration: $(\sigma_{1s})^2(\sigma^*_{1s})^2(\sigma_{2s})^2(\sigma^*_{2s})^2(\sigma_{2p})^2(\pi_{2p})^4(\pi^*_{2p})^2$

Bond order = 1/2(10 – 6) = 2

F_2^{2-} does not exist, so it has no bond energy and is not included in the list. For the other molecule and ions, bond energy increases as bond order increases: $F_2^- < F_2 < F_2^+ < F_2^{2+}$

Bond length decreases as bond energy increases, so the order of increasing bond length will be opposite that of increasing bond energy.

Increasing bond length: $F_2^{2+} < F_2^+ < F_2 < F_2^-$

F_2^{2-} will not form a bond, so it has no bond length and is not included in the list.

END–OF–CHAPTER PROBLEMS

11.1 Plan: Table 11.1 describes the types of hybrid orbitals that correspond to the various electron-group arrangements. The number of hybrid orbitals formed by a central atom is equal to the number of electron groups arranged around that central atom.

Solution:

a) trigonal planar: three electron groups - three hybrid orbitals: sp^2

b) octahedral: six electron groups - six hybrid orbitals: sp^3d^2

c) linear: two electron groups - two hybrid orbitals: sp

d) tetrahedral: four electron groups - four hybrid orbitals: sp^3

e) trigonal bipyramidal: five electron groups - five hybrid orbitals: sp^3d

11.3 Carbon and silicon have the same number of valence electrons, but the outer level of electrons is $n = 2$ for carbon and $n = 3$ for silicon. Thus, silicon has $3d$ orbitals in addition to $3s$ and $3p$ orbitals available for bonding in its outer level, to form up to six hybrid orbitals, whereas carbon has only $2s$ and $2p$ orbitals available in its outer level to form up to four hybrid orbitals.

11.5 Plan: The *number* of hybrid orbitals is the same as the number of atomic orbitals before hybridization. The *type* depends on the orbitals mixed. The name of the type of hybrid orbital comes from the number and type of atomic orbitals mixed. The number of each type of atomic orbital appears as a superscript in the name of the hybrid orbital.

Solution:

a) There are six unhybridized orbitals, and therefore **six** hybrid orbitals result. The type is sp^3d^2 since one s, three p, and two d atomic orbitals were mixed.

b) **Four** sp^3 hybrid orbitals form from three p and one s atomic orbitals.

11.7 Plan: To determine hybridization, draw the Lewis structure and count the number of electron groups around the central nitrogen atom. Hybridize that number of orbitals. Single, double, and triple bonds all count as one electron group. An unshared pair (lone pair) of electrons or one unshared electron also counts as one electron group.

Solution:

a) The three electron groups (one double bond, one lone pair, and one unpaired electron) around nitrogen require three hybrid orbitals. The hybridization is sp^2.

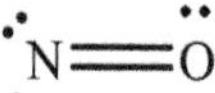

b) The nitrogen has three electron groups (one single bond, one double bond, and one unpaired electron), requiring three hybrid orbitals so the hybridization is ***sp*²**.

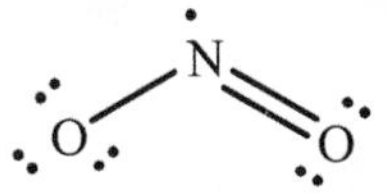

c) The nitrogen has three electron groups (one single bond, one double bond, and one lone pair) so the hybridization is ***sp*²**.

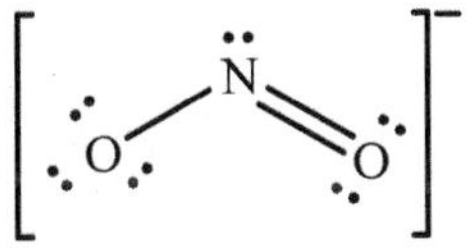

11.9 Plan: To determine hybridization, draw the Lewis structure and count the number of electron groups around the central chlorine atom. Hybridize that number of orbitals. Single, double, and triple bonds all count as one electron group. An unshared pair (lone pair) of electrons or one unshared electron also counts as one electron group.

Solution:

a) The Cl has four electron groups (one lone pair, one lone electron, and two double bonds) and therefore four hybrid orbitals are required; the hybridization is ***sp*³**. Note that in ClO_2, the π bond is formed by the overlap of *d* orbitals from chlorine with *p* orbitals from oxygen.

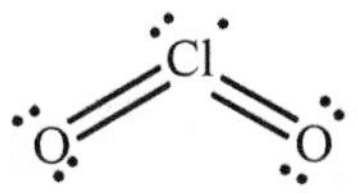

b) The Cl has four electron groups (one lone pair and three bonds) and therefore four hybrid orbitals are required; the hybridization is ***sp*³**.

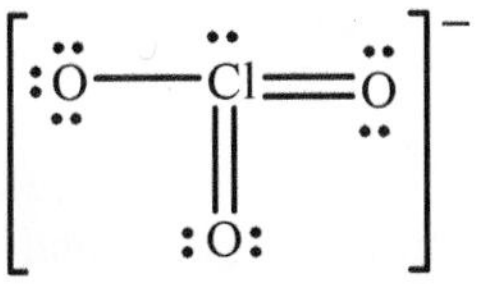

c) The Cl has four electron groups (four bonds) and therefore four hybrid orbitals are required; the hybridization is ***sp*³**.

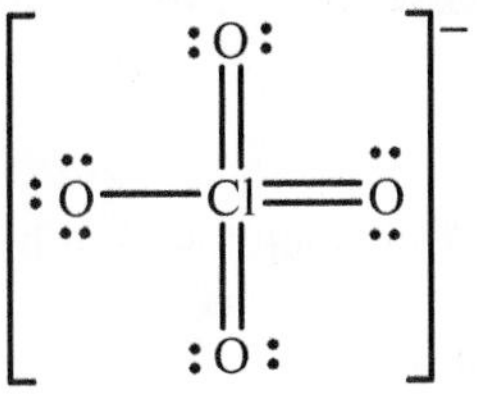

11.11 Plan: Draw the Lewis structure and count the number of electron groups around the central atom. Hybridize that number of orbitals. Single, double, and triple bonds all count as one electron group. An unshared pair (lone pair) of electrons or one unshared electron also counts as one electron group. Once the type of hybridization is known, the types of atomic orbitals that will mix to form those hybrid orbitals are also known.

Solution:
a) Silicon has four electron groups (four bonds) requiring four hybrid orbitals; four sp^3 hybrid orbitals are made from **one *s* and three *p* atomic orbitals.**

```
          H
          |
:Cl̤̈ — Si — H
          |
          H
```

b) Carbon has two electron groups (two double bonds) requiring two hybrid orbitals; two *sp* hybrid orbitals are made from **one *s* and one *p* orbital.**

```
S̤̈ = C = S̤̈
```

c) Sulfur is surrounded by five electron groups (four bonding pairs and one lone pair), requiring five hybrid orbitals; five sp^3d hybrid orbitals are formed from **one *s* orbital, three *p* orbitals, and one *d* orbital.**

```
        :F̤̈:
         |   Cl̤̈:
         |  /
:Cl̤̈ —— S :
         |
         |
       :Cl̤̈:
```

d) Nitrogen is surrounded by four electron groups (three bonding pairs and one lone pair) requiring four hybrid orbitals; four sp^3 hybrid orbitals are formed from **one *s* orbital and three *p* orbitals.**

```
:F̤̈ — N̈ — F̤̈:
       |
      :F̤̈:
```

11.13 Plan: To determine hybridization, draw the Lewis structure of the reactants and products and count the number of electron groups around the central atom. Hybridize that number of orbitals. Single, double, and triple bonds all count as one electron group. An unshared pair (lone pair) of electrons or one unshared electron also counts as one electron group. Recall that *sp* hydrid orbitals are oriented in a linear geometry, sp^2 in a trigonal planar geometry, sp^3 in a tetrahedral geometry, sp^3d in a trigonal bipyramidal geometry, and sp^3d^2 in an octahedral geometry.
Solution:
a) The P in PH_3 has four electron groups (one lone pair and three bonds) and therefore four hybrid orbitals are required; the hybridization is sp^3. The P in the product also has four electron groups (four bonds) and again four hybrid orbitals are required. The hybridization of P remains sp^3. There is no change in hybridization. Illustration **B** best shows the hybridization of P during the reaction as $\mathbf{sp^3 \rightarrow sp^3}$.

b) The B in BH_3 has three electron groups (three bonds) and therefore three hybrid orbitals are required; the hybridization is sp^2. The B in the product has four electron groups (four bonds) and four hybrid orbitals are required. The hybridization of B is now sp^3. The hybridization of B changes from $\boldsymbol{sp^2}$ **to** $\boldsymbol{sp^3}$; this is best shown by illustration **A**.

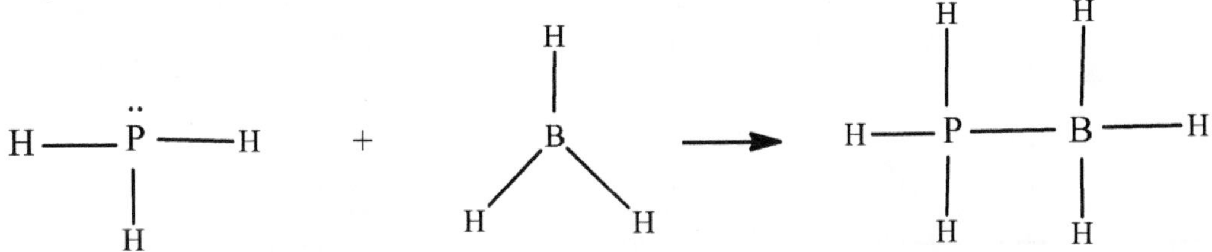

11.15 Plan: To determine hybridization, draw the Lewis structure and count the number of electron groups around the central atom. Hybridize that number of orbitals. Single, double, and triple bonds all count as one electron group. An unshared pair (lone pair) of electrons or one unshared electron also counts as one electron group. Write the electron configuration of the central atom and mix the appropriate atomic orbitals to form the hybrid orbitals.

Solution:

a) Germanium is the central atom in $GeCl_4$. Its electron configuration is $[Ar]4s^23d^{10}4p^2$. Ge has four electron groups (four bonds), requiring four hybrid orbitals. Hybridization is sp^3 around Ge. One of the 4s electrons is moved to a 4p orbital and the four orbitals are hybridized.

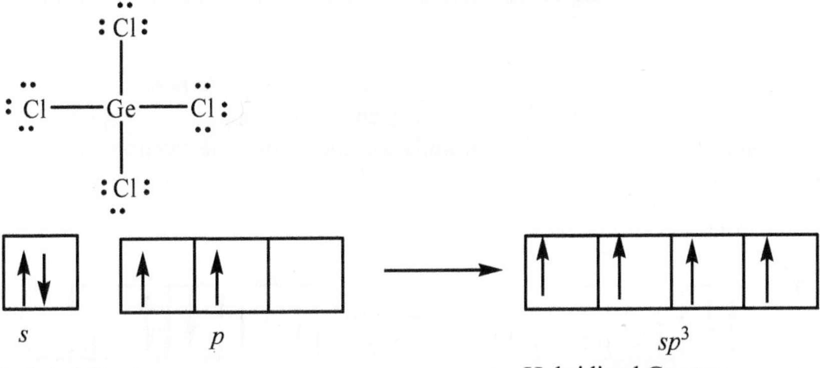

Isolated Ge atom Hybridized Ge atom

b) Boron is the central atom in BCl_3. Its electron configuration is $[He]2s^22p^1$. B has three electron groups (three bonds), requiring three hybrid orbitals. Hybridization is sp^2 around B. One of the 2s electrons is moved to an empty 2p orbital and the three atomic orbitals are hybridized. One of the 2p atomic orbitals is not involved in the hybridization.

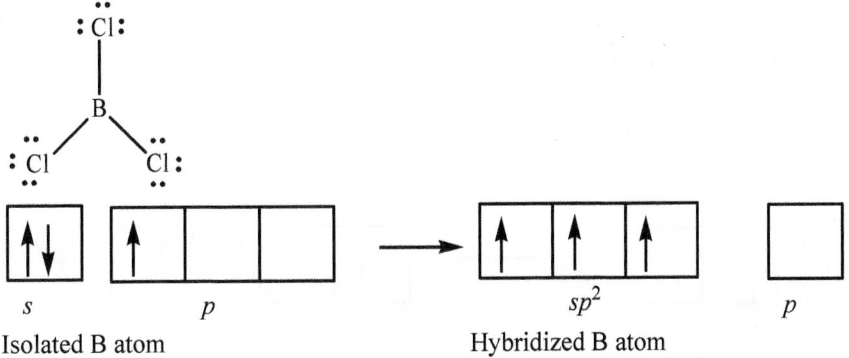

Isolated B atom Hybridized B atom

c) Carbon is the central atom in CH_3^+. Its electron configuration is $[He]2s^22p^2$. C has three electron groups (three bonds), requiring three hybrid orbitals. Hybridization is sp^2 around C.
One of the $2s$ electrons is moved to an empty $2p$ orbital; three orbitals are hybridized and one electron is removed to form the +1 ion.

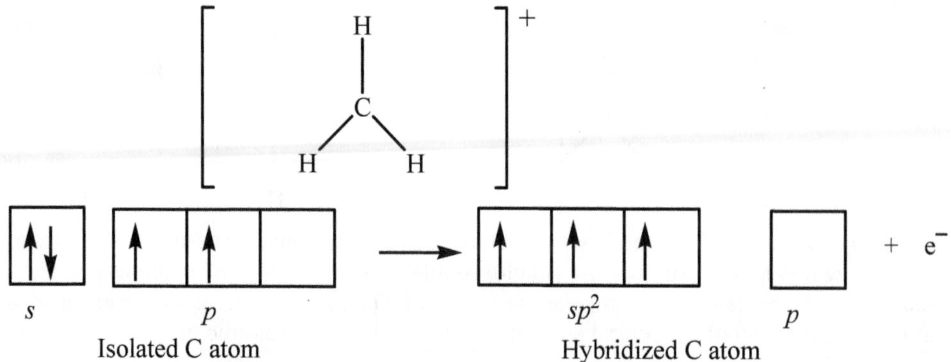

11.17 Plan: To determine hybridization, draw the Lewis structure and count the number of electron groups around the central atom. Hybridize that number of orbitals. Single, double, and triple bonds all count as one electron group. An unshared pair (lone pair) of electrons or one unshared electron also counts as one electron group. Write the electron configuration of the central atom and mix the appropriate atomic orbitals to form the hybrid orbitals.

Solution:

a) In $SeCl_2$, Se is the central atom and has four electron groups (two single bonds and two lone pairs), requiring four hybrid orbitals so Se is sp^3 hybridized. The electron configuration of Se is $[Ar]4s^23d^{10}4p^4$. The $4s$ and $4p$ atomic orbitals are hybridized. Two sp^3 hybrid orbitals are filled with lone electron pairs and two sp^3 orbitals bond with the chlorine atoms.

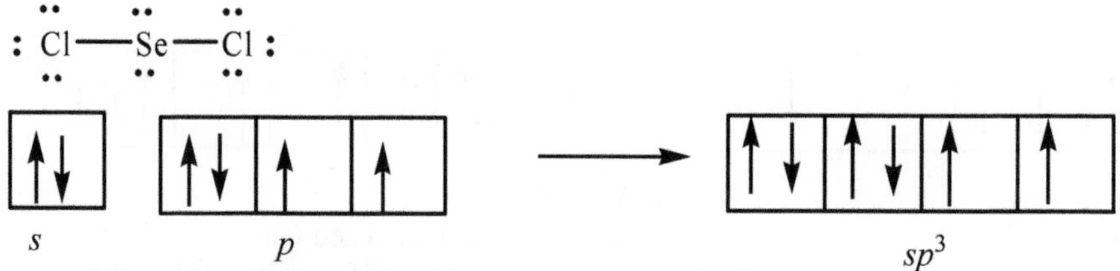

b) In H_3O^+, O is the central atom and has four electron groups (three single bonds and one lone pair), requiring four hybrid orbitals. O is sp^3 hybridized. The electron configuration of O is $[He]2s^22p^4$. The $2s$ and $2p$ orbitals are hybridized. One sp^3 hybrid orbital is filled with a lone electron pair and three sp^3 orbitals bond with the hydrogen atoms.

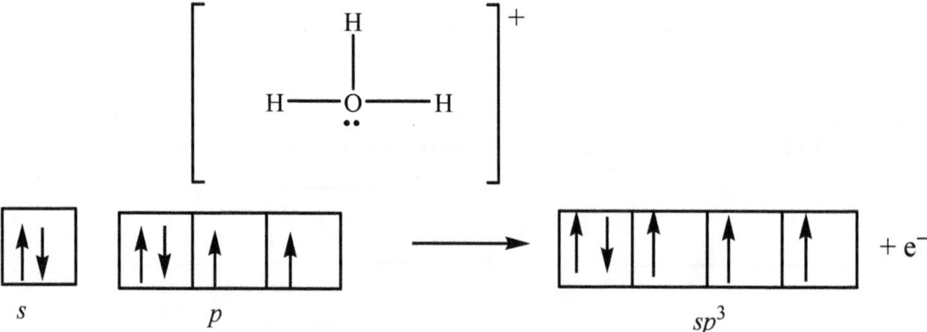

c) I is the central atom in IF_4^- with six electron groups (four single bonds and two lone pairs) surrounding it. Six hybrid orbitals are required and I has sp^3d^2 hybrid orbitals. The sp^3d^2 hybrid orbitals are composed of one *s* orbital, three *p* orbitals, and two *d* orbitals. Two sp^3d^2 orbitals are filled with a lone pair and four sp^3d^2 orbitals bond with the fluorine atoms.

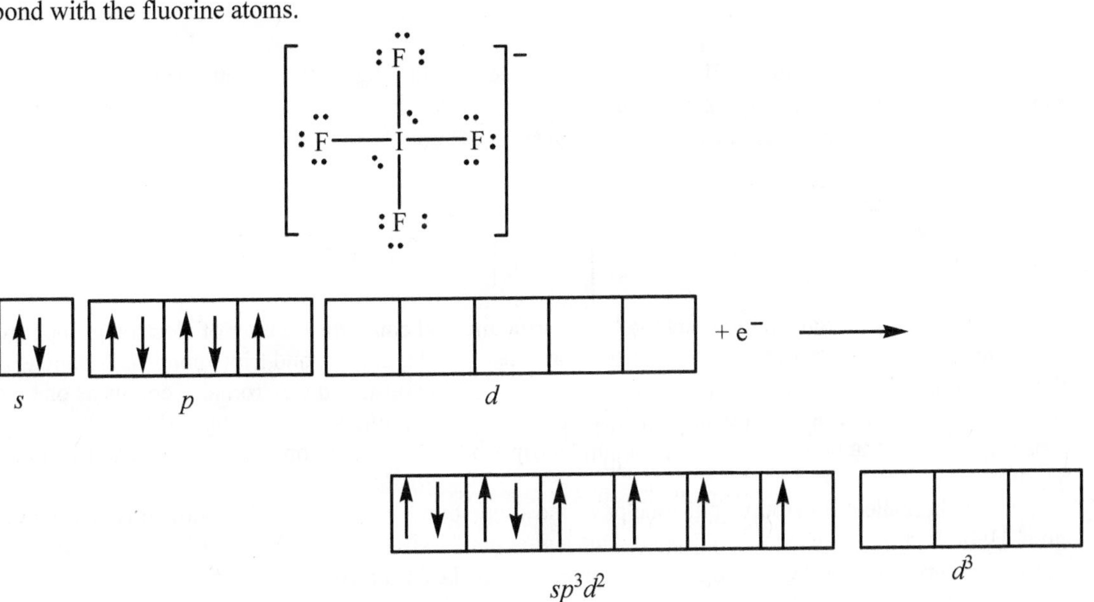

11.20 Plan: A single bond is a sigma bond which is the result of two orbitals overlapping end to end; a double bond consists of one sigma bond and one pi bond; and a triple bond consists of one sigma bond and two pi bonds. A pi bond is the result of orbitals overlapping side to side.

Solution:

a) **False**, a double bond is one sigma (σ) and one pi (π) bond.

b) **False**, a triple bond consists of one sigma (σ) and two pi (π) bonds.

c) **True**

d) **True**

e) **False**, a π bond consists of one pair of electrons; it occurs after a σ bond has been previously formed.

f) **False**, end-to-end overlap results in a bond with electron density along the bond axis.

11.21 Plan: To determine hybridization, draw the Lewis structure and count the number of electron groups around the central atom. Hybridize that number of orbitals. Single, double, and triple bonds all count as one electron group. An unshared pair (lone pair) of electrons or one unshared electron also counts as one electron group. A single bond is a sigma bond which is the result of two orbitals overlapping end to end; a double bond consists of one sigma bond and one pi bond; and a triple bond consists of one sigma bond and two pi bonds.

Solution:

a) Nitrogen is the central atom in NO_3^-. Nitrogen has three surrounding electron groups (two single bonds and one double bond), so it is sp^2 hybridized. Nitrogen forms **three σ bonds** (one each for the N–O bonds) and **one π bond** (part of the N=O double bond).

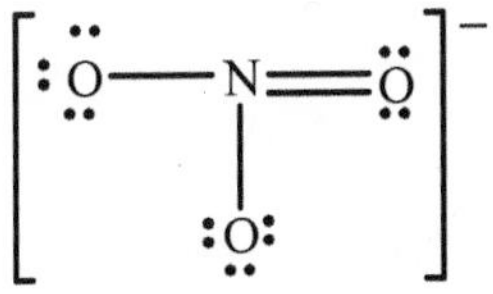

b) Carbon is the central atom in CS_2. Carbon has two surrounding electron groups (two double bonds), so it is ***sp*** hybridized. Carbon forms **two σ bonds** (one each for the C–S bonds) and **two π bonds** (part of the two C=S double bonds).

S=C=S

c) Carbon is the central atom in CH_2O. Carbon has three surrounding electron groups (two single bonds and one double bond), so it is ***sp***^{2} hybridized. Carbon forms **three σ bonds** (one each for the two C–H bonds and one C–O bond) and **one π bond** (part of the C=O double bond).

H

C=O

H

11.23 Plan: To determine hybridization, draw the Lewis structure and count the number of electron groups around the central nitrogen atom. Hybridize that number of orbitals. Single, double, and triple bonds all count as one electron group. An unshared pair (lone pair) of electrons or one unshared electron also counts as one electron group. A single bond is a sigma bond which is the result of two orbitals overlapping end to end; a double bond consists of one sigma bond and one pi bond; and a triple bond consists of one sigma bond and two pi bonds.
Solution:
a) In FNO, three electron groups (one lone pair, one single bond, and one double bond) surround the central N atom. Hybridization is ***sp***^{2} around nitrogen. One sigma bond exists between F and N, and one sigma and one pi bond exist between N and O. Nitrogen participates in a total of **2 σ and 1 π bonds.**

:F—N=O

b) In C_2F_4, each carbon has three electron groups (two single bonds and one double bond) with ***sp***^{2} hybridization. The bonds between C and F are sigma bonds. The C–C bond consists of one sigma and one pi bond. Each carbon participates in a total of **three σ and one π bonds.**

:F F:

C=C

:F F:

c) In $(CN)_2$, each carbon has two electron groups (one single bond and one triple bond) and is ***sp*** hybridized with a sigma bond between the two carbons and a sigma and two pi bonds comprising each C–N triple bond. Each carbon participates in a total of **two σ and two π bonds.**

:N≡C—C≡N:

11.25 Plan:. A single bond is a sigma bond which is the result of two orbitals overlapping end to end; a double bond consists of one sigma bond and one pi bond; and a triple bond consists of one sigma bond and two pi bonds.
Solution:
The double bond in 2-butene restricts rotation of the molecule, so that *cis* and *trans* structures result. The two structures are shown below:

cis

trans

The carbons participating in the double bond each have three surrounding groups, so they are sp^2 hybridized. The =C–H σ bonds result from the head-on overlap of a C sp^2 orbital and an H *s* orbital. The C–CH_3 bonds are also σ bonds, resulting from the head-on overlap of an sp^2 orbital and an sp^3 orbital. The C=C bond contains 1 σ bond (head on overlap of two sp^2 orbitals) and 1 π bond (sideways overlap of unhybridized *p* orbitals). Finally, C–H bonds in the methyl (–CH_3) groups are σ bonds resulting from the overlap of the sp^3 orbital of C with the *s* orbital of H.

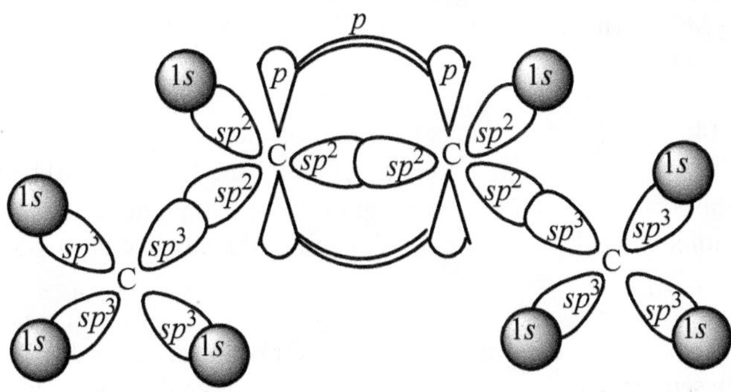

11.26 Four molecular orbitals form from the four *p* atomic orbitals. In forming molecular orbitals, the total number of molecular orbitals must equal the number of atomic orbitals. Two of the four molecular orbitals formed are bonding orbitals and two are antibonding.

11.28 a) Bonding MOs have lower energy than antibonding MOs. The bonding MO's lower energy, even lower than its constituent atomic orbitals, accounts for the stability of a molecule in relation to its individual atoms. However, the sum of energy of the MOs must equal the sum of energy of the AOs.
b) The node is the region of an orbital where the probability of finding the electron is zero, so the nodal plane is the plane that bisects the node perpendicular to the bond axis. There is no node along the bond axis (probability is positive between the two nuclei) for the bonding MO. The antibonding MO does have a nodal plane.
c) The bonding MO has higher electron density between nuclei than the antibonding MO.

11.30 Plan: Like atomic orbitals, any one MO holds a maximum of two electrons. Two atomic orbitals combine to form two molecular orbitals, a bonding and an antibonding MO.
Solution:
a) **Two** electrons are required to fill a σ-bonding molecular orbital. Each molecular orbital requires two electrons.
b) **Two** electrons are required to fill a π-antibonding molecular orbital. There are two π-antibonding orbitals, each holding a maximum of two electrons.
c) **Four** electrons are required to fill the two σ molecular orbitals (two electrons to fill the σ-bonding and two to fill the σ-antibonding) formed from two 1*s* atomic orbitals.

11.32 Plan: Recall that a bonding MO has a region of high electron density between the nuclei while an antibonding MO has a node, or region of zero electron density between the nuclei. MOs formed from *s* orbitals, or from *p* orbitals overlapping end to end, are called σ and MOs formed by the side-to-side overlap of *p* orbitals are called π. A superscript star (*) is used to designate an antibonding MO. To write the electron configuration of F_2^+, determine the number of valence electrons and write the sequence of MO energy levels, following the sequence order given in the text.
Solution:
a) A is the $\boldsymbol{\pi^*_{2p}}$ molecular orbital (two *p* orbitals overlapping side to side with a node between them); B is the $\boldsymbol{\sigma_{2p}}$ molecular orbital (two *p* orbitals overlapping end to end with no node); C is the $\boldsymbol{\pi_{2p}}$ molecular orbital (two *p* orbitals overlapping side to side with no node); D is the $\boldsymbol{\sigma^*_{2p}}$ molecular orbital (two *p* orbitals overlapping end to end with a node).

b) F_2^+ has thirteen valence electrons: [2 x F(7e$^-$) – 1 (from + charge)]. The MO electron configuration is $(\sigma_{2s})^2(\sigma^*_{2s})^2(\sigma_{2p})^2(\pi_{2p})^2(\pi_{2p})^2(\pi^*_{2p})^2(\pi^*_{2p})^1$. The $\boldsymbol{\pi^*_{2p}}$ molecular orbital, A, $\boldsymbol{\sigma_{2p}}$ molecular orbital, B, and $\boldsymbol{\pi_{2p}}$ molecular orbital, C, are all occupied by at least one electron. The $\boldsymbol{\sigma^*_{2p}}$ molecular orbital is unoccupied.
c) A $\boldsymbol{\pi^*_{2p}}$ molecular orbital, A, has only one electron.

11.34 Plan: To write the electron configuration of Be_2^+, determine the number of electrons and write the sequence of MO energy levels, following the sequence order given in the text.
Bond order = ½[(no. of electrons in bonding MO) – (no. of electrons in antibonding MO)]. Recall that a diamagnetic substance has no unpaired electrons.
Solution:
a) Be_2^+ has a total of seven electrons [2 x Be(4e$^-$) – 1 (from + charge)]. The molecular orbital configuration is $(\sigma_{1s})^2(\sigma^*_{1s})^2(\sigma_{2s})^2(\sigma^*_{2s})^1$ and bond order = ½(4 – 3) = 1/2. With a bond order of 1/2 the Be_2^+ ion will be **stable**.
b) No, the ion has one unpaired electron in the σ^*_{2s} MO, so it is **paramagnetic**, not diamagnetic.
c) Valence electrons would be those in the molecular orbitals at the $n = 2$ level, so the valence electron configuration is $\boldsymbol{(\sigma_{2s})^2(\sigma^*_{2s})^1}$.

11.36 Plan: Write the electron configuration of each species by determining the number of electrons and writing the sequence of MO energy levels, following the sequence order given in the text. Calculate the bond order: bond order = ½[(no. of electrons in bonding MO) – (no. of electrons in antibonding MO)]. Bond energy increases as bond order increases; bond length decreases as bond order increases.
Solution:

C_2^- Total electrons = 6 + 6 + 1 = 13
MO configuration: $(\sigma_{1s})^2(\sigma^*_{1s})^2(\sigma_{2s})^2(\sigma^*_{2s})^2(\pi_{2p})^4(\sigma_{2p})^1$
Bond order = 1/2(9 – 4) = 2.5

C_2 Total electrons = 6 + 6 = 12
MO configuration: $(\sigma_{1s})^2(\sigma^*_{1s})^2(\sigma_{2s})^2(\sigma^*_{2s})^2(\pi_{2p})^4$
Bond order = 1/2(8 – 4) = 2

C_2^+ Total electrons = 6 + 6 – 1 = 11
MO configuration: $(\sigma_{1s})^2(\sigma^*_{1s})^2(\sigma_{2s})^2(\sigma^*_{2s})^2(\pi_{2p})^3$
Bond order = 1/2(7 – 4) = 1.5

a) Bond energy increases as bond order increases: $\boldsymbol{C_2^+ < C_2 < C_2^-}$
b) Bond length decreases as bond energy increases, so the order of increasing bond length will be opposite that of increasing bond energy. Increasing bond length: $\boldsymbol{C_2^- < C_2 < C_2^+}$

11.40 Plan: To determine hybridization, count the number of electron groups around each of the C, O, and N atoms. Hybridize that number of orbitals. Single, double, and triple bonds all count as one electron group. An unshared pair (lone pair) of electrons or one unshared electron also counts as one electron group. A single bond is a sigma bond which is the result of two orbitals overlapping end to end; a double bond consists of one sigma bond and one pi bond; and a triple bond consists of one sigma bond and two pi bonds.
Solution:
a) Each of the six C atoms in the ring has three electron groups (two single bonds and a double bond) and has $\boldsymbol{sp^2}$ hybridization; all of the other C atoms have four electron groups (four single bonds) and have $\boldsymbol{sp^3}$ hybridization; all of the O atoms have four electron groups (two single bonds and two lone pairs) and have $\boldsymbol{sp^3}$ hybridization; the N atom has four electron groups (three single bonds and a lone pair) and has $\boldsymbol{sp^3}$ hybridization.
b) Each of the single bonds is a sigma bond; each of the double bonds has one sigma bond for a total of **26 sigma bonds**.
c) The ring has three double bonds each of which is composed of one sigma bond and one pi bond; so there are three pi bonds each with two electrons for a total of **six pi electrons.**

11.42 Plan: To determine hybridization, count the number of electron groups around each C and N atom. Hybridize that number of orbitals. Single, double, and triple bonds all count as one electron group. An unshared pair (lone pair) of electrons or one unshared electron also counts as one electron group. A single bond is a sigma bond which is the result of two orbitals overlapping end to end; a double bond consists of one sigma bond and one pi bond; and a triple bond consists of one sigma bond and two pi bonds.

Solution:

a) Every single bond is a sigma bond. There is one sigma bond in each double bond as well. There are **17 σ** bonds in isoniazid. Every atom-to-atom connection contains a σ bond.

b) All carbons have three surrounding electron groups (two single and one double bond), so their hybridization is ***sp*²**. The ring N also has three surrounding electron groups (one single bond, one double bond, and one lone pair), so its hybridization is also ***sp*²**. The other two N atoms have four surrounding electron groups (three single bonds and one lone pair) and are ***sp*³** hybridized.

11.44 Plan: To determine the hybridization in each species, count the number of electron groups around the underlined atom. Hybridize that number of orbitals. Single, double, and triple bonds all count as one electron group. An unshared pair (lone pair) of electrons or one unshared electron also counts as one electron group.

Solution:

a) B changes from $sp^2 \rightarrow sp^3$. Boron in BF_3 has three electron groups with sp^2 hybridization. In BF_4^-, four electron groups surround B with sp^3 hybridization.

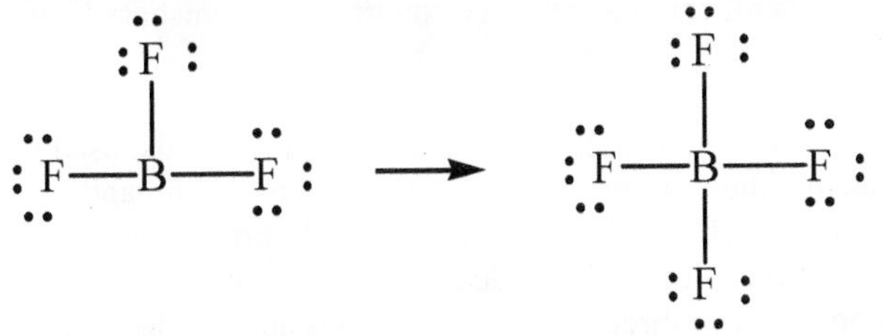

:F: — B(—F:)(—F:) → F—B(—F)(—F)—F (with lone pairs on each F)

b) P changes from $sp^3 \rightarrow sp^3d$. Phosphorus in PCl_3 is surrounded by four electron groups (three bonds to Cl and one lone pair) for sp^3 hybridization. In PCl_5, phosphorus is surrounded by five electron groups for sp^3d hybridization.

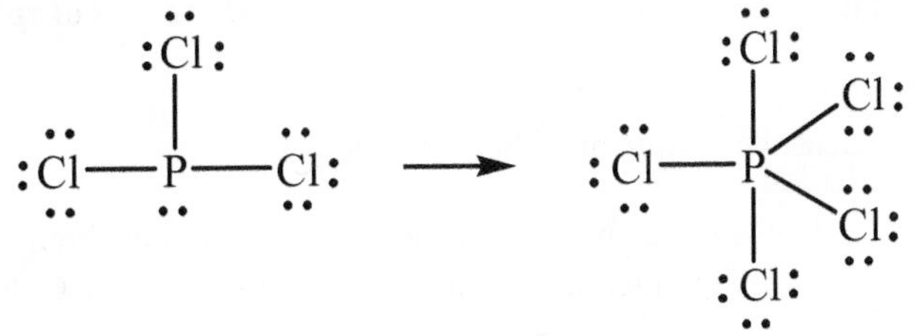

:Cl—P(—Cl:)—Cl: → :Cl—P(Cl)(Cl)(Cl)—Cl:

c) C changes from $sp \rightarrow sp^2$. Two electron groups surround C in C_2H_2 and three electron groups surround C in C_2H_4.

H—C≡C—H → $H_2C{=}CH_2$

d) Si changes from $sp^3 \rightarrow sp^3d^2$. Four electron groups surround Si in SiF_4 and six electron groups surround Si in SiF_6^{2-}.

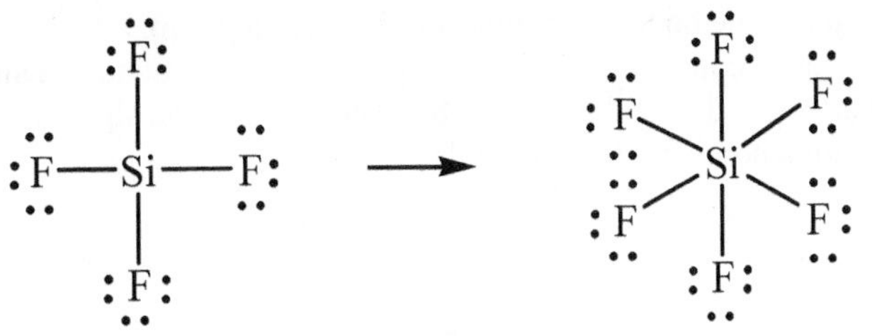

:F—Si(—F:)(—F:)—F: → Si(F)₆ (octahedral, lone pairs on each F)

e) **No change,** S in SO_2 is surrounded by three electron groups (one single bond, one double bond, and one lone pair) and in SO_3 is surrounded by three electron groups (two single bonds and one double bond); both have sp^2 hybridization.

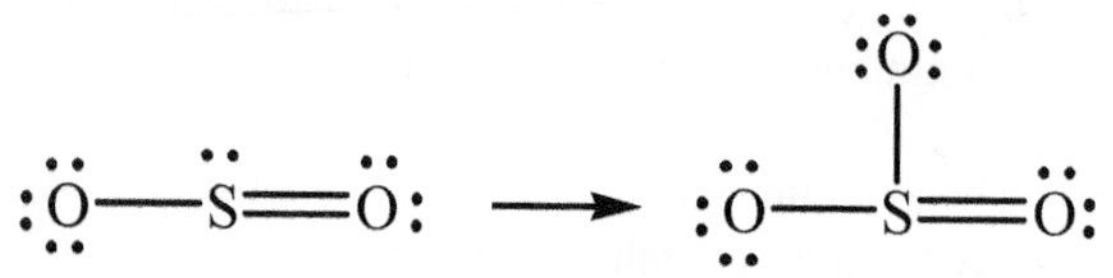

11.46 Plan: To determine the molecular shape and hybridization, count the number of electron groups around the P, N, and C atoms. Hybridize that number of orbitals. Single, double, and triple bonds all count as one electron group. An unshared pair (lone pair) of electrons or one unshared electron also counts as one electron group.
Solution:

P (3 single bonds and 1 double bond)	AX_4	**tetrahedral**	sp^3
N (3 single bonds and 1 lone pair)	AX_3E	**trigonal pyramidal**	sp^3
C_1 and C_2 (4 single bonds)	AX_4	**tetrahedral**	sp^3
C_3 (2 single bonds and 1 double bond)	AX_3	**trigonal planar**	sp^2

11.51 Plan: To determine the hybridization, count the number of electron groups around the atoms. Hybridize that number of orbitals. Single, double, and triple bonds all count as one electron group. An unshared pair (lone pair) of electrons or one unshared electron also counts as one electron group.
Solution:
a) **B and D** show hybrid orbitals that are present in the molecule. B shows sp^3 hybrid orbitals, used by atoms that have four groups of electrons. In the molecule, the C atom in the CH_3 group, the S atom, and the O atom all have four groups of electrons and would have sp^3 hybrid orbitals. D shows sp^2 hybrid orbitals, used by atoms that have three groups of electrons. In the molecule, the C bonded to the nitrogen atom, the C atoms involved in the C=C bond, and the nitrogen atom all have three groups of electrons and would have sp^2 hybrid orbitals.
b) The C atoms in the C≡C bond have only two electron groups and would have ***sp* hybrid orbitals**. These orbitals are not shown in the picture.
c) There are **two sets of *sp*** hybrid orbitals, **four sets of sp^2** hybrid orbitals, and **three sets of sp^3** hybrid orbitals in the molecule.

11.52 Plan: Draw a resonance structure that places the double bond between the C and N atoms.
Solution:
The resonance gives the C–N bond some double bond character, which hinders rotation about the C–N bond. The C–N single bond is a σ bond; the resonance interaction exchanges a C–O π bond for a C–N π bond.

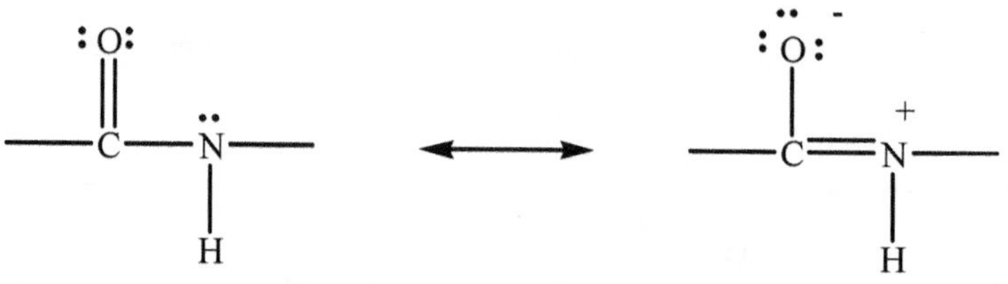

11.56 Plan: To determine hybridization, count the number of electron groups around each C and O atom. Hybridize that number of orbitals. Single, double, and triple bonds all count as one electron group. An unshared pair (lone pair) of electrons or one unshared electron also counts as one electron group. A single bond is a sigma bond which is the result of two orbitals overlapping end to end; a double bond consists of one sigma bond and one pi bond; and a triple bond consists of one sigma bond and two pi bonds.

Solution:
a) The six carbons in the ring each have three surrounding electron groups (two single bonds and one double bond) with sp^2 hybrid orbitals. The two carbons participating in the C=O bond are also sp^2 hybridized. The single carbon in the $–CH_3$ group has four electron groups (four single bonds) and is sp^3 hybridized. The two central oxygen atoms, one in a C–O–H configuration and the other in a C–O–C configuration, each have four surrounding electron groups (two single bonds and two lone pairs) and are sp^3 hybridized. The O atoms in the two C=O bonds have three electron groups (one double bond and two lone pairs) and are sp^2 hybridized.
Summary: C in $–CH_3$: $\boldsymbol{sp^3}$, all other C atoms (8 total): $\boldsymbol{sp^2}$, O in C=O (2 total): $\boldsymbol{sp^2}$, O in the C–O bonds (2 total): $\boldsymbol{sp^3}$.
b) The **two** C=O bonds are localized; the double bonds on the ring are delocalized as in benzene.
c) Each carbon with three surrounding groups has sp^2 hybridization and trigonal planar shape; therefore, **eight** carbons have this shape. Only **one** carbon in the CH_3 group has four surrounding groups with sp^3 hybridization and tetrahedral shape.

11.57 Plan: In the *cis* arrangement, the two H atoms are on the same side of the double bond; in the *trans* arrangement, the two H atoms are on different sides of the double bond.
Solution:
a) **Four** different isomeric fatty acids: *trans-cis*, *cis-cis*, *cis-trans*, *trans-trans*.
b) With three double bonds, there are $2^n = 2^3 = \mathbf{8}$ **isomers** possible.

cis-cis-cis	*trans-trans-trans*
cis-trans-cis	*trans-cis-trans*
cis-cis-trans	*trans-cis-cis*
cis-trans-trans	*trans-trans-cis*